Reference data

CIBSE Guide C

CIBSE

Note from the publisher

This publication is primarily intended to provide guidance to those responsible for the
design, installation, commissioning, operation and maintenance of building services. It is
not intended to be exhaustive or definitive and it will be necessary for users of the guidance
given to exercise their own professional judgement when deciding whether to abide by or
depart from it.

Foreword

CIBSE Guide C was comprehensively updated for the 2001 edition. Although basic physical data do not change with time, the refinement of measurement and calculation techniques and further research make regular review essential. Many of the changes to this edition are therefore small incremental changes, reflecting such refinement.

It was however recognised that section 4, *Flow of fluids in pipes and ducts*, while heavily revised for the 2001 edition, was at that time unable to take account of the latest European research. The report of this research has now been obtained and its results distilled into this edition of Guide C. The opportunity has also been taken to rewrite and clarify the text and to delete many pages of tabular data providing pre-calculated pressure drops through pipes. It was felt that these tables have outlived their usefulness now that accurate pressure drops can easily be calculated using spreadsheets or computer programs. Such a spreadsheet is provided on the CD-ROM that accompanies this Guide.

I would like to express my thanks to all the volunteer authors who agreed to review and update their work and particularly to Peter Koch for his effort and enthusiasm in revising section 4. I would also like to thank all contributors, reviewers and CIBSE staff for their valuable contributions.

Finally I hope that you will continue to find this Guide a useful and authoritative source of reference and guidance.

Paul Compton
Chairman, CIBSE Guide C

Authors, contributors and acknowledgements

Chapter 1: Properties of humid air

Principal author (2001 and 2007 editions)

W P Jones (consultant)

The tables of psychrometric data are reprinted unchanged from the 1986 edition of Guide C and were prepared by a task group, see below.

Task group members

W P Jones (Chairman) (consultant)
J F Armour
B G Lawrence

Chapter 2: Properties of water and steam

The tables of data are reprinted unchanged from the 1986 edition of Guide C.

Chapter 3: Heat transfer

This chapter is reprinted from the 2001 edition; the authors and contributors were as follows.

Principal authors (2001 edition)

D L Loveday (Loughborough University)
A H Taki (De Montfort University)

Contributors (2001 edition)

H B Awbi (University of Reading)
P D Compton (Colt International Ltd.)
R M Harris (Centre for Window and Cladding Technology)
M J Holmes (Ove Arup & Partners International Ltd.)
B P Holownia (Loughborough University)
J Moss (Ove Arup & Partners International Ltd.)

T Muneer (Napier University)
H K Versteeg (Loughborough University)

Acknowledgements

American Society of Heating, Refrigerating and Air-Conditioning Engineers Inc.
British Standards Institution
The McGraw-Hill Companies
Pearson Education Ltd.

Chapter 4: Flow of fluids in pipes and ducts

Principal author (2001 and 2007 editions)

P Koch (Université Joseph Fourier, Grenoble; Coventry University)

Contributor (2001 edition)

F Sprenger (Coventry University)

Acknowledgements

American Society of Heating, Refrigerating and Air-Conditioning Engineers Inc.
Centre Technique des Industries Aérauliques et Thermiques
Coventry University, School of Science and the Environment
Sheet Metal and Air Conditioning Contractors' National Association
Shell Chemicals, Rotterdam

Chapter 5: Fuels and combustion

Principal author (2001 and 2007 editions)

M R I Purvis (Chairman) (University of Portsmouth)

Task group members/Principal authors (2001 edition)

M R I Purvis (Chairman) (University of Portsmouth)
R Dando (Coal Research Establishment)
M Drew (BP Amoco plc)
R J Harris (Advantica Technologies Ltd.)
K Mildren (University of Portsmouth)

Acknowledgement

British Standards Institution

Chapter 6: Units, standard and mathematical data

Principal author (2001 and 2007 editions)

P D Compton (Colt International Ltd.)

Editor

Ken Butcher

CIBSE Publishing Manager

Jacqueline Balian

Contents

1   Properties of humid air

1.1   Psychrometric data

1.1.1   Basis of calculation

The method of formulation suggested by Goff and Gratch[1,2], based on the ideal gas laws with a modification to take account of intermolecular forces, has been adopted for calculating the thermodynamic properties of moist air. This approach remains in line with current practice[3,4].

The thermodynamic properties of dry air and saturated water vapour are well established and, although more recent research work[4–6] has been done, the results are not significantly different from those obtained in earlier work[7,8]. Hence the thermodynamic properties of dry air and water vapour, determined by the National Bureau of Standards[7] and the National Engineering Laboratory[8], have been retained for the evaluation of the thermodynamic properties of moist air.

Since the properties of dry air and saturated water vapour are accurately known, the properties of a mixture of the two can be established for the saturated case. For the enthalpy and specific volume of moist air, at a condition other than saturated, the method is exemplified by the following equations:

$$h = h_a + \mu \, (h_s - h_a) / 100 \qquad (1.1)$$

$$v = v_a + \mu \, (v_s - v_a) / 100 \qquad (1.2)$$

where h is the specific enthalpy of moist air (kJ·kg^{-1} dry air), h_a is the specific enthalpy of dry air (kJ·kg^{-1}), μ is the percentage saturation (%), h_s is the specific enthalpy of saturated moist air (kJ·kg^{-1} dry air), v is the specific volume of moist air (m^3·kg^{-1} dry air), v_a is the specific volume of dry air (m^3·kg^{-1}) and v_s is the specific volume of saturated moist air (m^3·kg^{-1} dry air).

The relevant specific property of moist, unsaturated air is determined by adding a proportion of the property of saturated water vapour to the same property of dry air, on a mass basis.

A consequence of this is that the humidity of moist air is expressed as percentage saturation (defined in terms of the mass of water vapour present), rather than relative humidity (defined in terms of vapour pressure). The details of the psychrometric calculations are given in references 9, 10 and 11.

1.1.2   Standards adopted

All data are tabulated for an internationally agreed standard atmospheric pressure[12] of 101.325 kPa.

The zero datum adopted by the National Engineering Laboratory[8] for the expression of the thermodynamic properties of steam is the triple point of water, +0.01 °C.

The zero datum for the specific enthalpies of both dry air and liquid water has been taken here as 273.15 K (0 °C).

1.1.3   Formulae used for calculations

Saturated vapour pressure over water[8]

$$\log p_s = 30.59051 - 8.2 \log (\theta + 273.16)$$
$$+ \, 2.4804 \times 10^{-3} \, (\theta + 273.16)$$
$$- \, [3142.31 / (\theta + 273.16)] \qquad (1.3)$$

where p_s is the saturated vapour pressure over water at temperature θ (kPa), θ is the temperature, greater than or equal to 0 °C (°C).

Saturated vapour pressure over ice[7]

$$\log p_s = 9.538\,099\,7 - [2\,663.91 / (\theta + 273.15)] \tag{1.4}$$

where p_s is the saturated vapour pressure over ice at temperature θ, less than 0 °C (kPa).

Moisture content

$$g_s = \frac{0.62197 f_s p_s}{101.325 - f_s p_s} \tag{1.5}$$

where g_s is the moisture content of saturated moist air (kg·kg^{-1} dry air) and f_s is a dimensionless enhancement factor[1–4,11].

Percentage saturation

$$\mu = \frac{100\,g}{g_s} \tag{1.6}$$

where μ is the percentage saturation (%) and g is the moisture content of unsaturated moist air (kg·kg^{-1} dry air).

Vapour pressure of water vapour in unsaturated moist air

$$p_v = \frac{p_a g}{f_s (0.62197 + g)} \tag{1.7}$$

where p_v is the vapour pressure of superheated water vapour in unsaturated moist air (kPa) and p_a is the atmospheric (barometric) pressure (kPa).

Relative humidity

$$\phi = \frac{100\,p_v}{p_s} \tag{1.8}$$

where ϕ is the relative humidity (%).

Wet bulb temperature

Knowing the value of the vapour pressure, p_v, from equation 1.7 the wet bulb temperature is derived from the following equations by an iterative technique:

$$p_v = p_{sl} - 101.325\,A\,(\theta - \theta'_{sl}) \tag{1.9}$$

where p_{sl} is the saturated vapour pressure at temperature θ'_{sl} (kPa), A is a coefficient (K^{-1}), θ is the dry bulb temperature (°C) and θ'_{sl} is the sling or mechanically aspirated wet bulb temperature (°C).

Values of A are as follows:

$$A = 6.66 \times 10^{-4}\ \mathrm{K}^{-1} \text{ when } \theta'_{sl} \geq 0\ °C$$

$$A = 5.94 \times 10^{-4}\ \mathrm{K}^{-1} \text{ when } \theta'_{sl} < 0\ °C$$

or:

$$p_v = p_{sc} - 101.325\,B\,(\theta - \theta'_{sc}) \tag{1.10}$$

where p_{sc} is the saturated vapour pressure at temperature θ'_{sc} (kPa), B is a coefficient (K^{-1}) and θ'_{sc} is the screen wet bulb temperature (°C).

Values of B are as follows:

$$B = 7.99 \times 10^{-4}\ \mathrm{K}^{-1} \text{ when } \theta'_{sc} \geq 0\ °C$$

$$B = 7.20 \times 10^{-4}\ \mathrm{K}^{-1} \text{ when } \theta'_{sc} < 0\ °C$$

Adiabatic saturation temperature

$$\theta^\star = \theta - \frac{h_{fg}\,(g_{sa} - g)}{(c_{pa} + g\,c_{ps})} \tag{1.11}$$

where $\theta^\star$ is the adiabatic saturation temperature (°C), h_{fg} is the latent heat of evaporation of water at temperature $\theta^\star$ (kJ·kg^{-1}), g_{sa} is the moisture content of saturated air at temperature $\theta^\star$ (kg·kg^{-1} dry air), g is the moisture content of moist air at the particular psychrometric state (kg·kg^{-1} dry air), c_{pa} is the mean specific heat capacity of dry air between temperatures θ and $\theta^\star$ (kJ·kg^{-1}·K^{-1}) and c_{ps} is the mean specific heat capacity of water vapour between temperatures θ and $\theta^\star$ (kJ·kg^{-1}·K^{-1}).

In the case of the adiabatic saturation temperature above ice, h_{fg} is replaced by h_{ig}, the latent heat of fusion of water at a temperature $\theta^\star$.

Dew-point

For a particular psychrometric state, equation 1.7 is used to calculate the vapour pressure. An iterative technique is then used with equation 1.3 or 1.4 to determine the temperature for which the calculated vapour pressure is a saturated vapour pressure.

Specific volume

$$v = \left[\frac{82.0567\,(273.15 + \theta)}{28.966\,(101.325 - p_v) / 101.325} \right]$$
$$- [A_{aa}\,x_a^2 + 2\,A_{aw}\,x_a\,(1 - x_a) + A_{ww}\,(1 - x_a)^2] \tag{1.12}$$

where v is the specific volume (m^3·kg^{-1} dry air), θ is the dry bulb temperature (°C), A_{aa} is the second virial coefficient for dry air[4] (m^3·kg^{-1}), A_{aw} is the interaction coefficient for moist air[4] (m^3·kg^{-1}), A_{ww} is the second virial coefficient for water vapour (m^3·kg^{-1}) and x_a is the mole fraction of dry air.

The mole fraction of dry air, x_a, is given by:

$$x_a = \frac{0.62197}{0.62197 + g} \tag{1.13}$$

In the original work[1,2] and in later research[4], a third virial coefficient for water vapour (A_{www}) appears in equation 1.12 but it is complicated to calculate and its influence is insignificant. It is ignored here, without any loss of accuracy.

Equation 1.2 yields answers of adequate precision and is easier to use than equation 1.12.

Specific enthalpy

$$h = h_a + g\,h_g \qquad (1.14)$$

where h is the specific enthalpy of moist air (kJ·kg^{-1} dry air), h_a is the specific enthalpy of dry air[7] (kJ·kg^{-1}), g is the moisture content (kg·kg^{-1} dry air) and h_g is the specific enthalpy of water vapour at the dry bulb temperature[8] (kg·kg^{-1} dry air).

Equation 1.1 gives answers having the same accuracy as those obtained from equation 1.14 and is simpler to use.

1.1.4 Psychrometric properties at non-standard barometric pressures

The tabulated psychrometric data are accurate within the range of barometric pressure from 95 kPa to 105 kPa and hence are suitable for the whole of the UK. For pressures outside these limits an application of the ideal gas laws will give answers of a little less accuracy. Better answers may be obtained by the use of equations 1.15 and 1.16.

$$g_s = \frac{0.624\,p_s}{(p_a - 1.004\,p_s)} \qquad (1.15)$$

$$v = \frac{(0.287 + 0.461\,g)\,(273.15 + \theta)}{p_a} \qquad (1.16)$$

Corrections to specific enthalpy may be taken from Table 1.1.

Figure 1.1, which gives the relationship between height above sea level and barometric pressure, is drawn from the equation:

$$p_a = 101.325\,\exp[(-9.81\,\rho\,z)\,/\,(101\,325)] \qquad (1.17)$$

where p_a is the particular atmospheric (barometric) pressure (kPa), ρ is the density of air (kg·m^{-3}) and z is the altitude above sea level (m).

Alternatively, the standard relationship[12] for altitude, atmospheric pressure and temperature may be used. This is reproduced in Table 1.2.

Table 1.1 Corrections to specific enthalpy at non-standard pressures

Adiabatic saturation temperature / °C	Approximate additive corrections to specific enthalpy (/ kJ·kg^{-1} dry air) at stated barometric pressure / kPa								
	82.5	85.0	87.5	90.0	92.5	95.0	97.5	101.325	102.5
30	16.90	14.23	11.68	9.29	6.95	4.80	2.86	0	−0.82
29	15.90	13.40	11.00	8.72	6.55	4.57	2.70	0	−0.77
28	14.95	12.58	10.30	8.18	6.16	4.30	2.54	0	−0.72
27	14.00	11.78	9.65	7.67	5.80	4.05	2.40	0	−0.68
26	13.05	11.02	9.03	7.18	5.44	3.82	2.27	0	−0.64
25	12.20	10.28	8.42	6.70	5.12	3.58	2.14	0	−0.60
24	11.43	9.64	7.90	6.30	4.80	3.36	2.00	0	−0.56
23	10.68	9.03	7.40	5.88	4.43	3.15	1.86	0	−0.52
22	10.00	8.45	6.93	5.51	4.20	2.94	1.73	0	−0.48
21	9.37	7.92	6.50	5.18	3.92	2.74	1.61	0	−0.45
20	8.77	7.42	6.10	4.84	3.65	2.55	1.50	0	−0.42
19	8.22	6.95	5.70	4.53	3.43	2.39	1.40	0	−0.39
18	7.73	6.49	5.35	4.24	3.20	2.23	1.30	0	−0.37
17	7.25	6.09	5.00	3.97	3.00	2.07	1.21	0	−0.35
16	6.79	5.68	4.65	3.72	2.80	1.94	1.13	0	−0.32
15	6.33	5.32	4.34	3.48	2.62	1.82	1.07	0	−0.30
14	5.90	4.95	4.07	3.24	2.44	1.70	1.00	0	−0.28
13	5.50	4.60	3.80	3.03	2.28	1.60	0.93	0	−0.26
12	5.13	4.30	3.53	2.82	2.12	1.50	0.86	0	−0.24
11	4.78	4.04	3.28	2.62	1.97	1.40	0.80	0	−0.22
10	4.44	3.77	3.08	2.46	1.82	1.30	0.74	0	−0.20
9	4.15	3.51	2.88	2.30	1.70	1.21	0.70	0	−0.20
8	3.88	3.30	2.68	2.14	1.60	1.12	0.66	0	−0.19
7	3.62	3.08	2.51	2.00	1.50	1.06	0.62	0	−0.19
6	3.40	2.88	2.37	1.87	1.40	1.00	0.59	0	−0.18
5	3.20	2.72	2.23	1.74	1.31	0.92	0.56	0	−0.17
4	3.06	2.60	2.10	1.64	1.24	0.88	0.53	0	−0.17
3	2.92	2.47	2.02	1.59	1.19	0.84	0.50	0	−0.16
2	2.78	2.36	1.94	1.54	1.15	0.80	0.48	0	−0.16
1	2.65	2.25	1.86	1.49	1.10	0.76	0.46	0	−0.15
0	2.52	2.16	1.79	1.44	1.08	0.72	0.44	0	−0.15

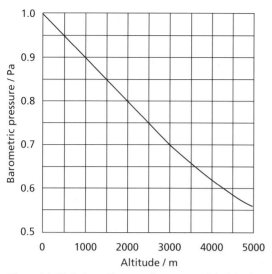

Figure 1.1 Variation of barometric pressure with altitude

Table 1.2 Standard atmospheric data for altitudes to 10 000 m

Altitude / m	Temperature / °C	Pressure / kPa
–500	18.2	107.478
0	15.0	101.325
500	11.8	95.461
1000	8.5	89.875
1500	5.2	84.556
2000	2.0	79.495
2500	–1.2	74.682
3000	–4.5	70.108
4000	–11.0	61.640
5000	–17.5	54.020
6000	–24.0	47.181
7000	–30.5	41.061
8000	–37.0	35.600
9000	–43.5	30.742
10000	–50.0	26.436

Atmospheric pressures and temperatures from –5000 m to +11 000 m may be accurately calculated[3] using the following equations:

$$p_a = 101.325 \, (1 - 2.25577 \times 10^{-5} \, z)^{5.2559} \qquad (1.18)$$

$$\theta = 15 - 0.0065 \, z \qquad (1.19)$$

where p_a is the barometric pressure (kPa), θ is the atmospheric temperature (°C) and z is the altitude above sea level (m).

1.2   CIBSE psychrometric chart (–10 to +60 °C)

The chart has been designed[13] and constructed using the two fundamental properties of mass (moisture content) and energy (specific enthalpy) as linear co-ordinates. Other physical properties are not then shown as linear scales[13,14]. The 30 °C dry-bulb line has been constructed at right angles to lines of constant moisture content, which are horizontal. The scale of specific enthalpy is obliquely inclined to the vertical scale of moisture content. In this way, lines of constant dry bulb temperature are approximately vertical, diverging slightly on each side of the 30 °C line, and the traditional appearance of the chart is preserved.

The wet-bulb values shown are those read from a sling or mechanically aspirated psychrometer and lines of percentage saturation are plotted instead of relative humidity. Within the comfort zone, there is no practical difference between percentage saturation and relative humidity. In any case, the difference diminishes as saturated or dry conditions are approached.

The psychrometric data used were taken from the tables of the properties of humid air presented in this chapter of CIBSE Guide C.

1.3   CIBSE psychrometric chart (10 to 120 °C)

The psychrometric chart for 10 to 120 °C has been based on the ideal gas laws. This does not give a significant difference when compared with a chart constructed using more accurate data, based on the method of Goff and Gratch[1,2]. The principles of calculation and drawing are detailed elsewhere[14].

References

1   Goff J A and Gratch S 'Thermodynamic properties of moist air' *Trans. ASHVE* **51** 125–164 (1945)

2   Goff J A 'Standardisation of thermodynamic properties of moist air' *Trans. ASHVE* **55** 459–484 (1949)

3   *Psychrometrics* ch. 6 in ASHRAE Handbook *Fundamentals* (Atlanta, GA: American Society of Heating, Refrigerating and Air-Conditioning Engineers) (2005)

4   Hyland R W and Wexler A 'Formulations for the thermodynamic properties of dry air from 173.15 K to 473.15 K and of saturated moist air from 173.15 K to 372.15 K at pressures to 5 MPa' *Trans. ASHRAE* **89**(2A) 520–535 (1982)

5   Hyland R W and Wexler A 'Formulations for the thermodynamic properties of the saturated phases of H₂O from 173.15 K to 473.15 K' *Trans. ASHRAE* **89**(2A) 500–519 (1983)

6   Stimson H F 'Some precise measurements of the vapour pressure of water in the range from 25 °C to 100 °C' *J. Res. NBS* **73A** (1969)

7   *Tables of thermal properties of gases* NBS Circular 564 (Gaithersburg, MD: National Bureau of Standards) (November 1955)

8   *National Engineering Laboratory steam tables* (London: Her Majesty's Stationery Office) (1964)

9   Jones W P and Lawrence B G *New psychrometric data for air* Technical Memorandum No. 11 (London: Polytechnic of the South Bank)

10   *Some fundamental data used by building services engineers* (London: Institution of Heating and Ventilating Engineers) (1973)

11   Jones W P 'A review of CIBSE psychrometry' *Building Serv. Eng. Res. Technol.* **15**(4) 189–198 (1994)

12   *US Standard Atmosphere* (Washington DC: U.S. Government Printing Office) (1976)

13   Jones W P 'The Psychrometric Chart in SI Units' *J. Inst. Heating and Ventilating Engineers* **38** 93 (1970)

14   Bull L C 'Design and use of the new IHVE psychrometric chart' *J. Inst. Heating and Ventilating Engineers* **32** 268 (1964)

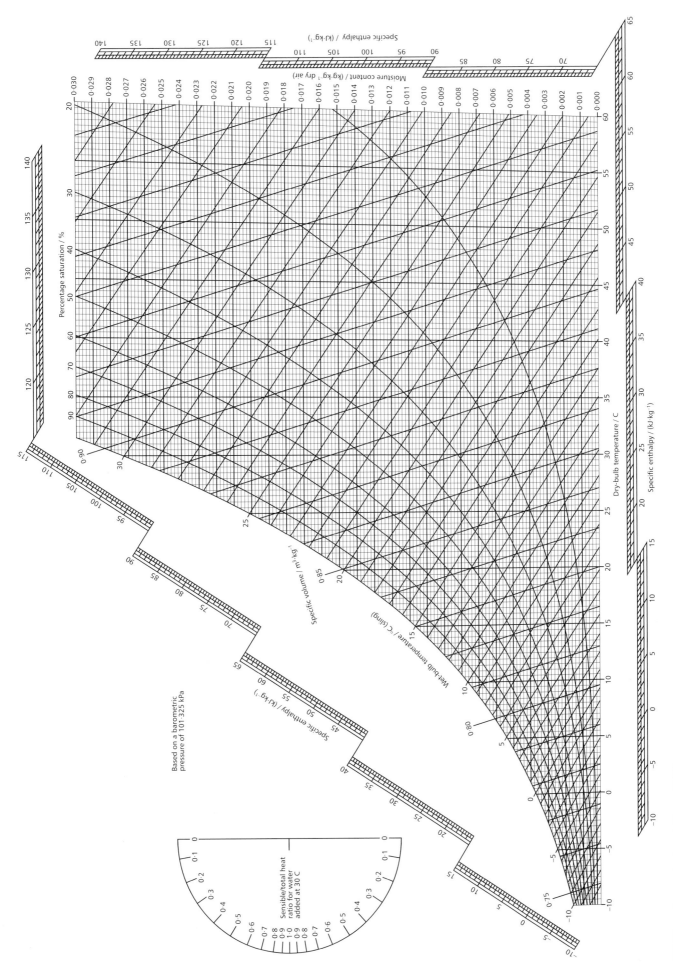

Figure 1.2 CIBSE psychrometric chart (−10 to +60 °C)

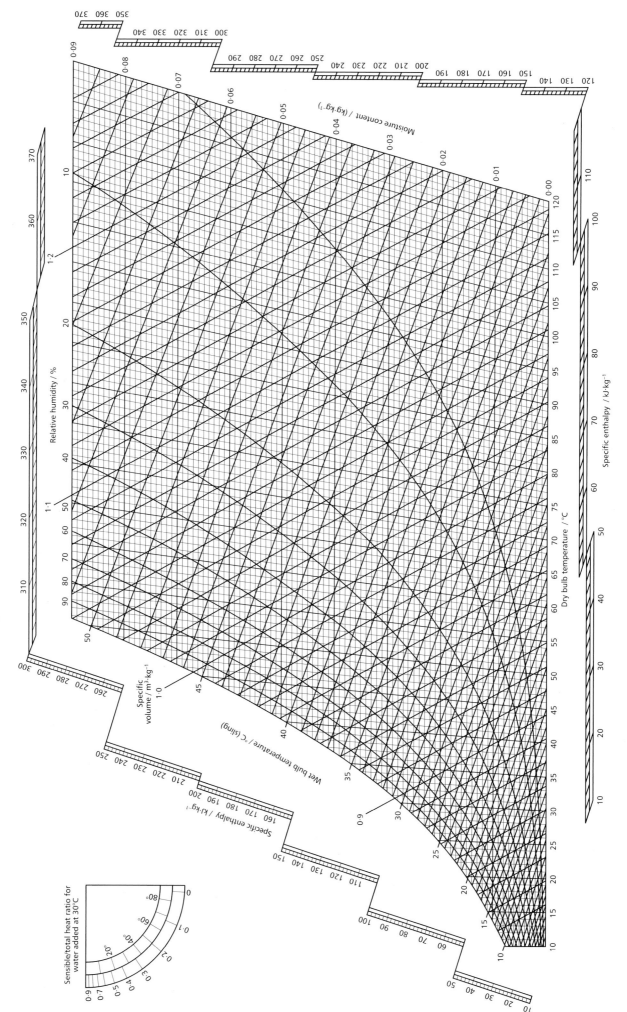

Figure 1.3 CIBSE psychrometric chart (+10 to +120 °C)

−10 °C DRY-BULB

Percentage saturation, μ / %	Relative humidity, ϕ /%	Value of stated parameter per kg dry air			Vapour pressure, p_v / kPa	Dew point temperature, θ_d / °C	Adiabatic saturation temperature, $\theta^\star$ / °C	Wet bulb temperature	
		Moisture content, g / (g·kg⁻¹)	Specific enthalpy, h / (kJ·kg⁻¹)	Specific volume, v / (m³·kg⁻¹)				Screen, θ'_{sc} / °C	Sling, θ'_{sl} / °C
100	100.00	1.607	−6.065	0.7468	0.2600	−10.0	−10.0	−10.0	−10.0
96	96.01	1.543	−6.224	0.7468	0.2496	−10.5	−10.1	−10.1	−10.1
92	92.02	1.479	−6.384	0.7467	0.2392	−10.9	−10.3	−10.2	−10.3
88	88.03	1.414	−6.544	0.7466	0.2288	−11.4	−10.4	−10.3	−10.4
84	84.03	1.350	−6.703	0.7465	0.2185	−11.9	−10.5	−10.4	−10.5
80	80.04	1.286	−6.863	0.7465	0.2081	−12.5	−10.7	−10.5	−10.6
76	76.05	1.221	−7.022	0.7464	0.1977	−13.1	−10.8	−10.7	−10.8
72	72.05	1.157	−7.182	0.7463	0.1873	−13.6	−10.9	−10.8	−10.9
70	70.05	1.125	−7.262	0.7463	0.1821	−14.0	−11.0	−10.8	−10.9
68	68.06	1.093	−7.342	0.7462	0.1769	−14.3	−11.0	−10.9	−11.0
66	66.06	1.061	−7.421	0.7462	0.1717	−14.6	−11.1	−10.9	−11.1
64	64.06	1.029	−7.501	0.7462	0.1665	−14.9	−11.2	−11.0	−11.1
62	62.06	0.996	−7.581	0.7461	0.1613	−15.3	−11.2	−11.0	−11.2
60	60.06	0.964	−7.661	0.7461	0.1562	−15.6	−11.3	−11.1	−11.3
58	58.06	0.932	−7.740	0.7460	0.1510	−16.0	−11.4	−11.1	−11.3
56	56.06	0.900	−7.820	0.7460	0.1458	−16.4	−11.4	−11.2	−11.4
54	54.06	0.868	−7.900	0.7460	0.1406	−16.8	−11.5	−11.3	−11.5
52	52.06	0.836	−7.980	0.7459	0.1354	−17.2	−11.6	−11.3	−11.5
50	50.06	0.804	−8.060	0.7459	0.1302	−17.6	−11.6	−11.4	−11.6
48	48.06	0.772	−8.139	0.7458	0.1250	−18.0	−11.7	−11.4	−11.7
46	46.06	0.739	−8.219	0.7458	0.1198	−18.5	−11.8	−11.5	−11.7
44	44.06	0.707	−8.299	0.7458	0.1146	−18.9	−11.8	−11.5	−11.8
42	42.06	0.675	−8.379	0.7457	0.1094	−19.4	−11.9	−11.6	−11.8
40	40.06	0.643	−8.459	0.7457	0.1042	−19.9	−12.0	−11.6	−11.9
38	38.06	0.611	−8.538	0.7457	0.0990	−20.5	−12.0	−11.7	−12.0
36	36.06	0.579	−8.618	0.7456	0.0938	−21.0	−12.1	−11.8	−12.0
34	34.06	0.546	−8.698	0.7456	0.0885	−21.6	−12.2	−11.8	−12.1
32	32.06	0.514	−8.778	0.7455	0.0833	−22.2	−12.3	−11.9	−12.2
30	30.05	0.482	−8.858	0.7455	0.0781	−22.9	−12.3	−11.9	−12.2
28	28.05	0.450	−8.937	0.7455	0.0729	−23.6	−12.4	−12.0	−12.3
24	24.05	0.386	−9.097	0.7454	0.0625	−25.2	−12.5	−12.1	−12.4
20	20.04	0.321	−9.256	0.7453	0.0521	−27.0	−12.7	−12.2	−12.6
16	16.03	0.257	−9.416	0.7452	0.0417	−29.2	−12.8	−12.3	−12.7
12	12.03	0.193	−9.576	0.7452	0.0313	−31.9	−12.9	−12.4	−12.8
8	8.02	0.129	−9.735	0.7451	0.0208	−35.7	−13.1	−12.6	−13.0
4	4.01	0.064	−9.895	0.7450	0.0104	−41.9	−13.2	−12.7	−13.1
0	0.00	0.000	−10.054	0.7449	0.0000	—	−13.4	−12.8	−13.2

−9.5 °C DRY-BULB

Percentage saturation, μ / %	Relative humidity, ϕ /%	Value of stated parameter per kg dry air			Vapour pressure, p_v / kPa	Dew point temperature, θ_d / °C	Adiabatic saturation temperature, $\theta^\star$ / °C	Wet bulb temperature	
		Moisture content, g / (g·kg⁻¹)	Specific enthalpy, h / (kJ·kg⁻¹)	Specific volume, v / (m³·kg⁻¹)				Screen, θ'_{sc} / °C	Sling, θ'_{sl} / °C
100	100.00	1.680	−5.380	0.7484	0.2717	−9.5	−9.5	−9.5	−9.5
96	96.01	1.613	−5.547	0.7483	0.2609	−10.0	−9.6	−9.6	−9.6
92	92.02	1.546	−5.713	0.7482	0.2500	−10.4	−9.8	−9.7	−9.8
88	88.03	1.478	−5.880	0.7481	0.2392	−10.9	−9.9	−9.8	−9.9
84	84.04	1.411	−6.047	0.7480	0.2284	−11.5	−10.0	−9.9	−10.0
80	80.04	1.344	−6.214	0.7480	0.2175	−12.0	−10.2	−10.1	−10.1
76	76.05	1.277	−6.381	0.7479	0.2066	−12.6	−10.3	−10.2	−10.3
72	72.05	1.210	−6.548	0.7478	0.1958	−13.2	−10.4	−10.3	−10.4
70	70.06	1.176	−6.631	0.7478	0.1904	−13.5	−10.5	−10.3	−10.5
68	68.06	1.142	−6.715	0.7477	0.1849	−13.8	−10.6	−10.4	−10.5
66	66.06	1.109	−6.798	0.7477	0.1795	−14.1	−10.6	−10.5	−10.6
64	64.06	1.075	−6.882	0.7476	0.1740	−14.5	−10.7	−10.5	−10.7
62	62.06	1.042	−6.965	0.7476	0.1686	−14.8	−10.8	−10.6	−10.7
60	60.06	1.008	−7.048	0.7476	0.1632	−15.2	−10.9	−10.6	−10.8
58	58.07	0.974	−7.132	0.7475	0.1578	−15.5	−10.9	−10.7	−10.9
56	56.07	0.940	−7.215	0.7475	0.1524	−15.9	−11.0	−10.7	−10.9
54	54.07	0.907	−7.299	0.7474	0.1469	−16.3	−11.1	−10.8	−11.0
52	52.07	0.874	−7.382	0.7474	0.1415	−16.7	−11.1	−10.9	−11.1
50	50.07	0.840	−7.466	0.7474	0.1360	−17.1	−11.2	−10.9	−11.1
48	48.07	0.806	−7.549	0.7473	0.1306	−17.5	−11.3	−11.0	−11.2
46	46.07	0.773	−7.633	0.7473	0.1252	−18.0	−11.3	−11.0	−11.3
44	44.07	0.739	−7.716	0.7472	0.1197	−18.5	−11.4	−11.1	−11.3
42	42.07	0.706	−7.800	0.7472	0.1143	−19.0	−11.5	−11.2	−11.4
40	40.06	0.672	−7.883	0.7472	0.1089	−19.5	−11.6	−11.2	−11.5
38	38.06	0.638	−7.966	0.7471	0.1034	−20.0	−11.6	−11.3	−11.5
36	36.06	0.605	−8.050	0.7471	0.0980	−20.6	−11.7	−11.3	−11.6
34	34.06	0.571	−8.133	0.7470	0.0926	−21.2	−11.8	−11.4	−11.7
32	32.06	0.538	−8.217	0.7470	0.0871	−21.8	−11.8	−11.4	−11.7
30	30.06	0.504	−8.300	0.7470	0.0817	−22.5	−11.9	−11.5	−11.8
28	28.05	0.470	−8.384	0.7469	0.0762	−23.2	−12.0	−11.6	−11.9
24	24.05	0.403	−8.550	0.7468	0.0654	−24.7	−12.1	−11.7	−12.0
20	20.04	0.336	−8.717	0.7467	0.0545	−26.5	−12.3	−11.8	−12.2
16	16.04	0.269	−8.884	0.7467	0.0436	−28.7	−12.4	−11.9	−12.3
12	12.03	0.201	−9.051	0.7466	0.0327	−31.5	−12.5	−12.0	−12.4
8	8.02	0.134	−9.218	0.7465	0.0218	−35.3	−12.7	−12.1	−12.6
4	4.01	0.067	−9.385	0.7464	0.0109	−41.5	−12.8	−12.3	−12.7
0	0.00	0.000	−9.552	0.7463	0.0000	—	−13.0	−12.4	−12.8

−9 °C DRY-BULB

Percentage saturation, μ / %	Relative humidity, ϕ /%	Value of stated parameter per kg dry air			Vapour pressure, p_v / kPa	Dew point temperature, θ_d / °C	Adiabatic saturation temperature, $\theta^\star$ / °C	Wet bulb temperature	
		Moisture content, g /(g·kg^{-1})	Specific enthalpy, h /(kJ·kg^{-1})	Specific volume, v /(m³·kg^{-1})				Screen, θ'_{sc} / °C	Sling, θ'_{sl} / °C
100	100.00	1.755	−4.687	0.7499	0.2840	−9.0	−9.0	−9.0	−9.0
96	96.01	1.686	−4.862	0.7498	0.2726	−9.5	−9.1	−9.1	−9.1
92	92.02	1.615	−5.036	0.7497	0.2613	−9.9	−9.3	−9.2	−9.3
88	88.03	1.545	−5.210	0.7496	0.2500	−10.4	−9.4	−9.3	−9.4
84	84.04	1.475	−5.385	0.7495	0.2386	−11.0	−9.6	−9.5	−9.5
80	80.04	1.405	−5.559	0.7494	0.2273	−11.5	−9.7	−9.6	−9.7
76	76.05	1.334	−5.734	0.7494	0.2160	−12.1	−9.8	−9.7	−9.8
72	72.06	1.264	−5.908	0.7493	0.2046	−12.7	−10.0	−9.8	−9.9
70	70.06	1.229	−5.996	0.7492	0.1989	−13.0	−10.0	−9.9	−10.0
68	68.06	1.194	−6.083	0.7492	0.1933	−13.3	−10.1	−9.9	−10.1
66	66.06	1.159	−6.170	0.7492	0.1876	−13.6	−10.2	−10.0	−10.1
64	64.06	1.124	−6.257	0.7491	0.1819	−14.0	−10.3	−10.1	−10.2
62	62.07	1.089	−6.345	0.7491	0.1762	−14.3	−10.3	−10.1	−10.3
60	60.07	1.054	−6.432	0.7490	0.1706	−14.7	−10.4	−10.2	−10.4
58	58.07	1.018	−6.519	0.7490	0.1649	−15.0	−10.5	−10.2	−10.4
56	56.07	0.983	−6.606	0.7489	0.1592	−15.4	−10.5	−10.3	−10.5
54	54.07	0.948	−6.694	0.7489	0.1535	−15.8	−10.6	−10.4	−10.6
52	52.07	0.913	−6.781	0.7489	0.1479	−16.2	−10.7	−10.4	−10.6
50	50.07	0.878	−6.868	0.7488	0.1422	−16.6	−10.8	−10.5	−10.7
48	48.07	0.843	−6.955	0.7488	0.1365	−17.1	−10.8	−10.5	−10.8
46	46.07	0.808	−7.042	0.7487	0.1308	−17.5	−10.9	−10.6	−10.8
44	44.07	0.773	−7.130	0.7487	0.1251	−18.0	−11.0	−10.6	−10.9
42	42.07	0.738	−7.217	0.7487	0.1195	−18.5	−11.0	−10.7	−11.0
40	40.07	0.702	−7.304	0.7486	0.1138	−19.0	−11.1	−10.8	−11.0
38	38.07	0.667	−7.391	0.7486	0.1081	−19.5	−11.2	−10.8	−11.1
36	36.06	0.632	−7.479	0.7485	0.1024	−20.1	−11.3	−10.9	−11.2
34	34.06	0.597	−7.566	0.7485	0.0967	−20.7	−11.3	−10.9	−11.3
32	32.06	0.562	−7.653	0.7484	0.0910	−21.3	−11.4	−11.0	−11.3
30	30.06	0.527	−7.740	0.7484	0.0854	−22.0	−11.5	−11.1	−11.4
28	28.06	0.492	−7.828	0.7484	0.0797	−22.7	−11.6	−11.1	−11.5
24	24.05	0.421	−8.002	0.7483	0.0683	−24.3	−11.7	−11.3	−11.6
20	20.04	0.351	−8.177	0.7482	0.0569	−26.1	−11.9	−11.4	−11.7
16	16.04	0.281	−8.351	0.7481	0.0455	−28.3	−12.0	−11.5	−11.9
12	12.03	0.211	−8.526	0.7480	0.0342	−31.1	−12.1	−11.6	−12.0
8	8.02	0.140	−8.700	0.7479	0.0228	−34.9	−12.3	−11.7	−12.2
4	4.01	0.070	−8.875	0.7479	0.0114	−41.1	−12.4	−11.9	−12.3
0	0.00	0.000	−9.049	0.7478	0.0000	—	−12.6	−12.0	−12.5

−8.5 °C DRY-BULB

Percentage saturation, μ / %	Relative humidity, ϕ /%	Value of stated parameter per kg dry air			Vapour pressure, p_v / kPa	Dew point temperature, θ_d / °C	Adiabatic saturation temperature, $\theta^\star$ / °C	Wet bulb temperature	
		Moisture content, g /(g·kg^{-1})	Specific enthalpy, h /(kJ·kg^{-1})	Specific volume, v /(m³·kg^{-1})				Screen, θ'_{sc} / °C	Sling, θ'_{sl} / °C
100	100.00	1.835	−3.986	0.7514	0.2967	−8.5	−8.5	−8.5	−8.5
96	96.01	1.761	−4.169	0.7513	0.2849	−9.0	−8.6	−8.6	−8.6
92	92.02	1.688	−4.351	0.7512	0.2730	−9.4	−8.8	−8.7	−8.8
88	88.03	1.615	−4.534	0.7511	0.2612	−9.9	−8.9	−8.9	−8.9
84	84.04	1.541	−4.716	0.7510	0.2493	−10.5	−9.1	−9.0	−9.1
80	80.05	1.468	−4.898	0.7509	0.2375	−11.0	−9.2	−9.1	−9.2
76	76.05	1.394	−5.081	0.7509	0.2256	−11.6	−9.4	−9.2	−9.3
72	72.06	1.321	−5.263	0.7508	0.2138	−12.2	−9.5	−9.3	−9.5
70	70.06	1.284	−5.354	0.7507	0.2079	−12.5	−9.6	−9.4	−9.5
68	68.06	1.248	−5.446	0.7507	0.2019	−12.8	−9.7	−9.5	−9.6
66	66.07	1.211	−5.537	0.7506	0.1960	−13.2	−9.7	−9.5	−9.7
64	64.07	1.174	−5.628	0.7506	0.1901	−13.5	−9.8	−9.6	−9.8
62	62.07	1.138	−5.719	0.7506	0.1842	−13.8	−9.9	−9.7	−9.8
60	60.07	1.101	−5.810	0.7505	0.1782	−14.2	−9.9	−9.7	−9.9
58	58.07	1.064	−5.902	0.7505	0.1723	−14.6	−10.0	−9.8	−10.0
56	56.07	1.028	−5.993	0.7504	0.1664	−14.9	−10.1	−9.8	−10.0
54	54.07	0.991	−6.084	0.7504	0.1604	−15.3	−10.2	−9.9	−10.1
52	52.07	0.954	−6.175	0.7503	0.1545	−15.7	−10.2	−10.0	−10.2
50	50.07	0.917	−6.266	0.7503	0.1486	−16.2	−10.3	−10.0	−10.3
48	48.07	0.881	−6.358	0.7502	0.1426	−16.6	−10.4	−10.1	−10.3
46	46.07	0.844	−6.449	0.7502	0.1367	−17.1	−10.5	−10.1	−10.4
44	44.07	0.807	−6.540	0.7502	0.1308	−17.5	−10.5	−10.2	−10.5
42	42.07	0.771	−6.631	0.7501	0.1248	−18.0	−10.6	−10.3	−10.5
40	40.07	0.734	−6.722	0.7501	0.1189	−18.5	−10.7	−10.3	−10.6
38	38.07	0.697	−6.814	0.7500	0.1130	−19.1	−10.8	−10.4	−10.7
36	36.07	0.660	−6.905	0.7500	0.1070	−19.7	−10.8	−10.5	−10.8
34	34.07	0.624	−6.996	0.7499	0.1011	−20.3	−10.9	−10.5	−10.8
32	32.06	0.587	−7.087	0.7499	0.0951	−20.9	−11.0	−10.6	−10.9
30	30.06	0.550	−7.178	0.7498	0.0892	−21.5	−11.1	−10.6	−11.0
28	28.06	0.514	−7.270	0.7498	0.0832	−22.3	−11.1	−10.7	−11.1
24	24.05	0.440	−7.452	0.7497	0.0714	−23.8	−11.3	−10.8	−11.2
20	20.05	0.367	−7.634	0.7496	0.0595	−25.7	−11.4	−11.0	−11.3
16	16.04	0.294	−7.817	0.7495	0.0476	−27.9	−11.6	−11.1	−11.5
12	12.03	0.220	−7.999	0.7495	0.0357	−30.7	−11.8	−11.2	−11.6
8	8.02	0.147	−8.182	0.7494	0.0238	−34.5	−11.9	−11.3	−11.8
4	4.01	0.073	−8.364	0.7493	0.0119	−40.7	−12.1	−11.5	−11.9
0	0.00	0.000	−8.546	0.7492	0.0000	—	−12.2	−11.6	−12.1

−8 °C DRY-BULB

Percentage saturation, μ / %	Relative humidity, ϕ /%	Value of stated parameter per kg dry air			Vapour pressure, p_v / kPa	Dew point temperature, θ_d / °C	Adiabatic saturation temperature, $\theta\star$ / °C	Wet bulb temperature	
		Moisture content, g / (g·kg^{-1})	Specific enthalpy, h / (kJ·kg^{-1})	Specific volume, v / (m^3·kg^{-1})				Screen, θ'_{sc} / °C	Sling, θ'_{sl} / °C
100	100.00	1.917	−3.278	0.7529	0.3100	−8.0	−8.0	−8.0	−8.0
96	96.01	1.840	−3.468	0.7528	0.2976	−8.5	−8.1	−8.1	−8.1
92	92.02	1.764	−3.659	0.7527	0.2852	−8.9	−8.3	−8.2	−8.3
88	88.03	1.687	−3.850	0.7526	0.2729	−9.5	−8.4	−8.4	−8.4
84	84.04	1.610	−4.040	0.7525	0.2605	−10.0	−8.6	−8.5	−8.6
80	80.05	1.534	−4.231	0.7524	0.2481	−10.5	−8.7	−8.6	−8.7
76	76.06	1.457	−4.421	0.7524	0.2357	−11.1	−8.9	−8.7	−8.9
72	72.06	1.380	−4.612	0.7523	0.2334	−11.7	−9.0	−8.9	−9.0
70	70.06	1.342	−4.707	0.7522	0.2172	−12.0	−9.1	−8.9	−9.1
68	68.07	1.304	−4.803	0.7522	0.2110	−12.3	−9.2	−9.0	−9.2
66	66.07	1.265	−4.898	0.7521	0.2048	−12.7	−9.3	−9.1	−9.2
64	64.07	1.227	−4.993	0.7521	0.1986	−13.0	−9.3	−9.1	−9.3
62	62.07	1.189	−5.089	0.7520	0.1924	−13.4	−9.4	−9.2	−9.4
60	60.07	1.150	−5.184	0.7520	0.1862	−13.7	−9.5	−9.3	−9.4
58	58.07	1.112	−5.279	0.7519	0.1800	−14.1	−9.6	−9.3	−9.5
56	56.08	1.074	−5.375	0.7519	0.1738	−14.5	−9.6	−9.4	−9.6
54	54.08	1.035	−5.470	0.7519	0.1676	−14.9	−9.7	−9.4	−9.7
52	52.08	0.997	−5.565	0.7518	0.1614	−15.3	−9.8	−9.5	−9.7
50	50.08	0.958	−5.661	0.7518	0.1552	−15.7	−9.9	−9.6	−9.8
48	48.08	0.920	−5.756	0.7517	0.1490	−16.1	−10.0	−9.6	−9.9
46	46.08	0.882	−5.851	0.7517	0.1428	−16.6	−10.0	−9.7	−10.0
44	44.08	0.844	−5.946	0.7516	0.1366	−17.1	−10.1	−9.8	−10.0
42	42.07	0.805	−6.042	0.7516	0.1304	−17.6	−10.2	−9.8	−10.1
40	40.07	0.767	−6.137	0.7515	0.1242	−18.1	−10.3	−9.9	−10.2
38	38.07	0.728	−6.232	0.7515	0.1180	−18.6	−10.3	−10.0	−10.3
36	36.07	0.690	−6.328	0.7514	0.1118	−19.2	−10.4	−10.0	−10.3
34	34.07	0.652	−6.423	0.7514	0.1056	−19.8	−10.5	−10.1	−10.4
32	32.07	0.614	−6.518	0.7513	0.0994	−20.4	−10.6	−10.2	−10.5
30	30.06	0.575	−6.614	0.7513	0.0932	−21.1	−10.7	−10.2	−10.6
28	28.06	0.537	−6.709	0.75113	0.0870	−21.8	−10.7	−10.3	−10.6
24	24.06	0.460	−6.900	0.7512	0.0746	−23.4	−10.9	−10.4	−10.8
20	20.05	0.383	−7.090	0.7511	0.0621	−25.2	−11.0	−10.5	−10.9
16	16.04	0.307	−7.281	0.7510	0.0497	−27.4	−11.2	−10.7	−11.1
12	12.03	0.230	−7.472	0.7509	0.0373	−30.2	−11.4	−10.8	−11.2
8	8.02	0.153	−7.662	0.7508	0.0249	−34.1	−11.5	−10.9	−11.4
4	4.01	0.077	−7.853	0.7507	0.0124	−40.4	−11.7	−11.1	−11.6
0	0.00	0.000	−8.044	0.7506	0.0000	—	−11.8	−11.2	−11.7

−7.5 °C DRY-BULB

Percentage saturation, μ / %	Relative humidity, ϕ /%	Value of stated parameter per kg dry air			Vapour pressure, p_v / kPa	Dew point temperature, θ_d / °C	Adiabatic saturation temperature, $\theta\star$ / °C	Wet bulb temperature	
		Moisture content, g / (g·kg^{-1})	Specific enthalpy, h / (kJ·kg^{-1})	Specific volume, v / (m^3·kg^{-1})				Screen, θ'_{sc} / °C	Sling, θ'_{sl} / °C
100	100.00	2.003	−2.560	0.7544	0.3238	−7.5	−7.5	−7.5	−7.5
96	96.01	1.922	−2.760	0.7543	0.3108	−8.0	−7.7	−7.6	−7.6
92	92.02	1.842	−2.959	0.7542	0.2979	−8.5	−7.8	−7.8	−7.8
88	88.03	1.762	−3.158	0.7541	0.2850	−9.0	−8.0	−7.9	−7.9
84	84.04	1.682	−3.357	0.7541	0.2721	−9.5	−8.1	−8.0	−8.1
80	80.05	1.602	−3.556	0.7540	0.2592	−10.0	−8.3	−8.1	−8.2
76	76.06	1.522	−3.756	0.7539	0.2462	−10.6	−8.4	−8.3	−8.4
72	72.06	1.442	−3.955	0.7538	0.2333	−11.2	−8.6	−8.4	−8.5
70	70.07	1.402	−4.054	0.7537	0.2268	−11.5	−8.7	−8.5	−8.6
68	68.07	1.362	−4.154	0.7537	0.2204	−11.9	−8.7	−8.5	−8.7
66	66.07	1.322	−4.254	0.7536	0.2139	−12.2	−8.8	−8.6	−8.8
64	64.07	1.282	−4.353	0.7536	0.2074	−12.5	−8.9	−8.7	−8.8
62	62.08	1.242	−4.453	0.7535	0.2010	−12.9	−9.0	−8.7	−8.9
60	60.08	1.202	−4.552	0.7535	0.1945	−13.2	−9.0	−8.8	−9.0
58	58.08	1.162	−4.652	0.7534	0.1880	−13.6	−9.1	−8.9	−9.1
56	56.08	1.122	−4.752	0.7534	0.1816	−14.0	−9.2	−8.9	−9.1
54	54.08	1.081	−4.851	0.7533	0.1751	−14.4	−9.3	−9.0	−9.2
52	52.08	1.041	−4.951	0.7533	0.1686	−14.8	−9.4	−9.1	−9.3
50	50.08	1.001	−5.051	0.7532	0.1621	−15.2	−9.4	−9.1	−9.4
48	48.08	0.961	−5.150	0.7532	0.1557	−15.7	−9.5	−9.2	−9.4
46	46.08	0.921	−5.250	0.7531	0.1492	−16.1	−9.6	−9.3	−9.5
44	44.08	0.881	−5.349	0.7531	0.1427	−16.6	−9.7	−9.3	−9.6
42	42.08	0.841	−5.449	0.7530	0.1362	−17.1	−9.8	−9.4	−9.7
40	40.08	0.801	−5.549	0.7530	0.1298	−17.6	−9.8	−9.5	−9.8
38	38.08	0.761	−5.648	0.7529	0.1233	−18.2	−9.9	−9.5	−9.8
36	36.07	0.721	−5.748	0.7529	0.1168	−18.7	−10.0	−9.6	−9.9
34	34.07	0.681	−5.848	0.7528	0.1103	−19.3	−10.1	−9.7	−10.0
32	32.07	0.641	−5.947	0.7528	0.1038	−20.0	−10.2	−9.7	−10.1
30	30.07	0.601	−6.047	0.7528	0.0973	−20.6	−10.2	−9.8	−10.1
28	28.06	0.561	−6.146	0.7527	0.0909	−21.4	−10.3	−9.9	−10.2
24	24.06	0.481	−6.346	0.7526	0.0779	−22.9	−10.5	−10.0	−10.4
20	20.05	0.400	−6.545	0.7525	0.0649	−24.8	−10.6	−10.1	−10.5
16	16.04	0.320	−6.744	0.7524	0.0519	−27.0	−10.8	−10.3	−10.7
12	12.03	0.240	−6.943	0.7523	0.0390	−29.8	−11.0	−10.4	−10.9
8	8.02	0.160	−7.142	0.7522	0.0260	−33.7	−11.1	−10.5	−11.0
4	4.01	0.080	−7.341	0.7521	0.0130	−40.0	−11.3	−10.7	−11.2
0	0.00	0.000	−7.541	0.7520	0.0000	—	−11.5	−10.8	−11.3

−7 °C DRY-BULB

Percentage saturation, μ / %	Relative humidity, ϕ /%	Moisture content, g / (g·kg⁻¹)	Specific enthalpy, h / (kJ·kg⁻¹)	Specific volume, v / (m³·kg⁻¹)	Vapour pressure, p_v / kPa	Dew point temperature, θ_d / °C	Adiabatic saturation temperature, $\theta\star$ / °C	Screen, θ'_{sc} / °C	Sling, θ'_{sl} / °C
100	100.00	2.092	−1.834	0.7560	0.3381	−7.0	−7.0	−7.0	−7.0
96	96.01	2.008	−2.042	0.7559	0.3246	−7.5	−7.2	−7.1	−7.2
92	92.02	1.924	−2.250	0.7558	0.3111	−8.0	−7.3	−7.3	−7.3
88	88.04	1.841	−2.458	0.7557	0.2976	−8.5	−7.5	−7.4	−7.5
84	84.04	1.757	−2.667	0.7556	0.2842	−9.0	−7.6	−7.5	−7.6
80	80.05	1.673	−2.875	0.7555	0.2707	−9.5	−7.8	−7.7	−7.8
76	76.06	1.590	−3.083	0.7554	0.2572	−10.1	−7.9	−7.8	−7.9
72	72.07	1.506	−3.291	0.7553	0.2437	−10.7	−8.1	−7.9	−8.1
70	70.07	1.464	−3.395	0.7552	0.2369	−11.0	−8.2	−8.0	−8.1
68	68.07	1.422	−3.499	0.7552	0.2302	−11.4	−8.3	−8.1	−8.2
66	66.07	1.380	−3.603	0.7551	0.2234	−11.7	−8.3	−8.1	−8.3
64	64.08	1.339	−3.708	0.7551	0.2166	−12.0	−8.4	−8.2	−8.4
62	62.08	1.297	−3.812	0.7550	0.2099	−12.4	−8.5	−8.3	−8.5
60	60.08	1.255	−3.916	0.7550	0.2031	−12.8	−8.6	−8.3	−8.5
58	58.08	1.213	−4.020	0.7549	0.1964	−13.1	−8.7	−8.4	−8.6
56	56.08	1.171	−4.124	0.7549	0.1896	−13.5	−8.8	−8.5	−8.7
54	54.08	1.130	−4.228	0.7548	0.1828	−13.9	−8.8	−8.5	−8.8
52	52.08	1.088	−4.332	0.7548	0.1761	−14.3	−8.9	−8.6	−8.9
50	50.08	1.046	−4.436	0.7457	0.1693	−14.8	−9.0	−8.7	−8.9
48	48.08	1.004	−4.540	0.7547	0.1626	−15.2	−9.1	−8.8	−9.0
46	46.08	0.962	−4.644	0.7546	0.1558	−15.7	−9.2	−8.8	−9.1
44	44.08	0.920	−4.748	0.7546	0.1490	−16.1	−9.2	−8.9	−9.2
42	42.08	0.878	−4.852	0.7545	0.1423	−16.6	−9.3	−9.0	−9.3
40	40.08	0.837	−4.956	0.7545	0.1355	−17.2	−9.4	−9.0	−9.3
38	38.08	0.795	−5.061	0.7544	0.1287	−17.7	−9.5	−9.1	−9.4
36	36.08	0.753	−5.165	0.7544	0.1220	−18.3	−9.6	−9.2	−9.5
34	34.07	0.711	−5.269	0.7543	0.1152	−18.9	−9.7	−9.2	−9.6
32	32.07	0.669	−5.373	0.7543	0.1084	−19.5	−9.7	−9.3	−9.7
30	30.07	0.628	−5.477	0.7542	0.1017	−20.2	−9.8	−9.4	−9.7
28	28.07	0.586	−5.581	0.7542	0.0949	−20.9	−9.9	−9.4	−9.8
24	24.06	0.502	−5.789	0.7541	0.0814	−22.5	−10.1	−9.6	−10.0
20	20.05	0.418	−5.997	0.7540	0.0678	−24.3	−10.3	−9.7	−10.1
16	16.04	0.335	−6.206	0.7539	0.0542	−26.6	−10.4	−9.9	−10.3
12	12.04	0.251	−6.414	0.7538	0.0407	−29.4	−10.6	−10.0	−10.5
8	8.02	0.167	−6.622	0.7537	0.0271	−33.3	−10.8	−10.1	−10.6
4	4.01	0.084	−6.830	0.7536	0.0136	−39.6	−10.9	−10.3	−10.8
0	0.00	0.000	−7.038	0.7535	0.0000	—	−11.1	−10.4	−11.0

−6.5 °C DRY-BULB

Percentage saturation, μ / %	Relative humidity, ϕ /%	Moisture content, g / (g·kg⁻¹)	Specific enthalpy, h / (kJ·kg⁻¹)	Specific volume, v / (m³·kg⁻¹)	Vapour pressure, p_v / kPa	Dew point temperature, θ_d / °C	Adiabatic saturation temperature, $\theta\star$ / °C	Screen, θ'_{sc} / °C	Sling, θ'_{sl} / °C
100	100.00	2.184	−1.099	0.7575	0.3530	−6.5	−6.5	−6.5	−6.5
96	96.01	2.097	−1.316	0.7574	0.3390	−7.0	−6.7	−6.6	−6.7
92	92.03	2.010	−1.534	0.7573	0.3249	−7.5	−6.8	−6.8	−6.8
88	88.04	1.922	−1.751	0.7572	0.3108	−8.0	−7.0	−6.9	−7.0
84	84.05	1.835	−1.969	0.7571	0.2967	−8.5	−7.1	−7.0	−7.1
80	80.06	1.748	−2.186	0.7570	0.2826	−9.1	−7.3	−7.2	−7.3
76	76.06	1.660	−2.404	0.7569	0.2685	−9.6	−7.5	−7.3	−7.4
72	72.07	1.573	−2.621	0.7568	0.2544	−10.2	−7.6	−7.5	−7.6
70	70.07	1.529	−2.730	0.7567	0.2474	−10.6	−7.7	−7.5	−7.7
68	68.08	1.485	−2.838	0.7567	0.2403	−10.9	−7.8	−7.6	−7.8
66	66.08	1.442	−2.947	0.7566	0.2333	−11.2	−7.9	−7.7	−7.8
64	64.08	1.398	−3.056	0.7566	0.2262	−11.6	−8.0	−7.7	−7.9
62	62.08	1.354	−3.165	0.7565	0.2192	−11.9	−8.1	−7.8	−8.0
60	60.08	1.311	−3.273	0.7565	0.2121	−12.3	−8.1	−7.9	−8.1
58	58.08	1.267	−3.382	0.7564	0.2051	−12.7	−8.2	−8.0	−8.2
56	56.09	1.223	−3.491	0.7563	0.1980	−13.0	−8.3	−8.0	−8.2
54	54.09	1.180	−3.600	0.7563	0.1909	−13.4	−8.4	−8.1	−8.3
52	52.09	1.136	−3.708	0.7562	0.1839	−13.9	−8.5	−8.2	−8.4
50	50.09	1.092	−3.817	0.7562	0.1768	−14.3	−8.6	−8.2	−8.5
48	48.09	1.048	−3.926	0.7561	0.1698	−14.7	−8.6	−8.3	−8.6
46	46.09	1.005	−4.034	0.7561	0.1627	−15.2	−8.7	−8.4	−8.7
44	44.09	0.961	−4.143	0.7560	0.1556	−15.7	−8.8	−8.5	−8.7
42	42.08	0.917	−4.252	0.7560	0.1486	−16.2	−8.9	−8.5	−8.8
40	40.08	0.874	−4.361	0.7559	0.1415	−16.7	−9.0	−8.6	−8.9
38	38.08	0.830	−4.470	0.7559	0.1344	−17.2	−9.1	−8.7	−9.0
36	36.08	0.786	−4.578	0.7558	0.1274	−17.8	−9.2	−8.7	−9.1
34	34.08	0.743	−4.687	0.7558	0.1203	−18.4	−9.2	−8.8	−9.2
32	32.08	0.699	−4.796	0.7557	0.1132	−19.1	−9.3	−8.9	−9.2
30	30.07	0.655	−4.904	0.7557	0.1062	−19.7	−9.4	−9.0	−9.3
28	28.07	0.612	−5.013	0.7556	0.0991	−20.5	−9.5	−9.0	−9.4
24	24.06	0.524	−5.230	0.7555	0.0850	−22.0	−9.7	−9.2	−9.6
20	20.06	0.437	−5.448	0.7554	0.0708	−23.9	−9.9	−9.3	−9.7
16	16.05	0.350	−5.666	0.7553	0.0566	−26.1	−10.0	−9.5	−9.9
12	12.04	0.262	−5.883	0.7552	0.0425	−29.0	−10.2	−9.6	−10.1
8	8.03	0.175	−6.100	0.7551	0.0283	−32.9	−10.4	−9.8	−10.3
4	4.01	0.087	−6.318	0.7550	0.0142	−39.2	−10.6	−9.9	−10.4
0	0.00	0.000	−6.535	0.7549	0.0000	—	−10.7	−10.0	−10.6

−6 °C DRY-BULB

Percentage saturation, μ / %	Relative humidity, ϕ /%	Value of stated parameter per kg dry air			Vapour pressure, p_v / kPa	Dew point temperature, θ_d / °C	Adiabatic saturation temperature, $\theta^\star$ / °C	Wet bulb temperature	
		Moisture content, g / (g·kg⁻¹)	Specific enthalpy, h / (kJ·kg⁻¹)	Specific volume, v / (m³·kg⁻¹)				Screen, θ'_{sc} / °C	Sling, θ'_{sl} / °C
100	100.00	2.281	−0.354	0.7590	0.3686	−6.0	−6.0	−6.0	−6.0
96	96.01	2.190	−0.581	0.7589	0.3539	−6.5	−6.2	−6.1	−6.2
92	92.03	2.098	−0.808	0.7588	0.3392	−7.0	−6.3	−6.3	−6.3
88	88.04	2.007	−1.035	0.7587	0.3245	−7.5	−6.5	−6.4	−6.5
84	84.05	1.916	−1.262	0.7586	0.3098	−8.0	−6.7	−6.6	−6.6
80	80.06	1.825	−1.490	0.7585	0.2950	−8.6	−6.8	−6.7	−6.8
76	76.07	1.733	−1.717	0.7584	0.2804	−9.1	−7.0	−6.9	−7.0
72	72.07	1.642	−1.944	0.7583	0.2656	−9.8	−7.2	−7.0	−7.1
70	70.08	1.597	−2.058	0.7582	0.2583	−10.1	−7.3	−7.1	−7.2
68	68.08	1.551	−2.171	0.7582	0.2509	−10.4	−7.3	−7.1	−7.3
66	66.08	1.505	−2.285	0.7581	0.2436	−10.7	−7.4	−7.2	−7.4
64	64.08	1.460	−2.398	0.7581	0.2362	−11.1	−7.5	−7.3	−7.5
62	62.09	1.414	−2.512	0.7580	0.2288	−11.4	−7.6	−7.4	−7.6
60	60.09	1.368	−2.625	0.7579	0.2215	−11.8	−7.7	−7.4	−7.6
58	58.09	1.323	−2.739	0.7579	0.2141	−12.2	−7.8	−7.5	−7.7
56	56.09	1.277	−2.852	0.7578	0.2067	−12.6	−7.9	−7.6	−7.8
54	54.09	1.232	−2.966	0.7578	0.1994	−13.0	−8.0	−7.6	−7.9
52	52.09	1.186	−3.080	0.7577	0.1920	−13.4	−8.0	−7.7	−8.0
50	50.09	1.140	−3.193	0.7577	0.1846	−13.8	−8.1	−7.8	−8.1
48	48.09	1.095	−3.307	0.7576	0.1772	−14.3	−8.2	−7.9	−8.1
46	46.09	1.049	−3.420	0.7576	0.1699	−14.7	−8.3	−7.9	−8.2
44	44.09	1.004	−3.534	0.7575	0.1625	−15.2	−8.4	−8.0	−8.3
42	42.09	0.958	−3.648	0.7575	0.1551	−15.7	−8.5	−8.1	−8.4
40	40.09	0.912	−3.761	0.7574	0.1478	−16.2	−8.6	−8.2	−8.5
38	38.09	0.867	−3.875	0.7573	0.1404	−16.8	−8.7	−8.2	−8.6
36	36.08	0.821	−3.988	0.7573	0.1330	−17.4	−8.7	−8.3	−8.7
34	34.08	0.776	−4.102	0.7572	0.1256	−18.0	−8.8	−8.4	−8.7
32	32.08	0.730	−4.216	0.7572	0.1182	−18.6	−8.9	−8.5	−8.8
30	30.08	0.684	−4.329	0.7571	0.1108	−19.3	−9.0	−8.5	−8.9
28	28.07	0.639	−4.443	0.7571	0.1035	−20.0	−9.1	−8.6	−9.0
24	24.07	0.547	−4.670	0.7570	0.0887	−21.6	−9.3	−8.8	−9.2
20	20.06	0.456	−4.897	0.7568	0.0739	−23.5	−9.5	−8.9	−9.3
16	16.05	0.365	−5.124	0.7567	0.0592	−25.7	−9.6	−9.1	−9.5
12	12.04	0.274	−5.351	0.7566	0.0444	−28.6	−9.8	−9.2	−9.7
8	8.03	0.182	−5.578	0.7565	0.0296	−32.4	−10.0	−9.4	−9.9
4	4.01	0.091	−5.806	0.7564	0.0148	−38.8	−10.2	−9.5	−10.1
0	0.00	0.000	−6.033	0.7563	0.0000	—	−10.4	−9.7	−10.2

−5.5 °C DRY-BULB

Percentage saturation, μ / %	Relative humidity, ϕ /%	Value of stated parameter per kg dry air			Vapour pressure, p_v / kPa	Dew point temperature, θ_d / °C	Adiabatic saturation temperature, $\theta^\star$ / °C	Wet bulb temperature	
		Moisture content, g / (g·kg⁻¹)	Specific enthalpy, h / (kJ·kg⁻¹)	Specific volume, v / (m³·kg⁻¹)				Screen, θ'_{sc} / °C	Sling, θ'_{sl} / °C
100	100.00	2.381	0.400	0.7606	0.3847	−5.5	−5.5	−5.5	−5.5
96	96.01	2.286	0.164	0.7605	0.3694	−6.0	−5.7	−5.6	−5.7
92	92.03	2.191	−0.074	0.7604	0.3540	−6.5	−5.8	−5.8	−5.8
88	88.04	2.095	−0.311	0.7602	0.3387	−7.0	−6.0	−5.9	−6.0
84	84.05	2.000	−0.548	0.7601	0.3234	−7.5	−6.2	−6.1	−6.2
80	80.06	1.905	−0.785	0.7600	0.3080	−8.1	−6.4	−6.2	−6.3
76	76.07	1.810	−1.022	0.7599	0.2926	−8.7	−6.5	−6.4	−6.5
72	72.08	1.714	−1.260	0.7598	0.2773	−9.3	−6.7	−6.5	−6.7
70	70.08	1.667	−1.378	0.7597	0.2696	−9.6	−6.8	−6.6	−6.8
68	68.08	1.619	−1.497	0.7597	0.2619	−9.9	−6.9	−6.7	−6.8
66	66.08	1.572	−1.616	0.7596	0.2542	−10.3	−7.0	−6.8	−6.9
64	64.09	1.524	−1.734	0.7596	0.2466	−10.6	−7.1	−6.8	−7.0
62	62.09	1.476	−1.853	0.7595	0.2389	−11.0	−7.2	−6.9	−7.1
60	60.09	1.429	−1.972	0.7594	0.2312	−11.3	−7.2	−7.0	−7.2
58	58.09	1.381	−2.090	0.7594	0.2235	−11.7	−7.3	−7.1	−7.3
56	56.09	1.334	−2.209	0.7593	0.2158	−12.1	−7.4	−7.1	−7.4
54	54.09	1.286	−2.327	0.7593	0.2081	−12.5	−7.5	−7.2	−7.4
52	52.09	1.238	−2.446	0.7592	0.2004	−12.9	−7.6	−7.3	−7.5
50	50.09	1.191	−2.565	0.7592	0.1927	−13.3	−7.7	−7.4	−7.6
48	48.09	1.143	−2.683	0.7591	0.1850	−13.8	−7.8	−7.4	−7.7
46	46.09	1.095	−2.802	0.7590	0.1773	−14.2	−7.9	−7.5	−7.8
44	44.09	1.048	−2.920	0.7590	0.1696	−14.7	−8.0	−7.6	−7.9
42	42.09	1.000	−3.039	0.7589	0.1619	−15.2	−8.1	−7.7	−8.0
40	40.09	0.952	−3.158	0.7589	0.1542	−15.8	−8.1	−7.7	−8.1
38	38.09	0.905	−3.276	0.7588	0.1465	−16.3	−8.2	−7.8	−8.1
36	36.09	0.857	−3.395	0.7588	0.1388	−16.9	−8.3	−7.9	−8.2
34	34.09	0.810	−3.514	0.7587	0.1311	−17.5	−8.4	−8.0	−8.3
32	32.08	0.762	−3.632	0.7586	0.1234	−18.1	−8.5	−8.0	−8.4
30	30.08	0.714	−3.751	0.7586	0.1157	−18.8	−8.6	−8.1	−8.5
28	28.08	0.667	−3.869	0.7585	0.1080	−19.6	−8.7	−8.2	−8.6
24	24.07	0.572	−4.107	0.7584	0.0926	−21.2	−8.9	−8.4	−8.8
20	20.06	0.476	−4.344	0.7583	0.0772	−23.0	−9.1	−8.5	−9.0
16	16.05	0.381	−4.581	0.7582	0.0618	−25.3	−9.3	−8.7	−9.1
12	12.04	0.286	−4.818	0.7581	0.0463	−28.1	−9.5	−8.8	−9.3
8	8.03	0.190	−5.056	0.7579	0.0309	−32.0	−9.6	−9.0	−9.5
4	4.01	0.095	−5.293	0.7578	0.0154	−38.4	−9.8	−9.1	−9.7
0	0.00	0.000	−5.530	0.7577	0.0000	—	−10.0	−9.3	−9.9

−5 °C DRY-BULB

Percentage saturation, μ / %	Relative humidity, ϕ /%	Value of stated parameter per kg dry air			Vapour pressure, p_v / kPa	Dew point temperature, θ_d / °C	Adiabatic saturation temperature, $\theta\star$ / °C	Wet bulb temperature	
		Moisture content, g /(g·kg⁻¹)	Specific enthalpy, h /(kJ·kg⁻¹)	Specific volume, v /(m³·kg⁻¹)				Screen, θ'_{sc} / °C	Sling, θ'_{sl} / °C
100	100.00	2.486	1.166	0.7621	0.4015	−5.0	−5.0	−5.0	−5.0
96	96.02	2.386	0.918	0.7620	0.3855	−5.5	−5.2	−5.1	−5.2
92	92.03	2.287	0.670	0.7619	0.3695	−6.0	−5.4	−5.3	−5.3
88	88.04	2.187	0.423	0.7618	0.3535	−6.5	−5.5	−5.5	−5.5
84	84.05	2.088	0.175	0.7617	0.3375	−7.0	−5.7	−5.6	−5.7
80	80.06	1.988	−0.073	0.7615	0.3215	−7.6	−5.9	−5.8	−5.9
76	76.07	1.889	−0.320	0.7614	0.3054	−8.2	−6.1	−5.9	−6.0
72	72.08	1.790	−0.568	0.7613	0.2894	−8.8	−6.2	−6.1	−6.2
70	70.08	1.740	−0.692	0.7612	0.2814	−9.1	−6.3	−6.1	−6.3
68	68.09	1.690	−0.816	0.7612	0.2734	−9.4	−6.4	−6.2	−6.4
66	66.09	1.640	−0.940	0.7611	0.2654	−9.8	−6.5	−6.3	−6.5
64	64.09	1.591	−1.064	0.7611	0.2573	−10.1	−6.6	−6.4	−6.6
62	62.09	1.541	−1.188	0.7610	0.2493	−10.5	−6.7	−6.4	−6.6
60	60.09	1.491	−1.311	0.7609	0.2413	−10.8	−6.8	−6.5	−6.7
58	58.10	1.442	−1.435	0.7609	0.2333	−11.2	−6.9	−6.6	−6.8
56	56.10	1.392	−1.559	0.7608	0.2252	−11.6	−7.0	−6.7	−6.9
54	54.10	1.342	−1.683	0.7608	0.2172	−12.0	−7.1	−6.8	−7.0
52	52.10	1.292	−1.807	0.7607	0.2092	−12.4	−7.2	−6.8	−7.1
50	50.10	1.243	−1.931	0.7606	0.2012	−12.9	−7.3	−6.9	−7.2
48	48.10	1.193	−2.055	0.7606	0.1931	−13.3	−7.4	−7.0	−7.3
46	46.10	1.143	−2.178	0.7605	0.1851	−13.8	−7.4	−7.1	−7.4
44	44.10	1.094	−2.302	0.7605	0.1771	−14.3	−7.5	−7.1	−7.5
42	42.10	1.044	−2.426	0.7604	0.1690	−14.8	−7.6	−7.2	−7.5
40	40.09	0.994	−2.550	0.7603	0.1610	−15.3	−7.7	−7.3	−7.6
38	38.09	0.944	−2.674	0.7603	0.1530	−15.9	−7.8	−7.4	−7.7
36	36.09	0.895	−2.798	0.7602	0.1449	−16.4	−7.9	−7.5	−7.8
34	34.09	0.845	−2.922	0.7602	0.1369	−17.0	−8.0	−7.5	−7.9
32	32.09	0.795	−3.045	0.7601	0.1288	−17.7	−8.1	−7.6	−8.0
30	30.08	0.746	−3.169	0.7600	0.1208	−18.4	−8.2	−7.7	−8.1
28	28.08	0.696	−3.293	0.7600	0.1127	−19.1	−8.3	−7.8	−8.2
24	24.07	0.597	−3.541	0.7599	0.0966	−20.7	−8.5	−7.9	−8.4
20	20.06	0.497	−3.789	0.7597	0.0806	−22.6	−8.7	−8.1	−8.6
16	16.05	0.398	−4.036	0.7596	0.0645	−24.9	−8.9	−8.3	−8.8
12	12.04	0.298	−4.284	0.7595	0.0484	−27.7	−9.1	−8.4	−8.9
8	8.03	0.199	−4.532	0.7594	0.0322	−31.6	−9.3	−8.6	−9.1
4	4.02	0.099	−4.780	0.7593	0.0161	−38.0	−9.5	−8.8	−9.3
0	0.00	0.000	−5.027	0.7591	0.0000	—	−9.7	−8.9	−9.5

−4.5 °C DRY-BULB

Percentage saturation, μ / %	Relative humidity, ϕ /%	Value of stated parameter per kg dry air			Vapour pressure, p_v / kPa	Dew point temperature, θ_d / °C	Adiabatic saturation temperature, $\theta\star$ / °C	Wet bulb temperature	
		Moisture content, g /(g·kg⁻¹)	Specific enthalpy, h /(kJ·kg⁻¹)	Specific volume, v /(m³·kg⁻¹)				Screen, θ'_{sc} / °C	Sling, θ'_{sl} / °C
100	100.00	2.594	1.941	0.7637	0.4190	−4.5	−4.5	−4.5	−4.5
96	96.02	2.490	1.683	0.7636	0.4023	−5.0	−4.7	−4.7	−4.7
92	92.03	2.387	1.424	0.7635	0.3856	−5.5	−4.9	−4.8	−4.9
88	88.04	2.283	1.166	0.7633	0.3689	−6.0	−5.0	−5.0	−5.0
84	84.06	2.179	0.907	0.7632	0.3522	−6.5	−5.2	−5.1	−5.2
80	80.07	2.075	0.648	0.7631	0.3355	−7.1	−5.4	−5.3	−5.4
76	76.08	1.972	0.390	0.7629	0.3187	−7.7	−5.6	−5.4	−5.6
72	72.08	1.868	0.131	0.7628	0.3020	−8.3	−5.8	−5.6	−5.7
70	70.09	1.816	0.002	0.7628	0.2936	−8.6	−5.9	−5.7	−5.8
68	68.09	1.764	−0.128	0.7627	0.2853	−8.9	−6.0	−5.8	−5.9
66	66.09	1.712	−0.257	0.7626	0.2769	−9.3	−6.1	−5.8	−6.0
64	64.10	1.660	−0.386	0.7626	0.2685	−9.6	−6.2	−5.9	−6.1
62	62.10	1.608	−0.516	0.7625	0.2602	−10.0	−6.3	−6.0	−6.2
60	60.10	1.556	−0.645	0.7624	0.2518	−10.4	−6.3	−6.1	−6.3
58	58.10	1.505	−0.774	0.7624	0.2434	−10.7	−6.4	−6.2	−6.4
56	56.10	1.453	−0.904	0.7623	0.2350	−11.1	−6.5	−6.2	−6.5
54	54.10	1.401	−1.033	0.7623	0.2267	−11.5	−6.6	−6.3	−6.6
52	52.10	1.349	−1.162	0.7622	0.2183	−12.0	−6.7	−6.4	−6.7
50	50.10	1.297	−1.292	0.7621	0.2099	−12.4	−6.8	−6.5	−6.8
48	48.10	1.245	−1.421	0.7621	0.2015	−12.8	−6.9	−6.6	−6.8
46	46.10	1.193	−1.550	0.7620	0.1932	−13.3	−7.0	−6.6	−6.9
44	44.10	1.141	−1.680	0.7619	0.1848	−13.8	−7.1	−6.7	−7.0
42	42.10	1.090	−1.809	0.7619	0.1764	−14.3	−7.2	−6.8	−7.1
40	40.10	1.038	−1.938	0.7618	0.1680	−14.8	−7.3	−6.9	−7.2
38	38.10	0.986	−2.068	0.7618	0.1596	−15.4	−7.4	−7.0	−7.3
36	36.10	0.934	−2.197	0.7617	0.1512	−16.0	−7.5	−7.0	−7.4
34	34.09	0.882	−2.326	0.7616	0.1428	−16.6	−7.6	−7.1	−7.5
32	32.09	0.830	−2.455	0.7616	0.1344	−17.2	−7.7	−7.2	−7.6
30	30.09	0.778	−2.585	0.7615	0.1261	−17.9	−7.8	−7.3	−7.7
28	28.08	0.726	−2.714	0.7614	0.1177	−18.7	−7.9	−7.4	−7.8
24	24.08	0.623	−2.973	0.7613	0.1009	−20.3	−8.1	−7.5	−8.0
20	20.07	0.519	−3.231	0.7612	0.0841	−22.2	−8.3	−7.7	−8.2
16	16.06	0.415	−3.490	0.7611	0.0673	−24.4	−8.5	−7.9	−8.4
12	12.04	0.311	−3.749	0.7609	0.0505	−27.3	−8.7	−8.0	−8.6
8	8.03	0.208	−4.007	0.7608	0.0336	−31.2	−8.9	−8.2	−8.8
4	4.02	0.104	−4.266	0.7607	0.0168	−37.7	−9.1	−8.4	−9.0
0	0.00	0.000	−4.524	0.7606	0.0000	—	−9.3	−8.5	−9.2

−4 °C DRY-BULB

Percentage saturation, μ / %	Relative humidity, ϕ /%	Value of stated parameter per kg dry air			Vapour pressure, p_v / kPa	Dew point temperature, θ_d / °C	Adiabatic saturation temperature, $\theta^\star$ / °C	Wet bulb temperature	
		Moisture content, g / (g·kg⁻¹)	Specific enthalpy, h / (kJ·kg⁻¹)	Specific volume, v / (m³·kg⁻¹)				Screen, θ'_{sc} / °C	Sling, θ'_{sl} / °C
100	100.00	2.707	2.729	0.7653	0.4371	−4.0	−4.0	−4.0	−4.0
96	96.02	2.599	2.458	0.7651	0.4197	−4.5	−4.2	−4.2	−4.2
92	92.03	2.490	2.188	0.7650	0.4023	−5.0	−4.4	−4.3	−4.4
88	88.05	2.382	1.918	0.7649	0.3849	−5.5	−4.6	−4.5	−4.5
84	84.06	2.274	1.648	0.7647	0.3674	−6.0	−4.7	−4.6	−4.7
80	80.07	2.166	1.378	0.7646	0.3500	−6.6	−4.9	−4.8	−4.9
76	76.08	2.057	1.108	0.7645	0.3326	−7.2	−5.1	−5.0	−5.1
72	72.09	1.949	0.838	0.7643	0.3151	−7.8	−5.3	−5.1	−5.3
70	70.09	1.895	0.703	0.7643	0.3064	−8.1	−5.4	−5.2	−5.4
68	68.09	1.841	0.568	0.7642	0.2977	−8.5	−5.5	−5.3	−5.5
66	66.10	1.787	0.433	0.7641	0.2889	−8.8	−5.6	−5.4	−5.6
64	64.10	1.732	0.298	0.7641	0.2802	−9.2	−5.7	−5.5	−5.7
62	62.10	1.678	0.163	0.7640	0.2715	−9.5	−5.8	−5.5	−5.7
60	60.10	1.624	0.028	0.7640	0.2627	−9.9	−5.9	−5.6	−5.8
58	58.10	1.570	−0.107	0.7639	0.2540	−10.3	−6.0	−5.7	−5.9
56	56.11	1.516	−0.242	0.7638	0.2452	−10.7	−6.1	−5.8	−6.0
54	54.11	1.462	−0.377	0.7638	0.2365	−11.1	−6.2	−5.9	−6.1
52	52.11	1.408	−0.512	0.7637	0.2278	−11.5	−6.3	−6.0	−6.2
50	50.11	1.353	−0.647	0.7636	0.2190	−11.9	−6.4	−6.0	−6.3
48	48.11	1.299	−0.782	0.7636	0.2103	−12.4	−6.5	−6.1	−6.4
46	46.11	1.245	−0.917	0.7635	0.2016	−12.8	−6.6	−6.2	−6.5
44	44.11	1.191	−1.052	0.7634	0.1928	−13.3	−6.7	−6.3	−6.6
42	42.10	1.137	−1.187	0.7634	0.1840	−13.8	−6.8	−6.4	−6.7
40	40.10	1.083	−1.322	0.7633	0.1753	−14.4	−6.9	−6.5	−6.8
38	38.10	1.029	−1.457	0.7632	0.1666	−14.9	−7.0	−6.5	−6.9
36	36.10	0.974	−1.592	0.7632	0.1578	−15.5	−7.1	−6.6	−7.0
34	34.10	0.920	−1.727	0.7631	0.1490	−16.1	−7.2	−6.7	−7.1
32	32.09	0.866	−1.862	0.7630	0.1403	−16.8	−7.3	−6.8	−7.2
30	30.09	0.812	−1.997	0.7630	0.1315	−17.5	−7.4	−6.9	−7.3
28	28.09	0.758	−2.132	0.7629	0.1228	−18.2	−7.5	−7.0	−7.4
24	24.08	0.650	−2.402	0.7628	0.1052	−19.8	−7.7	−7.1	−7.6
20	20.07	0.541	−2.672	0.7626	0.0877	−21.7	−7.9	−7.3	−7.8
16	16.06	0.433	−2.942	0.7625	0.0702	−24.0	−8.1	−7.5	−8.0
12	12.05	0.325	−3.212	0.7624	0.0526	−26.9	−8.3	−7.7	−8.2
8	8.03	0.217	−3.482	0.7622	0.0351	−30.8	−8.5	−7.8	−8.4
4	4.02	0.108	−3.752	0.7621	0.0176	−37.3	−8.8	−8.0	−8.6
0	0.00	0.000	−4.022	0.7620	0.0000	—	−9.0	−8.2	−8.8

−3.5 °C DRY-BULB

Percentage saturation, μ / %	Relative humidity, ϕ /%	Value of stated parameter per kg dry air			Vapour pressure, p_v / kPa	Dew point temperature, θ_d / °C	Adiabatic saturation temperature, $\theta^\star$ / °C	Wet bulb temperature	
		Moisture content, g / (g·kg⁻¹)	Specific enthalpy, h / (kJ·kg⁻¹)	Specific volume, v / (m³·kg⁻¹)				Screen, θ'_{sc} / °C	Sling, θ'_{sl} / °C
100	100.00	2.824	3.526	0.7668	0.4560	−3.5	−3.5	−3.5	−3.5
96	96.02	2.711	3.244	0.7667	0.4378	−4.0	−3.7	−3.7	−3.7
92	92.03	2.598	2.962	0.7666	0.4197	−4.5	−3.9	−3.8	−3.9
88	88.05	2.485	2.680	0.7664	0.4015	−5.0	−4.1	−4.0	−4.1
84	84.06	2.372	2.399	0.7663	0.3833	−5.5	−4.3	−4.2	−4.2
80	80.07	2.260	2.117	0.7662	0.3651	−6.1	−4.5	−4.3	−4.4
76	76.08	2.146	1.835	0.7660	0.3469	−6.7	−4.7	−4.5	−4.6
72	72.09	2.034	1.553	0.7659	0.3287	−7.3	−4.9	−4.7	−4.8
70	70.09	1.977	1.412	0.7658	0.3196	−7.6	−5.0	−4.7	−4.9
68	68.10	1.920	1.272	0.7657	0.3105	−8.0	−5.1	−4.8	−5.0
66	66.10	1.864	1.131	0.7657	0.3014	−8.3	−5.2	−4.9	−5.1
64	64.10	1.808	0.990	0.7656	0.2923	−8.7	−5.3	−5.0	−5.2
62	62.11	1.751	0.849	0.7655	0.2832	−9.0	−5.4	−5.1	−5.3
60	60.11	1.695	0.708	0.7655	0.2741	−9.4	−5.5	−5.2	−5.4
58	58.11	1.638	0.567	0.7654	0.2650	−9.8	−5.6	−5.3	−5.5
56	56.11	1.582	0.426	0.7653	0.2559	−10.2	−5.7	−5.3	−5.6
54	54.11	1.525	0.285	0.7653	0.2468	−10.6	−5.8	−5.4	−5.7
52	52.11	1.469	0.144	0.7652	0.2376	−11.0	−5.9	−5.5	−5.8
50	50.11	1.412	0.003	0.7651	0.2285	−11.4	−6.0	−5.6	−5.9
48	48.11	1.356	−0.138	0.7650	0.2194	−11.9	−6.1	−5.7	−6.0
46	46.11	1.299	−0.278	0.7650	0.2103	−12.4	−6.2	−5.8	−6.1
44	44.11	1.243	−0.419	0.7649	0.2011	−12.9	−6.3	−5.9	−6.2
42	42.11	1.186	−0.560	0.7648	0.1920	−13.4	−6.4	−5.9	−6.3
40	40.11	1.130	−0.701	0.7648	0.1829	−13.9	−6.5	−6.0	−6.4
38	38.11	1.073	−0.842	0.7647	0.1738	−14.5	−6.6	−6.1	−6.5
36	36.10	1.017	−0.983	0.7646	0.1646	−15.1	−6.7	−6.2	−6.6
34	34.10	0.960	−1.124	0.7646	0.1555	−15.7	−6.8	−6.3	−6.7
32	32.10	0.904	−1.265	0.7645	0.1464	−16.3	−6.9	−6.4	−6.8
30	30.09	0.847	−1.406	0.7644	0.1372	−17.0	−7.0	−6.5	−6.9
28	28.09	0.791	−1.546	0.7644	0.1281	−17.8	−7.1	−6.5	−7.0
24	24.08	0.678	−1.828	0.7642	0.1098	−19.4	−7.3	−6.5	−7.2
20	20.07	0.565	−2.110	0.7641	0.0915	−21.3	−7.5	−6.5	−7.4
16	16.06	0.452	−2.392	0.7639	0.0732	−23.6	−7.7	−6.5	−7.6
12	12.05	0.339	−2.674	0.7638	0.0549	−26.5	−8.0	−6.5	−7.8
8	8.03	0.226	−2.956	0.7637	0.0366	−30.4	−8.2	−6.5	−8.0
4	4.02	0.113	−3.237	0.7635	0.0183	−36.9	−8.4	−6.5	−8.2
0	0.00	0.000	−3.519	0.7634	0.0000	—	−8.6	−6.5	−8.5

−3 °C DRY-BULB

Percentage saturation, μ / %	Relative humidity, ϕ /%	Value of stated parameter per kg dry air			Vapour pressure, p_v / kPa	Dew point temperature, θ_d / °C	Adiabatic saturation temperature, $\theta\star$ / °C	Wet bulb temperature	
		Moisture content, g / (g·kg⁻¹)	Specific enthalpy, h / (kJ·kg⁻¹)	Specific volume, v / (m³·kg⁻¹)				Screen, θ'_{sc} / °C	Sling, θ'_{sl} / °C
100	100.00	2.946	4.336	0.7684	0.4756	−3.0	−3.0	−3.0	−3.0
96	96.02	2.828	4.042	0.7683	0.4567	−3.5	−3.2	−3.2	−3.2
92	92.03	2.711	3.747	0.7681	0.4377	−4.0	−3.4	−3.3	−3.4
88	88.05	2.593	3.453	0.7680	0.4188	−4.5	−3.6	−3.5	−3.6
84	84.06	2.475	3.159	0.7678	0.3998	−5.0	−3.8	−3.7	−3.8
80	80.07	2.357	2.865	0.7677	0.3808	−5.6	−4.0	−3.8	−4.0
76	76.09	2.239	2.571	0.7676	0.3619	−6.2	−4.2	−4.0	−4.2
72	72.09	2.121	2.277	0.7674	0.3429	−6.8	−4.4	−4.2	−4.4
70	70.10	2.062	2.130	0.7673	0.3334	−7.2	−4.5	−4.3	−4.5
68	68.10	2.004	1.983	0.7673	0.3239	−7.5	−4.6	−4.4	−4.6
66	66.11	1.945	1.836	0.7672	0.3144	−7.8	−4.7	−4.5	−4.6
64	64.11	1.886	1.689	0.7671	0.3049	−8.2	−4.8	−4.5	−4.7
62	62.11	1.827	1.542	0.7670	0.2954	−8.6	−4.9	−4.6	−4.8
60	60.11	1.768	1.395	0.7670	0.2859	−8.9	−5.0	−4.7	−4.9
58	58.11	1.709	1.248	0.7669	0.2764	−9.3	−5.1	−4.8	−5.1
56	56.12	1.650	1.101	0.7668	0.2669	−9.7	−5.2	−4.9	−5.2
54	54.12	1.591	0.954	0.7668	0.2574	−10.1	−5.3	−5.0	−5.3
52	52.12	1.532	0.807	0.7667	0.2479	−10.5	−5.4	−5.1	−5.4
50	50.12	1.473	0.660	0.7666	0.2384	−11.0	−5.5	−5.2	−5.5
48	48.12	1.414	0.513	0.7665	0.2288	−11.4	−5.6	−5.3	−5.6
46	46.12	1.355	0.366	0.7665	0.2193	−11.9	−5.7	−5.3	−5.7
44	44.12	1.296	0.218	0.7664	0.2098	−12.4	−5.9	−5.4	−5.8
42	42.11	1.238	0.072	0.7663	0.2003	−12.9	−6.0	−5.5	−5.9
40	40.11	1.178	−0.076	0.7663	0.1908	−13.4	−6.1	−5.6	−6.0
38	38.11	1.120	−0.223	0.7662	0.1812	−14.0	−6.2	−5.7	−6.1
36	36.11	1.061	−0.370	0.7661	0.1717	−14.6	−6.3	−5.8	−6.2
34	34.11	1.002	−0.517	0.7660	0.1622	−15.2	−6.4	−5.9	−6.3
32	32.10	0.943	−0.664	0.7660	0.1527	−15.9	−6.5	−6.0	−6.4
30	30.10	0.884	−0.811	0.7659	0.1432	−16.6	−6.6	−6.0	−6.5
28	28.09	0.825	−0.958	0.7658	0.1336	−17.3	−6.7	−6.2	−6.6
24	24.09	0.707	−1.252	0.7657	0.1146	−18.9	−6.9	−6.3	−6.8
20	20.08	0.589	−1.546	0.7655	0.0955	−20.8	−7.2	−6.5	−7.0
16	16.06	0.471	−1.840	0.7654	0.0764	−23.1	−7.4	−6.7	−7.2
12	12.05	0.354	−2.134	0.7652	0.0573	−26.0	−7.6	−6.9	−7.5
8	8.03	0.236	−2.428	0.7651	0.0382	−30.0	−7.8	−7.1	−7.7
4	4.02	0.118	−2.722	0.7650	0.0191	−36.5	−8.1	−7.3	−7.9
0	0.00	0.000	−3.016	0.7648	0.0000	—	−8.3	−7.5	−8.1

−2.5 °C DRY-BULB

Percentage saturation, μ / %	Relative humidity, ϕ /%	Value of stated parameter per kg dry air			Vapour pressure, p_v / kPa	Dew point temperature, θ_d / °C	Adiabatic saturation temperature, $\theta\star$ / °C	Wet bulb temperature	
		Moisture content, g / (g·kg⁻¹)	Specific enthalpy, h / (kJ·kg⁻¹)	Specific volume, v / (m³·kg⁻¹)				Screen, θ'_{sc} / °C	Sling, θ'_{sl} / °C
100	100.00	3.073	5.158	0.7700	0.4960	−2.5	−2.5	−2.5	−2.5
96	96.02	2.950	4.851	0.7698	0.4762	−3.0	−2.7	−2.7	−2.7
92	92.04	2.827	4.544	0.7697	0.4565	−3.5	−2.9	−2.8	−2.9
88	88.05	2.704	4.237	0.7695	0.4367	−4.0	−3.1	−3.0	−3.1
84	84.07	2.582	3.930	0.7694	0.4170	−4.6	−3.3	−3.2	−3.3
80	80.08	2.458	3.623	0.7692	0.3972	−5.1	−3.5	−3.4	−3.5
76	76.09	2.336	3.317	0.7691	0.3774	−5.7	−3.7	−3.6	−3.7
72	72.10	2.213	3.010	0.7689	0.3576	−6.4	−3.9	−3.7	−3.9
70	70.10	2.151	2.856	0.7689	0.3477	−6.7	−4.0	−3.8	−4.0
68	68.11	2.090	2.703	0.7688	0.3378	−7.0	−4.1	−3.9	−4.1
66	66.11	2.028	2.550	0.7687	0.3279	−7.4	−4.2	−4.0	−4.2
64	64.11	1.967	2.396	0.7686	0.3180	−7.7	−4.4	−4.1	−4.3
62	62.12	1.905	2.243	0.7686	0.3081	−8.1	−4.5	−4.2	−4.4
60	60.12	1.844	2.089	0.7685	0.2982	−8.4	−4.6	−4.3	−4.5
58	58.12	1.782	1.936	0.7684	0.2883	−8.8	−4.7	−4.4	−4.6
56	56.12	1.721	1.782	0.7683	0.2783	−9.2	−4.8	−4.5	−4.7
54	54.12	1.660	1.629	0.7683	0.2684	−9.6	−4.9	−4.5	−4.8
52	52.12	1.598	1.476	0.7682	0.2585	−10.1	−5.0	−4.6	−4.9
50	50.12	1.537	1.322	0.7681	0.2486	−10.5	−5.1	−4.7	−5.0
48	48.12	1.475	1.169	0.7680	0.2387	−11.0	−5.2	−4.8	−5.1
46	46.12	1.414	1.015	0.7680	0.2288	−11.4	−5.3	−4.9	−5.2
44	44.12	1.352	0.862	0.7679	0.2188	−11.9	−5.4	−5.0	−5.3
42	42.12	1.291	0.708	0.7678	0.2089	−12.4	−5.5	−5.1	−5.4
40	40.12	1.229	0.555	0.7677	0.1990	−13.0	−5.7	−5.2	−5.6
38	38.12	1.168	0.402	0.7677	0.1890	−13.5	−5.8	−5.3	−5.7
36	36.11	1.106	0.248	0.7676	0.1791	−14.1	−5.9	−5.4	−5.8
34	34.11	1.045	0.095	0.7675	0.1692	−14.8	−6.0	−5.5	−5.9
32	32.11	0.983	−0.059	0.7674	0.1592	−15.4	−6.1	−5.6	−6.0
30	30.10	0.922	−0.212	0.7674	0.1493	−16.1	−6.2	−5.7	−6.1
28	28.10	0.860	−0.366	0.7673	0.1394	−16.9	−6.3	−5.8	−6.2
24	24.09	0.738	−0.672	0.7671	0.1195	−18.5	−6.5	−5.9	−6.4
20	20.08	0.615	−0.979	0.7670	0.0996	−20.4	−6.8	−6.1	−6.6
16	16.07	0.492	−1.286	0.7668	0.0797	−22.7	−7.0	−6.3	−6.9
12	12.05	0.369	−1.593	0.7667	0.0598	−25.6	−7.2	−6.5	−7.1
8	8.04	0.246	−1.900	0.7665	0.0399	−29.6	−7.5	−6.7	−7.3
4	4.02	0.122	−2.207	0.7664	0.0199	−36.1	−7.7	−6.9	−7.5
0	0.00	0.000	−2.514	0.7662	0.0000	—	−7.9	−7.1	−7.8

–2 °C DRY-BULB

Percentage saturation, μ / %	Relative humidity, ϕ /%	Value of stated parameter per kg dry air			Vapour pressure, p_v / kPa	Dew point temperature, θ_d / °C	Adiabatic saturation temperature, $\theta^\star$ / °C	Wet bulb temperature	
		Moisture content, g / (g·kg^{-1})	Specific enthalpy, h / (kJ·kg^{-1})	Specific volume, v / (m^3·kg^{-1})				Screen, θ'_{sc} / °C	Sling, θ'_{sl} / °C
100	100.00	3.205	5.992	0.7716	0.5171	−2.0	−2.0	−2.0	−2.0
96	96.02	3.077	5.672	0.7714	0.4966	−2.5	−2.2	−2.2	−2.2
92	92.04	2.949	5.352	0.7713	0.4760	−3.0	−2.4	−2.4	−2.4
88	88.05	2.820	5.032	0.7711	0.4554	−3.5	−2.6	−2.5	−2.6
84	84.07	2.692	4.712	0.7710	0.4348	−4.1	−2.8	−2.7	−2.8
80	80.08	2.564	4.392	0.7708	0.4141	−4.6	−3.0	−2.9	−3.0
76	76.09	2.436	4.072	0.7706	0.3935	−5.2	−3.3	−3.1	−3.2
72	72.10	2.308	3.752	0.7705	0.3729	−5.9	−3.5	−3.3	−3.4
70	70.11	2.244	3.591	0.7704	0.3626	−6.2	−3.6	−3.4	−3.5
68	68.11	2.179	3.431	0.7703	0.3522	−6.5	−3.7	−3.4	−3.6
66	66.11	2.115	3.271	0.7703	0.3419	−6.9	−3.8	−3.5	−3.7
64	64.12	2.051	3.111	0.7702	0.3316	−7.2	−3.9	−3.6	−3.8
62	62.12	1.987	2.951	0.7701	0.3212	−7.6	−4.0	−3.7	−4.0
60	60.12	1.923	2.791	0.7700	0.3109	−8.0	−4.1	−3.8	−4.1
58	58.12	1.859	2.631	0.7699	0.3006	−8.4	−4.2	−3.9	−4.2
56	56.13	1.795	2.471	0.7699	0.2902	−8.8	−4.3	−4.0	−4.3
54	54.13	1.731	2.311	0.7698	0.2799	−9.2	−4.5	−4.1	−4.4
52	52.13	1.667	2.151	0.7697	0.2696	−9.6	−4.6	−4.2	−4.5
50	50.13	1.602	1.991	0.7696	0.2592	−10.0	−4.7	−4.3	−4.6
48	48.13	1.538	1.831	0.7695	0.2489	−10.5	−4.8	−4.4	−4.7
46	46.13	1.474	1.671	0.7695	0.2385	−11.0	−4.9	−4.5	−4.8
44	44.13	1.410	1.511	0.7694	0.2282	−11.5	−5.0	−4.6	−4.9
42	42.12	1.346	1.350	0.7693	0.2178	−12.0	−5.1	−4.7	−5.0
40	40.12	1.282	1.190	0.7692	0.2075	−12.5	−5.2	−4.8	−5.1
38	38.12	1.218	1.030	0.7692	0.1971	−13.1	−5.4	−4.9	−5.3
36	36.12	1.154	0.870	0.7691	0.1868	−13.7	−5.5	−5.0	−5.4
34	34.11	1.090	0.710	0.7690	0.1764	−14.3	−5.6	−5.0	−5.5
32	32.11	1.026	0.550	0.7689	0.1661	−15.0	−5.7	−5.1	−5.6
30	30.11	0.962	0.390	0.7688	0.1557	−15.7	−5.8	−5.2	−5.7
28	28.10	0.897	0.230	0.7688	0.1453	−16.4	−5.9	−5.4	−5.8
24	24.09	0.769	−0.090	0.7686	0.1246	−18.0	−6.2	−5.5	−6.0
20	20.08	0.641	−0.410	0.7684	0.1038	−20.0	−6.4	−5.8	−6.3
16	16.07	0.513	−0.730	0.7683	0.0831	−22.3	−6.6	−6.0	−6.5
12	12.05	0.385	−1.050	0.7681	0.0623	−25.2	−6.9	−6.1	−6.7
8	8.04	0.256	−1.371	0.7680	0.0416	−29.2	−7.1	−6.4	−7.0
4	4.02	0.128	−1.691	0.7678	0.0208	−35.7	−7.4	−6.6	−7.2
0	0.00	0.000	−2.011	0.7677	0.0000	—	−7.6	−6.7	−7.4

–1.5 °C DRY-BULB

Percentage saturation, μ / %	Relative humidity, ϕ /%	Value of stated parameter per kg dry air			Vapour pressure, p_v / kPa	Dew point temperature, θ_d / °C	Adiabatic saturation temperature, $\theta^\star$ / °C	Wet bulb temperature	
		Moisture content, g / (g·kg^{-1})	Specific enthalpy, h / (kJ·kg^{-1})	Specific volume, v / (m^3·kg^{-1})				Screen, θ'_{sc} / °C	Sling, θ'_{sl} / °C
100	100.00	3.342	6.840	0.7732	0.5391	−1.5	−1.5	−1.5	−1.5
96	96.02	3.208	6.506	0.7730	0.5177	−2.0	−1.7	−1.7	−1.7
92	92.04	3.075	6.172	0.7729	0.4962	−2.5	−1.9	−1.9	−1.9
88	88.06	2.941	5.838	0.7727	0.4747	−3.0	−2.1	−2.1	−2.1
84	84.07	2.807	5.504	0.7725	0.4533	−3.6	−2.4	−2.2	−2.3
80	80.09	2.674	5.171	0.7724	0.4318	−4.1	−2.6	−2.4	−2.5
76	76.10	2.540	4.837	0.7722	0.4103	−4.7	−2.8	−2.6	−2.8
72	72.11	2.406	4.503	0.7720	0.3888	−5.4	−3.0	−2.8	−3.0
70	70.11	2.339	4.336	0.7720	0.3780	−5.7	−3.1	−2.9	−3.1
68	68.12	2.272	4.169	0.7719	0.3672	−6.0	−3.2	−3.0	−3.2
66	66.12	2.206	4.002	0.7718	0.3565	−6.4	−3.3	−3.1	−3.3
64	64.12	2.139	3.835	0.7717	0.3457	−6.7	−3.5	−3.2	−3.4
62	62.13	2.072	3.668	0.7716	0.3349	−7.1	−3.6	−3.3	−3.5
60	60.13	2.005	3.501	0.7715	0.3242	−7.5	−3.7	−3.4	−3.6
58	58.13	1.938	3.334	0.7715	0.3134	−7.9	−3.8	−3.5	−3.7
56	56.13	1.872	3.167	0.7714	0.3026	−8.3	−3.9	−3.6	−3.8
54	54.13	1.805	3.000	0.7713	0.2918	−8.7	−4.0	−3.7	−3.9
52	52.13	1.738	2.833	0.7712	0.2810	−9.1	−4.1	−3.8	−4.1
50	50.13	1.671	2.666	0.7711	0.2703	−9.6	−4.3	−3.9	−4.2
48	48.13	1.604	2.499	0.7710	0.2595	−10.0	−4.4	−4.0	−4.3
46	46.13	1.537	2.332	0.7710	0.2487	−10.5	−4.5	−4.1	−4.4
44	44.13	1.470	2.165	0.7709	0.2379	−11.0	−4.6	−4.2	−4.5
42	42.13	1.404	1.998	0.7708	0.2271	−11.5	−4.7	−4.3	−4.6
40	40.13	1.337	1.831	0.7707	0.2163	−12.1	−4.8	−4.4	−4.7
38	38.13	1.270	1.664	0.7706	0.2056	−12.6	−5.0	−4.5	−4.8
36	36.12	1.203	1.497	0.7706	0.1948	−13.2	−5.1	−4.5	−5.0
34	34.12	1.136	1.330	0.7705	0.1840	−13.8	−5.2	−4.6	−5.1
32	32.12	1.069	1.163	0.7704	0.1732	−14.5	−5.3	−4.7	−5.2
30	30.11	1.003	0.996	0.7703	0.1623	−15.2	−5.4	−4.8	−5.3
28	28.11	0.936	0.829	0.7702	0.1515	−16.0	−5.5	−5.0	−5.4
24	24.10	0.802	0.496	0.7701	0.1299	−17.6	−5.8	−5.2	−5.7
20	20.09	0.668	0.162	0.7699	0.1083	−19.5	−6.0	−5.4	−5.9
16	16.07	0.535	−0.172	0.7697	0.0866	−21.8	−6.3	−5.6	−6.1
12	12.06	0.401	−0.506	0.7696	0.0650	−24.8	−6.5	−5.8	−6.4
8	8.04	0.267	−0.840	0.7694	0.0433	−28.8	−6.8	−6.0	−6.6
4	4.02	0.134	−1.174	0.7692	0.0217	−35.3	−7.0	−6.2	−6.8
0	0.00	0.000	−1.508	0.7691	0.0000	—	−7.3	−6.4	−7.1

−1 °C DRY-BULB

Percentage saturation, μ / %	Relative humidity, ϕ /%	Value of stated parameter per kg dry air			Vapour pressure, p_v / kPa	Dew point temperature, θ_d / °C	Adiabatic saturation temperature, $\theta^\star$ / °C	Wet bulb temperature	
		Moisture content, g /(g·kg^{-1})	Specific enthalpy, h /(kJ·kg^{-1})	Specific volume, v /(m³·kg^{-1})				Screen, θ'_{sc}/ °C	Sling, θ'_{sl}/ °C
100	100.00	3.484	7.702	0.7748	0.5620	−1.0	−1.0	−1.0	−1.0
96	96.02	3.345	7.354	0.7746	0.5396	−1.5	−1.2	−1.2	−1.2
92	92.04	3.206	7.005	0.7744	0.5172	−2.0	−1.4	−1.4	−1.4
88	88.06	3.066	6.657	0.7743	0.4949	−2.5	−1.7	−1.6	−1.6
84	84.07	2.927	6.309	0.7741	0.4725	−3.1	−1.9	−1.8	−1.9
80	80.09	2.787	5.960	0.7739	0.4501	−3.7	−2.1	−1.9	−2.1
76	76.10	2.648	5.612	0.7738	0.4277	−4.3	−2.3	−2.1	−2.3
72	72.11	2.509	5.264	0.7736	0.4052	−4.9	−2.5	−2.3	−2.5
70	70.12	2.439	5.090	0.7735	0.3940	−5.2	−2.7	−2.4	−2.6
68	68.12	2.369	4.916	0.7734	0.3828	−5.6	−2.8	−2.5	−2.7
66	66.12	2.300	4.741	0.7733	0.3716	−5.9	−2.9	−2.6	−2.8
64	64.13	2.230	4.567	0.7732	0.3604	−6.3	−3.0	−2.7	−2.9
62	62.13	2.160	4.393	0.7732	0.3492	−6.6	−3.1	−2.8	−3.1
60	60.13	2.091	4.219	0.7731	0.3379	−7.0	−3.2	−2.9	−3.2
58	58.14	2.021	4.045	0.7730	0.3267	−7.4	−3.4	−3.0	−3.3
56	56.14	1.951	3.871	0.7729	0.3155	−7.8	−3.5	−3.1	−3.4
54	54.14	1.882	3.696	0.7728	0.3042	−8.2	−3.6	−3.2	−3.5
52	52.14	1.812	3.522	0.7727	0.2930	−8.6	−3.7	−3.3	−3.6
50	50.14	1.742	3.348	0.7726	0.2818	−9.1	−3.8	−3.4	−3.7
48	48.14	1.672	3.174	0.7726	0.2705	−9.6	−3.9	−3.5	−3.9
46	46.14	1.603	3.000	0.7725	0.2593	−10.0	−4.1	−3.6	−4.0
44	44.14	1.533	2.826	0.7724	0.2480	−10.5	−4.2	−3.7	−4.1
42	42.14	1.463	2.652	0.7723	0.2368	−11.1	−4.3	−3.8	−4.2
40	40.13	1.394	2.477	0.7722	0.2255	−11.6	−4.4	−3.9	−4.3
38	38.13	1.324	2.303	0.7721	0.2143	−12.2	−4.5	−4.0	−4.4
36	36.13	1.254	2.129	0.7720	0.2030	−12.8	−4.7	−4.1	−4.6
34	34.12	1.185	1.955	0.7720	0.1918	−13.4	−4.8	−4.2	−4.7
32	32.12	1.115	1.781	0.7719	0.1805	−14.1	−4.9	−4.3	−4.8
30	30.12	1.045	1.607	0.7718	0.1692	−14.8	−5.0	−4.4	−4.9
28	28.11	0.976	1.433	0.7717	0.1580	−15.5	−5.2	−4.6	−5.0
24	24.10	0.836	1.084	0.7715	0.1354	−17.2	−5.4	−4.8	−5.3
20	20.09	0.697	0.736	0.7714	0.1129	−19.1	−5.7	−5.0	−5.5
16	16.07	0.558	0.388	0.7712	0.0903	−21.4	−5.9	−5.2	−5.8
12	12.06	0.418	0.039	0.7710	0.0678	−24.4	−6.2	−5.4	−6.0
8	8.04	0.279	−0.309	0.7708	0.0452	−28.4	−6.4	−5.6	−6.2
4	4.02	0.139	−0.657	0.7707	0.0226	−35.0	−6.7	−5.8	−6.5
0	0.00	0.000	−1.006	0.7705	0.0000	—	−6.9	−6.0	−6.7

−0.5 °C DRY-BULB

Percentage saturation, μ / %	Relative humidity, ϕ /%	Value of stated parameter per kg dry air			Vapour pressure, p_v / kPa	Dew point temperature, θ_d / °C	Adiabatic saturation temperature, $\theta^\star$ / °C	Wet bulb temperature	
		Moisture content, g /(g·kg^{-1})	Specific enthalpy, h /(kJ·kg^{-1})	Specific volume, v /(m³·kg^{-1})				Screen, θ'_{sc}/ °C	Sling, θ'_{sl}/ °C
100	100.00	3.632	8.577	0.7764	0.5857	−0.5	−0.5	−0.5	−0.5
96	96.02	3.487	8.214	0.7762	0.5624	−1.0	−0.7	−0.7	−0.7
92	92.04	3.342	7.851	0.7760	0.5391	−1.5	−0.9	−0.9	−0.9
88	88.06	3.196	7.485	0.7759	0.5158	−2.0	−1.2	−1.1	−1.2
84	84.08	3.051	7.124	0.7757	0.4924	−2.6	−1.4	−1.3	−1.4
80	80.09	2.906	6.761	0.7755	0.4691	−3.2	−1.6	−1.5	−1.6
76	76.11	2.760	6.398	0.7753	0.4457	−3.8	−1.9	−1.7	−1.8
72	72.12	2.615	6.035	0.7751	0.4224	−4.4	−2.1	−1.9	−2.0
70	70.12	2.542	5.853	0.7751	0.4107	−4.7	−2.2	−2.0	−2.2
68	68.13	2.470	5.672	0.7750	0.3990	−5.1	−2.3	−2.1	−2.3
66	66.13	2.397	5.490	0.7749	0.3873	−5.4	−2.4	−2.2	−2.4
64	64.13	2.325	5.309	0.7748	0.3756	−5.8	−2.6	−2.3	−2.5
62	62.14	2.252	5.127	0.7747	0.3639	−6.1	−2.7	−2.4	−2.6
60	60.14	2.179	4.945	0.7746	0.3522	−6.5	−2.8	−2.5	−2.7
58	58.14	2.107	4.764	0.7745	0.3405	−6.9	−2.9	−2.6	−2.8
56	56.14	2.034	4.582	0.7744	0.3288	−7.3	−3.0	−2.7	−3.0
54	54.14	1.961	4.400	0.7743	0.3171	−7.7	−3.2	−2.8	−3.1
52	52.14	1.889	4.219	0.7742	0.3054	−8.2	−3.3	−2.9	−3.2
50	50.14	1.816	4.037	0.7742	0.2937	−8.6	−3.4	−3.0	−3.3
48	48.14	1.744	3.856	0.7741	0.2820	−9.1	−3.5	−3.1	−3.4
46	46.14	1.671	3.674	0.7740	0.2702	−9.6	−3.6	−3.2	−3.6
44	44.14	1.598	3.492	0.7739	0.2585	−10.1	−3.8	−3.3	−3.7
42	42.14	1.526	3.311	0.7738	0.2468	−10.6	−3.9	−3.4	−3.8
40	40.14	1.453	3.129	0.7737	0.2351	−11.1	−4.0	−3.5	−3.9
38	38.14	1.380	2.948	0.7736	0.2234	−11.7	−4.1	−3.6	−4.0
36	36.13	1.308	2.766	0.7735	0.2116	−12.3	−4.3	−3.7	−4.2
34	34.13	1.235	2.584	0.7734	0.1999	−12.9	−4.4	−3.8	−4.3
32	32.13	1.162	2.403	0.7734	0.1882	−13.6	−4.5	−3.9	−4.4
30	30.12	1.090	2.221	0.7733	0.1764	−14.3	−4.6	−4.0	−4.5
28	28.12	1.017	2.040	0.7732	0.1647	−15.1	−4.8	−4.2	−4.6
24	24.11	0.872	1.676	0.7730	0.1412	−16.7	−5.0	−4.4	−4.9
20	20.09	0.726	1.313	0.7728	0.1177	−18.7	−5.3	−4.6	−5.1
16	16.08	0.581	0.950	0.7726	0.0942	−21.0	−5.5	−4.8	−5.4
12	12.06	0.436	0.587	0.7725	0.0706	−23.9	−5.8	−5.0	−5.6
8	8.04	0.291	0.224	0.7723	0.0471	−28.0	−6.1	−5.2	−5.9
4	4.02	0.145	−0.140	0.7721	0.0236	−34.6	−6.3	−5.5	−6.2
0	0.00	0.000	−0.503	0.7719	0.0000	—	−6.6	−5.7	−6.4

0 °C DRY-BULB

Percentage saturation, μ / %	Relative humidity, ϕ /%	Value of stated parameter per kg dry air			Vapour pressure, p_v / kPa	Dew point temperature, θ_d / °C	Adiabatic saturation temperature, $\theta^\star$ / °C	Wet bulb temperature	
		Moisture content, g / (g·kg^{-1})	Specific enthalpy, h / (kJ·kg^{-1})	Specific volume, v / (m^3·kg^{-1})				Screen, θ'_{sc} / °C	Sling, θ'_{sl} / °C
100	100.00	3.789	9.475	0.7780	0.6108	0.0	0.0	0.0	0.0
96	96.02	3.637	9.096	0.7778	0.5865	−0.5	−0.2	−0.2	−0.2
92	92.04	3.486	8.717	0.7776	0.5622	−1.0	−0.5	−0.4	−0.4
88	88.06	3.334	8.338	0.7775	0.5379	−1.5	−0.7	−0.6	−0.7
84	84.08	3.183	7.959	0.7773	0.5136	−2.1	−0.9	−0.8	−0.9
80	80.10	3.031	7.580	0.7771	0.4892	−2.7	−1.1	−1.0	−1.1
76	76.11	2.880	7.201	0.7769	0.4649	−3.3	−1.4	−1.2	−1.3
72	72.12	2.728	6.822	0.7767	0.4405	−3.9	−1.6	−1.4	−1.6
70	70.13	2.652	6.633	0.7766	0.4283	−4.2	−1.7	−1.5	−1.7
68	68.13	2.576	6.443	0.7765	0.4161	−4.6	−1.9	−1.6	−1.8
66	66.14	2.501	6.254	0.7764	0.4039	−4.9	−2.0	−1.7	−1.9
64	64.14	2.425	6.064	0.7763	0.3918	−5.3	−2.1	−1.8	−2.0
62	62.14	2.349	5.875	0.7762	0.3796	−5.7	−2.2	−1.9	−2.2
60	60.14	2.273	5.685	0.7761	0.3674	−6.0	−2.4	−2.0	−2.3
58	58.15	2.198	5.496	0.7761	0.3552	−6.4	−2.5	−2.1	−2.4
56	56.15	2.122	5.306	0.7760	0.3429	−6.8	−2.6	−2.2	−2.5
54	54.15	2.046	5.117	0.7759	0.3307	−7.3	−2.7	−2.4	−2.6
52	52.15	1.970	4.927	0.7758	0.3185	−7.7	−2.8	−2.5	−2.8
50	50.15	1.894	4.738	0.7757	0.3063	−8.1	−3.0	−2.6	−2.9
48	48.15	1.819	4.548	0.7756	0.2941	−8.6	−3.1	−2.7	−3.0
46	46.15	1.743	4.359	0.7755	0.2819	−9.1	−3.2	−2.8	−3.1
44	44.15	1.667	4.169	0.7754	0.2696	−9.6	−3.4	−2.9	−3.3
42	42.15	1.591	3.980	0.7753	0.2574	−10.1	−3.5	−3.0	−3.4
40	40.14	1.516	3.790	0.7752	0.2452	−10.7	−3.6	−3.1	−3.5
38	38.14	1.440	3.601	0.7751	0.2330	−11.2	−3.7	−3.2	−3.6
36	36.14	1.364	3.411	0.7750	0.2207	−11.8	−3.9	−3.3	−3.8
34	34.14	1.288	3.222	0.7749	0.2085	−12.5	−4.0	−3.4	−3.9
32	32.13	1.212	3.032	0.7748	0.1962	−13.1	−4.1	−3.5	−4.0
30	30.13	1.137	2.843	0.7747	0.1840	−13.8	−4.3	−3.6	−4.1
28	28.12	1.061	2.653	0.7747	0.1718	−14.6	−4.4	−3.8	−4.3
24	24.11	0.909	2.274	0.7745	0.1473	−16.3	−4.7	−4.0	−4.5
20	20.10	0.758	1.895	0.7743	0.1228	−18.2	−4.9	−4.2	−4.8
16	16.08	0.606	1.516	0.7741	0.0982	−20.5	−5.2	−4.4	−5.0
12	12.06	0.455	1.137	0.7739	0.0737	−23.5	−5.5	−4.7	−5.3
8	8.04	0.303	0.758	0.7737	0.0491	−27.6	−5.7	−4.9	−5.5
4	4.02	0.152	0.379	0.7735	0.0246	−34.2	−6.0	−5.1	−5.8
0	0.00	0.000	0.000	0.7733	0.0000	—	−6.3	−5.3	−6.1

0.5 °C DRY-BULB

Percentage saturation, μ / %	Relative humidity, ϕ /%	Value of stated parameter per kg dry air			Vapour pressure, p_v / kPa	Dew point temperature, θ_d / °C	Adiabatic saturation temperature, $\theta^\star$ / °C	Wet bulb temperature	
		Moisture content, g / (g·kg^{-1})	Specific enthalpy, h / (kJ·kg^{-1})	Specific volume, v / (m^3·kg^{-1})				Screen, θ'_{sc} / °C	Sling, θ'_{sl} / °C
100	100.00	3.930	10.334	0.7796	0.6333	0.5	0.5	0.5	0.5
96	96.02	3.772	9.941	0.7794	0.6082	0.0	0.3	0.3	0.3
92	92.05	3.615	9.548	0.7792	0.5830	−0.6	0.0	0.1	0.1
88	88.07	3.458	9.154	0.7790	0.5578	−1.1	−0.2	−0.1	−0.2
84	84.08	3.301	8.761	0.7788	0.5325	−1.6	−0.5	−0.3	−0.4
80	80.10	3.144	8.368	0.7787	0.5073	−2.2	−0.7	−0.5	−0.7
76	76.11	2.986	7.975	0.7785	0.4821	−2.8	−0.9	−0.8	−0.9
72	72.13	2.829	7.581	0.7783	0.3468	−3.5	−1.2	−1.0	−1.1
70	70.13	2.751	7.385	0.7782	0.4442	−3.8	−1.3	−1.1	−1.3
68	68.14	2.672	7.188	0.7781	0.4315	−4.2	−1.4	−1.2	−1.4
66	66.14	2.594	6.992	0.7780	0.4189	−4.5	−1.6	−1.3	−1.5
64	64.14	2.515	6.795	0.7779	0.4062	−4.9	−1.7	−1.4	−1.6
62	62.15	2.436	6.598	0.7778	0.3936	−5.2	−1.8	−1.5	−1.7
60	60.15	2.358	6.402	0.7777	0.3810	−5.6	−1.9	−1.6	−1.9
58	58.15	2.279	6.205	0.7776	0.3683	−6.0	−2.1	−1.7	−2.0
56	56.15	2.200	6.008	0.7775	0.3556	−6.4	−2.2	−1.8	−2.1
54	54.16	2.122	5.812	0.7774	0.3430	−6.8	−2.3	−1.9	−2.2
52	52.16	2.043	5.615	0.7773	0.3303	−7.3	−2.4	−2.0	−2.4
50	50.16	1.965	5.418	0.7772	0.3177	−7.7	−2.6	−2.1	−2.5
48	48.16	1.886	5.222	0.7771	0.3050	−8.2	−2.7	−2.3	−2.6
46	46.16	1.808	5.025	0.7770	0.2923	−8.7	−2.8	−2.4	−2.7
44	44.15	1.729	4.829	0.7769	0.2796	−9.2	−3.0	−2.5	−2.9
42	42.15	1.650	4.632	0.7768	0.2670	−9.7	−3.1	−2.6	−3.0
40	40.15	1.572	4.435	0.7767	0.2543	−10.2	−3.2	−2.7	−3.1
38	38.15	1.493	4.239	0.7766	0.2416	−10.8	−3.3	−2.8	−3.2
36	36.14	1.415	4.042	0.7765	0.2289	−11.4	−3.5	−2.9	−3.4
34	34.14	1.336	3.846	0.7764	0.2162	−12.1	−3.6	−3.0	−3.5
32	32.14	1.258	3.649	0.7763	0.2035	−12.7	−3.7	−3.1	−3.6
30	30.13	1.179	3.452	0.7762	0.1908	−13.4	−3.9	−3.3	−3.7
28	28.13	1.100	3.256	0.7761	0.1781	−14.2	−4.0	−3.4	−3.9
24	24.11	0.943	2.862	0.7759	0.1527	−15.9	−4.3	−3.6	−4.1
20	20.10	0.786	2.469	0.7757	0.1273	−17.8	−4.6	−3.8	−4.4
16	16.08	0.629	2.076	0.7755	0.1019	−20.2	−4.8	−4.1	−4.7
12	12.07	0.471	1.683	0.7753	0.0764	−23.1	−5.1	−4.3	−4.9
8	8.05	0.314	1.290	0.7752	0.0510	−27.2	−5.4	−4.5	−5.2
4	4.02	0.157	0.896	0.7750	0.0255	−33.8	−5.7	−4.8	−5.5
0	0.00	0.000	0.503	0.7748	0.0000	—	−6.0	−5.0	−5.8

1 °C DRY-BULB

Percentage saturation, μ / %	Relative humidity, ϕ /%	Value of stated parameter per kg dry air			Vapour pressure, p_v / kPa	Dew point temperature, θ_d / °C	Adiabatic saturation temperature, $\theta^\star$ / °C	Wet bulb temperature	
		Moisture content, g / (g·kg^{-1})	Specific enthalpy, h / (kJ·kg^{-1})	Specific volume, v / (m³·kg^{-1})				Screen, θ'_{sc} / °C	Sling, θ'_{sl} / °C
100	100.00	4.075	11.20	0.7812	0.6566	1.0	1.0	1.0	1.0
96	96.03	3.912	10.80	0.7810	0.6305	0.4	0.8	0.8	0.8
92	92.05	3.749	10.39	0.7808	0.6044	−0.1	0.5	0.6	0.5
88	88.07	3.586	9.98	0.7806	0.5783	−0.7	0.3	0.4	0.3
84	84.09	3.423	9.573	0.7804	0.5521	−1.2	0.1	0.2	0.1
80	80.10	3.260	9.165	0.7802	0.5260	−1.8	−0.3	−0.1	−0.2
76	76.12	3.097	8.757	0.7800	0.4998	−2.4	−0.5	−0.3	−0.5
72	72.13	2.934	8.349	0.7798	0.4736	−3.0	−0.7	−0.5	−0.7
70	70.14	2.852	8.145	0.7797	0.4605	−3.4	−0.9	−0.6	−0.8
68	68.14	2.771	7.941	0.7796	0.4474	−3.7	−1.0	−0.7	−0.9
66	66.15	2.690	7.737	0.7795	0.4343	−4.1	−1.1	−0.8	−1.1
64	64.15	2.608	7.533	0.7794	0.4212	−4.4	−1.3	−1.0	−1.2
62	62.15	2.526	7.329	0.7793	0.4081	−4.8	−1.4	−1.1	−1.3
60	60.16	2.445	7.125	0.7792	0.3950	−5.2	−1.5	−1.2	−1.4
58	58.16	2.364	6.921	0.7791	0.3819	−5.6	−1.6	−1.3	−1.6
56	56.16	2.282	6.717	0.7790	0.3688	−6.0	−1.8	−1.4	−1.7
54	54.16	2.200	6.513	0.7789	0.3556	−6.4	−1.9	−1.5	−1.8
52	52.16	2.119	6.309	0.7788	0.3425	−6.9	−2.0	−1.6	−1.9
50	50.16	2.038	6.105	0.7787	0.3294	−7.3	−2.2	−1.7	−2.1
48	48.16	1.956	5.901	0.7786	0.3162	−7.8	−2.3	−1.8	−2.2
46	46.16	1.874	5.697	0.7785	0.3031	−8.3	−2.4	−2.0	−2.3
44	44.16	1.793	5.493	0.7784	0.2900	−8.8	−2.6	−2.1	−2.5
42	42.16	1.712	5.289	0.7783	0.2768	−9.3	−2.7	−2.2	−2.6
40	40.16	1.630	5.085	0.7782	0.2637	−9.8	−2.8	−2.3	−2.7
38	38.15	1.548	4.881	0.7781	0.2505	−10.4	−3.0	−2.4	−2.8
36	36.15	1.467	4.678	0.7780	0.2374	−11.0	−3.1	−2.5	−3.0
34	34.15	1.386	4.474	0.7779	0.2242	−11.7	−3.2	−2.6	−3.1
32	32.14	1.304	4.270	0.7778	0.2110	−12.3	−3.4	−2.8	−3.2
30	30.14	1.222	4.066	0.7777	0.1979	−13.0	−3.5	−2.9	−3.4
28	28.13	1.141	3.862	0.7776	0.1847	−13.8	−3.6	−3.0	−3.5
24	24.12	0.978	3.454	0.7774	0.1584	−15.5	−3.9	−3.2	−3.8
20	20.10	0.815	3.046	0.7772	0.1320	−17.4	−4.2	−3.5	−4.0
16	16.09	0.652	2.638	0.7770	0.1056	−19.8	−4.5	−3.7	−4.3
12	12.07	0.489	2.230	0.7768	0.0792	−22.8	−4.8	−3.9	−4.6
8	8.05	0.326	1.822	0.7766	0.0528	−26.8	−5.1	−4.2	−4.9
4	4.02	0.163	1.414	0.7764	0.0264	−33.5	−5.3	−4.4	−5.1
0	0.00	0.000	1.006	0.7762	0.0000	—	−5.6	−4.7	−5.4

1.5 °C DRY-BULB

Percentage saturation, μ / %	Relative humidity, ϕ /%	Value of stated parameter per kg dry air			Vapour pressure, p_v / kPa	Dew point temperature, θ_d / °C	Adiabatic saturation temperature, $\theta^\star$ / °C	Wet bulb temperature	
		Moisture content, g / (g·kg^{-1})	Specific enthalpy, h / (kJ·kg^{-1})	Specific volume, v / (m³·kg^{-1})				Screen, θ'_{sc} / °C	Sling, θ'_{sl} / °C
100	100.00	4.225	12.09	0.7828	0.6807	1.5	1.5	1.5	1.5
96	96.03	4.056	11.66	0.7826	0.6536	0.9	1.3	1.3	1.3
92	92.05	3.887	11.24	0.7824	0.6265	0.4	1.0	1.1	1.0
88	88.07	3.718	10.82	0.7822	0.5995	−0.2	0.8	0.9	0.8
84	84.09	3.549	10.40	0.7820	0.5724	−0.8	0.5	0.7	0.6
80	80.11	3.380	9.972	0.7818	0.5453	−1.4	0.3	0.4	0.3
76	76.12	3.211	9.548	0.7816	0.5181	−2.0	−1.0	0.2	0.1
72	72.14	3.042	8.125	0.7814	0.4910	−2.6	−0.3	−0.1	−0.3
70	70.14	2.958	8.914	0.7813	0.4774	−3.0	−0.4	−0.2	−0.4
68	68.15	2.873	8.702	0.7812	0.4638	−3.3	−0.6	−0.3	−0.5
66	66.15	2.789	8.491	0.7811	0.4503	−3.7	−0.7	−0.4	−0.6
64	64.15	2.704	8.279	0.7810	0.4367	−4.0	−0.8	−0.5	−0.8
62	62.16	2.620	8.068	0.7809	0.4231	−4.4	−1.0	−0.6	−0.9
60	60.16	2.535	7.856	0.7808	0.4095	−4.8	−1.1	−0.8	−1.0
58	58.16	2.451	7.644	0.7806	0.3959	−5.2	−1.2	−0.9	−1.1
56	56.17	2.366	7.438	0.7805	0.3823	−5.6	−1.4	−1.0	−1.3
54	54.17	2.282	7.221	0.7804	0.3687	−6.0	−1.5	−1.1	−1.4
52	52.17	2.197	7.010	0.7803	0.3551	−6.4	−1.6	−1.2	−1.5
50	50.17	2.113	6.798	0.7802	0.3415	−6.9	−1.8	−1.3	−1.7
48	48.17	2.028	6.587	0.7801	0.3279	−7.4	−1.9	−1.4	−1.8
46	46.17	1.944	6.375	0.7800	0.3142	−7.8	−2.0	−1.6	−1.9
44	44.17	1.859	6.163	0.7799	0.3006	−8.4	−2.2	−1.7	−2.1
42	42.16	1.775	5.952	0.7798	0.2870	−8.9	−2.3	−1.8	−2.2
40	40.16	1.690	5.740	0.7797	0.2734	−9.4	−2.4	−1.9	−2.3
38	38.16	1.606	5.529	0.7796	0.2597	−10.0	−2.6	−2.0	−2.5
36	36.16	1.521	5.317	0.7795	0.2461	−10.6	−2.7	−2.1	−2.6
34	34.15	1.436	5.106	0.7794	0.2324	−11.3	−2.9	−2.3	−2.7
32	32.15	1.352	4.894	0.7793	0.2188	−11.9	−3.0	−2.4	−2.9
30	30.14	1.268	4.682	0.7792	0.2052	−12.6	−3.1	−2.5	−3.0
28	28.14	1.183	4.471	0.7791	0.1915	−13.4	−3.3	−2.6	−3.1
24	24.12	1.014	4.048	0.7789	0.1642	−15.1	−3.6	−2.9	−3.4
20	20.11	0.845	3.625	0.7787	0.1369	−17.0	−3.8	−3.1	−3.7
16	16.09	0.676	3.202	0.7784	0.1095	−19.4	−4.1	−3.3	−4.0
12	12.07	0.507	2.778	0.7782	0.0822	−22.4	−4.4	−3.6	−4.2
8	8.05	0.338	2.355	0.7780	0.0548	−26.5	−4.7	−3.8	−4.5
4	4.03	0.169	1.932	0.7778	0.0274	−33.2	−5.0	−4.1	−4.6
0	0.00	0.000	1.509	0.7776	0.0000	—	−5.3	−4.3	−5.1

2 °C DRY-BULB

Percentage saturation, μ / %	Relative humidity, ϕ / %	Value of stated parameter per kg dry air			Vapour pressure, p_v / kPa	Dew point temperature, θ_d / °C	Adiabatic saturation temperature, $\theta\star$ / °C	Wet bulb temperature	
		Moisture content, g / (g·kg^{-1})	Specific enthalpy, h / (kJ·kg^{-1})	Specific volume, v / (m^3·kg^{-1})				Screen, θ'_{sc} / °C	Sling, θ'_{sl} / °C
100	100.00	4.380	12.98	0.7845	0.7055	2.0	2.0	2.0	2.0
96	96.03	4.205	12.54	0.7843	0.6774	1.4	1.8	1.8	1.8
92	92.05	4.030	12.10	0.7840	0.6494	0.8	1.5	1.6	1.5
88	88.07	3.855	11.67	0.7838	0.6213	0.2	1.3	1.4	1.3
84	84.09	3.679	11.23	0.7836	0.5933	−0.3	1.0	1.1	1.0
80	80.11	3.504	10.79	0.7834	0.5652	−0.9	0.8	0.9	0.8
76	76.13	3.329	10.35	0.7832	0.5371	−1.5	0.5	0.7	0.5
72	72.14	3.154	9.911	0.7829	0.5089	−2.2	0.3	0.5	0.3
70	70.15	3.066	9.692	0.7828	0.4949	−2.5	0.1	0.4	0.2
68	68.15	2.979	9.472	0.7827	0.4808	−2.9	−0.1	0.3	−0.1
66	66.16	2.891	9.253	0.7826	0.4667	−3.2	−0.3	0.1	−0.2
64	64.16	2.803	9.033	0.7825	0.4526	−3.6	−0.4	−0.1	−0.3
62	62.16	2.716	8.814	0.7824	0.4386	−4.0	−0.5	−0.2	−0.5
60	60.17	2.628	8.594	0.7823	0.4245	−4.3	−0.7	−0.3	−0.6
58	58.17	2.540	8.375	0.7822	0.4104	−4.7	−0.8	−0.4	−0.7
56	56.17	2.453	8.156	0.7821	0.3963	−5.2	−0.9	−0.6	−0.9
54	54.17	2.365	7.936	0.7820	0.3822	−5.6	−1.1	−0.7	−1.0
52	52.17	2.278	7.717	0.7819	0.3681	−6.0	−1.2	−0.8	−1.1
50	50.17	2.190	7.497	0.7817	0.3540	−6.5	−1.4	−0.9	−1.3
48	48.17	2.102	7.278	0.7816	0.3399	−6.9	−1.5	−1.0	−1.4
46	46.17	2.015	7.058	0.7815	0.3257	−7.4	−1.6	−1.1	−1.5
44	44.17	1.927	6.839	0.7814	0.3116	−7.9	−1.8	−1.3	−1.7
42	42.17	1.840	6.620	0.7813	0.2975	−8.5	−1.9	−1.4	−1.8
40	40.17	1.752	6.400	0.7812	0.2834	−9.0	−2.0	−1.5	−1.9
38	38.16	1.664	6.181	0.7811	0.2692	−9.6	−2.2	−1.6	−2.1
36	36.16	1.577	5.961	0.7810	0.2551	−10.2	−2.3	−1.7	−2.2
34	34.16	1.489	5.742	0.7809	0.2410	−10.9	−2.5	−1.9	−2.3
32	32.15	1.402	5.523	0.7808	0.2268	−11.5	−2.6	−2.0	−2.5
30	30.15	1.314	5.303	0.7807	0.2127	−12.2	−2.8	−2.1	−2.6
28	28.14	1.226	5.084	0.7805	0.1985	−13.0	−2.9	−2.2	−2.8
24	24.13	1.051	4.645	0.7803	0.1702	−14.7	−3.2	−2.5	−3.0
20	20.11	0.876	4.206	0.7801	0.1419	−16.7	−3.5	−2.7	−3.3
16	16.09	0.701	3.767	0.7799	0.1135	−19.0	−3.8	−3.0	−3.6
12	12.07	0.526	3.328	0.7797	0.0852	−22.0	−4.1	−3.2	−3.9
8	8.05	0.350	2.890	0.7795	0.0568	−26.1	−4.4	−3.5	−4.2
4	4.03	0.175	2.451	0.7792	0.0284	−32.8	−4.7	−3.7	−4.5
0	0.00	0.000	2.012	0.7790	0.0000	—	−5.0	−4.0	−4.8

2.5 °C DRY-BULB

Percentage saturation, μ / %	Relative humidity, ϕ / %	Value of stated parameter per kg dry air			Vapour pressure, p_v / kPa	Dew point temperature, θ_d / °C	Adiabatic saturation temperature, $\theta\star$ / °C	Wet bulb temperature	
		Moisture content, g / (g·kg^{-1})	Specific enthalpy, h / (kJ·kg^{-1})	Specific volume, v / (m^3·kg^{-1})				Screen, θ'_{sc} / °C	Sling, θ'_{sl} / °C
100	100.00	4.540	13.89	0.7861	0.7311	2.5	2.5	2.5	2.5
96	96.03	4.359	13.44	0.7859	0.7020	1.9	2.3	2.3	2.3
92	92.05	4.177	12.98	0.7856	0.6730	1.3	2.0	2.1	2.0
88	88.08	3.996	12.53	0.7854	0.6439	0.7	1.7	1.8	1.8
84	84.10	3.814	12.07	0.7852	0.6148	0.1	1.5	1.6	1.5
80	80.12	3.632	11.62	0.7850	0.5857	−0.5	1.2	1.4	1.3
76	76.13	3.451	11.16	0.7847	0.5566	−1.1	1.0	1.2	1.0
72	72.15	3.269	10.71	0.7845	0.5274	−1.8	0.7	0.9	0.8
70	70.15	3.178	10.48	0.7844	0.5129	−2.1	0.6	0.8	0.6
68	68.16	3.088	10.25	0.7843	0.4983	−2.4	0.5	0.7	0.5
66	66.16	2.997	10.02	0.7842	0.4837	−2.8	0.3	0.6	0.4
64	64.17	2.906	9.796	0.7841	0.4691	−3.2	0.2	0.5	0.2
62	62.17	2.815	9.568	0.7840	0.4545	−3.5	0.1	0.4	0.1
60	60.17	2.724	9.341	0.7838	0.4399	−3.9	−0.3	0.3	−0.2
58	58.18	2.633	9.113	0.7837	0.4253	−4.3	−0.4	0.1	−0.3
56	56.18	2.543	8.886	0.7836	0.4107	−4.7	−0.5	−0.1	−0.4
54	54.18	2.452	8.658	0.7835	0.3961	−5.2	−0.7	−0.3	−0.6
52	52.18	2.361	8.430	0.7834	0.3815	−5.6	−0.8	−0.4	−0.7
50	50.18	2.270	8.203	0.7833	0.3669	−6.1	−1.0	−0.5	−0.9
48	48.18	2.179	7.976	0.7832	0.3522	−6.5	−1.1	−0.6	−1.0
46	46.18	2.089	7.748	0.7830	0.3376	−7.0	−1.2	−0.7	−1.1
44	44.18	1.998	7.520	0.7829	0.3230	−7.5	−1.4	−0.9	−1.3
42	42.18	1.907	7.293	0.7829	0.3083	−8.1	−1.5	−1.0	−1.4
40	40.17	1.816	7.065	0.7827	0.2937	−8.6	−1.7	−1.1	−1.5
38	38.17	1.725	6.838	0.7826	0.2791	−9.2	−1.8	−1.2	−1.7
36	36.17	1.635	6.610	0.7825	0.2644	−9.8	−2.0	−1.4	−1.8
34	34.16	1.544	6.383	0.7824	0.2498	−10.5	−2.1	−1.5	−2.0
32	32.16	1.453	6.155	0.7823	0.2351	−11.1	−2.2	−1.6	−2.1
30	30.15	1.362	5.928	0.7821	0.2204	−11.8	−2.4	−1.7	−2.3
28	28.15	1.271	5.700	0.7820	0.2058	−12.6	−2.5	−1.9	−2.4
24	24.13	1.090	5.245	0.7818	0.1764	−14.3	−2.8	−2.1	−2.7
20	20.12	0.908	4.790	0.7816	0.1471	−16.3	−3.1	−2.4	−3.0
16	16.10	0.727	4.335	0.7813	0.1177	−18.7	−3.4	−2.6	−3.3
12	12.08	0.545	3.880	0.7811	0.0883	−21.7	−3.8	−2.9	−3.6
8	8.05	0.363	3.425	0.7809	0.0589	−25.8	−4.1	−3.1	−3.9
4	4.03	0.182	2.970	0.7807	0.0294	−32.5	−4.4	−3.4	−4.2
0	0.00	0.000	2.515	0.7804	0.0000	—	−4.7	−3.7	−4.5

3 °C DRY-BULB

Percentage saturation, μ / %	Relative humidity, ϕ /%	Value of stated parameter per kg dry air			Vapour pressure, p_v / kPa	Dew point temperature, θ_d / °C	Adiabatic saturation temperature, $\theta\star$ / °C	Wet bulb temperature	
		Moisture content, g /(g·kg⁻¹)	Specific enthalpy, h /(kJ·kg⁻¹)	Specific volume, v /(m³·kg⁻¹)				Screen, θ'_{sc} / °C	Sling, θ'_{sl} / °C
100	100.00	4.706	14.81	0.7877	0.7575	3.0	3.0	3.0	3.0
96	96.03	4.518	14.34	0.7875	0.7274	2.4	2.7	2.8	2.8
92	92.06	4.329	13.87	0.7873	0.6973	1.8	2.5	2.6	2.5
88	88.08	4.141	13.40	0.7870	0.6672	1.2	2.2	2.3	2.2
84	84.10	3.953	12.93	0.7868	0.6371	0.6	2.0	2.1	2.0
80	80.12	3.765	12.45	0.7866	0.6069	−0.1	1.7	1.9	1.7
76	76.14	3.576	11.98	0.7863	0.5768	−0.7	1.4	1.6	1.5
72	72.15	3.388	11.51	0.7861	0.5466	−1.3	1.2	1.4	1.2
70	70.16	3.294	11.27	0.7860	0.5314	−1.7	1.0	1.3	1.1
68	68.16	3.200	11.04	0.7859	0.5164	−2.0	0.9	1.2	1.0
66	66.17	3.106	10.80	0.7857	0.5012	−2.4	0.8	1.1	0.8
64	64.17	3.012	10.57	0.7856	0.4861	−2.7	0.6	0.9	0.7
62	62.18	2.918	10.33	0.7855	0.4710	−3.1	0.5	0.8	0.6
60	60.18	2.824	10.09	0.7854	0.4559	−3.5	0.4	0.7	0.4
58	58.18	2.729	9.859	0.7853	0.4407	−3.9	0.2	0.6	0.3
56	56.18	2.635	9.623	0.7852	0.4256	−4.3	0.1	0.5	0.2
54	54.19	2.541	9.387	0.7850	0.4105	−4.7	−0.3	0.3	−0.2
52	52.19	2.447	9.151	0.7849	0.3953	−5.2	−0.4	0.2	−0.3
50	50.19	2.353	8.915	0.7848	0.3802	−5.6	−0.5	0.1	−0.5
48	48.19	2.259	8.679	0.7847	0.3650	−6.1	−0.7	−0.2	−0.6
46	46.19	2.166	8.444	0.7846	0.3499	−6.6	−0.8	−0.3	−0.7
44	44.18	2.071	8.208	0.7844	0.3347	−7.1	−1.0	−0.5	−0.9
42	42.18	1.976	7.972	0.7843	0.3195	−7.7	−1.1	−0.6	−1.0
40	40.18	1.882	7.736	0.7842	0.3044	−8.2	−1.3	−0.7	−1.2
38	38.18	1.788	7.500	0.7841	0.2892	−8.8	−1.4	−0.8	−1.3
36	36.17	1.694	7.264	0.7840	0.2740	−9.4	−1.6	−1.0	−1.4
34	34.17	1.600	7.028	0.7839	0.2588	−10.1	−1.7	−1.1	−1.6
32	32.16	1.506	6.792	0.7837	0.2436	−10.7	−1.9	−1.2	−1.7
30	30.16	1.412	6.556	0.7836	0.2284	−11.5	−2.0	−1.4	−1.9
28	28.15	1.318	6.320	0.7835	0.2132	−12.2	−2.2	−1.5	−2.0
24	24.14	1.129	5.849	0.7833	0.1828	−13.9	−2.5	−1.7	−2.3
20	20.12	0.941	5.377	0.7830	0.1524	−15.9	−2.8	−2.0	−2.6
16	16.10	0.753	4.905	0.7828	0.1220	−18.3	−3.1	−2.3	−2.9
12	12.08	0.565	4.433	0.7826	0.0915	−21.3	−3.4	−2.5	−3.2
8	8.06	0.376	3.962	0.7823	0.0610	−25.4	−3.7	−2.8	−3.5
4	4.03	0.188	3.490	0.7821	0.0305	−32.1	−4.1	−3.1	−3.8
0	0.00	0.000	3.018	0.7819	0.0000	—	−4.4	−3.3	−4.2

3.5 °C DRY-BULB

Percentage saturation, μ / %	Relative humidity, ϕ /%	Value of stated parameter per kg dry air			Vapour pressure, p_v / kPa	Dew point temperature, θ_d / °C	Adiabatic saturation temperature, $\theta\star$ / °C	Wet bulb temperature	
		Moisture content, g /(g·kg⁻¹)	Specific enthalpy, h /(kJ·kg⁻¹)	Specific volume, v /(m³·kg⁻¹)				Screen, θ'_{sc} / °C	Sling, θ'_{sl} / °C
100	100.00	4.877	15.75	0.7894	0.7848	3.5	3.5	3.5	3.5
96	96.03	4.682	15.26	0.7891	0.7536	2.9	3.2	3.3	3.2
92	92.06	4.486	14.77	0.7889	0.7225	2.3	3.0	3.0	3.0
88	88.08	4.291	14.28	0.7887	0.6913	1.7	2.7	2.8	2.7
84	84.10	4.096	13.79	0.7884	0.6600	1.1	2.4	2.6	2.5
80	80.12	3.901	13.30	0.7882	0.6288	0.4	2.2	2.3	2.2
76	76.14	3.706	12.81	0.7879	0.5976	−0.3	1.9	2.1	1.9
72	72.16	3.511	12.32	0.7877	0.5663	−0.9	1.6	1.9	1.7
70	70.16	3.414	12.08	0.7876	0.5506	−1.2	1.5	1.7	1.5
68	68.17	3.316	11.84	0.7874	0.5350	−1.6	1.4	1.6	1.4
66	66.17	3.218	11.59	0.7873	0.5193	−1.9	1.2	1.5	1.3
64	64.18	3.121	11.35	0.7872	0.5037	−2.3	1.1	1.4	1.1
62	62.18	3.024	11.10	0.7871	0.4880	−2.7	0.9	1.3	1.0
60	60.19	2.926	10.86	0.7869	0.4723	−3.1	0.8	1.1	0.9
58	58.19	2.828	10.61	0.7868	0.4567	−3.5	0.7	1.0	0.7
56	56.19	2.731	10.37	0.7867	0.4410	−3.9	0.5	0.9	0.6
54	54.19	2.633	10.12	0.7866	0.4253	−4.3	0.4	0.8	0.5
52	52.19	2.536	9.879	0.7865	0.4096	−4.8	0.2	0.7	0.3
50	50.19	2.438	9.634	0.7663	0.3939	−5.2	0.1	0.5	0.2
48	48.19	2.341	9.390	0.7862	0.3782	−5.7	−0.3	0.4	−0.2
46	46.19	2.243	9.146	0.7861	0.3625	−6.2	−0.4	0.3	−0.3
44	44.19	2.146	8.901	0.7860	0.3468	−6.7	−0.6	0.2	−0.5
42	42.19	2.048	8.656	0.7858	0.3311	−7.2	−0.7	−0.2	−0.6
40	40.19	1.951	8.412	0.7857	0.3154	−7.8	−0.9	−0.3	−0.8
38	38.18	1.853	8.167	0.7856	0.2997	−8.4	−1.0	−0.5	−0.9
36	36.18	1.756	7.923	0.7855	0.2839	−9.0	−1.2	−0.6	−1.1
34	34.17	1.658	7.678	0.7854	0.2682	−9.6	−1.4	−0.7	−1.2
32	32.17	1.560	7.434	0.7852	0.2525	−10.3	−1.5	−0.8	−1.4
30	30.16	1.463	7.189	0.7851	0.2367	−11.1	−1.7	−1.0	−1.5
28	28.16	1.365	6.944	0.7850	0.2210	−11.8	−1.8	−1.1	−1.7
24	24.14	1.170	6.455	0.7847	0.1895	−13.5	−2.1	−1.4	−2.0
20	20.12	0.975	5.966	0.7845	0.1579	−15.5	−2.4	−1.6	−2.3
16	16.10	0.780	5.477	0.7843	0.1264	−17.9	−2.8	−1.9	−2.6
12	12.08	0.585	4.988	0.7840	0.0948	−20.9	−3.1	−2.2	−2.9
8	8.06	0.390	4.499	0.7838	0.0632	−25.0	−3.4	−2.5	−3.2
4	4.03	0.195	4.010	0.7835	0.0316	−31.8	−3.7	−2.7	−3.5
0	0.00	0.000	3.520	0.7833	0.0000	—	−4.1	−3.0	−3.9

4 °C DRY-BULB

Percentage saturation, μ / %	Relative humidity, ϕ /%	Value of stated parameter per kg dry air			Vapour pressure, p_v / kPa	Dew point temperature, θ_d / °C	Adiabatic saturation temperature, $\theta\star$ / °C	Wet bulb temperature	
		Moisture content, g / (g·kg^{-1})	Specific enthalpy, h / (kJ·kg^{-1})	Specific volume, v / (m^3·kg^{-1})				Screen, θ'_{sc} / °C	Sling, θ'_{sl} / °C
100	100.00	5.053	16.70	0.7910	0.8129	4.0	4.0	4.0	4.0
96	96.03	4.851	16.19	0.7908	0.7807	3.4	3.7	3.8	3.7
92	92.06	4.649	15.68	0.7905	0.7484	2.8	3.5	3.5	3.5
88	88.08	4.446	15.18	0.7903	0.7161	2.2	3.2	3.3	3.2
84	84.11	4.244	14.67	0.7900	0.6937	1.6	2.9	3.1	2.9
80	80.13	4.042	14.16	0.7898	0.6514	0.9	2.7	2.8	2.7
76	76.15	3.840	13.66	0.7895	0.6190	0.2	2.4	2.6	2.4
72	72.16	3.638	13.15	0.7893	0.5866	−0.5	2.1	2.3	2.1
70	70.17	3.537	12.90	0.7891	0.5704	−0.8	2.0	2.2	2.0
68	68.17	3.436	12.64	0.7890	0.5542	−1.2	1.8	2.1	1.9
66	66.18	3.335	12.39	0.7889	0.5380	−1.5	1.7	2.0	1.7
64	64.19	3.234	12.14	0.7888	0.5218	−1.9	1.5	1.8	1.6
62	62.19	3.133	11.88	0.7886	0.5056	−2.3	1.4	1.7	1.4
60	60.19	3.032	11.63	0.7885	0.4893	−2.7	1.2	1.6	1.3
58	58.20	2.931	11.38	0.7884	0.4731	−3.1	1.1	1.5	1.2
56	56.20	2.830	11.12	0.7883	0.4568	−3.5	1.0	1.3	1.0
54	54.20	2.728	10.87	0.7881	0.4406	−3.9	0.8	1.2	0.9
52	52.20	2.628	10.61	0.7880	0.4244	−4.3	0.7	1.1	0.7
50	50.20	2.526	10.36	0.7879	0.4081	−4.8	0.5	1.0	0.6
48	48.20	2.425	10.11	0.7877	0.3918	−5.3	0.4	0.8	0.5
46	46.20	2.324	9.854	0.7876	0.3756	−5.8	0.2	0.7	0.3
44	44.20	2.223	9.600	0.7875	0.3593	−6.3	0.1	0.6	0.2
42	42.20	2.122	9.347	0.7874	0.3430	−6.8	−0.4	0.4	−0.2
40	40.19	2.021	9.093	0.7872	0.3267	−7.4	−0.5	0.3	−0.4
38	38.19	1.920	8.840	0.7871	0.3105	−8.0	−0.7	0.2	−0.5
36	36.19	1.819	8.586	0.7870	0.2942	−8.6	−0.8	0.1	−0.7
34	34.18	1.718	8.333	0.7869	0.2779	−9.2	−1.0	−0.3	−0.8
32	32.18	1.617	8.080	0.7867	0.2616	−9.9	−1.1	−0.5	−1.0
30	30.17	1.516	7.826	0.7866	0.2453	−10.7	−1.3	−0.6	−1.1
28	28.16	1.415	7.573	0.7865	0.2289	−11.4	−1.5	−0.7	−1.3
24	24.15	1.213	7.066	0.7862	0.1963	−13.1	−1.8	−1.0	−1.6
20	20.13	1.011	6.559	0.7860	0.1636	−15.1	−2.1	−1.3	−1.9
16	16.11	0.808	6.052	0.7857	0.1310	−17.5	−2.4	−1.6	−2.2
12	12.09	0.606	5.545	0.7855	0.0982	−20.5	−2.8	−1.8	−2.6
8	8.06	0.404	5.038	0.7852	0.0655	−24.7	−3.1	−2.1	−2.9
4	4.03	0.202	4.531	0.7850	0.0328	−31.5	−3.4	−2.4	−3.2
0	0.00	0.000	4.024	0.7847	0.0000	—	−3.8	−2.7	−3.5

4.5 °C DRY-BULB

Percentage saturation, μ / %	Relative humidity, ϕ /%	Value of stated parameter per kg dry air			Vapour pressure, p_v / kPa	Dew point temperature, θ_d / °C	Adiabatic saturation temperature, $\theta\star$ / °C	Wet bulb temperature	
		Moisture content, g / (g·kg^{-1})	Specific enthalpy, h / (kJ·kg^{-1})	Specific volume, v / (m^3·kg^{-1})				Screen, θ'_{sc} / °C	Sling, θ'_{sl} / °C
100	100.00	5.235	17.66	0.7927	0.8420	4.5	4.5	4.5	4.5
96	96.03	5.025	17.14	0.7924	0.8086	3.9	4.2	4.3	4.2
92	92.06	4.816	16.61	0.7922	0.7751	3.3	4.0	4.0	4.0
88	88.09	4.607	16.09	0.7919	0.7417	2.7	3.7	3.8	3.7
84	84.11	4.397	15.56	0.7916	0.7082	2.1	3.4	3.5	3.4
80	80.13	4.188	15.04	0.7914	0.6747	1.4	3.1	3.3	3.2
76	76.15	3.978	14.51	0.7911	0.6412	0.7	2.8	3.0	2.9
72	72.17	3.769	13.98	0.7909	0.6076	−0.1	2.6	2.8	2.6
70	70.17	3.664	13.72	0.7907	0.5908	−0.4	2.4	2.7	2.5
68	68.18	3.560	13.46	0.7906	0.5741	−0.7	2.3	2.5	2.3
66	66.19	3.455	13.20	0.7905	0.5573	−1.1	2.1	2.4	2.2
64	64.19	3.350	12.93	0.7903	0.5405	−1.5	2.0	2.3	2.0
62	62.20	3.246	12.67	0.7902	0.5237	−1.8	1.8	2.2	1.9
60	60.20	3.141	12.41	0.7901	0.5069	−2.2	1.7	2.0	1.7
58	58.20	3.036	12.15	0.7899	0.4900	−2.6	1.5	1.9	1.6
56	56.21	2.932	11.88	0.7898	0.4732	−3.1	1.4	1.8	1.5
54	54.21	2.827	11.62	0.7897	0.4564	−3.5	1.2	1.6	1.3
52	52.21	2.722	11.36	0.7895	0.4396	−3.9	1.1	1.5	1.2
50	50.21	2.617	11.09	0.7894	0.4227	−4.4	0.9	1.4	1.0
48	48.21	2.513	10.83	0.7893	0.4059	−4.9	0.8	1.3	0.9
46	46.21	2.408	10.57	0.7891	0.3890	−5.4	0.6	1.1	0.7
44	44.21	2.303	10.31	0.7890	0.3722	−5.9	0.5	1.0	0.6
42	42.20	2.199	10.04	0.7889	0.3553	−6.4	0.3	0.9	0.4
40	40.20	2.094	9.781	0.7888	0.3385	−7.0	0.2	0.7	0.3
38	38.20	1.989	9.518	0.7886	0.3216	−7.6	−0.3	0.6	0.1
36	36.19	1.884	9.256	0.7885	0.3047	−8.2	−0.5	0.5	−0.3
34	34.19	1.780	8.993	0.7884	0.2878	−8.8	−0.6	0.3	−0.5
32	32.18	1.675	8.730	0.7882	0.2710	−9.5	−0.8	0.2	−0.6
30	30.18	1.570	8.467	0.7881	0.2541	−10.3	−0.9	0.1	−0.8
28	28.17	1.466	8.205	0.7880	0.2372	−11.0	−1.1	−0.4	−0.9
24	24.15	1.256	7.679	0.7877	0.2034	−12.7	−1.4	−0.6	−1.3
20	20.13	1.047	7.154	0.7874	0.1695	−14.7	−1.8	−0.9	−1.6
16	16.11	0.838	6.628	0.7872	0.1357	−17.1	−2.1	−1.2	−1.9
12	12.09	0.628	6.103	0.7869	0.1018	−20.2	−2.4	−1.5	−2.2
8	8.06	0.419	5.578	0.7867	0.0679	−24.3	−2.8	−1.8	−2.6
4	4.03	0.209	5.052	0.7864	0.0340	−31.1	−3.1	−2.1	−2.9
0	0.00	0.000	4.527	0.7861	0.0000	—	−3.5	−2.4	−3.2

5 °C DRY-BULB

Percentage saturation, μ / %	Relative humidity, ϕ /%	Value of stated parameter per kg dry air			Vapour pressure, p_v / kPa	Dew point temperature, θ_d / °C	Adiabatic saturation temperature, $\theta\star$ / °C	Wet bulb temperature	
		Moisture content, g / (g·kg^{-1})	Specific enthalpy, h / (kJ·kg^{-1})	Specific volume, v / (m^3·kg^{-1})				Screen, θ'_{sc} / °C	Sling, θ'_{sl} / °C
100	100.00	5.422	18.64	0.7944	0.8719	5.0	5.0	5.0	5.0
96	96.03	5.206	18.10	0.7941	0.8373	4.4	4.7	4.8	4.7
92	92.06	4.989	17.55	0.7938	0.8027	3.8	4.4	4.5	4.5
88	88.09	4.772	17.01	0.7935	0.7681	3.2	4.2	4.3	4.2
84	84.12	4.555	16.46	0.7933	0.7334	2.5	3.9	4.0	3.9
80	80.14	4.338	15.92	0.7930	0.6987	1.9	3.6	3.8	3.6
76	76.16	4.121	15.37	0.7927	0.6640	1.2	3.3	3.5	3.3
72	72.17	3.904	14.83	0.7925	0.6293	0.4	3.0	3.2	3.1
70	70.18	3.796	14.56	0.7923	0.6119	0.0	2.9	3.1	2.9
68	68.19	3.687	14.29	0.7922	0.5945	−0.3	2.7	3.0	2.8
66	66.19	3.579	14.01	0.7920	0.5771	−0.7	2.6	2.9	2.6
64	64.20	3.470	13.74	0.7919	0.5598	−1.0	2.4	2.7	2.5
62	62.20	3.362	13.47	0.7918	0.5424	−1.4	2.3	2.6	2.3
60	60.21	3.254	13.20	0.7916	0.5250	−1.8	2.1	2.5	2.2
58	58.21	3.145	12.92	0.7915	0.5075	−2.2	2.0	2.3	2.0
56	56.21	3.037	12.65	0.7914	0.4901	−2.6	1.8	2.2	1.9
54	54.21	2.928	12.38	0.7912	0.4727	−3.1	1.7	2.1	1.7
52	52.22	2.820	12.11	0.7911	0.4553	−3.5	1.5	1.9	1.6
50	50.22	2.711	11.84	0.7910	0.4378	−4.0	1.4	1.8	1.4
48	48.22	2.603	11.56	0.7908	0.4204	−4.5	1.2	1.7	1.3
46	46.21	2.494	11.29	0.7907	0.4030	−5.0	1.1	1.5	1.1
44	44.21	2.386	11.02	0.7905	0.3855	−5.5	0.9	1.4	1.0
42	42.21	2.278	10.75	0.7904	0.3680	−6.0	0.7	1.3	0.8
40	40.21	2.169	10.47	0.7903	0.3506	−6.6	0.6	1.1	0.7
38	38.20	2.061	10.20	0.7901	0.3331	−7.2	0.4	1.0	0.5
36	36.20	1.952	9.930	0.7900	0.3156	−7.8	0.3	0.9	0.4
34	34.19	1.884	9.658	0.7899	0.2981	−8.4	0.1	0.7	0.2
32	32.19	1.735	9.385	0.7897	0.2806	−9.1	−0.4	0.6	0.1
30	30.18	1.627	9.113	0.7896	0.2632	−9.9	−0.6	0.5	−0.4
28	28.17	1.518	8.841	0.7895	0.2456	−10.6	−0.7	0.3	−0.6
24	24.16	1.301	8.296	0.7892	0.2106	−12.4	−1.1	−0.3	−0.9
20	20.14	1.084	7.752	0.7889	0.1756	−14.4	−1.4	−0.6	−1.2
16	16.12	0.868	7.208	0.7886	0.1405	−16.8	−1.8	−0.9	−1.6
12	12.09	0.651	6.663	0.7884	0.1054	−19.8	−2.1	−1.2	−1.9
8	8.06	0.434	6.119	0.7881	0.0703	−24.0	−2.5	−1.5	−2.2
4	4.03	0.217	5.574	0.7878	0.0352	−30.8	−2.8	−1.8	−2.6
0	0.00	0.000	5.030	0.7875	0.0000	—	−3.2	−2.1	−2.9

5.5 °C DRY-BULB

Percentage saturation, μ / %	Relative humidity, ϕ /%	Value of stated parameter per kg dry air			Vapour pressure, p_v / kPa	Dew point temperature, θ_d / °C	Adiabatic saturation temperature, $\theta\star$ / °C	Wet bulb temperature	
		Moisture content, g / (g·kg^{-1})	Specific enthalpy, h / (kJ·kg^{-1})	Specific volume, v / (m^3·kg^{-1})				Screen, θ'_{sc} / °C	Sling, θ'_{sl} / °C
100	100.00	5.618	19.64	0.7960	0.9028	5.5	5.5	5.5	5.5
96	96.03	5.393	19.07	0.7958	0.8670	4.9	5.2	5.2	5.2
92	92.07	5.167	18.51	0.7955	0.8312	4.3	4.9	5.0	4.9
88	88.09	4.942	17.94	0.7952	0.7953	3.7	4.6	4.7	4.7
84	84.12	4.718	17.38	0.7949	0.7594	3.0	4.4	4.5	4.4
80	80.14	4.493	16.82	0.7916	0.7235	2.4	4.1	4.2	4.1
76	76.16	4.268	16.25	0.7943	0.6876	1.6	3.8	4.0	3.8
72	72.18	4.044	15.69	0.7941	0.6516	0.9	3.5	3.7	3.5
70	70.19	3.931	15.40	0.7939	0.6336	0.5	3.3	3.6	3.4
68	68.19	3.819	15.12	0.7938	0.6156	0.1	3.2	3.4	3.2
66	66.20	3.707	14.84	0.7936	0.5976	−0.3	3.0	3.3	3.1
64	64.21	3.594	14.56	0.7935	0.5796	−0.6	2.9	3.2	2.9
62	62.21	3.482	14.28	0.7934	0.5616	−0.1	2.7	3.0	2.8
60	60.21	3.370	13.99	0.7932	0.5436	−1.4	2.6	2.9	2.6
58	58.22	3.257	13.71	0.7931	0.5256	−1.8	2.4	2.8	2.5
56	56.22	3.145	13.43	0.7929	0.5076	−2.2	2.3	2.6	2.3
54	54.22	3.033	13.15	0.7928	0.4895	−2.7	2.1	2.5	2.2
52	52.22	2.920	12.87	0.7926	0.4715	−3.1	1.9	2.4	2.0
50	50.22	2.808	12.58	0.7925	0.4534	−3.6	1.8	2.2	1.9
48	48.22	2.696	12.30	0.7924	0.4354	−4.0	1.6	2.1	1.7
46	46.22	2.584	12.02	0.7922	0.4173	−4.5	1.5	2.0	1.6
44	44.22	2.471	11.74	0.7921	0.3992	−5.1	1.3	1.8	1.4
42	42.22	2.359	11.46	0.7919	0.3811	−5.6	1.1	1.7	1.2
40	40.21	2.246	11.17	0.7918	0.3630	−6.2	1.0	1.5	1.1
38	38.21	2.134	10.89	0.7917	0.3450	−6.8	0.8	1.4	0.9
36	36.21	2.022	10.61	0.7915	0.3269	−7.4	0.7	1.3	0.8
34	34.20	1.910	10.33	0.7914	0.3088	−8.0	0.5	1.1	0.6
32	32.19	1.797	10.05	0.7912	0.2906	−8.7	0.3	1.0	0.5
30	30.19	1.685	9.764	0.7911	0.2725	−9.5	0.2	0.8	0.3
28	28.18	1.573	9.482	0.7909	0.2544	−10.2	−0.4	0.7	0.1
24	24.16	1.348	8.918	0.7907	0.2181	−12.0	−0.7	0.4	−0.4
20	20.14	1.123	8.353	0.7904	0.1818	−14.0	−1.1	0.1	−0.9
16	16.12	0.899	7.789	0.7901	0.1455	−16.4	−1.4	−0.5	−1.2
12	12.09	0.674	7.225	0.7898	0.1092	−19.4	−1.8	−0.8	−1.6
8	8.07	0.449	6.661	0.7895	0.0728	−23.6	−2.1	−1.2	−1.9
4	4.03	0.225	6.097	0.7892	0.0364	−30.5	−2.5	−1.4	−2.3
0	0.00	0.000	5.533	0.7890	0.0000	—	−2.9	−1.8	−2.6

6 °C DRY-BULB

Percentage saturation, μ / %	Relative humidity, ϕ /%	Value of stated parameter per kg dry air			Vapour pressure, p_v / kPa	Dew point temperature, θ_d / °C	Adiabatic saturation temperature, $\theta^\star$ / °C	Wet bulb temperature	
		Moisture content, g / (g·kg⁻¹)	Specific enthalpy, h / (kJ·kg⁻¹)	Specific volume, v / (m³·kg⁻¹)				Screen, θ'_{sc} / °C	Sling, θ'_{sl} / °C
100	100.00	5.816	20.65	0.7977	0.9346	6.0	6.0	6.0	6.0
96	96.04	5.584	20.06	0.7974	0.8976	5.4	5.7	5.7	5.7
92	92.07	5.351	19.48	0.7971	0.8605	4.8	5.4	5.5	5.4
88	88.10	5.118	18.89	0.7968	0.8234	4.2	5.1	5.2	5.1
84	84.12	4.886	18.31	0.7966	0.7862	3.5	4.8	5.0	4.9
80	80.15	4.653	17.72	0.7963	0.7491	2.8	4.5	4.7	4.6
76	76.17	4.420	17.14	0.7960	0.7119	2.1	4.2	4.4	4.3
72	72.19	4.188	16.56	0.7957	0.6747	1.4	3.9	4.2	4.0
70	70.19	4.071	16.26	0.7955	0.6560	1.0	3.8	4.0	3.8
68	68.20	3.955	15.97	0.7954	0.6374	0.6	3.6	3.9	3.7
66	66.21	3.839	15.68	0.7952	0.6188	0.2	3.5	3.8	3.5
64	64.21	3.722	15.39	0.7951	0.6002	−0.2	3.3	3.6	3.4
62	62.22	3.606	15.09	0.7949	0.5815	−0.6	3.2	3.5	3.2
60	60.22	3.490	14.80	0.7948	0.5628	−1.0	3.0	3.4	3.1
58	58.23	3.373	14.51	0.7946	0.5442	−1.4	2.8	3.2	2.9
56	56.23	3.257	14.22	0.7945	0.5255	−1.8	2.7	3.1	2.8
54	54.23	3.141	13.93	0.7944	0.5068	−2.2	2.5	2.9	2.6
52	52.23	3.024	13.63	0.7942	0.4882	−2.7	2.4	2.8	2.4
50	50.23	2.907	13.34	0.7941	0.4695	−3.2	2.2	2.7	2.3
48	48.23	2.792	13.05	0.7939	0.4508	−3.6	2.0	2.5	2.1
46	46.23	2.675	12.76	0.7938	0.4321	−4.1	1.9	2.4	2.0
44	44.23	2.559	12.46	0.7936	0.4134	−4.7	1.7	2.2	1.8
42	42.23	2.443	12.17	0.7935	0.3946	−5.2	1.6	2.1	1.7
40	40.22	2.326	11.88	0.7933	0.3759	−5.8	1.4	2.0	1.5
38	38.22	2.210	11.59	0.7932	0.3572	−6.4	1.2	1.8	1.3
36	36.21	2.094	11.30	0.7930	0.3385	−7.0	1.1	1.7	1.2
34	34.21	1.978	11.00	0.7929	0.3197	−7.6	0.9	1.5	1.0
32	32.20	1.861	10.71	0.7927	0.3010	−8.3	0.7	1.4	0.8
30	30.19	30.19	10.42	0.7926	0.2822	−9.1	0.6	1.2	0.7
28	28.19	1.628	10.13	0.7924	0.2634	−9.9	0.4	1.1	0.5
24	24.17	1.396	9.542	0.7921	0.2259	−11.6	−0.4	0.8	0.2
20	20.15	1.163	8.958	0.7919	0.1883	−13.6	−0.7	0.5	−0.6
16	16.12	0.931	8.373	0.7916	0.1507	−16.0	−1.1	0.2	−0.9
12	12.10	0.698	7.789	0.7913	0.1131	−19.1	−1.5	−0.5	−1.3
8	8.07	0.465	7.205	0.7910	0.0754	−23.3	−1.8	−0.8	−1.6
4	4.04	0.233	6.620	0.7907	0.0377	−30.1	−2.2	−1.1	−2.0
0	0.00	0.000	6.036	0.7904	0.0000	—	−2.6	−1.4	−2.3

6.5 °C DRY-BULB

Percentage saturation, μ / %	Relative humidity, ϕ /%	Value of stated parameter per kg dry air			Vapour pressure, p_v / kPa	Dew point temperature, θ_d / °C	Adiabatic saturation temperature, $\theta^\star$ / °C	Wet bulb temperature	
		Moisture content, g / (g·kg⁻¹)	Specific enthalpy, h / (kJ·kg⁻¹)	Specific volume, v / (m³·kg⁻¹)				Screen, θ'_{sc} / °C	Sling, θ'_{sl} / °C
100	100.00	6.022	21.67	0.7994	0.9674	6.5	6.5	6.5	6.5
96	96.04	5.782	21.08	0.7991	0.9291	5.9	6.2	6.2	6.2
92	92.07	5.541	20.46	0.7988	0.8907	5.3	5.9	6.0	5.9
88	88.10	5.300	19.86	0.7985	0.8523	4.7	5.6	5.7	5.6
84	84.13	5.059	19.25	0.7982	0.8139	4.0	5.3	5.4	5.3
80	80.15	4.818	18.65	0.7979	0.7754	3.3	5.0	5.2	5.0
76	76.17	4.577	18.04	0.7976	0.7370	2.6	4.7	4.9	4.7
72	72.19	4.336	17.44	0.7973	0.6984	1.9	4.4	4.6	4.4
70	70.20	4.216	17.13	0.7971	0.6792	1.5	4.2	4.5	4.3
68	68.21	4.095	16.83	0.7970	0.6599	1.1	4.1	4.4	4.1
66	66.21	3.975	16.53	0.7968	0.6406	0.7	3.9	4.2	4.0
64	64.22	3.854	16.22	0.7967	0.6213	0.2	3.8	4.1	3.8
62	62.23	3.734	15.92	0.7965	0.6020	−0.2	3.6	3.9	3.7
60	60.23	3.614	15.62	0.7964	0.5827	−0.6	3.4	3.8	3.5
58	58.23	3.493	15.32	0.7962	0.5634	−1.0	3.3	3.7	3.3
56	56.24	3.373	15.01	0.7961	0.5441	−1.4	3.1	3.5	3.2
54	54.24	3.252	14.71	0.7959	0.5247	−1.8	3.0	3.4	3.0
52	52.24	3.132	14.41	0.7958	0.5054	−2.3	2.8	3.2	2.9
50	50.24	3.011	14.11	0.7956	0.4860	−2.7	2.6	3.1	2.7
48	48.24	2.891	13.80	0.7955	0.4667	−3.2	2.5	2.9	2.5
46	46.24	2.770	13.50	0.7953	0.4473	−3.7	2.3	2.8	2.4
44	44.24	2.650	13.20	0.7952	0.4280	−4.3	2.1	2.7	2.2
42	42.23	2.529	12.90	0.7950	0.4086	−4.8	2.0	2.5	2.1
40	40.23	2.409	12.59	0.7949	0.3892	−5.4	1.8	2.4	1.9
38	38.23	2.289	12.29	0.7947	0.3698	−6.0	1.6	2.2	1.7
36	36.22	2.168	11.99	0.7945	0.3504	−6.6	1.4	2.1	1.6
34	34.22	2.048	11.68	0.7944	0.3310	−7.2	1.3	1.9	1.4
32	32.21	1.927	11.38	0.7942	0.3116	−7.9	1.1	1.8	1.2
30	30.20	1.807	11.08	0.7941	0.2922	−8.7	0.9	1.6	1.1
28	28.19	1.686	10.78	0.7939	0.2728	−9.5	0.8	1.5	0.9
24	24.18	1.445	10.17	0.7936	0.2339	−11.2	0.4	1.2	0.5
20	20.15	1.204	9.566	0.7933	0.1950	−13.2	0.1	0.9	0.2
16	16.13	0.964	8.960	0.7930	0.1560	−15.6	−0.8	0.6	−0.6
12	12.10	0.723	8.355	0.7927	0.1171	−18.7	−1.2	0.3	−0.9
8	8.07	0.482	7.750	0.7924	0.0781	−22.9	−1.5	−0.5	−1.3
4	4.04	0.241	7.144	0.7921	0.0391	−29.8	−1.9	−0.8	−1.7
0	0.00	0.000	6.539	0.7918	0.0000	—	−2.3	−1.1	−2.1

7 °C DRY-BULB

Percentage saturation, μ / %	Relative humidity, ϕ /%	Value of stated parameter per kg dry air			Vapour pressure, p_v / kPa	Dew point temperature, θ_d / °C	Adiabatic saturation temperature, $\theta^\star$ / °C	Wet bulb temperature	
		Moisture content, g /(g·kg⁻¹)	Specific enthalpy, h /(kJ·kg⁻¹)	Specific volume, v /(m³·kg⁻¹)				Screen, θ'_{sc} / °C	Sling, θ'_{sl} / °C
100	100.00	6.235	22.72	0.8011	1.001	7.0	7.0	7.0	7.0
96	96.04	5.986	22.09	0.8008	0.9616	6.4	6.7	6.7	6.7
92	92.07	5.736	21.46	0.8005	0.9219	5.8	6.4	6.5	6.4
88	88.10	5.487	20.84	0.8002	0.8822	5.2	6.1	6.2	6.1
84	84.13	5.238	20.21	0.7999	0.8424	4.5	5.8	5.9	5.8
80	80.16	4.988	19.58	0.7995	0.8026	3.8	5.5	5.6	5.5
76	76.18	4.739	18.95	0.7992	0.7628	3.1	5.2	5.4	5.2
72	72.20	4.489	18.33	0.7989	0.7229	2.3	4.8	5.1	4.9
70	70.21	4.365	18.01	0.7988	0.7030	2.0	4.7	5.0	4.7
68	68.22	4.240	17.70	0.7986	0.6830	1.5	4.5	4.8	4.6
66	66.22	4.115	17.39	0.7984	0.6631	1.1	4.4	4.7	4.4
64	64.23	3.990	17.07	0.7983	0.6431	0.7	4.2	4.5	4.3
62	62.23	3.866	16.76	0.7981	0.6231	0.3	4.0	4.4	4.1
60	60.24	3.741	16.45	0.7980	0.6032	−0.1	3.9	4.2	3.9
58	58.24	3.616	16.13	0.7978	0.5832	−0.6	3.7	4.1	3.8
56	56.24	3.492	15.82	0.7977	0.5632	−1.0	3.5	4.0	3.6
54	54.25	3.367	15.51	0.7975	0.5432	−1.4	3.4	3.8	3.5
52	52.25	3.242	15.19	0.7973	0.5232	−1.9	3.2	3.7	3.3
50	50.25	3.118	14.88	0.7972	0.5031	−2.3	3.0	3.5	3.1
48	48.25	2.993	14.57	0.7970	0.4831	−2.8	2.9	3.4	3.0
46	46.25	2.868	14.25	0.7969	0.4631	−3.3	2.7	3.2	2.8
44	44.24	2.744	13.94	0.7967	0.4430	−3.8	2.5	3.1	2.6
42	42.24	2.619	13.62	0.7965	0.4230	−4.4	2.4	2.9	2.5
40	40.24	2.494	13.31	0.7964	0.4029	−5.0	2.2	2.8	2.3
38	38.23	2.369	13.00	0.7962	0.3828	−5.6	2.0	2.6	2.1
36	36.23	2.245	12.68	0.7961	0.3628	−6.2	1.8	2.5	2.0
34	34.22	2.120	12.37	0.7959	0.3427	−6.8	1.7	2.3	1.8
32	32.22	1.995	12.06	0.7958	0.3226	−7.5	1.5	2.2	1.6
30	30.21	1.871	11.74	0.7956	0.3025	−8.3	1.3	2.0	1.4
28	28.20	1.746	11.43	0.7954	0.2824	−9.1	1.1	1.9	1.3
24	24.18	1.496	10.80	0.7951	0.2421	−10.8	0.8	1.6	0.9
20	20.16	1.247	10.18	0.7948	0.2018	−12.8	0.4	1.2	0.6
16	16.13	0.998	9.550	0.7945	0.1616	−15.3	−0.5	0.9	0.2
12	12.11	0.748	8.923	0.7942	0.1212	−18.3	−0.8	0.6	−0.6
8	8.07	0.499	8.296	0.7939	0.0808	−22.6	−1.2	0.3	−1.0
4	4.04	0.249	7.669	0.7935	0.0404	−29.5	−1.6	−0.5	−1.4
0	0.00	0.000	7.042	0.7932	0.0000	—	−2.0	−0.8	−1.8

7.5 °C DRY-BULB

Percentage saturation, μ / %	Relative humidity, ϕ /%	Value of stated parameter per kg dry air			Vapour pressure, p_v / kPa	Dew point temperature, θ_d / °C	Adiabatic saturation temperature, $\theta^\star$ / °C	Wet bulb temperature	
		Moisture content, g /(g·kg⁻¹)	Specific enthalpy, h /(kJ·kg⁻¹)	Specific volume, v /(m³·kg⁻¹)				Screen, θ'_{sc} / °C	Sling, θ'_{sl} / °C
100	100.00	6.455	23.78	0.8028	1.036	7.5	7.5	7.5	7.5
96	96.04	6.196	23.13	0.8025	0.9951	6.9	7.2	7.2	7.2
92	92.08	5.938	22.48	0.8022	0.9541	6.3	6.9	7.0	6.9
88	88.11	5.680	21.83	0.8019	0.9130	5.7	6.6	6.7	6.6
84	84.14	5.422	21.18	0.8015	0.8718	5.0	6.3	6.4	6.3
80	80.16	5.164	20.53	0.8012	0.8306	4.3	6.0	6.1	6.0
76	76.19	4.906	19.88	0.8009	0.7894	3.6	5.6	5.8	5.7
72	72.21	4.647	19.23	0.8005	0.7482	2.8	5.3	5.6	5.3
70	70.22	4.518	18.91	0.8004	0.7276	2.4	5.1	5.4	5.2
68	68.22	4.389	18.58	0.8002	0.7069	2.0	5.0	5.3	5.0
66	66.23	4.260	18.26	0.8001	0.6863	1.6	4.8	5.1	4.9
64	64.24	4.131	17.93	0.7999	0.6656	1.2	4.7	5.0	4.7
62	62.24	4.002	17.61	0.7997	0.6449	0.8	4.5	4.8	4.5
60	60.25	3.873	17.28	0.7996	0.6243	0.3	4.3	4.7	4.4
58	58.25	3.744	16.96	0.7994	0.6036	−0.1	4.1	4.5	4.2
56	56.25	3.615	16.63	0.7992	0.5829	−0.6	4.0	4.4	4.0
54	54.25	3.486	16.31	0.7991	0.5622	−1.0	3.8	4.2	3.9
52	52.26	3.356	15.99	0.7989	0.5415	−1.4	3.6	4.1	3.7
50	50.26	3.227	15.66	0.7987	0.5208	−1.9	3.5	3.9	3.5
48	48.26	3.098	15.34	0.7986	0.5000	−2.4	3.3	3.8	3.4
46	46.26	2.969	15.01	0.7984	0.4793	−2.9	3.1	3.6	3.2
44	44.25	2.840	14.69	0.7983	0.4585	−3.4	2.9	3.5	3.0
42	42.25	2.711	14.36	0.7981	0.4378	−4.0	2.8	3.3	2.9
40	40.25	2.582	14.04	0.7979	0.4170	−4.6	2.6	3.2	2.7
38	38.24	2.453	13.71	0.7978	0.3963	−5.2	2.4	3.0	2.5
36	36.24	2.324	13.39	0.7976	0.3755	−5.8	2.2	2.9	2.3
34	34.23	2.195	13.06	0.7974	0.3547	−6.4	2.1	2.7	2.2
32	32.22	2.066	12.74	0.7973	0.3339	−7.1	1.9	2.6	2.0
30	30.22	1.936	12.41	0.7971	0.3131	−7.9	1.7	2.4	1.8
28	28.21	1.807	12.09	0.7969	0.2923	−8.7	1.5	2.2	1.6
24	24.19	1.549	11.44	0.7966	0.2506	−10.4	1.1	1.9	1.3
20	20.16	1.291	10.79	0.7963	0.2089	−12.4	0.8	1.6	0.9
16	16.14	1.033	10.14	0.7960	0.1672	−14.9	0.4	1.3	0.6
12	12.11	0.775	9.493	0.7956	0.1255	−18.0	−0.5	1.0	0.2
8	8.08	0.516	8.843	0.7953	0.0837	−22.2	−0.9	0.6	−0.7
4	4.04	0.258	8.194	0.7950	0.0419	−29.1	−1.3	0.3	−1.1
0	0.00	0.000	7.545	0.7946	0.0000	—	−1.7	−0.5	−1.5

8 °C DRY-BULB

Percentage saturation, μ / %	Relative humidity, ϕ /%	Value of stated parameter per kg dry air			Vapour pressure, p_v / kPa	Dew point temperature, θ_d / °C	Adiabatic saturation temperature, $\theta\star$ / °C	Wet bulb temperature	
		Moisture content, g / (g·kg^{-1})	Specific enthalpy, h / (kJ·kg^{-1})	Specific volume, v / (m^3·kg^{-1})				Screen, θ'_{sc} / °C	Sling, θ'_{sl} / °C
100	100.00	6.681	24.86	0.8046	1.072	8.0	8.0	8.0	8.0
96	96.04	6.414	24.18	0.8042	1.030	7.4	7.7	7.7	7.7
92	92.08	6.146	23.51	0.8039	0.9872	6.8	7.4	7.4	7.4
88	88.11	5.879	22.84	0.8035	0.9447	6.2	7.1	7.2	7.1
84	84.14	5.612	22.17	0.8032	0.9021	5.5	6.7	6.9	6.8
80	80.17	5.345	21.49	0.8029	0.8595	4.8	6.4	6.6	6.4
76	76.19	5.078	20.82	0.8025	0.8169	4.1	6.1	6.3	6.1
72	72.21	4.810	20.15	0.8022	0.7742	3.3	5.8	6.0	5.8
70	70.22	4.677	19.81	0.8020	0.7529	2.9	5.6	5.9	5.6
68	68.23	4.543	19.48	0.8018	0.7315	2.5	5.4	5.7	5.5
66	66.24	4.909	19.14	0.8017	0.7102	2.1	5.3	5.6	5.3
64	64.24	4.276	18.80	0.8015	0.6888	1.7	5.1	5.4	5.2
62	62.25	4.142	18.47	0.8013	0.6674	1.2	4.9	5.3	5.0
60	60.25	4.009	18.13	0.8012	0.6460	0.8	4.8	5.1	4.8
58	58.26	3.875	17.80	0.8010	0.6246	0.3	4.6	5.0	4.6
56	56.26	3.741	17.46	0.8008	0.6032	−0.1	4.4	4.8	4.5
54	54.26	3.608	17.12	0.8007	0.5818	−0.6	4.2	4.7	4.3
52	52.27	3.474	16.79	0.8005	0.5604	−1.0	4.1	4.5	4.1
50	50.27	3.340	16.45	0.8003	0.5389	−1.5	3.9	4.4	4.0
48	48.27	3.207	16.12	0.8001	0.5175	−2.0	3.7	4.2	3.8
46	46.26	3.073	15.78	0.8000	0.4960	−2.5	3.5	4.0	3.6
44	44.26	2.940	15.44	0.7998	0.4745	−3.0	3.4	3.9	3.4
42	42.26	2.806	15.11	0.7996	0.4531	−3.6	3.2	3.7	3.3
40	40.26	2.672	14.77	0.7995	0.4316	−4.2	3.0	3.6	3.1
38	38.25	2.539	14.43	0.7993	0.4101	−4.8	2.8	3.4	2.9
36	36.25	2.405	14.10	0.7991	0.3886	−5.4	2.6	3.3	2.7
34	34.24	2.272	13.76	0.7990	0.3671	−6.0	2.4	3.1	2.6
32	32.23	2.138	13.43	0.7988	0.3456	−6.7	2.3	2.9	2.4
30	30.22	2.004	13.09	0.7986	0.3240	−7.5	2.1	2.8	2.2
28	28.21	1.871	12.75	0.7984	0.3025	−8.3	1.9	2.6	2.0
24	24.19	1.603	12.08	0.7981	0.2594	−10.0	1.5	2.3	1.6
20	20.17	1.336	11.41	0.7978	0.2162	−12.1	1.1	2.0	1.3
16	16.14	1.069	10.74	0.7974	0.1731	−14.5	0.7	1.6	0.9
12	12.11	0.8017	10.06	0.7971	0.1299	−17.6	0.3	1.3	0.5
8	8.08	0.5345	9.392	0.7967	0.0866	−21.9	−0.6	1.0	0.1
4	4.04	0.2672	8.720	0.7964	0.0433	−28.8	−1.0	0.6	−0.8
0	0.00	0.0000	8.048	0.7961	0.0000	—	−1.5	0.3	−1.2

8.5 °C DRY-BULB

Percentage saturation, μ / %	Relative humidity, ϕ /%	Value of stated parameter per kg dry air			Vapour pressure, p_v / kPa	Dew point temperature, θ_d / °C	Adiabatic saturation temperature, $\theta\star$ / °C	Wet bulb temperature	
		Moisture content, g / (g·kg^{-1})	Specific enthalpy, h / (kJ·kg^{-1})	Specific volume, v / (m^3·kg^{-1})				Screen, θ'_{sc} / °C	Sling, θ'_{sl} / °C
100	100.00	6.914	25.95	0.8063	1.109	8.5	8.5	8.5	8.5
96	96.04	6.638	25.26	0.8059	1.065	7.9	8.2	8.2	8.2
92	92.08	6.361	24.56	0.8056	1.021	7.3	7.9	7.9	7.9
88	88.12	6.085	23.86	0.8052	0.9774	6.6	7.5	7.6	7.6
84	84.15	5.808	23.17	0.8049	0.9333	6.0	7.2	7.4	7.2
80	80.18	5.532	22.47	0.8045	0.8893	5.3	6.9	7.1	6.9
76	76.20	5.255	21.78	0.8042	0.8452	4.6	6.6	6.8	6.6
72	72.22	4.978	21.08	0.8038	0.8011	3.8	6.2	6.5	6.3
70	70.23	4.840	20.73	0.8037	0.7790	3.4	6.1	6.3	6.1
68	68.24	4.702	20.38	0.8035	0.7569	3.0	5.9	6.2	5.9
66	66.25	4.564	20.04	0.8033	0.7348	2.6	5.7	6.0	5.8
64	64.25	4.425	19.69	0.8031	0.7127	2.1	5.5	5.9	5.6
62	62.26	4.287	19.34	0.8029	0.6906	1.7	5.4	5.7	5.4
60	60.26	4.149	18.99	0.8028	0.6684	1.2	5.2	5.6	5.3
58	58.27	4.010	18.64	0.8026	0.6463	0.8	5.0	5.4	5.1
56	56.27	3.872	18.29	0.8024	0.6241	0.3	4.8	5.3	4.9
54	54.27	3.734	17.95	0.8022	0.6020	−0.2	4.7	5.1	4.7
52	52.27	3.596	17.60	0.8021	0.5798	−0.6	4.5	4.9	4.6
50	50.27	3.457	17.25	0.8019	0.5576	−1.1	4.3	4.8	4.4
48	48.27	3.319	16.90	0.8017	0.5354	−1.6	4.1	4.6	4.2
46	46.27	3.181	16.55	0.8015	0.5132	−2.1	3.9	4.5	4.0
44	44.27	3.042	16.21	0.8014	0.4910	−2.6	3.8	4.3	3.9
42	42.27	2.904	15.86	0.8012	0.4688	−3.2	3.6	4.1	3.7
40	40.26	2.766	15.51	0.8010	0.4466	−3.7	3.4	4.0	3.5
38	38.26	2.627	15.16	0.8008	0.4244	−4.3	3.2	3.8	3.3
36	36.25	2.489	14.81	0.8007	0.4021	−5.0	3.0	3.7	3.1
34	34.25	2.351	14.47	0.8005	0.3799	−5.6	2.8	3.5	2.9
32	32.24	2.213	14.12	0.8003	0.3576	−6.4	2.6	3.3	2.8
30	30.23	2.074	13.77	0.8001	0.3353	−7.1	2.4	3.2	2.6
28	28.22	1.936	13.42	0.8000	0.3130	−7.9	2.3	3.0	2.4
24	24.20	1.659	12.73	0.7996	0.2684	−9.6	1.9	2.7	2.0
20	20.18	1.383	12.03	0.7993	0.2238	−11.7	1.5	2.3	1.6
16	16.15	1.106	11.33	0.7989	0.1791	−14.1	1.1	2.0	1.2
12	12.12	0.831	10.64	0.7985	0.1344	−17.2	0.7	1.7	0.9
8	8.08	0.553	9.943	0.7982	0.0896	−21.5	0.3	1.3	0.5
4	4.04	0.278	9.247	0.7978	0.0448	−28.5	−0.7	1.0	0.1
0	0.00	0.000	8.551	0.7975	0.0000	—	−1.2	0.6	−0.9

9 °C DRY-BULB

Percentage saturation, μ / %	Relative humidity, ϕ /%	Value of stated parameter per kg dry air			Vapour pressure, p_v / kPa	Dew point temperature, θ_d / °C	Adiabatic saturation temperature, $\theta\star$ / °C	Wet bulb temperature	
		Moisture content, g / (g·kg^{-1})	Specific enthalpy, h / (kJ·kg^{-1})	Specific volume, v / (m^3·kg^{-1})				Screen, θ'_{sc} / °C	Sling, θ'_{sl} / °C
100	100.00	7.155	27.07	0.8080	1.147	9.0	9.0	9.0	9.0
96	96.04	6.869	26.35	0.8077	1.102	8.4	8.7	8.7	8.7
92	92.08	6.583	25.63	0.8073	1.056	7.8	8.4	8.4	8.4
88	88.12	6.296	24.90	0.8069	1.011	7.1	8.0	8.1	8.0
84	84.15	6.010	24.18	0.8066	0.9655	6.5	7.7	7.8	7.7
80	80.18	5.724	23.46	0.8062	0.9200	5.8	7.4	7.5	7.4
76	76.21	5.438	22.74	0.8058	0.8744	5.0	7.0	7.2	7.1
72	72.23	5.152	22.02	0.8055	0.8287	4.3	6.7	6.9	6.7
70	70.24	5.008	21.66	0.8053	0.8059	3.9	6.5	6.8	6.6
68	68.25	4.865	21.30	0.8051	0.7830	3.5	6.3	6.6	6.4
66	66.25	4.722	20.94	0.8049	0.7602	3.0	6.2	6.5	6.2
64	64.26	4.579	20.58	0.8048	0.7373	2.6	6.0	6.3	6.0
62	62.27	4.436	20.22	0.8046	0.7144	2.2	5.8	6.2	5.9
60	60.27	4.293	19.86	0.8044	0.6915	1.7	5.6	6.0	5.7
58	58.28	4.150	19.50	0.8042	0.6686	1.3	5.4	5.8	5.5
56	56.28	4.007	19.14	0.8040	0.6457	0.8	5.3	5.7	5.3
54	54.28	3.864	18.78	0.8038	0.6228	0.3	5.1	5.5	5.2
52	52.28	3.721	18.42	0.8037	0.5999	−0.2	4.9	5.4	5.0
50	50.28	3.578	18.06	0.8035	0.5769	−0.7	4.7	5.2	4.8
48	48.28	3.434	17.70	0.8033	0.5540	−1.2	4.5	5.0	4.6
46	46.28	3.291	17.34	0.8031	0.5310	−1.7	4.4	4.9	4.4
44	44.28	3.148	16.98	0.8029	0.5080	−2.2	4.2	4.7	4.3
42	42.28	3.005	16.62	0.8027	0.4851	−2.8	4.0	4.6	4.1
40	40.27	2.862	16.26	0.8026	0.4621	−3.3	3.8	4.4	3.9
38	38.27	2.719	15.90	0.8024	0.4391	−3.9	3.6	4.2	3.7
36	36.26	2.576	15.54	0.8022	0.4160	−4.6	3.4	4.1	3.5
34	34.26	2.433	15.18	0.8020	0.3930	−5.3	3.2	3.9	3.3
32	32.25	2.290	14.82	0.8018	0.3700	−6.0	3.0	3.7	3.1
30	30.24	2.146	14.46	0.8016	0.3470	−6.7	2.8	3.6	3.0
28	28.23	2.003	14.10	0.8015	0.3239	−7.5	2.6	3.4	2.8
24	24.21	1.717	13.38	0.8011	0.2778	−9.3	2.2	3.0	2.4
20	20.18	1.431	12.66	0.8007	0.2316	−11.3	1.8	2.7	2.0
16	16.15	1.145	11.94	0.8004	0.1853	−13.8	1.4	2.4	1.6
12	12.12	0.857	11.22	0.8000	0.1391	−16.9	1.0	2.0	1.2
8	8.08	0.572	10.50	0.7996	0.0928	−21.1	0.6	1.6	0.8
4	4.04	0.286	9.774	0.7993	0.0464	−28.1	0.2	1.3	0.4
0	0.00	0.000	9.054	0.7989	0.0000	—	−0.9	0.9	−0.6

9.5 °C DRY-BULB

Percentage saturation, μ / %	Relative humidity, ϕ /%	Value of stated parameter per kg dry air			Vapour pressure, p_v / kPa	Dew point temperature, θ_d / °C	Adiabatic saturation temperature, $\theta\star$ / °C	Wet bulb temperature	
		Moisture content, g / (g·kg^{-1})	Specific enthalpy, h / (kJ·kg^{-1})	Specific volume, v / (m^3·kg^{-1})				Screen, θ'_{sc} / °C	Sling, θ'_{sl} / °C
100	100.00	7.403	28.20	0.8098	1.188	9.5	9.5	9.5	9.5
96	96.05	7.107	27.45	0.8094	1.141	8.9	9.2	9.2	9.2
92	92.09	6.811	26.71	0.8090	1.094	8.3	8.8	8.9	8.9
88	88.12	6.515	25.96	0.8087	1.047	7.6	8.5	8.6	8.5
84	84.16	6.219	25.22	0.8083	0.9987	7.0	8.2	8.3	8.2
80	80.19	5.923	24.47	0.8079	0.9516	6.3	7.8	8.0	7.9
76	76.21	5.626	23.73	0.8075	0.9044	5.5	7.5	7.7	7.5
72	72.24	5.330	22.98	0.8071	0.8572	4.8	7.1	7.4	7.2
70	70.25	5.182	22.61	0.8070	0.8336	4.4	7.0	7.2	7.0
68	68.26	5.034	22.23	0.8068	0.8100	3.9	6.8	7.1	6.8
66	66.26	4.886	21.86	0.8066	0.7863	3.5	6.6	6.9	6.7
64	64.27	4.738	21.49	0.8064	0.7627	3.1	6.4	6.8	6.5
62	62.28	4.590	21.12	0.8062	0.7390	2.7	6.2	6.6	6.3
60	60.28	4.442	20.74	0.8060	0.7154	2.2	6.1	6.4	6.1
58	58.29	4.294	20.37	0.8058	0.6917	1.7	5.9	6.3	5.9
56	56.29	4.146	20.00	0.8056	0.6680	1.2	5.7	6.1	5.8
54	54.29	3.998	19.62	0.8054	0.6443	0.7	5.5	6.0	5.6
52	52.29	3.850	19.25	0.8053	0.6206	0.2	5.3	5.8	5.4
50	50.29	3.702	18.88	0.8051	0.5968	−0.3	5.1	5.6	5.2
48	48.29	3.554	18.51	0.8049	0.5731	−0.8	4.9	5.5	5.0
46	46.29	3.405	18.13	0.8047	0.5493	−1.3	4.8	5.3	4.9
44	44.29	3.257	17.76	0.8045	0.5256	−1.8	4.6	5.1	4.7
42	42.29	3.109	17.39	0.8043	0.5018	−2.4	4.4	5.0	4.5
40	40.28	2.961	17.01	0.8041	0.4780	−2.9	4.2	4.8	4.3
38	38.28	2.813	16.64	0.8039	0.4542	−3.5	4.0	4.6	4.1
36	36.27	2.665	16.27	0.8037	0.4304	−4.2	3.8	4.5	3.9
34	34.26	2.517	15.90	0.8035	0.4066	−4.9	3.6	4.3	3.7
32	32.26	2.369	15.52	0.8034	0.3828	−5.6	3.4	4.1	3.5
30	30.25	2.221	15.15	0.8032	0.3589	−6.3	3.2	3.9	3.3
28	28.24	2.073	14.78	0.8030	0.3351	−7.1	3.0	3.8	3.1
24	24.22	1.777	14.03	0.8026	0.2874	−8.9	2.6	3.4	2.7
20	20.19	1.481	13.29	0.8022	0.2396	−10.9	2.2	3.1	2.3
16	16.16	1.184	12.54	0.8018	0.1918	−13.4	1.8	2.7	1.9
12	12.12	0.888	11.79	0.8015	0.1439	−16.5	1.3	2.3	1.5
8	8.09	0.592	11.05	0.8011	0.0960	−20.8	0.9	2.0	1.1
4	4.05	0.296	10.30	0.8007	0.0480	−27.8	0.5	1.6	0.7
0	0.00	0.000	9.557	0.8003	0.0000	—	−0.6	1.2	0.3

10 °C DRY-BULB

Percentage saturation, μ / %	Relative humidity, ϕ / %	Value of stated parameter per kg dry air			Vapour pressure, p_v / kPa	Dew point temperature, θ_d / °C	Adiabatic saturation temperature, $\theta^\star$ / °C	Wet bulb temperature	
		Moisture content, g / (g·kg^{-1})	Specific enthalpy, h / (kJ·kg^{-1})	Specific volume, v / $(\text{m}^3\text{·kg}^{-1})$				Screen, θ'_{sc} / °C	Sling, θ'_{sl} / °C
100	100.00	7.659	29.35	0.8116	1.227	10.0	10.0	10.0	10.0
96	96.05	7.352	28.58	0.8112	1.180	9.4	9.7	9.7	9.7
92	92.09	7.046	27.81	0.8108	1.130	8.8	9.3	9.4	9.3
88	88.13	6.740	27.04	0.8104	1.081	8.1	9.0	9.1	9.0
84	84.16	6.433	26.27	0.8100	1.034	7.5	8.7	8.8	8.7
80	80.19	6.127	25.50	0.8096	0.9841	6.7	8.3	8.5	8.3
76	76.22	5.821	24.72	0.8092	0.9354	6.0	8.0	8.2	8.0
72	72.24	5.514	23.95	0.8088	0.8866	5.2	7.6	7.8	7.6
70	70.26	5.361	23.57	0.8086	0.8622	4.8	7.4	7.7	7.5
68	68.26	5.208	23.18	0.8084	0.8377	4.4	7.2	7.5	7.3
66	66.27	5.055	22.79	0.8082	0.8133	4.0	7.1	7.4	7.1
64	64.28	4.902	22.41	0.8080	0.7888	3.6	6.9	7.2	6.9
62	62.29	4.748	22.02	0.8078	0.7644	3.1	6.7	7.0	6.7
60	60.29	4.595	21.64	0.8076	0.7398	2.7	6.5	6.9	6.6
58	58.30	4.442	21.25	0.8074	0.7154	2.2	6.3	6.7	6.4
56	56.30	4.289	20.86	0.8072	0.6909	1.7	6.1	6.5	6.2
54	54.30	4.136	20.48	0.8070	0.6664	1.2	5.9	6.4	6.0
52	52.30	3.983	20.09	0.8069	0.6419	0.7	5.7	6.2	5.8
50	50.30	3.829	19.71	0.8067	0.6173	0.1	5.6	6.0	5.6
48	48.30	3.676	19.32	0.8065	0.5928	−0.4	5.4	5.9	5.5
46	46.30	3.523	18.94	0.8063	0.5682	−0.9	5.2	5.7	5.3
44	44.30	3.370	18.55	0.8061	0.5436	−1.4	5.0	5.5	5.1
42	42.30	3.217	18.16	0.8059	0.5190	−2.0	4.8	5.4	4.9
40	40.29	3.064	17.78	0.8057	0.4945	−2.5	4.6	5.2	4.7
38	38.29	2.910	17.39	0.8055	0.4698	−3.1	4.4	5.0	4.5
36	36.28	2.757	17.00	0.8053	0.4452	−3.8	4.2	4.8	4.3
34	34.27	2.604	16.62	0.8051	0.4206	−4.5	4.0	4.7	4.1
32	32.27	2.451	16.23	0.8049	0.3960	−5.2	3.8	4.5	3.9
30	30.26	2.298	15.85	0.8047	0.3713	−5.9	3.6	4.3	3.7
28	28.25	2.144	15.46	0.8045	0.3466	−6.7	3.4	4.1	3.5
24	24.22	1.838	14.69	0.8041	0.2973	−8.5	3.0	3.8	3.1
20	20.20	1.532	13.92	0.8037	0.2478	−10.5	2.5	3.4	2.7
16	16.16	1.225	13.15	0.8033	0.1984	−13.0	2.1	3.1	2.3
12	12.13	0.919	12.38	0.8029	0.1488	−16.1	1.7	2.7	1.9
8	8.09	0.613	11.60	0.8025	0.0993	−20.4	1.2	2.3	1.4
4	4.05	0.306	10.83	0.8021	0.0497	−27.4	0.8	1.9	1.0
0	0.00	0.000	10.06	0.8018	0.0000	—	0.3	1.6	0.6

10.5 °C DRY-BULB

Percentage saturation, μ / %	Relative humidity, ϕ / %	Value of stated parameter per kg dry air			Vapour pressure, p_v / kPa	Dew point temperature, θ_d / °C	Adiabatic saturation temperature, $\theta^\star$ / °C	Wet bulb temperature	
		Moisture content, g / (g·kg^{-1})	Specific enthalpy, h / (kJ·kg^{-1})	Specific volume, v / $(\text{m}^3\text{·kg}^{-1})$				Screen, θ'_{sc} / °C	Sling, θ'_{sl} / °C
100	100.00	7.922	30.53	0.8133	1.269	10.5	10.5	10.5	10.5
96	96.05	7.606	29.73	0.8129	1.219	9.9	10.2	10.2	10.2
92	92.09	7.289	28.93	0.8125	1.169	9.3	9.8	9.9	9.8
88	88.13	6.972	28.13	0.8121	1.118	8.6	9.5	9.6	9.5
84	84.17	6.655	27.33	0.8117	1.068	7.9	9.1	9.3	9.2
80	80.20	6.338	26.54	0.8113	1.018	7.2	8.8	8.9	8.8
76	76.23	6.021	25.74	0.8109	0.9673	6.5	8.4	8.6	8.5
72	72.25	5.704	24.94	0.8105	0.9168	5.7	8.1	8.3	8.1
70	70.26	5.546	24.54	0.8103	0.8916	5.3	7.9	8.1	7.9
68	68.27	5.387	24.14	0.8101	0.8663	4.9	7.7	8.0	7.7
66	66.28	5.229	23.74	0.8099	0.8410	4.5	7.5	7.8	7.6
64	64.29	5.070	23.34	0.8097	0.8158	4.0	7.3	7.6	7.4
62	62.30	4.912	22.94	0.8095	0.7905	3.6	7.1	7.5	7.2
60	60.30	4.754	22.54	0.8093	0.7652	3.1	6.9	7.3	7.0
58	58.31	4.595	22.14	0.8091	0.7398	2.7	6.7	7.1	6.8
56	56.31	4.437	21.74	0.8089	0.7145	2.2	6.6	7.0	6.6
54	54.31	4.278	21.34	0.8087	0.6892	1.7	6.4	6.8	6.4
52	52.31	4.120	20.95	0.8085	0.6638	1.2	6.2	6.6	6.2
50	50.31	3.961	20.55	0.8083	0.6384	0.6	6.0	6.5	6.1
48	48.31	3.803	20.15	0.8080	0.6131	0.1	5.8	6.3	5.9
46	46.31	3.644	19.75	0.8078	0.5877	−0.5	5.6	6.1	5.7
44	44.31	3.486	19.35	0.8076	0.5623	−1.0	5.4	5.9	5.5
42	42.31	3.328	18.95	0.8074	0.5368	−1.6	5.2	5.8	5.3
40	40.30	3.169	18.55	0.8072	0.5114	−2.1	5.0	5.6	5.1
38	38.30	3.011	18.15	0.8070	0.4860	−2.7	4.8	5.4	4.9
36	36.29	2.852	17.75	0.8068	0.4605	−3.4	4.6	5.2	4.7
34	34.28	2.694	17.35	0.8066	0.4350	−4.1	4.4	5.1	4.5
32	32.27	2.535	16.95	0.8064	0.4095	−4.8	4.2	4.9	4.3
30	30.27	2.377	16.55	0.8062	0.3840	−5.5	3.9	4.7	4.1
28	28.25	2.218	16.15	0.8060	0.3585	−6.3	3.7	4.5	3.9
24	24.23	1.901	15.35	0.8056	0.3075	−8.1	3.3	4.1	3.5
20	20.20	1.584	14.56	0.8052	0.2560	−10.2	2.9	3.8	3.0
16	16.17	1.268	13.76	0.8048	0.2052	−12.6	2.4	3.4	2.6
12	12.13	0.951	12.96	0.8044	0.1540	−15.8	2.0	3.0	2.2
8	8.09	0.634	12.16	0.8040	0.1027	−20.1	1.6	2.6	1.8
4	4.05	0.317	11.36	0.8036	0.0514	−27.1	1.1	2.3	1.3
0	0.00	0.000	10.56	0.8032	0.0000	—	0.6	1.9	0.9

11 °C DRY-BULB

Percentage saturation, μ / %	Relative humidity, ϕ /%	Value of stated parameter per kg dry air			Vapour pressure, p_v / kPa	Dew point temperature, θ_d / °C	Adiabatic saturation temperature, $\theta^\star$ / °C	Wet bulb temperature	
		Moisture content, g / (g·kg^{-1})	Specific enthalpy, h / (kJ·kg^{-1})	Specific volume, v / (m^3·kg^{-1})				Screen, θ'_{sc} / °C	Sling, θ'_{sl} / °C
100	100.00	8.194	31.72	0.8151	1.312	11.0	11.0	11.0	11.0
96	96.05	7.866	30.90	0.8147	1.260	10.4	10.7	10.7	10.7
92	92.09	7.539	30.07	0.8143	1.208	9.8	10.3	10.4	10.3
88	88.14	7.211	29.25	0.8139	1.156	9.1	10.0	10.1	10.0
84	84.17	6.883	28.42	0.8134	1.104	8.4	9.6	9.7	9.6
80	80.21	6.555	27.59	0.8130	1.052	7.7	9.2	9.4	9.3
76	76.24	6.228	26.77	0.8126	1.000	7.0	8.9	9.1	8.9
72	72.26	5.900	25.94	0.8122	0.9480	6.2	8.5	8.8	8.6
70	70.27	5.736	25.53	0.8120	0.9219	5.8	8.3	8.6	8.4
68	68.28	5.572	25.11	0.8117	0.8959	5.4	8.1	8.4	8.2
66	66.29	5.408	24.70	0.8115	0.8696	5.0	7.9	8.3	8.0
64	64.30	5.244	24.29	0.8113	0.8435	4.5	7.8	8.1	7.8
62	62.31	5.080	23.87	0.8111	0.8174	4.1	7.6	7.9	7.6
60	60.31	4.916	23.46	0.8109	0.7912	3.6	7.4	7.8	7.4
58	58.32	4.753	23.05	0.8107	0.7650	3.1	7.2	7.6	7.2
56	56.32	4.589	22.63	0.8105	0.7388	2.6	7.0	7.4	7.1
54	54.32	4.425	22.22	0.8103	0.7126	2.1	6.8	7.2	6.9
52	52.32	4.261	21.81	0.8101	0.6864	1.6	6.6	7.1	6.7
50	50.33	4.097	21.40	0.8099	0.6602	1.1	6.4	6.9	6.5
48	48.32	3.933	20.98	0.8096	0.6339	0.5	6.2	6.7	6.3
46	46.32	3.769	20.57	0.8094	0.6077	−0.1	6.0	6.5	6.1
44	44.32	3.605	20.16	0.8092	0.5814	−0.6	5.8	6.4	5.9
42	42.32	3.442	19.74	0.8090	0.5551	−1.1	5.6	6.2	5.7
40	40.31	3.278	19.33	0.8088	0.5288	−1.7	5.4	6.0	5.5
38	38.31	3.114	18.92	0.8086	0.5025	−2.3	5.2	5.8	5.3
36	36.30	2.950	18.50	0.8084	0.4762	−3.0	5.0	5.6	5.1
34	34.29	2.786	18.09	0.8082	0.4499	−3.7	4.7	5.4	4.9
32	32.28	2.622	17.68	0.8080	0.4235	−4.4	4.5	5.3	4.7
30	30.27	2.458	17.26	0.8077	0.3972	−5.1	4.3	5.1	4.5
28	28.26	2.294	16.85	0.8075	0.3708	−5.9	4.1	4.9	4.2
24	24.24	1.967	16.02	0.8071	0.3180	−7.7	3.7	4.5	3.8
20	20.21	1.639	15.20	0.8067	0.2651	−9.8	3.2	4.1	3.4
16	16.18	1.311	14.37	0.8063	0.2122	−12.3	2.8	3.8	3.0
12	12.14	0.983	13.54	0.8059	0.1592	−15.4	2.3	3.4	2.5
8	8.10	0.655	12.72	0.8054	0.1062	−19.7	1.9	3.0	2.1
4	4.05	0.328	11.89	0.8050	0.0531	−26.8	1.4	2.6	1.6
0	0.00	0.000	11.06	0.8046	0.0000	—	0.9	2.2	1.2

11.5 °C DRY-BULB

Percentage saturation, μ / %	Relative humidity, ϕ /%	Value of stated parameter per kg dry air			Vapour pressure, p_v / kPa	Dew point temperature, θ_d / °C	Adiabatic saturation temperature, $\theta^\star$ / °C	Wet bulb temperature	
		Moisture content, g / (g·kg^{-1})	Specific enthalpy, h / (kJ·kg^{-1})	Specific volume, v / (m^3·kg^{-1})				Screen, θ'_{sc} / °C	Sling, θ'_{sl} / °C
100	100.00	8.474	32.94	0.8169	1.356	11.5	11.5	11.5	11.5
96	96.05	8.135	32.09	0.8165	1.303	10.9	11.2	11.2	11.2
92	92.10	7.796	31.23	0.8160	1.249	10.3	10.8	10.9	10.8
88	88.14	7.457	30.38	0.8156	1.195	9.6	10.4	10.5	10.5
84	84.18	7.118	29.52	0.8152	1.142	8.9	10.1	10.2	10.1
80	80.21	6.779	28.67	0.8147	1.088	8.2	9.7	9.9	9.7
76	76.24	6.440	27.81	0.8143	1.034	7.5	9.3	9.6	9.4
72	72.27	6.102	26.96	0.8139	0.9800	6.7	9.0	9.2	9.0
70	70.28	5.932	26.53	0.8136	0.9531	6.3	8.8	9.1	8.8
68	68.29	5.762	26.10	0.8134	0.9261	5.9	8.6	8.9	8.6
66	66.30	5.593	25.67	0.8132	0.8991	5.4	8.4	8.7	8.4
64	64.31	5.424	25.25	0.8130	0.8721	5.0	8.2	8.5	8.3
62	62.32	5.254	24.82	0.8128	0.8451	4.6	8.0	8.4	8.1
60	60.32	5.085	24.39	0.8126	0.8180	4.1	7.8	8.2	7.9
58	58.33	4.915	23.96	0.8123	0.7910	3.6	7.6	8.0	7.7
56	56.33	4.746	23.54	0.8121	0.7639	3.1	7.4	7.8	7.5
54	54.33	4.576	23.11	0.8119	0.7368	2.6	7.2	7.7	7.3
52	52.34	4.407	22.68	0.8117	0.7097	2.1	7.0	7.5	7.1
50	50.34	4.237	22.26	0.8115	0.6826	1.5	6.8	7.3	6.9
48	48.34	4.068	21.83	0.8112	0.6555	1.0	6.6	7.1	6.7
46	46.33	3.898	21.40	0.8110	0.6283	0.4	6.4	6.9	6.5
44	44.33	3.729	20.97	0.8108	0.6012	−0.2	6.2	6.8	6.3
42	42.33	3.559	20.55	0.8106	0.5740	−0.7	6.0	6.6	6.1
40	40.32	3.390	20.12	0.8104	0.5468	−1.3	5.8	6.4	5.9
38	38.32	3.220	19.69	0.8102	0.5196	−1.9	5.6	6.2	5.7
36	36.31	3.051	19.26	0.8099	0.4924	−2.6	5.3	6.0	5.5
34	34.30	2.881	18.84	0.8097	0.4652	−3.3	5.1	5.8	5.2
32	32.29	2.712	18.41	0.8095	0.4379	−4.0	4.9	5.6	5.0
30	30.28	2.542	17.98	0.8093	0.4107	−4.7	4.7	5.5	4.8
28	28.27	2.373	17.55	0.8091	0.3834	−5.5	4.5	5.3	4.6
24	24.25	2.034	16.70	0.8086	0.3288	−7.3	4.0	4.9	4.2
20	20.22	1.695	15.84	0.8082	0.2742	−9.4	3.6	4.5	3.7
16	16.18	1.356	14.99	0.8078	0.2194	−11.9	3.1	4.1	3.3
12	12.14	1.017	14.13	0.8073	0.1647	−15.1	2.7	3.7	2.8
8	8.10	0.678	13.28	0.8069	0.1098	−19.4	2.2	3.3	2.4
4	4.05	0.339	12.42	0.8064	0.0549	−26.4	1.7	2.9	1.9
0	0.00	0.000	11.57	0.8060	0.0000	—	1.2	2.5	1.4

12 °C DRY-BULB

Percentage saturation, μ / %	Relative humidity, ϕ /%	Value of stated parameter per kg dry air			Vapour pressure, p_v / kPa	Dew point temperature, θ_d / °C	Adiabatic saturation temperature, $\theta^\star$ / °C	Wet bulb temperature	
		Moisture content, g / (g·kg^{-1})	Specific enthalpy, h / (kJ·kg^{-1})	Specific volume, v / (m^3·kg^{-1})				Screen, θ'_{sc} / °C	Sling, θ'_{sl} / °C
100	100.00	8.763	34.18	0.8187	1.402	12.0	12.0	12.0	12.0
96	96.05	8.412	33.30	0.8183	1.346	11.4	11.6	11.7	11.7
92	92.10	8.062	32.41	0.8178	1.291	10.8	11.3	11.4	11.3
88	88.15	7.711	31.53	0.8174	1.236	10.1	10.8	11.0	10.9
84	84.19	7.361	30.64	0.8169	1.180	9.4	10.6	10.7	10.6
80	80.22	7.010	29.76	0.8165	1.124	8.7	10.2	10.4	10.2
76	76.25	6.660	28.87	0.8160	1.069	8.0	9.8	10.0	9.8
72	72.28	6.309	27.99	0.8156	1.013	7.2	9.4	9.7	9.5
70	70.29	6.134	27.55	0.8153	0.9852	6.8	9.2	9.5	9.3
68	68.30	5.959	27.11	0.8151	0.9574	6.3	9.0	9.3	9.1
66	66.31	5.784	26.66	0.8149	0.9294	5.9	8.8	9.2	8.9
64	64.32	5.608	26.22	0.8147	0.9015	5.5	8.6	9.0	8.7
62	62.33	5.433	25.78	0.8144	0.8736	5.0	8.4	8.8	8.5
60	60.33	5.258	25.34	0.8142	0.8457	4.6	8.2	8.6	8.3
58	58.34	5.082	24.89	0.8140	0.8177	4.1	8.0	8.4	8.1
56	56.34	4.907	24.45	0.8138	0.7897	3.6	7.8	8.3	7.9
54	54.35	4.732	24.01	0.8135	0.7617	3.1	7.6	8.1	7.7
52	52.35	4.557	23.57	0.8133	0.7337	2.6	7.4	7.9	7.5
50	50.35	4.382	23.13	0.8131	0.7057	2.0	7.2	7.7	7.3
48	48.35	4.206	22.68	0.8129	0.6777	1.4	7.0	7.5	7.1
46	46.35	4.031	22.24	0.8126	0.6496	0.9	6.8	7.4	6.9
44	44.34	3.856	21.80	0.8124	0.6215	0.2	6.6	7.2	6.7
42	42.34	3.680	21.36	0.8122	0.5934	−0.3	6.4	7.0	6.5
40	40.34	3.505	20.92	0.8120	0.5654	−0.9	6.2	6.8	6.3
38	38.33	3.330	20.47	0.8117	0.5372	−1.5	5.9	6.6	6.1
36	36.32	3.155	20.03	0.8115	0.5091	−2.2	5.7	6.4	5.8
34	34.31	2.979	19.59	0.8113	0.4810	−2.9	5.5	6.2	5.6
32	32.30	2.804	19.15	0.8110	0.4528	−3.6	5.3	5.0	5.4
30	30.29	2.629	18.70	0.8108	0.4246	−4.3	5.1	5.8	5.2
28	28.28	2.454	18.26	0.8106	0.3964	−5.2	4.8	5.6	5.0
24	24.26	2.103	17.38	0.8101	0.3400	−6.9	4.4	5.2	4.5
20	20.22	1.753	16.49	0.8097	0.2835	−9.0	3.9	4.8	4.1
16	16.19	1.402	15.61	0.8092	0.2269	−11.5	3.5	4.4	3.6
12	12.15	1.052	14.72	0.8088	0.1703	−14.7	3.0	4.0	3.2
8	8.10	0.701	13.84	0.8083	0.1136	−19.0	2.5	3.6	2.7
4	4.05	0.350	12.96	0.8079	0.0568	−26.1	2.0	3.2	2.2
0	0.00	0.000	12.07	0.8074	0.0000	—	1.5	2.8	1.7

12.5 °C DRY-BULB

Percentage saturation, μ / %	Relative humidity, ϕ /%	Value of stated parameter per kg dry air			Vapour pressure, p_v / kPa	Dew point temperature, θ_d / °C	Adiabatic saturation temperature, $\theta^\star$ / °C	Wet bulb temperature	
		Moisture content, g / (g·kg^{-1})	Specific enthalpy, h / (kJ·kg^{-1})	Specific volume, v / (m^3·kg^{-1})				Screen, θ'_{sc} / °C	Sling, θ'_{sl} / °C
100	100.00	9.060	35.44	0.8205	1.449	12.5	12.5	12.5	12.5
96	96.06	8.698	34.53	0.8201	1.391	11.9	12.1	12.2	12.1
92	92.11	8.336	33.61	0.8196	1.334	11.3	11.8	11.8	11.8
88	88.15	7.973	32.70	0.8191	1.277	10.6	11.4	11.5	11.4
84	84.19	7.611	31.78	0.8187	1.220	9.9	11.0	11.2	11.1
80	80.23	7.248	30.87	0.8182	1.162	9.2	10.7	10.8	10.7
76	76.26	6.886	29.95	0.8177	1.105	8.4	10.3	10.5	10.3
72	72.29	6.524	29.04	0.8173	1.047	7.7	9.9	10.1	9.9
70	70.30	6.342	28.58	0.8170	1.018	7.2	9.7	10.0	9.7
68	68.31	6.161	28.12	0.8168	0.9895	6.8	9.5	9.8	9.5
66	66.32	5.980	27.67	0.8166	0.9607	6.4	9.3	9.6	9.3
64	64.33	5.799	27.21	0.8163	0.9319	6.0	9.1	9.4	9.1
62	62.34	5.618	26.75	0.8161	0.9030	5.5	8.9	9.2	8.9
60	60.35	5.436	26.30	0.8159	0.8741	5.0	8.7	9.1	8.7
58	58.35	5.255	25.84	0.8156	0.8452	4.6	8.5	8.9	8.5
56	56.36	5.074	25.38	0.8154	0.8163	4.1	8.3	8.7	8.3
54	54.36	4.893	24.92	0.8152	0.7874	3.5	8.1	8.5	8.1
52	52.36	4.711	24.47	0.8149	0.7584	3.0	7.8	8.3	7.9
50	50.36	4.530	24.01	0.8147	0.7295	2.5	7.6	8.1	7.7
48	48.36	4.349	23.55	0.8145	0.7005	1.9	7.4	8.0	7.5
46	46.36	4.168	23.09	0.8142	0.6715	1.3	7.2	7.8	7.3
44	44.36	3.987	22.64	0.8140	0.6425	0.7	7.0	7.6	7.1
42	42.35	3.805	22.18	0.8138	0.6135	0.1	6.8	7.4	6.9
40	40.35	3.624	21.72	0.8135	0.5844	−0.5	6.6	7.2	6.7
38	38.34	3.443	21.26	0.8133	0.5554	−1.1	6.3	7.0	6.4
36	36.33	3.262	20.81	0.8131	0.5263	−1.8	6.1	6.8	6.2
34	34.32	3.080	20.35	0.8128	0.4972	−2.5	5.9	6.6	6.0
32	32.31	2.899	19.89	0.8126	0.4681	−3.2	5.7	6.4	5.8
30	30.30	2.718	19.44	0.8124	0.4390	−4.0	5.4	6.2	5.6
28	28.29	2.537	18.98	0.8121	0.4098	−4.8	5.2	6.0	5.3
24	24.26	2.174	18.06	0.8117	0.3515	−6.6	4.7	5.6	4.9
20	20.23	1.812	17.15	0.8112	0.2931	−8.6	4.3	5.2	4.4
16	16.19	1.450	16.23	0.8107	0.2346	−11.2	3.8	4.8	4.0
12	12.15	1.087	15.32	0.8103	0.1760	−14.3	3.3	4.4	3.5
8	8.11	0.724	14.40	0.8098	0.1174	−18.7	2.8	3.9	3.0
4	4.06	0.362	13.49	0.8093	0.0587	−25.8	2.3	3.5	2.5
0	0.00	0.000	12.58	0.8089	0.0000	—	1.8	3.1	2.0

13 °C DRY-BULB

Percentage saturation, μ / %	Relative humidity, ϕ /%	Value of stated parameter per kg dry air			Vapour pressure, p_v / kPa	Dew point temperature, θ_d / °C	Adiabatic saturation temperature, $\theta^\star$ / °C	Wet bulb temperature	
		Moisture content, g / (g·kg^{-1})	Specific enthalpy, h / (kJ·kg^{-1})	Specific volume, v / (m^3·kg^{-1})				Screen, θ'_{sc} / °C	Sling, θ'_{sl} / °C
100	100.00	9.367	36.73	0.8224	1.497	13.0	13.0	13.0	13.0
96	96.06	8.992	35.78	0.8219	1.438	12.4	12.6	12.7	12.6
92	92.11	8.618	34.84	0.8214	1.379	11.7	12.3	12.3	12.3
88	88.16	8.243	33.89	0.8209	1.320	11.1	11.9	12.0	11.9
84	84.20	7.868	32.94	0.8204	1.260	10.4	11.5	11.6	11.5
80	80.24	7.494	32.00	0.8200	1.201	9.7	11.1	11.3	11.2
76	76.27	7.119	31.05	0.8195	1.142	8.9	10.7	11.0	10.8
72	72.30	6.744	30.11	0.8190	1.082	8.1	10.3	10.6	10.4
70	70.31	6.557	29.63	0.8188	1.052	7.7	10.1	10.4	10.2
68	68.33	6.370	29.16	0.8185	1.023	7.3	9.9	10.2	10.0
66	66.34	6.182	28.69	0.8183	0.9929	6.9	9.7	10.1	9.8
64	64.34	5.995	28.21	0.8180	0.9631	6.4	9.5	9.9	9.6
62	62.35	5.808	27.74	0.8178	0.9333	6.0	9.3	9.7	9.4
60	60.36	5.620	27.27	0.8175	0.9034	5.5	9.1	9.5	9.2
58	58.36	5.433	26.79	0.8173	0.8736	5.0	8.9	9.3	9.0
56	56.37	5.245	26.32	0.8171	0.8437	4.5	8.7	9.1	8.8
54	54.37	5.058	25.85	0.8168	0.8138	4.0	8.5	8.9	8.6
52	52.37	4.871	25.38	0.8166	0.7839	3.5	8.3	8.7	8.3
50	50.37	0.4683	24.90	0.8163	0.7540	2.9	8.1	8.6	8.1
48	48.37	4.496	24.43	0.8161	0.7240	2.4	7.8	8.4	7.9
46	46.37	4.309	23.96	0.8158	0.6941	1.8	7.6	8.2	7.7
44	44.37	4.121	23.48	0.8156	0.6641	1.2	7.4	8.0	7.5
42	42.36	3.934	23.01	0.8154	0.6341	0.5	7.2	7.8	7.3
40	40.36	3.747	22.54	0.8151	0.6041	−0.1	6.9	7.6	7.1
38	38.35	3.559	22.06	0.8149	0.5740	−0.7	6.7	7.4	6.8
36	36.34	3.372	21.59	0.8146	0.5440	−1.4	6.5	7.2	6.6
34	34.34	3.185	21.12	0.8144	0.5139	−2.1	6.3	7.0	6.4
32	32.33	2.997	20.65	0.8141	0.4838	−2.8	6.0	6.8	6.2
30	30.31	2.810	20.17	0.8139	0.4537	−3.6	5.8	6.6	5.9
28	28.30	2.623	19.70	0.8137	0.4236	−4.4	5.6	6.4	5.7
24	24.27	2.248	18.75	0.8132	0.3633	−6.2	5.1	6.0	5.2
20	20.24	1.873	17.81	0.8127	0.3029	−8.3	4.6	5.6	4.8
16	16.20	1.499	16.86	0.8122	0.2425	−10.8	4.1	5.1	4.3
12	12.16	1.124	15.92	0.8117	0.1820	−14.0	3.6	4.7	3.8
8	8.11	0.7493	14.97	0.8112	0.1214	−18.3	3.1	4.3	3.3
4	4.06	0.3747	14.02	0.8108	0.0607	−25.5	2.6	3.8	2.8
0	0.00	0.000	13.08	0.8103	0.0000	—	2.1	3.4	2.3

13.5 °C DRY-BULB

Percentage saturation, μ / %	Relative humidity, ϕ /%	Value of stated parameter per kg dry air			Vapour pressure, p_v / kPa	Dew point temperature, θ_d / °C	Adiabatic saturation temperature, $\theta^\star$ / °C	Wet bulb temperature	
		Moisture content, g / (g·kg^{-1})	Specific enthalpy, h / (kJ·kg^{-1})	Specific volume, v / (m^3·kg^{-1})				Screen, θ'_{sc} / °C	Sling, θ'_{sl} / °C
100	100.00	9.683	38.04	0.8242	1.546	13.5	13.5	13.5	13.5
96	96.06	9.295	37.06	0.8237	1.486	12.9	13.1	13.2	13.1
92	92.11	8.908	36.08	0.8232	1.424	12.2	12.8	12.8	12.8
88	88.16	8.521	35.10	0.8227	1.363	11.6	12.4	12.5	12.4
84	84.21	8.133	34.12	0.8222	1.302	10.8	12.0	12.1	12.0
80	80.25	7.746	33.14	0.8217	1.241	10.2	11.6	11.8	11.6
76	76.28	7.359	32.17	0.8212	1.180	9.4	11.2	11.4	11.2
72	72.31	6.972	31.19	0.8207	1.118	8.6	10.8	11.1	10.8
70	70.32	6.778	30.70	0.8205	1.088	8.2	10.6	10.9	10.6
68	68.34	6.584	30.21	0.8202	1.057	7.8	10.4	10.7	10.4
66	66.35	6.390	29.72	0.8200	1.026	7.4	10.2	10.5	10.2
64	64.36	6.197	29.23	0.8197	0.9952	6.9	10.0	10.3	10.0
62	62.36	6.003	28.74	0.8195	0.9644	6.5	9.8	10.1	9.8
60	60.37	5.810	28.25	0.8192	0.9336	6.0	9.6	9.9	9.6
58	58.38	5.616	27.76	0.8190	0.9028	5.5	9.3	9.7	9.4
56	56.38	5.422	27.28	0.8187	0.8719	5.0	9.1	9.6	9.2
54	54.38	5.229	26.79	0.8185	0.8410	4.5	8.9	9.4	9.0
52	52.39	5.036	26.30	0.8182	0.8101	4.0	8.7	9.2	8.8
50	50.39	4.841	25.81	0.8180	0.7792	3.4	8.5	9.0	8.6
48	48.39	4.648	25.32	0.8177	0.7482	2.8	8.2	8.8	8.3
46	46.38	4.454	24.83	0.8175	0.7173	2.2	8.0	8.6	8.1
44	44.38	4.260	24.34	0.8172	0.6863	1.6	7.8	8.4	7.9
42	42.38	4.067	23.85	0.8170	0.6553	1.0	7.6	8.2	7.7
40	40.37	3.873	23.36	0.8167	0.6243	0.3	7.3	8.0	7.4
38	38.36	3.679	22.87	0.8165	0.5933	−0.3	7.1	7.8	7.2
36	36.36	3.486	22.38	0.8162	0.5622	−1.0	6.9	7.6	7.0
34	34.35	3.292	21.90	0.8160	0.5312	−1.7	6.6	7.4	6.8
32	32.34	3.098	21.41	0.8157	0.5000	−2.4	6.4	7.2	6.5
30	30.33	2.905	20.92	0.8155	0.4690	−3.2	6.2	7.0	6.3
28	28.31	2.711	20.43	0.8152	0.4378	−4.0	5.9	6.8	6.1
24	24.28	2.324	19.45	0.8147	0.3755	−5.8	5.4	6.3	5.6
20	20.25	1.936	18.47	0.8142	0.3131	−7.9	4.9	5.9	5.1
16	16.21	1.549	17.49	0.8137	0.2506	−10.4	4.4	5.5	4.6
12	12.16	1.162	16.52	0.8132	0.1881	−13.6	3.9	5.0	4.1
8	8.11	0.7746	15.54	0.8127	0.1255	−18.0	3.4	4.6	3.6
4	4.06	0.3873	14.56	0.8122	0.0628	−25.1	2.9	4.1	3.1
0	0.00	0.000	13.58	0.8117	0.0000	—	2.4	3.7	2.6

14 °C DRY-BULB

Percentage saturation, μ / %	Relative humidity, ϕ /%	Value of stated parameter per kg dry air			Vapour pressure, p_v / kPa	Dew point temperature, θ_d / °C	Adiabatic saturation temperature, $\theta^\star$ / °C	Wet bulb temperature	
		Moisture content, g / (g·kg^{-1})	Specific enthalpy, h / (kJ·kg^{-1})	Specific volume, v / (m^3·kg^{-1})				Screen, θ'_{sc} / °C	Sling, θ'_{sl} / °C
100	100.00	10.010	39.37	0.8261	1.598	14.0	14.0	14.0	14.0
96	96.06	9.608	38.36	0.8256	1.535	13.4	13.6	13.7	13.6
92	92.12	9.207	37.37	0.8251	1.472	12.7	13.2	13.3	13.3
88	88.17	8.807	35.34	0.8245	1.409	12.1	12.9	13.0	12.9
84	84.21	8.407	35.32	0.8240	1.345	11.4	12.5	12.6	12.5
80	80.26	8.006	34.31	0.8235	1.282	10.7	12.1	12.2	12.1
76	76.29	7.606	33.30	0.8230	1.219	9.9	11.7	11.9	11.7
72	72.32	7.206	32.29	0.8225	1.155	9.1	11.3	11.5	11.3
70	70.34	7.005	31.78	0.8222	1.124	8.7	11.0	11.3	11.1
68	68.35	6.805	31.28	0.8219	1.092	8.3	10.8	11.1	10.9
66	66.36	6.605	30.77	0.8217	1.060	7.8	10.6	10.9	10.7
64	64.37	6.405	30.27	0.8214	1.028	7.4	10.4	10.8	10.5
62	62.38	6.205	29.76	0.8212	0.9965	6.9	10.2	10.6	10.3
60	60.38	6.005	29.26	0.8209	0.9647	6.5	10.0	10.4	10.0
58	58.39	5.804	28.75	0.8206	0.9328	6.0	9.8	10.2	9.8
56	56.39	5.604	28.24	0.8204	0.9009	5.5	9.6	10.0	9.6
54	54.40	5.404	27.74	0.8201	0.8690	5.0	9.3	9.8	9.4
52	52.40	5.204	27.23	0.8199	0.8371	4.4	9.1	9.6	9.2
50	50.40	5.004	26.73	0.8196	0.8052	3.9	8.9	9.4	9.0
48	48.40	4.804	26.22	0.8193	0.7732	3.3	8.7	9.2	8.7
46	46.40	4.604	25.72	0.8191	0.7412	2.7	8.4	9.0	8.5
44	44.39	4.403	25.21	0.8188	0.7092	2.1	8.2	8.8	8.3
42	42.39	4.203	24.70	0.8186	0.6772	1.4	8.0	8.6	8.1
40	40.38	4.003	24.20	0.8183	0.6452	0.8	7.7	8.4	7.8
38	38.38	3.803	23.69	0.8180	0.6131	0.1	7.5	8.2	7.6
36	36.37	3.603	23.17	0.8178	0.5810	−0.6	7.3	8.0	7.4
34	34.36	3.403	22.68	0.8175	0.5489	−1.3	7.0	7.8	7.1
32	32.35	3.202	22.18	0.8173	0.5168	−2.0	6.8	7.5	6.9
30	30.34	3.002	21.67	0.8170	0.4846	−2.8	6.5	7.3	6.7
28	28.32	2.802	21.16	0.8167	0.4525	−3.6	6.3	7.1	6.4
24	24.29	2.402	20.15	0.8162	0.3881	−5.4	5.8	6.7	5.9
20	20.26	2.002	19.14	0.8157	0.3236	−7.5	5.3	6.3	5.5
16	16.22	1.601	18.13	0.8152	0.2590	−10.0	4.8	5.8	5.0
12	12.17	1.201	17.12	0.8147	0.1944	−13.2	4.3	5.4	4.4
8	8.12	0.8006	16.11	0.8142	0.1297	−17.6	3.7	4.9	3.9
4	4.06	0.4003	15.10	0.8136	0.0649	−24.8	3.2	4.4	3.4
0	0.00	0.0000	14.08	0.8131	0.0000	—	2.6	4.0	2.9

14.5 °C DRY-BULB

Percentage saturation, μ / %	Relative humidity, ϕ /%	Value of stated parameter per kg dry air			Vapour pressure, p_v / kPa	Dew point temperature, θ_d / °C	Adiabatic saturation temperature, $\theta^\star$ / °C	Wet bulb temperature	
		Moisture content, g / (g·kg^{-1})	Specific enthalpy, h / (kJ·kg^{-1})	Specific volume, v / (m^3·kg^{-1})				Screen, θ'_{sc} / °C	Sling, θ'_{sl} / °C
100	100.00	10.340	40.73	0.8280	1.650	14.5	14.5	14.5	14.5
96	96.06	9.929	39.68	0.8274	1.585	13.9	14.1	14.2	14.1
92	92.12	9.515	38.64	0.8269	1.520	13.2	13.7	13.8	13.7
88	88.17	9.102	37.59	0.8264	1.455	12.6	13.3	13.4	13.4
84	84.22	8.688	36.55	0.8258	1.390	11.9	12.9	13.1	13.0
80	80.26	8.274	35.50	0.8253	1.324	11.1	12.5	12.7	12.6
76	76.30	7.860	34.45	0.8248	1.259	10.4	12.1	12.3	12.2
72	72.33	7.447	33.41	0.8242	1.194	9.6	11.7	12.0	11.8
70	70.35	7.240	32.89	0.8239	1.161	9.2	11.5	11.8	11.5
68	68.36	7.033	32.36	0.8237	1.128	8.7	11.3	11.6	11.3
66	66.37	6.826	31.84	0.8234	1.095	8.3	11.1	11.4	11.1
64	64.38	6.619	31.32	0.8231	1.062	7.9	10.9	11.2	10.9
62	62.39	6.412	30.79	0.8229	1.030	7.4	10.6	11.0	10.7
60	60.40	6.206	30.27	0.8226	0.9966	6.9	10.4	10.8	10.5
58	58.40	5.999	29.75	0.8223	0.9937	6.4	10.2	10.6	10.3
56	56.41	5.792	29.23	0.8221	0.9308	5.9	10.0	10.4	10.0
54	54.41	5.585	28.70	0.8218	0.8978	5.4	9.8	10.2	9.8
52	52.41	5.378	28.18	0.8215	0.8649	4.9	9.5	10.0	9.6
50	50.41	5.171	27.66	0.8213	0.8329	4.3	9.3	9.8	9.4
48	48.41	4.964	27.13	0.8210	0.7989	3.8	9.1	9.6	9.2
46	46.41	4.758	26.61	0.8207	0.7658	3.2	8.8	9.4	8.9
44	44.41	4.551	26.09	0.8204	0.7328	2.5	8.6	9.2	8.7
42	42.40	4.344	25.57	0.8202	0.6997	1.9	8.4	9.0	8.5
40	40.40	4.137	25.04	0.8199	0.6666	1.2	8.1	8.8	8.2
38	38.39	3.930	24.52	0.8196	0.6335	0.5	7.9	8.6	8.0
36	36.38	3.723	24.00	0.8194	0.6003	−0.2	7.6	8.4	7.8
34	34.37	3.516	23.47	0.8191	0.5672	−0.9	7.4	8.1	7.5
32	32.36	3.310	22.95	0.8188	0.5340	−1.6	7.2	7.9	7.3
30	30.35	3.103	22.43	0.8186	0.5008	−2.4	6.9	7.7	7.0
28	28.33	2.896	21.91	0.8183	0.4675	−3.2	6.7	7.5	6.8
24	24.30	2.482	20.86	0.8178	0.4010	−5.0	6.1	7.0	6.3
20	20.27	2.068	19.81	0.8172	0.3344	−7.1	5.6	6.6	5.8
16	16.22	1.655	18.77	0.8167	0.2677	−9.7	5.1	6.1	5.3
12	12.18	1.241	17.72	0.8161	0.2009	−12.9	4.6	5.7	4.8
8	8.12	0.827	16.68	0.8156	0.1340	−17.3	4.0	5.2	4.2
4	4.06	0.413	15.63	0.8151	0.0670	−24.5	3.5	4.7	3.7
0	0.00	0.000	14.59	0.8145	0.0000	—	2.9	4.3	3.2

15 °C DRY-BULB

Percentage saturation, μ / %	Relative humidity, ϕ /%	Value of stated parameter per kg dry air			Vapour pressure, p_v / kPa	Dew point temperature, θ_d / °C	Adiabatic saturation temperature, $\theta^\star$ / °C	Wet bulb temperature	
		Moisture content, g /(g·kg⁻¹)	Specific enthalpy, h /(kJ·kg⁻¹)	Specific volume, v /(m³·kg⁻¹)				Screen, θ'_{sc} / °C	Sling, θ'_{sl} / °C
100	100.00	10.697	42.11	0.8299	1.704	15.0	15.0	15.0	15.0
96	96.06	10.260	41.03	0.8293	1.637	14.4	14.6	14.6	14.6
92	92.13	9.833	39.95	0.8288	1.570	13.7	14.2	14.3	14.2
88	88.18	9.405	38.87	0.8282	1.503	13.1	13.8	13.9	13.8
84	84.23	8.978	37.79	0.8276	1.435	12.4	13.4	13.6	13.4
80	80.27	8.550	36.71	0.8271	1.368	11.6	13.0	13.2	13.0
76	76.31	8.123	35.63	0.8265	1.301	10.9	12.6	12.8	12.6
72	72.34	7.695	34.55	0.8260	1.233	10.1	12.2	12.4	12.2
70	70.36	7.481	34.01	0.8257	1.199	9.7	12.0	12.2	12.0
68	68.37	7.268	33.47	0.8254	1.165	9.2	11.7	12.0	11.8
66	66.38	7.054	32.93	0.8251	1.131	8.8	11.5	11.8	11.6
64	64.39	6.840	32.28	0.8249	1.097	8.3	11.3	11.6	11.4
62	62.40	6.626	31.84	0.8246	1.064	7.9	11.1	11.4	11.1
60	60.41	6.413	31.30	0.8243	1.030	7.4	10.9	11.2	10.9
58	58.42	6.199	30.76	0.8240	0.9956	6.9	10.6	11.0	10.7
56	56.42	5.985	30.22	0.8237	0.9616	6.4	10.4	10.8	10.5
54	54.42	5.771	29.68	0.8235	0.9275	5.9	10.2	10.6	10.3
52	52.43	5.558	29.14	0.8232	0.8935	5.4	9.9	10.4	10.0
50	50.43	5.344	28.60	0.8229	0.8594	4.8	9.7	10.2	9.8
48	48.43	5.130	28.06	0.8226	0.8253	4.2	9.5	10.0	9.6
46	46.42	4.916	27.52	0.8224	0.7912	3.6	9.2	9.8	9.3
44	44.42	4.703	26.98	0.8221	0.7570	3.0	9.0	9.6	9.1
42	42.42	4.489	26.44	0.8218	0.7229	2.3	8.8	9.4	8.9
40	40.41	4.275	25.90	0.8215	0.6887	1.7	8.5	9.2	8.6
38	38.40	4.061	25.36	0.8212	0.6545	1.0	8.3	9.0	8.4
36	36.39	3.848	24.82	0.8210	0.6202	0.2	8.0	8.7	8.1
34	34.38	3.634	24.28	0.8207	0.5860	−0.5	7.8	8.5	7.9
32	32.37	3.420	23.74	0.8204	0.5517	−1.2	7.5	8.3	7.7
30	30.36	3.206	23.20	0.8201	0.5174	−2.0	7.3	8.1	7.4
28	28.35	2.993	22.66	0.8198	0.4831	−2.8	7.0	7.9	7.2
24	24.31	2.565	21.58	0.8193	0.4143	−4.6	6.5	7.4	6.7
20	20.27	2.138	20.49	0.8187	0.3455	−6.7	6.0	6.9	6.1
16	16.23	1.710	19.41	0.8182	0.2766	−9.3	5.4	6.5	5.6
12	12.18	1.282	18.33	0.8176	0.2076	−12.5	4.9	6.0	5.1
8	8.13	0.855	17.25	0.8171	0.1385	−16.9	4.3	5.5	4.5
4	4.07	0.427	16.17	0.8165	0.0692	−24.1	3.8	5.0	4.0
0	0.00	0.000	15.09	0.8159	0.0000	—	3.2	4.6	3.4

15.5 °C DRY-BULB

Percentage saturation, μ / %	Relative humidity, ϕ /%	Value of stated parameter per kg dry air			Vapour pressure, p_v / kPa	Dew point temperature, θ_d / °C	Adiabatic saturation temperature, $\theta^\star$ / °C	Wet bulb temperature	
		Moisture content, g /(g·kg⁻¹)	Specific enthalpy, h /(kJ·kg⁻¹)	Specific volume, v /(m³·kg⁻¹)				Screen, θ'_{sc} / °C	Sling, θ'_{sl} / °C
00	100.00	11.04	43.52	0.8318	1.760	15.5	15.5	15.5	15.5
96	96.07	10.60	42.41	0.8312	1.691	14.9	15.1	15.1	15.1
92	92.13	10.16	41.29	0.8306	1.621	14.2	14.7	14.8	14.7
88	88.19	9.718	40.17	0.8300	1.552	13.6	14.3	14.4	14.3
84	84.24	9.276	39.06	0.8295	1.482	12.9	13.9	14.0	13.9
80	80.28	8.834	37.94	0.8289	1.413	12.1	13.5	13.7	13.5
76	76.32	8.393	36.82	0.8283	1.343	11.4	13.1	13.3	13.1
72	72.36	7.951	35.70	0.8277	1.273	10.6	12.6	12.9	12.7
70	70.37	7.730	35.14	0.8275	1.238	10.1	12.4	12.7	12.5
68	68.38	7.509	34.59	0.8272	1.204	9.7	12.2	12.5	12.2
66	66.40	7.288	34.03	0.8269	1.168	9.3	12.0	12.3	12.0
64	64.41	7.068	33.47	0.8266	1.134	8.8	11.7	12.1	11.8
62	62.42	6.847	32.91	0.8263	1.098	8.4	11.5	11.9	11.6
60	60.42	6.626	32.35	0.8260	1.063	7.9	11.3	11.7	11.4
58	58.43	6.405	31.79	0.8257	1.028	7.4	11.1	11.5	11.1
56	56.44	6.184	31.24	0.8254	0.9932	6.9	10.8	11.3	10.9
54	54.44	5.963	30.68	0.8252	0.9581	6.4	10.6	11.1	10.7
52	52.44	5.742	30.12	0.8249	0.9229	5.8	10.4	10.9	10.4
50	50.44	5.522	29.56	0.8246	0.8877	5.3	10.1	10.6	10.2
48	48.44	5.301	29.00	0.8243	0.8525	4.7	9.9	10.4	10.0
46	46.44	5.080	28.44	0.8240	0.8173	4.1	9.6	10.2	9.7
44	44.44	4.859	27.88	0.8237	0.7820	3.4	9.4	10.0	9.5
42	42.43	4.638	27.32	0.8234	0.7467	2.8	9.2	9.8	9.3
40	40.42	4.417	26.77	0.8231	0.7114	2.1	8.9	9.6	9.0
38	38.42	4.196	26.21	0.8228	0.6761	1.4	8.7	9.3	8.8
36	36.41	3.976	25.65	0.8226	0.6407	0.7	8.4	9.1	8.5
34	34.40	3.755	25.09	0.8223	0.6053	−0.1	8.2	8.9	8.3
32	32.39	3.534	24.53	0.8220	0.5699	−0.8	7.9	8.7	8.0
30	30.37	3.313	23.97	0.8217	0.5345	−1.6	7.6	8.4	7.8
28	28.36	3.092	23.41	0.8214	0.4990	−2.4	7.4	8.2	7.5
24	24.32	2.650	22.30	0.8208	0.4280	−4.2	6.8	7.8	7.0
20	20.28	2.209	21.18	0.8203	0.3570	−6.4	6.3	7.3	6.5
16	16.24	1.767	20.06	0.8197	0.2858	−8.9	5.8	6.8	5.9
12	12.19	1.325	18.94	0.8191	0.2145	−12.2	5.2	6.3	5.4
8	8.13	0.883	17.83	0.8185	0.1431	−16.6	4.6	5.8	4.8
4	4.07	0.442	16.71	0.8179	0.0716	−23.8	4.0	5.3	4.3
0	0.00	0.000	15.59	0.8174	0.0000	—	3.5	4.8	3.7

16 °C DRY-BULB

Percentage saturation, μ / %	Relative humidity, ϕ /%	Value of stated parameter per kg dry air			Vapour pressure, p_v / kPa	Dew point temperature, θ_d / °C	Adiabatic saturation temperature, $\theta\star$ / °C	Wet bulb temperature	
		Moisture content, g / (g·kg^{-1})	Specific enthalpy, h / (kJ·kg^{-1})	Specific volume, v / (m^3·kg^{-1})				Screen, θ'_{sc} / °C	Sling, θ'_{sl} / °C
100	100.00	11.41	44.96	0.8337	1.817	16.0	16.0	16.0	16.0
96	96.07	10.95	43.81	0.8331	1.746	15.4	15.6	15.6	15.6
92	92.13	10.50	42.65	0.8325	1.674	14.7	15.2	15.3	15.2
88	88.19	10.04	41.50	0.8319	1.603	14.0	14.8	14.9	14.8
84	84.24	9.583	40.34	0.8313	1.531	13.3	14.4	14.5	14.4
80	80.29	9.127	39.19	0.8307	1.459	12.6	14.0	14.1	14.0
76	76.33	8.671	38.04	0.8301	1.387	11.8	13.5	13.7	13.6
72	72.37	8.214	36.88	0.8295	1.315	11.0	13.1	13.3	13.1
70	70.38	7.986	36.30	0.8292	1.279	10.6	12.9	13.1	12.9
68	68.40	7.758	35.73	0.8289	1.243	10.2	12.6	12.9	12.7
66	66.41	7.530	35.15	0.8286	1.207	9.7	12.4	12.7	12.5
64	64.42	7.302	34.57	0.8283	1.171	9.3	12.2	12.5	12.2
62	62.43	7.074	33.99	0.8280	1.134	8.8	12.0	12.3	12.0
60	60.44	6.845	33.42	0.8277	1.098	8.4	11.7	12.1	11.8
58	58.45	6.617	32.84	0.8274	1.062	7.9	11.5	11.9	11.6
56	56.45	6.389	32.26	0.8271	1.026	7.4	11.3	11.7	11.3
54	54.45	6.161	31.68	0.8268	0.9895	6.8	11.0	11.5	11.1
52	52.46	5.933	31.11	0.8265	0.9532	6.3	10.8	11.3	10.9
50	50.46	5.704	30.53	0.8262	0.9169	5.7	10.5	11.1	10.6
48	48.46	5.476	29.95	0.8259	0.8805	5.1	10.3	10.8	10.4
46	46.45	5.248	29.37	0.8257	0.8441	4.5	10.1	10.6	10.1
44	44.45	5.020	28.80	0.8254	0.8077	3.9	9.8	10.4	9.9
42	42.45	4.792	28.22	0.8251	0.7713	3.3	9.6	10.2	9.7
40	40.44	4.564	27.64	0.8248	0.7348	2.6	9.3	10.0	9.4
38	38.43	4.335	27.07	0.8245	0.6983	1.9	9.0	9.7	9.2
36	36.42	4.107	26.49	0.8242	0.6618	1.1	8.8	9.5	8.9
34	34.41	3.879	25.91	0.8239	0.6253	0.3	8.5	9.3	8.7
32	32.40	3.651	25.33	0.8236	0.5887	−0.4	8.3	9.1	8.4
30	30.38	3.423	24.76	0.8233	0.5521	−1.2	8.0	8.8	8.1
28	28.37	3.194	24.17	0.8230	0.5155	−2.0	7.7	8.6	7.9
24	24.33	2.738	23.02	0.8224	0.4422	−3.9	7.2	8.1	7.4
20	20.29	2.282	21.87	0.8218	0.3688	−6.0	6.6	7.6	6.8
16	16.25	1.825	20.71	0.8212	0.2952	−8.6	6.1	7.2	6.3
12	12.19	1.369	19.56	0.8206	0.2216	−11.8	5.5	6.7	5.7
8	8.13	0.912	18.40	0.8200	0.1478	−16.2	4.9	6.2	5.1
4	4.07	0.456	17.25	0.8194	0.0740	−23.5	4.3	5.6	4.6
0	0.00	0.000	16.10	0.8188	0.0000	—	3.7	5.1	4.0

16.5 °C DRY-BULB

Percentage saturation, μ / %	Relative humidity, ϕ /%	Value of stated parameter per kg dry air			Vapour pressure, p_v / kPa	Dew point temperature, θ_d / °C	Adiabatic saturation temperature, $\theta\star$ / °C	Wet bulb temperature	
		Moisture content, g / (g·kg^{-1})	Specific enthalpy, h / (kJ·kg^{-1})	Specific volume, v / (m^3·kg^{-1})				Screen, θ'_{sc} / °C	Sling, θ'_{sl} / °C
100	100.00	11.79	46.43	0.8356	1.876	16.5	16.5	16.5	16.5
96	96.07	11.31	45.24	0.8350	1.802	15.9	16.1	16.1	16.1
92	92.14	10.84	44.04	0.8344	1.728	15.2	15.7	15.8	15.7
88	88.20	10.37	42.85	0.8338	1.655	14.5	15.3	15.4	15.3
84	84.25	9.900	41.66	0.8332	1.581	13.8	14.9	15.0	14.9
80	80.30	9.428	40.46	0.8326	1.506	13.1	14.4	14.6	14.4
76	76.34	8.957	39.27	0.8319	1.432	12.3	14.0	14.2	14.0
72	72.38	8.486	38.08	0.8313	1.358	11.5	13.5	13.8	13.6
70	70.40	8.250	37.48	0.8310	1.321	11.1	13.3	13.6	13.4
68	68.41	8.014	36.88	0.8307	1.283	10.7	13.1	13.4	13.1
66	66.42	7.778	36.29	0.8304	1.246	10.2	12.9	13.2	12.9
64	64.43	7.543	35.69	0.8301	1.209	9.8	12.6	13.0	12.7
62	62.44	7.307	35.09	0.8298	1.171	9.3	12.4	12.8	12.5
60	60.45	7.071	34.50	0.8295	1.134	8.8	12.2	12.6	12.2
58	58.46	6.836	33.90	0.8292	1.097	8.3	11.9	12.3	12.0
56	56.47	6.600	33.30	0.8289	1.059	7.8	11.7	12.1	11.8
54	54.47	6.364	32.71	0.8285	1.022	7.3	11.4	11.9	11.5
52	52.47	6.128	32.11	0.8282	0.9844	6.8	11.2	11.7	11.3
50	50.47	5.893	31.51	0.8279	0.9469	6.2	11.0	11.5	11.0
48	48.47	5.657	30.92	0.8276	0.9093	5.6	10.7	11.3	10.8
46	46.47	5.421	30.32	0.8273	0.8718	5.0	10.5	11.0	10.6
44	44.47	5.186	29.72	0.8270	0.8342	4.4	10.2	10.8	10.4
42	42.46	4.950	29.13	0.8267	0.7965	3.7	10.0	10.6	10.1
40	40.45	4.714	28.53	0.8264	0.7589	3.0	9.7	10.4	9.8
38	38.45	4.478	27.93	0.8261	0.7212	2.3	9.4	10.1	9.5
36	36.44	4.243	27.34	0.8258	0.6835	1.6	9.2	9.9	9.3
34	34.42	4.007	26.74	0.8255	0.6458	0.8	8.9	9.7	9.0
32	32.41	3.771	26.14	0.8251	0.6080	−0.1	8.6	9.4	8.8
30	30.40	3.536	25.55	0.8248	0.5702	−0.8	8.4	9.2	8.5
28	28.38	3.300	24.95	0.8245	0.5324	−1.7	8.1	9.0	8.2
24	24.35	2.828	23.76	0.8239	0.4567	−3.5	7.5	8.5	7.7
20	20.30	2.357	22.56	0.8233	0.3809	−5.6	7.0	8.0	7.2
16	16.25	1.886	21.37	0.8227	0.3049	−8.2	6.4	7.5	6.6
12	12.20	1.414	20.18	0.8221	0.2289	−11.4	5.8	7.0	6.0
8	8.14	0.943	18.98	0.8214	0.1527	−15.9	5.2	6.5	5.4
4	4.07	0.471	17.79	0.8208	0.0764	−23.1	4.6	5.9	4.8
0	0.00	0.000	16.60	0.8202	0.0000	—	4.0	5.4	4.2

17 °C DRY-BULB

Percentage saturation, μ / %	Relative humidity, ϕ /%	Value of stated parameter per kg dry air			Vapour pressure, p_v / kPa	Dew point temperature, θ_d / °C	Adiabatic saturation temperature, $\theta^\star$ / °C	Wet bulb temperature	
		Moisture content, g / (g·kg^{-1})	Specific enthalpy, h / (kJ·kg^{-1})	Specific volume, v / (m^3·kg^{-1})				Screen, θ'_{sc} / °C	Sling, θ'_{sl} / °C
100	100.00	12.17	47.93	0.8376	1.936	17.0	17.0	17.0	17.0
96	96.07	11.69	46.69	0.8370	1.860	16.4	16.6	16.6	16.6
92	92.14	11.20	45.46	0.8363	1.784	15.7	16.2	16.2	16.2
88	88.20	10.71	44.23	0.8357	1.708	15.0	15.8	15.9	15.8
84	84.26	10.23	42.99	0.8350	1.632	14.3	15.3	15.5	15.4
80	80.31	9.739	41.76	0.8344	1.555	13.6	14.9	15.1	14.9
76	76.35	9.252	40.53	0.8338	1.479	12.8	14.5	14.7	14.5
72	72.39	8.765	39.30	0.8331	1.402	12.0	14.0	14.3	14.0
70	70.41	8.521	38.68	0.8328	1.363	11.6	13.8	14.0	13.8
68	68.42	8.278	38.06	0.8325	1.325	11.2	13.5	13.8	13.6
66	66.44	8.034	37.45	0.8322	1.287	10.7	13.3	13.6	13.4
64	64.45	7.791	36.83	0.8318	1.248	10.3	13.1	13.4	13.1
62	62.46	7.547	36.21	0.8315	1.210	9.8	12.8	13.2	12.9
60	60.47	7.304	35.60	0.8312	1.171	9.3	12.6	13.0	12.7
58	58.47	7.060	34.98	0.8309	1.132	8.8	12.4	12.8	12.4
56	56.48	6.817	34.36	0.8306	1.094	8.3	12.1	12.6	12.2
54	54.48	6.574	33.75	0.8303	1.055	7.8	11.9	12.3	11.9
52	52.49	6.330	33.13	0.8299	1.016	7.2	11.6	12.1	11.7
50	50.49	6.087	32.51	0.8296	0.9777	6.7	11.4	11.9	11.5
48	48.49	5.843	31.90	0.8293	0.9390	6.1	11.1	11.7	11.2
46	46.49	5.600	31.28	0.8290	0.9002	5.5	10.9	11.4	11.0
44	44.48	5.356	30.66	0.8287	0.8614	4.8	10.6	11.2	10.7
42	42.48	5.113	30.05	0.8283	0.8225	4.2	10.3	11.0	10.4
40	40.47	4.869	29.43	0.8280	0.7837	3.5	10.1	10.7	10.2
38	38.46	4.626	28.81	0.8277	0.7448	2.8	9.8	10.5	9.9
36	36.45	4.382	28.20	0.8274	0.7058	2.0	9.6	10.3	9.7
34	34.44	4.139	27.58	0.8271	0.6669	1.2	9.3	10.0	9.4
32	32.43	3.896	26.97	0.8267	0.6279	0.4	9.0	9.8	9.1
30	30.41	3.652	26.35	0.8264	0.5889	−0.4	8.7	9.6	8.9
28	28.39	3.409	25.73	0.8261	0.5498	−1.3	8.5	9.3	8.6
24	24.36	2.922	24.50	0.8255	0.4717	−3.1	7.9	8.8	8.0
20	20.31	2.435	23.27	0.8248	0.3934	−5.2	7.3	8.3	7.5
16	16.26	1.948	22.03	0.8242	0.3149	−7.8	6.7	7.8	6.9
12	12.21	1.461	20.80	0.8235	0.2364	−11.1	6.1	7.3	6.3
8	8.14	0.974	19.57	0.8229	0.1577	−15.5	5.5	6.8	5.7
4	4.08	0.487	18.33	0.8223	0.0789	−22.8	4.9	6.2	5.1
0	0.00	0.000	17.10	0.8216	0.0000	—	4.3	5.7	4.5

17.5 °C DRY-BULB

Percentage saturation, μ / %	Relative humidity, ϕ /%	Value of stated parameter per kg dry air			Vapour pressure, p_v / kPa	Dew point temperature, θ_d / °C	Adiabatic saturation temperature, $\theta^\star$ / °C	Wet bulb temperature	
		Moisture content, g / (g·kg^{-1})	Specific enthalpy, h / (kJ·kg^{-1})	Specific volume, v / (m^3·kg^{-1})				Screen, θ'_{sc} / °C	Sling, θ'_{sl} / °C
00	100.00	12.57	49.45	0.8396	1.999	17.5	17.5	17.5	17.5
96	96.08	12.07	48.18	0.8389	1.920	16.9	17.1	17.1	17.1
92	92.15	11.57	46.90	0.8382	1.842	16.2	16.7	16.7	16.7
88	88.21	11.06	45.63	0.8376	1.763	15.5	16.2	16.3	16.3
84	84.27	10.56	44.36	0.8369	1.684	14.8	15.8	15.9	15.8
80	80.32	10.06	43.08	0.8363	1.605	14.1	15.4	15.5	15.4
76	76.37	9.555	41.81	0.8356	1.526	13.3	14.9	15.1	14.9
72	72.40	9.052	40.53	0.8349	1.447	12.5	14.5	14.7	14.5
70	70.42	8.801	39.90	0.8346	1.408	12.1	14.2	14.5	14.5
68	68.44	8.549	39.26	0.8343	1.368	11.6	14.0	14.3	14.0
66	66.45	8.298	38.62	0.8340	1.328	11.2	13.8	14.1	13.8
64	64.46	8.046	37.99	0.8336	1.288	10.7	13.5	13.9	13.6
62	62.47	7.795	37.35	0.8333	1.249	10.3	13.3	13.6	13.3
60	60.48	7.544	36.71	0.8330	1.209	9.8	13.0	13.4	13.1
58	58.49	7.292	36.08	0.8326	1.169	9.3	12.8	13.2	12.9
56	56.50	7.041	35.44	0.8323	1.129	8.8	12.5	13.0	12.6
54	54.50	6.789	34.80	0.8320	1.089	8.2	12.3	12.8	12.4
52	52.50	6.538	34.16	0.8316	1.049	7.7	12.0	12.5	12.1
50	50.50	6.286	33.53	0.8313	1.009	7.1	11.8	12.3	11.9
48	48.50	6.035	32.89	0.8310	0.9695	6.5	11.5	12.1	11.6
46	46.50	5.783	32.25	0.8307	0.9294	5.9	11.3	11.8	11.4
44	44.50	5.532	31.62	0.8303	0.8894	5.3	11.0	11.6	11.1
42	42.49	5.280	30.98	0.8300	0.8493	4.6	10.7	11.4	10.8
40	40.48	5.029	30.34	0.8297	0.8092	3.9	10.5	11.1	10.6
38	38.48	4.778	29.71	0.8293	0.7690	3.2	10.2	10.9	10.3
36	36.46	4.526	29.07	0.8290	0.7288	2.5	9.9	10.7	10.1
34	34.45	4.275	28.43	0.8287	0.6886	1.7	9.7	10.4	9.8
32	32.44	4.023	27.80	0.8283	0.6484	0.8	9.4	10.2	9.5
30	30.42	3.772	27.16	0.8280	0.6081	0.0	9.1	9.9	9.2
28	28.41	3.520	26.52	0.8277	0.5678	−0.9	8.8	9.7	9.0
24	24.37	3.017	25.25	0.8270	0.4871	−2.7	8.2	9.2	8.4
20	20.32	2.514	23.97	0.8264	0.4062	−4.9	7.7	8.7	7.8
16	16.27	2.012	22.70	0.8257	0.3252	−7.4	7.1	8.1	7.2
12	12.21	1.509	21.43	0.8250	0.2441	−10.7	6.4	7.6	6.6
8	8.15	1.006	20.15	0.8244	0.1629	−15.2	5.8	7.1	6.0
4	4.08	0.503	18.88	0.8237	0.0815	−22.5	5.2	6.5	5.4
0	0.00	0.000	17.60	0.8230	0.0000	—	4.5	6.0	4.8

18 °C DRY-BULB

Percentage saturation, μ / %	Relative humidity, ϕ /%	Value of stated parameter per kg dry air			Vapour pressure, p_v / kPa	Dew point temperature, θ_d / °C	Adiabatic saturation temperature, $\theta^\star$ / °C	Wet bulb temperature	
		Moisture content, g / (g·kg^{-1})	Specific enthalpy, h / (kJ·kg^{-1})	Specific volume, v / (m^3·kg^{-1})				Screen, θ'_{sc} / °C	Sling, θ'_{sl} / °C
100	100.00	12.98	51.01	0.8416	2.063	18.0	18.0	18.0	18.0
96	96.08	12.46	49.69	0.8409	1.982	17.4	17.6	17.6	17.6
92	92.15	11.94	48.38	0.8402	1.901	16.7	17.2	17.2	17.2
88	88.22	11.43	47.06	0.8395	1.820	16.0	16.7	16.8	16.7
84	84.28	10.91	45.74	0.8388	1.738	15.3	16.3	16.4	16.3
80	80.33	10.39	44.43	0.8381	1.657	14.6	15.8	16.0	15.9
76	76.38	9.868	43.11	0.8375	1.576	13.8	15.4	15.6	15.4
72	72.42	9.348	41.80	0.8368	1.494	13.0	14.9	15.2	15.0
70	70.44	9.088	41.14	0.8364	1.453	12.5	14.7	15.0	14.7
68	68.45	8.829	40.48	0.8361	1.412	12.1	14.4	14.7	14.5
66	66.47	8.569	39.82	0.8357	1.371	11.7	14.2	14.5	14.3
64	64.48	8.309	39.16	0.8354	1.330	11.2	14.0	14.3	14.0
62	62.49	8.050	38.51	0.8351	1.289	10.7	13.7	14.1	13.8
60	60.50	7.790	37.85	0.8347	1.248	10.3	13.5	13.9	13.5
58	58.51	7.530	37.19	0.8344	1.207	9.8	13.2	13.6	13.3
56	56.51	7.271	36.53	0.8340	1.166	9.2	13.0	13.4	13.0
54	54.52	7.011	35.87	0.8337	1.125	8.7	12.7	13.2	12.8
52	52.52	6.751	35.22	0.8334	1.083	8.2	12.5	13.0	12.5
50	50.52	6.492	34.56	0.8330	1.042	7.6	12.2	12.7	12.3
48	48.52	6.232	33.90	0.8327	1.001	7.0	11.9	12.5	12.0
46	46.52	5.972	33.24	0.8323	0.9595	6.4	11.7	12.3	11.8
44	44.51	5.713	32.58	0.8320	0.9182	5.7	11.4	12.0	11.5
42	42.51	5.453	31.93	0.8316	0.8768	5.1	11.1	11.8	11.2
40	40.50	5.193	31.27	0.8313	0.8354	4.4	10.9	11.5	11.0
38	38.49	4.934	30.61	0.8310	0.7940	3.7	10.6	11.3	10.7
36	36.48	4.674	29.95	0.8306	0.7525	2.9	10.3	11.0	10.4
34	34.47	4.414	29.29	0.8303	0.7110	2.1	10.0	10.8	10.2
32	32.45	4.155	28.64	0.8299	0.6694	1.3	9.7	10.5	9.9
30	30.44	3.895	27.98	0.8296	0.6278	0.4	9.5	10.3	9.6
28	28.42	3.635	27.32	0.8293	0.5862	−0.5	9.2	10.0	9.3
24	24.38	3.116	26.00	0.8286	0.5029	−2.5	8.6	9.5	8.7
20	20.33	2.597	24.69	0.8279	0.4194	−4.5	8.0	9.0	8.2
16	16.28	2.077	23.37	0.8272	0.3358	−7.1	7.4	8.5	7.6
12	12.22	1.558	22.06	0.8265	0.2521	−10.3	6.7	7.9	6.9
8	8.15	1.039	20.74	0.8258	0.1682	−14.8	6.1	7.4	6.3
4	4.08	0.519	19.42	0.8252	0.0842	−22.1	5.5	6.8	5.7
0	0.00	0.000	18.11	0.8245	0.0000	—	4.8	6.3	5.0

18.5 °C DRY-BULB

Percentage saturation, μ / %	Relative humidity, ϕ /%	Value of stated parameter per kg dry air			Vapour pressure, p_v / kPa	Dew point temperature, θ_d / °C	Adiabatic saturation temperature, $\theta^\star$ / °C	Wet bulb temperature	
		Moisture content, g / (g·kg^{-1})	Specific enthalpy, h / (kJ·kg^{-1})	Specific volume, v / (m^3·kg^{-1})				Screen, θ'_{sc} / °C	Sling, θ'_{sl} / °C
100	100.00	13.41	52.59	0.8436	2.128	18.5	18.5	18.5	18.5
96	96.08	12.87	51.24	0.8429	2.045	17.9	18.1	18.1	18.1
92	92.16	12.33	49.88	0.8421	1.962	17.2	17.6	17.7	17.7
88	88.22	11.80	48.52	0.8414	1.878	16.5	17.2	17.3	17.2
84	84.29	11.26	47.16	0.8407	1.794	15.8	16.8	16.9	16.8
80	80.34	10.73	45.80	0.8400	1.710	15.1	16.3	16.5	16.3
76	76.39	10.19	44.44	0.8393	1.626	14.3	15.8	16.1	15.9
72	72.43	9.653	43.08	0.8386	1.542	13.5	15.4	15.6	15.4
70	70.45	9.384	42.40	0.8383	1.500	13.0	15.1	15.4	15.2
68	68.47	9.116	41.72	0.8379	1.457	12.6	14.9	15.2	14.9
66	66.48	8.848	41.04	0.8376	1.415	12.1	14.6	15.0	14.7
64	64.49	8.580	40.36	0.8372	1.373	11.7	14.4	14.7	14.5
62	62.50	8.312	39.68	0.8368	1.330	11.2	14.2	14.5	14.2
60	60.51	8.044	39.00	0.8365	1.288	10.7	13.9	14.3	14.0
58	58.52	7.776	38.32	0.8361	1.246	10.2	13.7	14.1	13.7
56	56.53	7.508	37.64	0.8358	1.203	9.7	13.4	13.8	13.5
54	54.53	7.240	36.96	0.8354	1.161	9.2	13.1	13.6	13.2
52	52.54	6.971	36.28	0.8351	1.118	8.6	12.9	13.4	13.0
50	50.54	6.703	35.60	0.8347	1.076	8.0	12.6	13.1	12.7
48	48.54	6.435	34.92	0.8344	1.033	7.5	12.3	12.9	12.4
46	46.53	6.167	34.24	0.8340	0.9904	6.8	12.1	12.7	12.2
44	44.53	5.899	33.56	0.8337	0.9478	6.2	11.8	12.4	11.9
42	42.52	5.631	32.88	0.8333	0.9051	5.5	11.5	12.2	11.6
40	40.52	5.363	32.20	0.8330	0.8624	4.8	11.3	11.9	11.4
38	38.51	5.094	31.52	0.8326	0.8196	4.1	11.0	11.7	11.1
36	36.50	4.826	30.84	0.8323	0.7278	3.4	10.7	11.4	10.8
34	34.48	4.558	30.16	0.8319	0.7340	2.6	10.4	11.2	10.5
32	32.47	4.290	29.49	0.8315	0.6911	1.7	10.1	10.9	10.2
30	30.45	4.022	28.81	0.8312	0.6482	0.8	9.8	10.7	10.0
28	28.43	3.754	28.13	0.8308	0.6052	−0.1	9.5	10.4	9.7
24	24.39	3.218	26.77	0.8301	0.5192	−2.0	8.9	9.9	9.1
20	20.34	2.681	25.41	0.8294	0.4330	−4.1	8.3	9.3	8.5
16	16.29	2.145	24.05	0.8287	0.3477	−6.7	7.7	8.8	7.9
12	12.23	1.609	22.69	0.8280	0.2603	−10.0	7.1	8.2	7.3
8	8.16	1.072	21.33	0.8273	0.1747	−14.5	6.4	7.7	6.6
4	4.08	0.536	19.97	0.8266	0.0869	−21.8	5.7	7.1	6.0
0	0.00	0.000	18.61	0.8259	0.0000	—	5.0	6.5	5.3

19 °C DRY-BULB

Percentage saturation, μ / %	Relative humidity, ϕ / %	Value of stated parameter per kg dry air			Vapour pressure, p_v / kPa	Dew point temperature, θ_d / °C	Adiabatic saturation temperature, $\theta\star$ / °C	Wet bulb temperature	
		Moisture content, g / (g·kg⁻¹)	Specific enthalpy, h / (kJ·kg⁻¹)	Specific volume, v / (m³·kg⁻¹)				Screen, θ'_{sc} / °C	Sling, θ'_{sl} / °C
100	100.00	13.84	54.21	0.8456	2.196	19.0	19.0	19.0	19.0
96	96.08	13.29	52.81	0.8449	2.110	18.4	18.6	18.6	18.6
92	92.16	12.74	51.41	0.8441	2.024	17.7	18.1	18.2	18.1
88	88.23	12.18	50.00	0.8434	1.938	17.0	17.7	17.8	17.7
84	84.30	11.63	48.60	0.8427	1.851	16.3	17.2	17.4	17.3
80	80.35	11.07	47.19	0.8419	1.765	15.5	16.8	17.0	16.8
76	76.40	10.52	45.79	0.8412	1.678	14.8	16.3	16.5	16.3
72	72.44	9.966	44.39	0.8405	1.591	13.9	15.8	16.1	15.9
70	70.46	9.689	43.68	0.8401	1.547	13.5	15.6	15.9	15.6
68	68.48	9.412	42.98	0.8397	1.504	13.1	15.3	15.6	15.4
66	66.50	9.136	42.28	0.8394	1.460	12.6	15.1	15.4	15.1
64	64.51	8.859	41.58	0.8390	1.417	12.2	14.8	15.2	14.9
62	62.52	8.582	40.88	0.8386	1.373	11.7	14.6	15.0	14.7
60	60.53	8.305	40.17	0.8383	1.329	11.2	14.3	14.7	14.4
58	58.54	8.028	39.47	0.8379	1.286	10.7	14.1	14.5	14.1
56	56.55	7.751	38.77	0.8375	1.242	10.2	13.8	14.3	13.9
54	54.55	7.475	38.07	0.8372	1.198	9.6	13.6	14.0	13.6
52	52.55	7.198	37.37	0.8368	1.154	9.1	13.3	13.8	13.4
50	50.55	6.921	36.66	0.8365	1.110	8.5	13.0	13.5	13.1
48	48.55	6.644	35.96	0.8361	1.066	7.9	12.8	13.3	12.8
46	46.55	6.367	35.26	0.8357	1.022	7.3	12.5	13.1	12.6
44	44.55	6.090	34.56	0.8354	0.9782	6.7	12.2	12.8	12.3
42	42.54	5.814	33.86	0.8350	0.9342	6.0	11.9	12.6	12.0
40	40.53	5.537	33.15	0.8346	0.8902	5.3	11.6	12.3	11.8
38	38.52	5.260	32.45	0.8343	0.8460	4.6	11.4	12.1	11.5
36	36.51	4.983	31.75	0.8339	0.8018	3.8	11.1	11.8	11.2
34	34.50	4.706	31.05	0.8335	0.7576	3.0	10.8	11.6	10.9
32	32.48	4.429	30.35	0.8332	0.7134	2.2	10.5	11.3	10.6
30	30.47	4.153	29.64	0.8328	0.6691	1.3	10.2	11.0	10.3
28	28.45	3.876	28.94	0.8324	0.6248	0.3	9.9	10.8	10.0
24	24.41	3.322	27.54	0.8317	0.5360	−1.6	9.3	10.2	9.4
20	20.36	2.768	26.13	0.8310	0.4470	−3.7	8.7	9.7	8.8
16	16.30	2.215	24.73	0.8302	0.3580	−6.3	8.0	9.1	8.2
12	12.24	1.661	23.33	0.8295	0.2687	−9.6	7.4	8.6	7.6
8	8.16	1.107	21.92	0.8288	0.1792	−14.1	6.7	8.0	6.9
4	4.09	0.554	20.52	0.8280	0.0897	−21.5	6.0	7.4	6.2
0	0.00	0.000	19.11	0.8273	0.0000	—	5.3	6.8	5.6

19.5 °C DRY-BULB

Percentage saturation, μ / %	Relative humidity, ϕ / %	Value of stated parameter per kg dry air			Vapour pressure, p_v / kPa	Dew point temperature, θ_d / °C	Adiabatic saturation temperature, $\theta\star$ / °C	Wet bulb temperature	
		Moisture content, g / (g·kg⁻¹)	Specific enthalpy, h / (kJ·kg⁻¹)	Specific volume, v / (m³·kg⁻¹)				Screen, θ'_{sc} / °C	Sling, θ'_{sl} / °C
100	100.00	14.29	55.87	0.8476	2.266	19.5	19.5	19.5	19.5
96	96.09	13.72	54.42	0.8469	2.177	18.9	19.1	19.1	19.1
92	92.17	13.15	52.97	0.8461	2.088	18.2	18.6	18.7	18.6
88	88.24	12.58	51.52	0.8454	1.999	17.5	18.2	18.3	18.2
84	84.30	12.00	50.07	0.8446	1.910	16.8	17.7	17.9	17.7
80	80.36	11.43	48.62	0.8438	1.821	16.0	17.3	17.4	17.3
76	76.41	10.86	47.17	0.8431	1.731	15.2	16.8	17.0	16.8
72	72.46	10.29	45.72	0.8423	1.642	14.4	16.3	16.5	16.3
70	70.48	10.00	44.99	0.8420	1.597	14.0	16.0	16.3	16.1
68	68.50	9.717	44.27	0.8416	1.552	13.6	15.8	16.1	15.8
66	66.51	9.431	43.54	0.8412	1.507	13.1	15.5	15.9	15.6
64	64.53	9.146	42.82	0.8408	1.462	12.6	15.3	15.6	15.3
62	62.54	8.860	42.09	0.8405	1.417	12.2	15.0	15.4	15.1
60	60.55	8.574	41.37	0.8401	1.372	11.7	14.8	15.2	14.8
58	58.56	8.288	40.64	0.8397	1.327	11.2	14.5	14.9	14.6
56	56.56	8.002	39.92	0.8393	1.282	10.6	14.3	14.7	14.3
54	54.57	7.716	39.19	0.8389	1.236	10.1	14.0	14.5	14.1
52	52.57	7.431	38.47	0.8386	1.191	9.6	13.7	14.2	13.8
50	50.57	7.145	37.74	0.8382	1.146	9.0	13.4	14.0	13.5
48	48.57	6.859	37.02	0.8378	1.100	8.4	13.2	13.7	13.3
46	46.57	6.573	36.29	0.8374	1.055	7.8	12.9	13.5	13.0
44	44.56	6.288	35.57	0.8370	1.010	7.1	12.6	13.2	12.7
42	42.56	6.002	34.84	0.8367	0.9642	6.5	12.3	13.0	12.4
40	40.55	5.716	34.12	0.8363	0.9187	5.8	12.0	12.7	12.1
38	38.54	5.430	33.39	0.8359	0.8732	5.0	11.7	12.5	11.9
36	36.53	5.144	32.67	0.8355	0.8276	4.3	11.5	12.2	11.6
34	34.52	4.859	31.94	0.8352	0.7820	3.4	11.2	11.9	11.3
32	32.50	4.573	31.22	0.8348	0.7363	2.6	10.9	11.7	11.0
30	30.48	4.287	30.49	0.8344	0.6906	1.7	10.6	11.4	10.7
28	28.46	4.001	29.77	0.8340	0.6448	0.7	10.2	11.1	10.4
24	24.42	3.430	28.32	0.8333	0.5532	−1.2	9.6	10.6	9.8
20	20.37	2.858	26.87	0.8325	0.4614	−3.4	9.0	10.0	9.2
16	16.31	2.286	25.42	0.8318	0.3695	−6.0	8.3	9.5	8.5
12	12.24	1.715	23.97	0.8310	0.2774	−9.3	7.7	8.9	7.9
8	8.17	1.143	22.52	0.8302	0.1851	−13.8	7.0	8.3	7.2
4	4.09	0.572	21.07	0.8295	0.0926	−21.2	6.3	7.7	6.5
0	0.00	0.000	19.62	0.8287	0.0000	—	5.6	7.1	5.8

20 °C DRY-BULB

Percentage saturation, μ / %	Relative humidity, ϕ /%	Value of stated parameter per kg dry air			Vapour pressure, p_v / kPa	Dew point temperature, θ_d / °C	Adiabatic saturation temperature, $\theta^\star$ / °C	Wet bulb temperature	
		Moisture content, g / (g·kg^{-1})	Specific enthalpy, h / (kJ·kg^{-1})	Specific volume, v / (m^3·kg^{-1})				Screen, θ'_{sc} / °C	Sling, θ'_{sl} / °C
100	100.00	14.75	57.55	0.8497	2.337	20.0	20.0	20.0	20.0
96	96.09	14.16	56.05	0.8489	2.246	19.4	19.6	19.6	19.6
92	92.17	13.57	54.56	0.8481	2.154	18.7	19.1	19.2	19.1
88	88.25	12.98	53.06	0.8473	2.062	18.0	18.7	18.8	18.7
84	84.31	12.39	51.56	0.8466	1.970	17.3	18.2	18.3	18.2
80	80.37	11.80	50.06	0.8458	1.878	16.5	17.7	17.9	17.7
76	76.43	11.21	48.57	0.8450	1.786	15.7	17.2	17.5	17.3
72	72.47	10.62	47.07	0.8442	1.694	14.9	16.7	17.0	16.8
70	70.49	10.33	46.32	0.8438	1.647	14.5	16.5	16.8	16.5
68	68.51	10.03	45.57	0.8434	1.601	14.0	16.2	16.5	16.3
66	66.53	9.736	44.82	0.8431	1.555	13.6	16.0	16.3	16.0
64	64.54	9.441	44.08	0.8427	1.508	13.1	15.7	16.1	15.8
62	62.55	9.146	43.33	0.8423	1.462	12.6	15.5	15.8	15.5
60	60.56	8.851	42.58	0.8419	1.415	12.1	15.2	15.6	15.3
58	58.57	8.556	41.83	0.8415	1.369	11.6	14.9	15.4	15.0
56	56.58	8.260	41.08	0.8411	1.322	11.1	14.7	15.1	14.7
54	54.59	7.966	40.33	0.8407	1.276	10.6	14.4	14.9	14.5
52	52.59	7.670	39.58	0.8403	1.229	10.0	14.1	14.6	14.2
50	50.59	7.376	38.84	0.8399	1.182	9.4	13.9	14.4	13.9
48	48.59	7.080	38.09	0.8395	1.136	8.8	13.6	14.1	13.7
46	46.59	6.785	37.34	0.8391	1.089	8.2	13.3	13.9	13.4
44	44.58	6.490	36.59	0.8388	1.042	7.6	13.0	13.6	13.1
42	42.58	6.195	35.84	0.8384	0.9945	6.9	12.7	13.4	12.8
40	40.57	5.900	35.09	0.8380	0.9480	6.2	12.4	13.1	12.5
38	38.56	5.605	34.34	0.8376	0.9011	5.5	12.1	12.8	12.2
36	36.55	5.310	33.60	0.8372	0.8541	4.7	11.8	12.6	12.0
34	34.53	5.015	32.85	0.8368	0.8070	3.9	11.5	12.3	11.7
32	32.52	4.720	32.10	0.8364	0.7600	3.0	11.2	12.0	11.4
30	30.50	4.425	31.35	0.8360	0.7127	2.1	10.9	11.8	11.1
28	28.48	4.130	30.60	0.8356	0.6656	1.2	10.6	11.5	10.7
24	24.43	3.540	29.10	0.8348	0.5710	−0.8	10.0	10.9	10.1
20	20.38	2.950	27.61	0.8341	0.4763	−3.0	9.3	10.4	9.5
16	16.32	2.360	26.11	0.8333	0.3814	−5.6	8.6	9.8	8.8
12	12.25	1.770	24.61	0.8325	0.2863	−8.9	8.0	9.2	8.2
8	8.17	1.180	23.11	0.8317	0.1910	−13.4	7.3	8.6	7.5
4	4.09	0.590	21.62	0.8309	0.0956	−20.8	6.5	8.0	6.8
0	0.00	0.000	20.11	0.8301	0.0000	—	5.8	7.3	6.1

20.5 °C DRY-BULB

Percentage saturation, μ / %	Relative humidity, ϕ /%	Value of stated parameter per kg dry air			Vapour pressure, p_v / kPa	Dew point temperature, θ_d / °C	Adiabatic saturation temperature, $\theta^\star$ / °C	Wet bulb temperature	
		Moisture content, g / (g·kg^{-1})	Specific enthalpy, h / (kJ·kg^{-1})	Specific volume, v / (m^3·kg^{-1})				Screen, θ'_{sc} / °C	Sling, θ'_{sl} / °C
100	100.00	15.22	59.27	0.8518	2.410	20.5	20.5	20.5	20.5
96	96.09	14.62	57.73	0.8510	2.316	19.9	20.1	20.1	20.1
92	92.18	14.01	56.18	0.8502	2.222	19.2	19.6	19.7	19.6
88	88.25	13.49	54.63	0.8493	2.127	18.5	19.1	19.2	19.2
84	84.32	12.79	53.09	0.8485	2.032	17.8	18.7	18.8	18.7
80	80.39	12.18	51.54	0.8477	1.938	17.0	18.2	18.4	18.2
76	76.44	11.57	50.00	0.8469	1.842	16.2	17.7	17.9	17.7
72	72.49	10.96	48.45	0.8461	1.747	15.4	17.2	17.5	17.2
70	70.51	10.66	47.68	0.8457	1.699	15.0	17.0	17.2	17.0
68	68.53	10.35	46.90	0.8453	1.652	14.5	16.7	17.0	16.7
66	66.54	10.05	46.13	0.8449	1.604	14.1	16.4	16.8	16.5
64	64.56	9.744	45.36	0.8445	1.556	13.6	16.2	16.5	16.2
62	62.57	9.440	44.59	0.8441	1.508	13.1	15.9	16.3	16.0
60	60.58	9.135	43.81	0.8437	1.460	12.6	15.6	16.0	15.7
58	58.59	8.831	43.04	0.8433	1.412	12.1	15.4	15.8	15.4
56	56.60	8.526	42.27	0.8429	1.364	11.6	15.1	15.5	15.2
54	54.60	8.222	41.49	0.8425	1.316	11.0	14.8	15.3	14.9
52	52.61	7.917	40.72	0.8421	1.268	10.5	14.6	15.0	14.6
50	50.61	7.613	39.95	0.8417	1.220	9.9	14.3	14.8	14.4
48	48.61	7.308	39.18	0.8413	1.172	9.3	14.0	14.5	14.1
46	46.61	7.004	38.40	0.8409	1.123	8.7	13.7	14.3	13.8
44	44.60	6.699	37.63	0.8405	1.075	8.0	13.4	14.0	13.5
42	42.59	6.395	36.86	0.8401	1.027	7.4	13.1	13.8	13.2
40	40.59	6.090	36.08	0.8397	0.9782	6.7	12.8	13.5	12.9
38	38.58	5.786	35.31	0.8393	0.9298	5.9	12.5	13.2	12.6
36	36.56	5.481	34.54	0.8388	0.8813	5.2	12.2	13.0	12.3
34	34.55	5.177	33.76	0.8384	0.8327	4.3	11.9	12.7	12.0
32	32.53	4.872	32.99	0.8380	0.7841	3.5	11.6	12.4	11.7
30	30.51	4.568	32.22	0.8376	0.7355	2.6	11.3	12.1	11.4
28	28.49	4.263	31.44	0.8372	0.6868	1.6	11.0	11.8	11.1
24	24.45	3.654	29.90	0.8364	0.5892	−0.4	10.3	11.3	10.5
20	20.39	3.045	28.35	0.8356	0.4915	−2.6	9.6	10.7	9.8
16	16.33	2.436	26.81	0.8348	0.3936	−5.2	9.0	10.1	9.2
12	12.26	1.827	25.26	0.8340	0.2955	−8.5	8.3	9.5	8.5
8	8.18	1.218	23.71	0.8332	0.1972	−13.1	7.5	8.9	7.8
4	4.09	0.609	22.17	0.8324	0.0986	−20.5	6.8	8.2	7.1
0	0.00	0.000	20.62	0.8316	0.0000	—	6.1	7.6	6.3

21 °C DRY-BULB

Percentage saturation, μ / %	Relative humidity, ϕ /%	Value of stated parameter per kg dry air			Vapour pressure, p_v / kPa	Dew point temperature, θ_d / °C	Adiabatic saturation temperature, $\theta\star$ / °C	Wet bulb temperature	
		Moisture content, g / (g·kg^{-1})	Specific enthalpy, h / (kJ·kg^{-1})	Specific volume, v / (m^3·kg^{-1})				Screen, θ'_{sc} / °C	Sling, θ'_{sl} / °C
100	100.00	15.71	61.03	0.8539	2.486	21.0	21.0	21.0	21.0
96	96.09	15.09	59.43	0.8530	2.389	20.4	20.6	20.6	20.6
92	92.18	14.46	57.84	0.8522	2.291	19.7	20.1	20.2	20.1
88	88.26	13.83	56.24	0.8514	2.194	19.0	19.6	19.7	19.6
84	84.33	13.20	54.64	0.8505	2.096	18.3	19.2	19.3	19.2
80	80.40	12.57	53.05	0.8497	1.998	17.5	18.7	18.8	18.7
76	76.45	11.94	51.45	0.8489	1.900	16.7	18.2	18.4	18.2
72	72.50	11.31	49.86	0.8480	1.802	15.9	17.7	17.9	17.7
70	70.52	11.00	49.06	0.8476	1.753	15.4	17.4	17.7	17.5
68	68.54	10.69	48.26	0.8472	1.704	15.0	17.1	17.4	17.2
66	66.56	10.37	47.46	0.8468	1.654	14.5	16.9	17.2	16.9
64	64.58	10.06	46.66	0.8464	1.605	14.1	16.6	17.0	16.7
62	62.59	9.742	45.87	0.8459	1.556	13.6	16.4	16.7	16.4
60	60.60	9.428	45.07	0.8455	1.506	13.1	16.1	16.5	16.1
58	58.61	9.114	44.27	0.8451	1.457	12.6	15.8	16.2	15.9
56	56.62	8.800	43.47	0.8447	1.407	12.1	15.5	16.0	15.6
54	54.62	8.485	42.67	0.8443	1.358	11.5	15.3	15.7	15.3
52	52.63	8.171	41.88	0.8439	1.308	11.0	15.0	15.5	15.0
50	50.63	7.857	41.08	0.8434	1.258	10.4	14.7	15.2	14.8
48	48.63	7.542	40.28	0.8430	1.209	9.8	14.4	14.9	14.5
46	46.62	7.228	39.48	0.8426	1.159	9.1	14.1	14.7	14.2
44	44.62	6.914	38.68	0.8422	1.109	8.5	13.8	14.4	13.9
42	42.61	6.600	37.89	0.8418	1.059	7.8	13.5	14.2	13.6
40	40.60	6.285	37.09	0.8413	1.009	7.1	13.2	13.9	13.3
38	38.59	5.971	36.29	0.8409	0.9593	6.4	12.9	13.6	13.0
36	36.58	5.657	35.49	0.8405	0.9093	5.6	12.6	13.3	12.7
34	34.57	5.343	34.69	0.8401	0.8592	4.8	12.3	13.1	12.4
32	32.55	5.028	33.89	0.8397	0.8091	3.9	12.0	12.8	12.1
30	30.53	4.714	33.10	0.8393	0.7589	3.0	11.6	12.5	11.8
28	28.51	4.400	32.30	0.8388	0.7087	2.1	11.3	12.2	11.5
24	24.46	3.771	30.70	0.8380	0.6080	−0.1	10.7	11.6	10.8
20	20.40	3.143	29.11	0.8372	0.5072	−2.2	10.0	11.0	10.1
16	16.34	2.514	27.51	0.8363	0.4062	−4.9	9.3	10.4	9.5
12	12.27	1.886	25.91	0.8355	0.3049	−8.2	8.6	9.8	8.8
8	8.19	1.257	24.32	0.8347	0.2035	−12.7	7.8	9.2	8.1
4	4.10	0.628	22.72	0.8338	0.1018	−20.2	7.1	8.5	7.3
0	0.00	0.000	21.13	0.8330	0.0000	—	6.3	7.9	6.6

21.5 °C DRY-BULB

Percentage saturation, μ / %	Relative humidity, ϕ /%	Value of stated parameter per kg dry air			Vapour pressure, p_v / kPa	Dew point temperature, θ_d / °C	Adiabatic saturation temperature, $\theta\star$ / °C	Wet bulb temperature	
		Moisture content, g / (g·kg^{-1})	Specific enthalpy, h / (kJ·kg^{-1})	Specific volume, v / (m^3·kg^{-1})				Screen, θ'_{sc} / °C	Sling, θ'_{sl} / °C
100	100.00	16.22	62.82	0.8560	2.563	21.5	21.5	21.5	21.5
96	96.10	15.57	61.17	0.8551	2.463	20.9	21.0	21.1	21.1
92	92.19	14.92	59.53	0.8543	2.363	20.2	20.6	20.6	20.6
88	88.27	14.27	57.88	0.8534	2.262	19.5	20.1	20.2	20.1
84	84.34	13.62	56.23	0.8525	2.162	18.7	19.6	19.8	19.6
80	80.41	12.97	54.58	0.8517	2.061	18.0	19.1	19.3	19.2
76	76.47	12.32	52.94	0.8508	1.960	17.2	18.6	18.8	18.7
72	72.52	11.68	51.29	0.8500	1.859	16.4	18.1	18.4	18.2
70	70.54	11.35	50.46	0.8495	1.808	15.9	17.9	18.1	17.9
68	68.56	11.03	49.64	0.8491	1.757	15.5	17.6	17.9	17.6
66	66.58	10.70	48.82	0.8487	1.706	15.0	17.3	17.7	17.4
64	64.59	10.38	47.99	0.8482	1.656	14.6	17.1	17.4	17.1
62	62.61	10.05	47.17	0.8478	1.605	14.1	16.8	17.2	16.9
60	60.62	9.730	46.34	0.8474	1.554	13.6	16.5	16.9	16.6
58	58.63	9.405	45.52	0.8469	1.503	13.1	16.2	16.7	16.3
56	56.64	9.081	44.70	0.8465	1.452	12.5	16.0	16.4	16.0
54	54.64	8.756	43.87	0.8461	1.401	12.0	15.7	16.1	15.8
52	52.65	8.432	43.05	0.8456	1.349	11.4	15.4	15.9	15.5
50	50.65	8.108	42.23	0.8452	1.298	10.8	15.1	15.6	15.2
48	48.65	7.784	41.40	0.8448	1.247	10.2	14.8	15.4	14.9
46	46.64	7.459	40.58	0.8443	1.196	9.6	14.5	15.1	14.6
44	44.64	7.135	39.75	0.8439	1.144	9.0	14.2	14.8	14.3
42	42.63	6.811	38.93	0.8435	1.093	8.3	13.9	14.5	14.0
40	40.62	6.486	38.11	0.8431	1.041	7.6	13.6	14.3	13.7
38	38.61	6.162	37.28	0.8426	0.9897	6.8	13.3	14.0	13.4
36	36.60	5.838	36.46	0.8422	0.9381	6.1	13.0	13.7	13.1
34	34.58	5.513	35.64	0.8418	0.8864	5.2	12.7	13.4	12.8
32	32.57	5.189	34.81	0.8413	0.8347	4.4	12.3	13.1	12.5
30	30.55	4.865	33.99	0.8409	0.7829	3.5	12.0	12.9	12.1
28	28.53	4.540	33.16	0.8405	0.7311	2.5	11.7	12.6	11.8
24	24.48	3.892	31.52	0.8396	0.6273	0.4	11.0	12.0	11.2
20	20.42	3.243	29.87	0.8387	0.5233	−1.9	10.3	11.4	10.5
16	16.35	2.594	28.22	0.8379	0.4191	−4.5	9.6	10.7	9.8
12	12.28	1.946	26.57	0.8370	0.3146	−7.8	8.9	10.1	9.1
8	8.19	1.297	24.92	0.8361	0.2100	−12.4	8.1	9.5	8.3
4	4.10	0.648	23.28	0.8353	0.1051	−19.8	7.3	8.8	7.6
0	0.00	0.000	21.63	0.8344	0.0000	—	6.6	8.1	6.8

22 °C DRY-BULB

Percentage saturation, μ / %	Relative humidity, ϕ /%	Value of stated parameter per kg dry air			Vapour pressure, p_v / kPa	Dew point temperature, θ_d / °C	Adiabatic saturation temperature, $\theta^\star$ / °C	Wet bulb temperature	
		Moisture content, g / (g·kg^{-1})	Specific enthalpy, h / (kJ·kg^{-1})	Specific volume, v / (m^3·kg^{-1})				Screen, θ'_{sc} / °C	Sling, θ'_{sl} / °C
100	100.00	16.73	64.65	0.8581	2.643	22.0	22.0	22.0	22.0
96	96.10	16.06	62.95	0.8572	2.540	21.3	21.5	21.6	21.5
92	92.19	15.39	61.25	0.8564	2.436	20.7	21.1	21.1	21.1
88	88.28	14.72	59.55	0.8555	2.333	20.0	20.6	20.7	20.6
84	84.36	14.06	57.85	0.8546	2.229	19.2	20.1	20.2	20.1
80	80.42	13.39	56.15	0.8537	2.125	18.5	19.6	19.8	19.6
76	76.48	12.72	54.45	0.8528	2.021	17.7	19.1	19.3	19.1
72	72.53	12.05	52.75	0.8519	1.917	16.8	18.6	18.8	18.6
70	70.56	11.71	51.90	0.8515	1.865	16.4	18.3	18.6	18.4
68	68.58	11.38	51.05	0.8510	1.812	16.0	18.1	18.3	18.1
66	66.60	11.04	50.20	0.8506	1.760	15.5	17.8	18.1	17.8
64	64.61	10.71	49.35	0.8501	1.707	15.0	17.5	17.9	17.6
62	62.63	10.37	48.50	0.8497	1.655	14.5	17.2	17.6	17.3
60	60.64	10.04	47.64	0.8492	1.602	14.0	17.0	17.3	17.0
58	58.65	9.705	46.79	0.8488	1.550	13.5	16.7	17.1	16.7
56	56.66	9.370	45.94	0.8483	1.497	13.0	16.4	16.8	16.5
54	54.66	9.036	45.09	0.8479	1.445	12.5	16.1	16.6	16.2
52	52.67	8.701	44.24	0.8474	1.392	11.9	15.8	16.3	15.9
50	50.67	8.366	43.39	0.8470	1.339	11.3	15.5	16.0	15.6
48	48.67	8.032	42.54	0.8465	1.286	10.7	15.2	15.8	15.3
46	46.66	7.697	41.69	0.8461	1.233	10.1	14.9	15.5	15.0
44	44.66	7.362	40.84	0.8457	1.180	9.4	14.6	15.2	14.7
42	42.65	7.028	39.99	0.8452	1.127	8.7	14.3	14.9	14.4
40	40.64	6.693	39.14	0.8448	1.074	8.0	14.0	14.7	14.1
38	38.63	6.358	38.29	0.8443	1.021	7.3	13.7	14.4	13.8
36	36.62	6.024	37.44	0.8439	0.9677	6.5	13.4	14.1	13.5
34	34.60	5.689	36.59	0.8434	0.9144	5.7	13.0	13.8	13.2
32	32.58	5.354	35.74	0.8430	0.8611	4.8	12.7	13.5	12.8
30	30.56	5.020	34.89	0.8425	0.8077	3.9	12.4	13.2	12.5
28	28.54	4.685	34.04	0.8421	0.7542	2.9	12.0	12.9	12.2
24	24.49	4.016	32.34	0.8412	0.6472	0.8	11.3	12.3	11.5
20	20.43	3.346	30.64	0.8403	0.5399	−1.5	10.6	11.7	10.8
16	16.36	2.677	28.94	0.8394	0.4324	−4.1	9.9	11.1	10.1
12	12.28	2.008	27.24	0.8385	0.3246	−7.5	9.2	10.4	9.4
8	8.20	1.339	25.53	0.8376	0.2166	−12.0	8.4	9.8	8.6
4	4.10	0.669	23.83	0.8367	0.1084	−19.5	7.6	9.1	7.9
0	0.00	0.000	22.13	0.8358	0.0000	—	6.8	8.4	7.1

22.5 °C DRY-BULB

Percentage saturation, μ / %	Relative humidity, ϕ /%	Value of stated parameter per kg dry air			Vapour pressure, p_v / kPa	Dew point temperature, θ_d / °C	Adiabatic saturation temperature, $\theta^\star$ / °C	Wet bulb temperature	
		Moisture content, g / (g·kg^{-1})	Specific enthalpy, h / (kJ·kg^{-1})	Specific volume, v / (m^3·kg^{-1})				Screen, θ'_{sc} / °C	Sling, θ'_{sl} / °C
100	100.00	17.26	66.52	0.8603	2.724	22.5	22.5	22.5	22.5
96	96.10	16.57	64.77	0.8594	2.618	21.8	22.0	22.1	22.0
92	92.20	15.88	63.01	0.8585	2.512	21.2	21.6	21.6	21.6
88	88.29	15.19	61.26	0.8575	2.405	20.5	21.1	21.2	21.1
84	84.37	14.50	59.50	0.8566	2.298	19.7	20.6	20.7	20.6
80	80.44	13.81	57.75	0.8557	2.191	19.0	20.1	20.3	20.1
76	76.50	13.12	55.99	0.8548	2.084	18.2	19.6	19.8	19.6
72	72.55	12.43	54.23	0.8539	1.976	17.3	19.0	19.3	19.1
70	70.58	12.08	53.36	0.8534	1.923	16.9	18.8	19.0	18.8
68	68.60	11.74	52.48	0.8529	1.869	16.4	18.5	18.8	18.6
66	66.62	11.39	51.60	0.8525	1.815	16.0	18.2	18.5	18.3
64	64.63	11.05	50.72	0.8520	1.761	15.5	18.0	18.3	18.0
62	62.65	10.70	49.85	0.8516	1.707	15.0	17.7	18.0	17.7
60	60.66	10.36	48.97	0.8511	1.653	14.5	17.4	17.8	17.5
58	58.67	10.01	48.09	0.8506	1.598	14.0	17.1	17.5	17.2
56	56.68	9.668	47.21	0.8502	1.544	13.5	16.8	17.3	16.9
54	54.68	9.322	46.33	0.8497	1.490	12.9	16.5	17.0	16.6
52	52.69	8.977	45.46	0.8492	1.435	12.4	16.2	16.7	16.3
50	50.69	8.632	44.58	0.8488	1.381	11.8	15.9	16.5	16.0
48	48.69	8.287	43.70	0.8483	1.326	11.2	15.6	16.2	15.7
46	46.69	7.941	42.82	0.8479	1.272	10.5	15.3	15.9	15.4
44	44.68	7.596	41.95	0.8474	1.217	9.9	15.0	15.6	15.1
42	42.67	7.251	41.07	0.8469	1.163	9.2	14.7	15.3	14.8
40	40.66	6.906	40.19	0.8465	1.108	8.5	14.4	15.1	14.5
38	38.65	6.560	39.31	0.8460	1.053	7.7	14.1	14.8	14.2
36	36.64	6.215	38.43	0.8456	0.9981	7.0	13.7	14.5	13.8
34	34.62	5.870	37.56	0.8451	0.9432	6.1	13.4	14.2	13.5
32	32.60	5.524	36.68	0.8446	0.8882	5.3	13.1	13.9	13.2
30	30.58	5.179	35.80	0.8442	0.8331	4.3	12.7	13.6	12.9
28	28.56	4.834	34.92	0.8437	0.7780	3.4	12.4	13.3	12.5
24	24.51	4.143	33.17	0.8428	0.6676	1.2	11.7	12.7	11.8
20	20.44	3.453	31.41	0.8419	0.5570	−1.1	11.0	12.0	11.1
16	16.37	2.762	29.66	0.8409	0.4461	−3.8	10.2	11.4	10.4
12	12.29	2.072	27.90	0.8400	0.3349	−7.1	9.5	10.7	9.7
8	8.20	1.381	26.15	0.8391	0.2235	−11.7	8.7	10.1	8.9
4	4.11	0.690	24.39	0.8382	0.1119	−19.2	7.9	9.4	8.1
0	0.00	0.000	22.64	0.8372	0.0000	—	7.0	8.7	7.3

23 °C DRY-BULB

Percentage saturation, μ / %	Relative humidity, ϕ /%	Value of stated parameter per kg dry air			Vapour pressure, p_v / kPa	Dew point temperature, θ_d / °C	Adiabatic saturation temperature, $\theta^\star$ / °C	Wet bulb temperature	
		Moisture content, g / (g·kg^{-1})	Specific enthalpy, h / (kJ·kg^{-1})	Specific volume, v / (m³·kg^{-1})				Screen, θ'_{sc} / °C	Sling, θ'_{sl} / °C
100	100.00	17.81	68.43	0.8625	2.808	23.0	23.0	23.0	23.0
96	96.11	17.10	66.62	0.8615	2.699	22.3	22.5	22.6	22.5
92	92.21	16.39	64.81	0.8606	2.589	21.7	22.1	22.1	22.1
88	88.30	15.67	63.00	0.8596	2.479	21.0	21.6	21.7	21.6
84	84.38	14.96	61.18	0.8587	2.369	20.2	21.1	21.2	21.1
80	80.45	14.25	59.37	0.8577	2.259	19.5	20.6	20.7	20.6
76	76.51	13.54	57.56	0.8568	2.149	18.6	20.0	20.2	20.1
72	72.57	12.82	55.75	0.8558	2.038	17.8	19.5	19.7	19.5
70	70.59	12.47	54.84	0.8554	1.982	17.4	19.2	19.5	19.3
68	68.61	12.11	53.94	0.8549	1.927	16.9	19.0	19.2	19.0
66	66.63	11.76	53.03	0.8544	1.871	16.5	18.7	19.0	18.7
64	64.65	11.40	52.13	0.8539	1.815	16.0	18.4	18.7	18.5
62	62.67	11.04	51.22	0.8535	1.760	15.5	18.1	18.5	18.2
60	60.68	10.69	50.31	0.8530	1.704	15.0	17.8	18.2	17.9
58	58.69	10.33	49.41	0.8525	1.648	14.5	17.5	18.0	17.6
56	56.70	9.974	48.50	0.8520	1.592	13.9	17.2	17.7	17.3
54	54.70	9.618	47.60	0.8515	1.536	13.4	17.0	17.4	17.0
52	52.71	9.262	46.69	0.8511	1.480	12.8	16.7	17.1	16.7
50	50.71	8.905	45.79	0.8506	1.424	12.2	16.3	16.9	16.4
48	48.71	8.549	44.88	0.8501	1.368	11.6	16.0	16.6	16.1
46	46.71	8.193	43.97	0.8496	1.312	11.0	15.7	16.3	15.8
44	44.70	7.837	43.07	0.8392	1.255	10.3	15.4	16.0	15.5
42	42.69	7.480	42.16	0.8487	1.199	9.7	15.1	15.7	15.2
40	40.68	7.124	41.26	0.8482	1.142	8.9	14.8	15.4	14.9
38	38.67	6.768	40.35	0.8477	1.086	8.2	14.4	15.2	14.6
36	36.66	6.412	39.44	0.8473	1.029	7.4	14.1	14.9	14.2
34	34.64	6.056	38.54	0.8468	0.9727	6.6	13.8	14.6	13.9
32	32.62	5.699	37.63	0.8463	0.9160	5.7	13.4	14.3	13.6
30	30.60	5.343	36.73	0.8458	0.8593	4.8	13.1	13.9	13.2
28	28.58	4.987	35.82	0.8453	0.8024	3.8	12.7	13.6	12.9
24	24.52	4.275	34.01	0.8444	0.6886	1.7	12.0	13.0	12.2
20	20.46	3.562	32.20	0.8434	0.5745	−0.7	11.3	12.4	11.5
16	16.39	2.850	30.39	0.8425	0.4601	−3.4	10.5	11.7	10.7
12	12.30	2.137	28.57	0.8415	0.3455	−6.8	9.8	11.0	10.0
8	8.21	1.425	26.76	0.8406	0.2306	−11.3	9.0	10.3	9.2
4	4.11	0.712	24.95	0.8396	0.1154	−18.9	8.1	9.6	8.4
0	0.00	0.000	23.14	0.8387	0.0000	—	7.3	8.9	7.6

23.5 °C DRY-BULB

Percentage saturation, μ / %	Relative humidity, ϕ /%	Value of stated parameter per kg dry air			Vapour pressure, p_v / kPa	Dew point temperature, θ_d / °C	Adiabatic saturation temperature, $\theta^\star$ / °C	Wet bulb temperature	
		Moisture content, g / (g·kg^{-1})	Specific enthalpy, h / (kJ·kg^{-1})	Specific volume, v / (m³·kg^{-1})				Screen, θ'_{sc} / °C	Sling, θ'_{sl} / °C
100	100.00	18.37	70.38	0.8467	2.894	23.5	23.5	23.5	23.5
96	96.11	17.64	68.51	0.8637	2.782	22.8	23.0	23.1	23.0
92	92.21	16.90	66.64	0.8627	2.669	22.2	22.5	22.6	22.6
88	88.31	16.17	64.77	0.8618	2.556	21.5	22.0	22.1	22.1
84	84.39	15.43	62.90	0.8608	2.442	20.7	21.5	21.7	21.6
80	80.46	14.70	61.03	0.8598	2.329	19.9	21.0	21.2	21.1
76	76.53	13.96	59.16	0.8588	2.215	19.1	20.5	20.7	20.5
72	72.59	13.23	57.29	0.8578	2.101	18.3	20.0	20.2	20.0
70	70.61	12.86	56.36	0.8573	2.044	17.9	19.7	20.0	19.7
68	68.63	12.49	55.42	0.8568	1.986	17.4	19.4	19.7	19.5
66	66.65	12.13	54.49	0.8563	1.929	16.9	19.1	19.4	19.2
64	64.67	11.76	53.56	0.8559	1.872	16.5	18.8	19.2	18.9
62	62.69	11.39	52.62	0.8554	1.814	16.0	18.6	18.9	18.6
60	60.70	11.02	51.69	0.8549	1.757	15.5	18.3	18.7	18.3
58	58.71	10.66	50.75	0.8544	1.699	15.0	18.0	18.4	18.0
56	56.72	10.29	49.82	0.8539	1.642	14.4	17.7	18.1	17.7
54	54.73	9.921	48.88	0.8534	1.584	13.9	17.4	17.8	17.4
52	52.73	9.554	47.95	0.8529	1.526	13.3	17.1	17.6	17.1
50	50.73	9.187	47.01	0.8524	1.468	12.7	16.8	17.3	16.8
48	48.73	8.819	46.08	0.8519	1.410	12.1	16.5	17.0	16.5
46	46.73	8.452	45.14	0.8514	1.352	11.5	16.1	16.7	16.2
44	44.72	8.804	44.21	0.8509	1.294	10.8	15.8	16.4	15.9
42	42.72	7.717	43.27	0.8504	1.236	10.1	15.5	16.1	15.6
40	40.71	7.349	42.34	0.8499	1.178	9.4	15.2	15.8	15.3
38	38.69	6.982	41.40	0.8495	1.120	8.6	14.8	15.5	14.9
36	36.68	6.614	40.47	0.8490	1.062	7.9	14.5	15.2	14.6
34	34.66	6.247	39.53	0.8485	1.003	7.0	14.1	14.9	14.3
32	32.64	5.879	38.60	0.8480	0.9447	6.2	13.8	14.6	13.9
30	30.62	5.512	37.66	0.8475	0.8862	5.2	13.4	14.3	13.6
28	28.59	5.144	36.73	0.8470	0.8276	4.3	13.1	14.0	13.2
24	24.54	4.410	34.86	0.8460	0.7102	2.1	12.4	13.4	12.5
20	20.47	3.675	32.99	0.8450	0.5925	−0.4	11.6	12.7	11.8
16	16.40	2.940	31.12	0.8440	0.4746	−3.0	10.8	12.0	11.0
12	12.31	2.205	29.25	0.8430	0.3564	−6.4	10.1	11.3	10.3
8	8.22	1.470	27.38	0.8421	0.2379	−11.0	9.2	10.6	9.5
4	4.11	0.735	25.51	0.8411	0.1191	−18.5	8.4	9.9	8.7
0	0.00	0.000	23.64	0.8401	0.0000	—	7.5	9.2	7.8

24 °C DRY-BULB

Percentage saturation, μ / %	Relative humidity, ϕ /%	Value of stated parameter per kg dry air			Vapour pressure, p_v / kPa	Dew point temperature, θ_d / °C	Adiabatic saturation temperature, $\theta\star$ / °C	Wet bulb temperature	
		Moisture content, g / (g·kg^{-1})	Specific enthalpy, h / (kJ·kg^{-1})	Specific volume, v / (m^3·kg^{-1})				Screen, θ'_{sc} / °C	Sling, θ'_{sl} / °C
100	100.00	18.95	72.37	0.8669	2.983	24.0	24.0	24.0	24.0
96	96.11	18.19	70.44	0.8659	2.867	23.3	23.5	23.6	23.5
92	92.22	17.44	68.52	0.8649	2.751	22.7	23.0	23.1	23.0
88	88.31	16.68	66.59	0.8639	2.634	21.9	22.5	22.6	22.5
84	84.40	15.92	64.66	0.8629	2.517	21.2	22.0	22.2	22.0
80	80.48	15.16	62.73	0.8619	2.400	20.4	21.5	21.7	21.5
76	76.55	14.40	60.80	0.8608	2.283	19.6	21.0	21.2	21.0
72	72.60	13.64	58.87	0.8598	2.165	18.8	20.4	20.7	20.5
70	70.63	13.27	57.90	0.8593	2.107	18.3	20.1	20.4	20.2
68	68.65	12.89	56.94	0.8588	2.048	17.9	19.9	20.2	19.9
66	66.67	12.51	55.98	0.8583	1.989	17.4	19.6	19.9	19.6
64	64.69	12.13	55.01	0.8578	1.930	16.9	19.3	19.6	19.3
62	62.71	11.75	54.05	0.8573	1.870	16.5	19.0	19.4	19.1
60	60.72	11.37	53.08	0.8568	1.811	15.9	18.7	19.1	18.8
58	58.73	10.99	52.12	0.8563	1.752	15.4	18.4	18.8	18.5
56	56.74	10.61	51.15	0.8558	1.692	14.9	18.1	18.5	18.2
54	54.75	10.23	50.19	0.8553	1.633	14.3	17.8	18.3	17.9
52	52.75	9.855	49.22	0.8547	1.573	13.8	17.5	18.0	17.6
50	50.75	9.476	48.26	0.8542	1.514	13.2	17.2	17.7	17.3
48	48.75	9.097	47.29	0.8537	1.454	12.6	16.9	17.4	16.9
46	46.75	8.718	46.33	0.8532	1.394	11.9	16.5	17.1	16.6
44	44.75	8.339	45.37	0.8527	1.335	11.3	16.2	16.8	16.3
42	42.74	7.960	44.40	0.8522	1.275	10.6	15.9	16.5	16.0
40	40.73	7.580	43.44	0.8517	1.215	9.8	15.6	16.2	15.7
38	38.71	7.202	42.47	0.8512	1.155	9.1	15.2	15.9	15.3
36	36.70	6.822	41.51	0.8507	1.095	8.3	14.9	15.6	15.0
34	34.68	6.444	40.54	0.8502	1.034	7.5	14.5	15.3	14.6
32	32.66	6.064	39.58	0.8497	0.9741	6.6	14.2	15.0	14.3
30	30.64	5.685	38.61	0.8491	0.9138	5.7	13.8	14.7	13.9
28	28.61	5.306	37.65	0.8486	0.8534	4.7	13.4	14.4	13.6
24	24.56	4.548	35.72	0.8476	0.7324	2.5	12.7	13.7	12.9
20	20.49	3.790	33.79	0.8466	0.6111	−0.0	11.9	13.0	12.1
16	16.41	3.032	31.86	0.8456	0.4894	−2.7	11.2	12.3	11.4
12	12.32	2.274	29.93	0.8446	0.3675	−6.0	10.4	11.6	10.6
8	8.22	1.516	28.00	0.8435	0.2453	−10.7	9.5	10.9	9.8
4	4.12	0.758	26.07	0.8425	0.1228	−18.2	8.7	10.2	8.9
0	0.00	0.000	24.14	0.8415	0.0000	—	7.8	9.4	8.1

24.5 °C DRY-BULB

Percentage saturation, μ / %	Relative humidity, ϕ /%	Value of stated parameter per kg dry air			Vapour pressure, p_v / kPa	Dew point temperature, θ_d / °C	Adiabatic saturation temperature, $\theta\star$ / °C	Wet bulb temperature	
		Moisture content, g / (g·kg^{-1})	Specific enthalpy, h / (kJ·kg^{-1})	Specific volume, v / (m^3·kg^{-1})				Screen, θ'_{sc} / °C	Sling, θ'_{sl} / °C
100	100.00	19.55	74.41	0.8692	3.073	24.5	24.5	24.5	24.5
96	96.12	18.76	72.42	0.8682	2.954	23.8	24.0	24.0	24.0
92	92.23	17.98	70.43	0.8671	2.834	23.2	23.5	23.6	23.5
88	88.32	17.20	68.44	0.8661	2.714	22.4	23.0	23.1	23.0
84	84.41	16.42	66.45	0.8650	2.594	21.7	22.5	22.6	22.5
80	80.49	15.64	64.46	0.8640	2.474	20.9	22.0	22.1	22.0
76	76.56	14.86	62.47	0.8629	2.353	20.1	21.4	21.6	21.5
72	72.62	14.07	60.48	0.8619	2.232	19.3	20.9	21.1	20.9
70	70.65	13.68	59.48	0.8613	2.171	18.8	20.6	20.9	20.6
68	68.67	13.29	58.48	0.8608	2.111	18.4	20.3	20.6	20.4
66	66.69	12.90	57.49	0.8603	2.050	17.9	20.0	20.3	20.1
64	64.71	12.51	56.49	0.8598	1.989	17.4	19.7	20.1	19.8
62	62.73	12.12	55.50	0.8592	1.928	16.9	19.4	19.8	19.5
60	60.74	11.73	54.50	0.8587	1.867	16.4	19.1	19.5	19.2
58	58.76	11.34	53.51	0.8582	1.806	15.9	18.8	19.3	18.9
56	56.77	10.95	52.51	0.8577	1.745	15.4	18.5	19.0	18.6
54	54.77	10.56	51.52	0.8571	1.658	14.8	18.2	18.7	18.3
52	52.78	10.16	50.52	0.8566	1.622	14.2	17.9	18.4	18.0
50	50.78	9.773	49.53	0.8561	1.561	13.6	17.6	18.1	17.7
48	48.78	9.382	48.53	0.8556	1.499	13.0	17.3	17.8	17.4
46	46.77	8.991	47.54	0.8550	1.439	12.4	16.9	17.5	17.0
44	44.77	8.600	46.54	0.8545	1.376	11.7	16.6	17.2	16.7
42	42.76	8.209	45.55	0.8540	1.314	11.0	16.3	16.9	16.4
40	40.75	7.818	44.55	0.8535	1.252	10.3	15.9	16.6	16.0
38	38.74	7.428	43.56	0.8529	1.190	9.5	15.6	16.3	15.7
36	36.72	7.037	42.56	0.8524	1.129	8.8	15.2	16.0	15.4
34	34.70	6.646	41.57	0.8519	1.067	7.9	14.9	15.7	15.0
32	32.68	6.255	40.57	0.8513	1.004	7.0	14.5	15.4	14.7
30	30.66	5.864	39.58	0.8508	0.9422	6.1	14.2	15.0	14.3
28	28.63	5.473	38.58	0.8503	0.8800	5.1	13.8	14.7	13.9
24	24.57	4.691	36.59	0.8492	0.7552	3.0	13.0	14.0	13.2
20	20.50	3.909	34.60	0.8482	0.6301	0.4	12.3	13.4	12.4
16	16.42	3.127	32.61	0.8471	0.5047	−2.3	11.5	12.7	11.7
12	12.33	2.346	30.62	0.8461	0.3790	−5.7	10.6	11.9	10.9
8	8.23	1.564	28.63	0.8450	0.2530	−10.3	9.8	11.2	10.0
4	4.12	0.782	26.64	0.8440	0.1267	−17.9	8.9	10.4	9.2
0	0.00	0.000	24.65	0.8429	0.0000	—	8.0	9.7	8.3

25 °C DRY-BULB

Percentage saturation, μ / %	Relative humidity, ϕ /%	Value of stated parameter per kg dry air			Vapour pressure, p_v / kPa	Dew point temperature, θ_d / °C	Adiabatic saturation temperature, $\theta\star$ / °C	Wet bulb temperature	
		Moisture content, g /(g·kg^{-1})	Specific enthalpy, h /(kJ·kg^{-1})	Specific volume, v /(m³·kg^{-1})				Screen, θ'_{sc} / °C	Sling, θ'_{sl} / °C
100	100.00	20.16	76.49	0.8715	3.166	25.0	25.0	25.0	25.0
96	96.12	19.35	74.43	0.8704	3.044	24.3	24.5	24.5	24.5
92	92.23	18.55	72.38	0.8693	2.921	23.7	24.0	24.1	24.0
88	88.33	17.74	70.33	0.8682	2.797	22.9	23.5	23.6	23.5
84	84.43	16.93	68.27	0.8672	2.673	22.2	23.0	23.1	23.0
80	80.51	16.13	66.22	0.8661	2.549	21.4	22.4	22.6	22.5
76	76.58	15.32	64.17	0.8650	2.425	20.6	21.9	22.1	21.9
72	72.64	14.51	62.11	0.8639	2.300	19.7	21.3	21.6	21.4
70	70.67	14.11	61.09	0.8634	2.238	19.3	21.1	21.3	21.1
68	68.69	13.71	60.06	0.8628	2.175	18.8	20.8	21.1	20.8
66	66.72	13.30	59.03	0.8623	2.113	18.4	20.5	20.8	20.5
64	64.74	12.90	58.01	0.8617	2.050	17.9	20.2	20.5	20.2
62	62.75	12.50	56.98	0.8612	1.987	17.4	19.9	20.2	19.9
60	60.77	12.10	55.95	0.8606	1.924	16.9	19.6	20.0	19.6
58	58.78	11.69	54.93	0.8601	1.861	16.4	19.3	19.7	19.3
56	56.79	11.29	53.90	0.8596	1.798	15.8	19.0	19.4	19.0
54	54.80	10.89	52.87	0.8590	1.735	15.3	18.7	19.1	18.7
52	52.80	10.48	51.85	0.8585	1.672	14.7	18.3	18.8	18.4
50	50.80	10.08	50.82	0.8579	1.609	14.1	18.0	18.5	18.1
48	48.80	9.676	49.79	0.8574	1.545	13.5	17.7	18.2	17.8
46	46.80	9.273	48.76	0.8568	1.482	12.8	17.4	17.9	17.4
44	44.79	8.870	47.74	0.8563	1.418	12.2	17.0	17.6	17.1
42	42.78	8.466	46.71	0.8558	1.355	11.5	16.7	17.3	16.8
40	40.77	8.063	45.69	0.8552	1.291	10.8	16.3	17.0	16.4
38	38.76	7.660	44.66	0.8547	1.227	10.0	16.0	16.7	16.1
36	36.74	7.257	43.63	0.8541	1.163	9.2	15.6	16.4	15.7
34	34.72	6.854	42.60	0.8536	1.100	8.4	15.3	16.1	15.4
32	32.70	6.450	41.58	0.8530	1.036	7.5	14.9	15.7	15.0
30	30.68	6.047	40.55	0.8525	0.9714	6.6	14.5	15.4	14.7
28	28.65	5.644	39.52	0.8520	0.9072	5.6	14.2	15.1	14.3
24	24.59	4.838	37.47	0.8509	0.7786	3.4	13.4	14.4	13.5
20	20.52	4.032	35.42	0.8498	0.6497	0.9	12.6	13.7	12.8
16	16.44	3.225	33.36	0.8487	0.5204	−1.9	11.8	13.0	12.0
12	12.34	2.419	31.31	0.8476	0.3908	−5.3	10.9	12.2	11.2
8	8.24	1.613	29.26	0.8465	0.2609	−10.0	10.1	11.5	10.3
4	4.12	0.806	27.20	0.8454	0.1306	−17.5	9.2	10.7	9.4
0	0.00	0.000	25.15	0.8443	0.0000	—	8.2	9.9	8.5

25.5 °C DRY-BULB

Percentage saturation, μ / %	Relative humidity, ϕ /%	Value of stated parameter per kg dry air			Vapour pressure, p_v / kPa	Dew point temperature, θ_d / °C	Adiabatic saturation temperature, $\theta\star$ / °C	Wet bulb temperature	
		Moisture content, g /(g·kg^{-1})	Specific enthalpy, h /(kJ·kg^{-1})	Specific volume, v /(m³·kg^{-1})				Screen, θ'_{sc} / °C	Sling, θ'_{sl} / °C
100	100.00	20.79	78.61	0.8738	3.262	25.5	25.5	25.5	25.5
96	96.12	20.00	76.49	0.8727	3.136	24.8	25.0	25.0	25.0
92	92.24	19.12	74.37	0.8716	3.009	24.1	24.5	24.6	24.5
88	88.34	18.29	72.26	0.8704	2.882	23.4	24.0	24.1	24.0
84	84.44	17.46	70.14	0.8693	2.754	22.7	23.5	23.6	23.5
80	80.52	16.63	68.02	0.8682	2.627	21.9	22.9	23.1	22.9
76	76.60	15.80	65.90	0.8671	2.499	21.1	22.4	22.6	22.4
72	72.66	14.97	63.78	0.8660	2.370	20.2	21.8	22.0	21.8
70	70.69	14.55	62.72	0.8654	2.306	19.8	21.5	21.8	21.6
68	68.71	14.14	61.66	0.8648	2.242	19.3	21.2	21.5	21.3
66	66.74	13.72	60.61	0.8643	2.177	18.9	20.9	21.2	21.0
64	64.76	13.30	59.55	0.8637	2.112	18.4	20.6	21.0	20.7
62	62.78	12.89	58.49	0.8632	2.048	17.9	20.3	20.7	20.4
60	60.79	12.47	57.43	0.8626	1.983	17.4	20.0	20.4	20.1
58	58.80	12.06	56.37	0.8620	1.918	16.9	19.7	20.1	19.8
56	56.81	11.64	55.31	0.8615	1.853	16.3	19.4	19.8	19.5
54	54.82	11.22	54.25	0.8609	1.788	15.7	19.1	19.5	19.2
52	52.82	10.81	53.19	0.8604	1.723	15.2	18.8	19.2	18.8
50	50.83	10.39	52.13	0.8598	1.658	14.6	18.4	18.9	18.5
48	48.83	9.978	51.07	0.8592	1.593	14.0	18.1	18.6	18.2
46	46.82	9.562	50.01	0.8587	1.527	13.3	17.8	18.3	17.9
44	44.82	9.146	48.95	0.8581	1.462	12.6	17.4	18.0	17.5
42	42.81	8.730	47.90	0.8576	1.396	11.9	17.1	17.7	17.2
40	40.80	8.315	46.84	0.8570	1.331	11.2	16.7	17.4	16.8
38	38.78	7.899	45.78	0.8564	1.265	10.5	16.4	17.1	16.5
36	36.77	7.483	44.72	0.8559	1.199	9.7	16.0	16.8	16.1
34	34.75	7.068	43.66	0.8553	1.133	8.8	15.6	16.4	15.8
32	32.72	6.652	42.60	0.8548	1.067	7.9	15.3	16.1	15.4
30	30.70	6.236	41.54	0.8542	1.001	7.0	14.9	15.8	15.0
28	28.67	5.820	40.48	0.8536	0.9353	6.0	14.5	15.4	14.7
24	24.61	4.989	38.36	0.8525	0.8027	3.8	13.7	14.7	13.9
20	20.53	4.157	36.25	0.8514	0.6698	1.3	12.9	14.0	13.1
16	16.45	3.326	34.13	0.8503	0.5366	−1.6	12.1	13.3	12.3
12	12.35	2.494	32.01	0.8491	0.4030	−5.0	11.2	12.5	11.4
8	8.25	1.663	29.89	0.8480	0.2690	−9.6	10.3	11.8	10.6
4	4.13	0.831	27.77	0.8469	0.1347	−17.2	9.4	11.0	9.7
0	0.00	0.000	25.65	0.8458	0.0000	—	8.5	10.2	8.8

26 °C DRY-BULB

Percentage saturation, μ / %	Relative humidity, ϕ /%	Value of stated parameter per kg dry air			Vapour pressure, p_v / kPa	Dew point temperature, θ_d / °C	Adiabatic saturation temperature, $\theta\star$ / °C	Wet bulb temperature	
		Moisture content, g / (g·kg^{-1})	Specific enthalpy, h / (kJ·kg^{-1})	Specific volume, v / (m^3·kg^{-1})				Screen, θ'_{sc} / °C	Sling, θ'_{sl} / °C
100	100.00	21.43	80.78	0.8761	3.360	26.0	26.0	26.0	26.0
96	96.13	20.58	78.60	0.8750	3.230	25.3	25.5	25.5	25.5
92	92.25	19.72	76.41	0.8738	3.100	24.6	25.0	25.1	25.0
88	88.35	18.86	74.23	0.8727	2.969	23.9	24.5	24.6	24.5
84	84.45	18.00	72.04	0.8715	2.838	23.2	23.9	24.1	24.0
80	80.54	17.15	69.86	0.8704	2.706	22.4	23.4	23.6	23.4
76	76.62	16.29	67.67	0.8692	2.574	21.6	22.8	23.0	22.9
72	72.68	15.43	65.49	0.8680	2.442	20.7	22.3	22.5	22.3
70	70.71	15.00	64.39	0.8675	2.376	20.3	22.0	22.2	22.0
68	68.74	14.58	63.30	0.8669	2.310	19.8	21.7	22.0	21.7
66	66.76	14.15	62.21	0.8663	2.243	19.3	21.4	21.7	21.4
64	64.78	13.72	61.12	0.8657	2.177	18.9	21.1	21.4	21.1
62	62.80	13.29	60.02	0.8652	2.110	18.4	20.8	21.1	20.8
60	60.81	12.86	58.93	0.8646	2.043	17.9	20.5	20.8	20.5
58	58.83	12.43	57.84	0.8640	1.977	17.3	20.1	20.6	20.2
56	56.84	12.00	56.75	0.8634	1.910	16.8	19.8	20.3	19.9
54	54.85	11.57	55.65	0.8628	1.843	16.2	19.5	20.0	19.6
52	52.85	11.15	54.56	0.8623	1.776	15.6	19.2	19.7	19.3
50	50.85	10.72	53.47	0.8617	1.709	15.0	18.8	19.4	18.9
48	48.85	10.29	52.38	0.8611	1.641	14.4	18.5	19.1	18.6
46	46.85	9.860	51.28	0.8605	1.574	13.8	18.2	18.7	18.3
44	44.84	9.431	50.19	0.8599	1.507	13.1	17.8	18.4	17.9
42	42.83	9.002	49.10	0.8594	1.439	12.4	17.5	18.1	17.6
40	40.82	8.574	48.01	0.8588	1.372	11.7	17.1	17.8	17.2
38	38.81	8.145	46.91	0.8582	1.304	10.9	16.8	17.5	16.9
36	36.79	7.716	45.82	0.8576	1.236	10.1	16.4	17.1	16.5
34	34.77	7.288	44.73	0.8570	1.168	9.3	16.0	16.8	16.1
32	32.75	6.859	43.64	0.8565	1.100	8.4	15.6	16.5	15.8
30	30.72	6.430	42.54	0.8559	1.032	7.4	15.3	16.1	15.4
28	28.69	6.002	41.45	0.8553	0.9641	6.4	14.9	15.8	15.0
24	24.63	5.144	39.27	0.8541	0.8275	4.3	14.1	15.1	14.2
20	20.55	4.287	37.08	0.8530	0.6905	1.7	13.2	14.3	13.4
16	16.46	3.429	34.90	0.8518	0.5532	−1.2	12.4	13.6	12.6
12	12.36	2.572	32.71	0.8507	0.4155	−4.6	11.5	12.8	11.7
8	8.25	1.715	30.53	0.8495	0.2774	−9.3	10.6	12.1	10.9
4	4.13	0.857	28.34	0.8483	0.1389	−16.9	9.7	11.2	9.9
0	0.00	0.000	26.16	0.8472	0.0000	—	8.7	10.4	9.0

26.5 °C DRY-BULB

Percentage saturation, μ / %	Relative humidity, ϕ /%	Value of stated parameter per kg dry air			Vapour pressure, p_v / kPa	Dew point temperature, θ_d / °C	Adiabatic saturation temperature, $\theta\star$ / °C	Wet bulb temperature	
		Moisture content, g / (g·kg^{-1})	Specific enthalpy, h / (kJ·kg^{-1})	Specific volume, v / (m^3·kg^{-1})				Screen, θ'_{sc} / °C	Sling, θ'_{sl} / °C
100	100.00	22.10	83.00	0.8785	3.461	26.5	26.5	26.5	26.5
96	96.13	21.22	80.75	0.8773	3.327	25.8	26.0	26.0	26.0
92	92.26	20.33	78.49	0.8761	3.193	25.1	25.5	25.5	25.5
88	88.37	19.45	76.24	0.8749	3.058	24.4	25.0	25.0	25.0
84	84.47	18.56	73.99	0.8737	2.923	23.7	24.4	24.5	24.4
80	80.56	17.68	71.73	0.8725	2.788	22.9	23.9	24.0	23.9
76	76.63	16.80	69.48	0.8713	2.652	22.1	23.3	23.5	23.3
72	72.70	15.91	67.23	0.8702	2.516	21.2	22.7	23.0	22.8
70	70.73	15.47	66.10	0.8696	2.448	20.8	22.4	22.7	22.5
68	68.76	15.03	64.97	0.8690	2.380	20.3	22.1	22.4	22.2
66	66.78	14.59	63.84	0.8684	2.311	19.8	21.8	22.1	21.9
64	64.81	14.14	62.72	0.8678	2.243	19.3	21.5	21.9	21.6
62	62.82	13.70	61.59	0.8672	2.174	18.8	21.2	21.6	21.3
60	60.84	13.26	60.46	0.8666	2.106	18.3	20.9	21.3	21.0
58	58.85	12.82	59.34	0.8660	2.037	17.8	20.6	21.0	20.6
56	56.86	12.38	58.21	0.8654	1.968	17.3	20.3	20.7	20.3
54	54.87	11.93	57.08	0.8648	1.899	16.7	19.9	20.4	20.0
52	52.88	11.49	55.96	0.8642	1.830	16.1	19.6	20.1	19.7
50	50.88	11.05	54.83	0.8636	1.761	15.5	19.3	19.8	19.3
48	48.88	10.61	53.70	0.8630	1.692	14.9	18.9	19.5	19.0
46	46.87	10.18	52.58	0.8624	1.622	14.2	18.6	19.2	18.7
44	44.87	9.723	51.45	0.8618	1.553	13.6	18.2	18.8	18.3
42	42.86	9.281	50.32	0.8612	1.483	12.9	17.9	18.5	18.0
40	40.85	8.840	49.20	0.8606	1.414	12.1	17.5	18.2	17.6
38	38.83	8.400	48.07	0.8600	1.344	11.4	17.1	17.9	17.3
36	36.81	7.956	46.94	0.8594	1.274	10.6	16.8	17.5	16.9
34	34.79	7.514	45.82	0.8588	1.204	9.7	16.4	17.2	16.5
32	32.77	7.072	44.69	0.8582	1.134	8.8	16.0	16.8	16.1
30	30.74	6.630	43.56	0.8576	1.064	7.9	15.6	16.5	15.8
28	28.71	6.188	42.44	0.8570	0.9937	6.9	15.2	16.1	15.4
24	24.65	5.304	40.18	0.8558	0.8530	4.7	14.4	15.4	14.6
20	20.57	4.420	37.93	0.8546	0.7118	2.1	13.6	14.7	13.8
16	16.48	3.536	35.67	0.8534	0.5703	−0.8	12.7	13.9	12.9
12	12.38	2.652	33.42	0.8522	0.4283	−4.2	11.8	13.1	12.0
8	8.26	1.768	31.17	0.8510	0.2860	−8.9	10.9	12.3	11.1
4	4.14	0.884	28.91	0.8498	0.1432	−16.6	9.9	11.5	10.2
0	0.00	0.000	26.66	0.8486	0.0000	—	8.9	10.7	9.2

27 °C DRY-BULB

Percentage saturation, μ / %	Relative humidity, ϕ /%	Value of stated parameter per kg dry air			Vapour pressure, p_v / kPa	Dew point temperature, θ_d / °C	Adiabatic saturation temperature, $\theta\star$ / °C	Wet bulb temperature	
		Moisture content, g / (g·kg^{-1})	Specific enthalpy, h / (kJ·kg^{-1})	Specific volume, v / (m^3·kg^{-1})				Screen, θ'_{sc} / °C	Sling, θ'_{sl} / °C
100	100.00	22.78	85.29	0.8809	3.564	27.0	27.0	27.0	27.0
96	96.14	21.87	82.94	0.8797	3.426	26.3	26.5	26.5	26.5
92	92.26	20.96	80.62	0.8784	3.288	25.6	26.0	26.0	26.0
88	88.38	20.05	78.30	0.8772	3.150	24.9	25.4	25.5	25.5
84	84.48	19.14	75.97	0.8760	3.011	24.2	24.9	25.0	24.9
80	80.57	18.23	73.65	0.8747	2.872	23.4	24.3	24.5	24.4
76	76.66	17.32	71.32	0.8735	2.732	22.5	23.8	24.0	23.8
72	72.72	16.40	69.00	0.8723	2.592	21.7	23.2	23.4	23.2
70	70.76	15.95	67.84	0.8717	2.522	21.2	22.9	23.1	22.9
68	68.78	15.49	66.67	0.8710	2.452	20.8	22.6	22.9	22.6
66	66.81	15.04	65.51	0.8704	2.381	20.3	22.3	22.6	22.3
64	64.83	14.58	64.35	0.8698	2.311	19.8	22.0	22.3	22.0
62	62.85	14.13	63.19	0.8692	2.240	19.3	21.7	22.0	21.7
60	60.87	13.67	62.03	0.8686	2.169	18.8	21.3	21.7	21.4
58	58.88	13.21	60.86	0.8680	2.099	18.3	21.0	21.4	21.1
56	56.89	12.76	59.70	0.8673	2.028	17.7	20.7	21.1	20.8
54	54.90	12.30	58.54	0.8667	1.957	17.2	20.4	20.8	20.4
52	52.90	11.85	57.38	0.8661	1.886	16.6	20.0	20.5	20.1
50	50.91	11.39	56.22	0.8655	1.814	16.0	19.7	20.2	19.8
48	48.90	10.94	55.05	0.8649	1.743	15.3	19.3	19.9	19.4
46	46.90	10.48	53.89	0.8642	1.672	14.7	19.0	19.6	19.1
44	44.89	10.02	52.73	0.8636	1.600	14.0	18.6	19.2	18.7
42	42.88	9.569	51.57	0.8630	1.528	13.3	18.3	18.9	18.4
40	40.87	9.113	50.41	0.8624	1.459	12.6	17.9	18.6	18.0
38	38.86	8.658	49.24	0.8618	1.385	11.8	17.5	18.2	17.6
36	36.84	8.202	48.08	0.8612	1.313	11.0	17.2	17.9	17.3
34	34.82	7.746	46.92	0.8605	1.241	10.2	16.8	17.6	16.9
32	32.79	7.291	45.76	0.8599	1.169	9.3	16.4	17.2	16.5
30	30.77	6.835	44.60	0.8593	1.097	8.3	16.0	16.9	16.1
28	28.74	6.379	43.43	0.8587	1.024	7.3	15.6	16.5	15.7
24	24.67	5.468	41.11	0.8574	0.8792	5.1	14.8	15.8	14.9
20	20.59	4.557	38.78	0.8562	0.7337	2.6	13.9	15.0	14.1
16	16.49	3.645	36.46	0.8550	0.5878	−0.5	13.0	14.2	13.2
12	12.39	2.734	34.14	0.8537	0.4415	−3.9	12.1	13.4	12.3
8	8.27	1.823	31.81	0.8525	0.2948	−8.6	11.2	12.6	11.4
4	4.14	0.911	29.49	0.8513	0.1476	−16.2	10.2	11.8	10.4
0	0.00	0.000	27.16	0.8500	0.0000	—	9.2	10.9	9.5

27.5 °C DRY-BULB

Percentage saturation, μ / %	Relative humidity, ϕ /%	Value of stated parameter per kg dry air			Vapour pressure, p_v / kPa	Dew point temperature, θ_d / °C	Adiabatic saturation temperature, $\theta\star$ / °C	Wet bulb temperature	
		Moisture content, g / (g·kg^{-1})	Specific enthalpy, h / (kJ·kg^{-1})	Specific volume, v / (m^3·kg^{-1})				Screen, θ'_{sc} / °C	Sling, θ'_{sl} / °C
100	100.00	23.49	87.59	0.8833	3.670	27.5	27.5	27.5	27.5
96	96.14	22.55	85.19	0.8821	3.528	26.8	27.0	27.0	27.0
92	92.27	21.61	82.79	0.8808	3.386	26.1	26.5	26.5	26.5
88	88.39	20.67	80.40	0.8795	3.244	25.4	25.9	26.0	25.9
84	84.50	19.73	78.00	0.8782	3.101	24.7	25.4	25.5	25.4
80	80.59	18.79	75.60	0.8770	2.958	23.9	24.8	25.0	24.8
76	76.68	17.85	73.21	0.8757	2.814	23.0	24.2	24.4	24.3
72	72.75	16.91	70.81	0.8744	2.670	22.2	23.7	23.9	23.7
70	70.78	16.44	69.61	0.8738	2.598	21.7	23.3	23.6	23.4
68	68.81	15.97	68.41	0.8731	2.525	21.3	23.0	23.3	23.1
66	66.83	15.50	67.21	0.8725	2.453	20.8	22.7	23.0	22.8
64	64.86	15.03	66.02	0.8719	2.380	20.3	22.4	22.7	22.5
62	62.88	14.56	64.82	0.8712	2.308	19.8	22.1	22.5	22.2
60	60.89	14.09	63.62	0.8706	2.235	19.3	21.8	22.2	21.8
58	58.91	13.62	62.42	0.8700	2.162	18.7	21.5	21.9	21.5
56	56.92	13.15	61.22	0.8693	2.089	18.2	21.1	21.5	21.2
54	54.93	12.68	60.02	0.8687	2.016	17.6	20.8	21.2	20.9
52	52.93	12.21	58.82	0.8680	1.943	17.0	20.4	20.9	20.5
50	50.93	11.74	57.63	0.8674	1.869	16.4	20.1	20.6	20.2
48	48.93	11.27	56.43	0.8668	1.796	15.8	19.7	20.3	19.8
46	46.93	10.80	55.23	0.8661	1.722	15.2	19.4	20.0	19.5
44	44.92	10.33	54.03	0.8655	1.649	14.5	19.0	19.6	19.1
42	42.91	9.864	52.83	0.8649	1.575	13.8	18.7	19.3	18.8
40	40.90	9.395	51.63	0.8642	1.501	13.0	18.3	19.0	18.4
38	38.88	8.925	50.44	0.8636	1.427	12.3	17.9	18.6	18.0
36	36.86	8.455	49.24	0.8629	1.353	11.5	17.5	18.3	17.6
34	34.84	7.986	48.04	0.8623	1.279	10.6	17.1	17.9	17.3
32	32.82	7.516	46.84	0.8617	1.204	9.7	16.7	17.6	16.9
30	30.79	7.046	45.64	0.8610	1.130	8.8	16.3	17.2	16.5
28	28.76	6.576	44.44	0.8604	1.055	7.8	15.9	16.8	16.1
24	24.69	5.637	42.05	0.8591	0.9060	5.6	15.1	16.1	15.3
20	20.60	4.697	39.65	0.8578	0.7562	3.0	14.2	15.3	14.4
16	16.51	3.758	37.25	0.8566	0.6059	−0.1	13.3	14.5	13.5
12	12.40	2.818	34.86	0.8553	0.4551	−3.5	12.4	13.7	12.6
8	8.28	1.879	32.46	0.8540	0.3039	−8.2	11.4	12.9	11.7
4	4.15	0.939	30.06	0.8527	0.1522	−15.9	10.4	12.0	10.7
0	0.00	0.000	27.67	0.8514	0.0000	—	9.4	11.1	9.7

28 °C DRY-BULB

Percentage saturation, μ / %	Relative humidity, ϕ /%	Value of stated parameter per kg dry air			Vapour pressure, p_v / kPa	Dew point temperature, θ_d / °C	Adiabatic saturation temperature, $\theta^\star$ / °C	Wet bulb temperature	
		Moisture content, g / (g·kg^{-1})	Specific enthalpy, h / (kJ·kg^{-1})	Specific volume, v / (m^3·kg^{-1})				Screen, θ'_{sc} / °C	Sling, θ'_{sl} / °C
100	100.00	24.21	89.96	0.8858	3.779	28.0	28.0	28.0	28.0
96	96.14	23.24	87.49	0.8845	3.633	27.3	27.5	27.5	27.5
92	92.28	22.27	85.01	0.8832	3.487	26.6	27.0	27.0	27.0
88	88.40	21.30	82.54	0.8818	3.340	25.9	26.4	26.5	26.4
84	84.51	20.34	80.07	0.8805	3.194	25.1	25.9	26.0	25.9
80	80.61	19.37	77.60	0.8792	3.046	24.4	25.3	25.5	25.3
76	76.70	18.40	75.13	0.8779	2.898	23.5	24.7	24.9	24.7
72	72.77	17.43	72.66	0.8766	2.750	22.7	24.1	24.3	24.2
70	70.80	16.95	71.42	0.8759	2.675	22.2	23.8	24.1	23.8
68	68.83	16.46	70.18	0.8753	2.601	21.7	23.5	23.8	23.5
66	66.86	15.98	68.95	0.8746	2.526	21.3	23.2	23.5	23.2
64	64.88	15.49	67.71	0.8740	2.452	20.8	22.9	23.2	22.9
62	62.90	15.01	66.48	0.8733	2.377	20.3	22.5	22.9	22.6
60	60.92	14.53	65.24	0.8726	2.302	19.8	22.2	22.6	22.3
58	58.94	14.04	64.01	0.8720	2.227	19.2	21.9	22.3	22.0
56	56.95	13.56	62.77	0.8713	2.152	18.7	21.6	22.0	21.6
54	54.95	13.07	61.53	0.8707	2.077	18.1	21.2	21.7	21.3
52	52.96	12.59	60.30	0.8700	2.001	17.5	20.9	21.3	20.9
50	50.96	12.10	59.06	0.8693	1.926	16.9	20.5	21.0	20.6
48	48.96	11.62	57.83	0.8687	1.850	16.3	20.2	20.7	20.2
46	46.96	11.14	56.59	0.8680	1.774	15.6	19.8	20.4	19.9
44	44.95	10.65	55.36	0.8674	1.699	14.9	19.4	20.0	19.5
42	42.94	10.17	54.12	0.8667	1.624	14.2	19.1	19.7	19.2
40	40.93	9.684	52.88	0.8661	1.547	13.5	18.7	19.4	18.8
38	38.91	9.200	51.65	0.8654	1.470	12.7	18.3	19.0	18.4
36	36.89	8.716	50.41	0.8647	1.394	11.9	17.9	18.7	18.0
34	34.87	8.231	49.18	0.8641	1.318	11.1	17.5	18.3	17.6
32	32.84	7.747	47.94	0.8634	1.241	10.2	17.1	17.9	17.2
30	30.81	7.263	46.70	0.8628	1.164	9.2	16.7	17.6	16.8
28	28.78	6.779	45.47	0.8621	1.088	8.2	16.3	17.2	16.4
24	24.71	5.810	43.00	0.8608	0.9337	6.0	15.4	16.4	15.6
20	20.62	4.842	40.53	0.8595	0.7793	3.4	14.6	15.7	14.7
16	16.52	3.874	38.06	0.8581	0.6244	0.3	13.6	14.9	13.8
12	12.41	2.905	35.58	0.8568	0.4690	−3.2	12.7	14.0	12.9
8	8.29	1.937	33.11	0.8555	0.3132	−7.9	11.7	13.2	11.9
4	4.15	0.968	30.64	0.8542	0.1568	−15.6	10.7	12.3	10.9
0	0.00	0.000	28.17	0.8529	0.0000	—	9.6	11.4	9.9

28.5 °C DRY-BULB

Percentage saturation, μ / %	Relative humidity, ϕ /%	Value of stated parameter per kg dry air			Vapour pressure, p_v / kPa	Dew point temperature, θ_d / °C	Adiabatic saturation temperature, $\theta^\star$ / °C	Wet bulb temperature	
		Moisture content, g / (g·kg^{-1})	Specific enthalpy, h / (kJ·kg^{-1})	Specific volume, v / (m^3·kg^{-1})				Screen, θ'_{sc} / °C	Sling, θ'_{sl} / °C
100	100.00	24.95	92.38	0.8883	3.890	28.5	28.5	28.5	28.5
96	96.15	23.96	89.83	0.8869	3.740	27.8	28.0	28.0	28.0
92	92.29	22.96	87.28	0.8856	3.590	27.1	27.4	27.5	27.5
88	88.41	21.96	84.74	0.8842	3.439	26.4	26.9	27.0	26.9
84	84.53	20.96	82.19	0.8828	3.288	25.6	26.3	26.5	26.4
80	80.63	19.96	79.64	0.8815	3.137	24.8	25.8	25.9	25.8
76	76.72	18.96	77.09	0.8801	2.985	24.0	25.2	25.4	25.2
72	72.79	17.97	74.54	0.8788	2.832	23.1	24.6	24.8	24.6
70	70.83	17.47	73.27	0.8781	2.755	22.7	24.3	24.5	24.3
68	68.86	16.97	71.99	0.8774	2.679	22.2	24.0	24.2	24.0
66	66.89	16.47	70.72	0.8767	2.602	21.7	23.6	23.9	23.7
64	64.91	15.97	69.45	0.8761	2.525	21.3	23.3	23.6	23.4
62	62.93	15.47	68.17	0.8754	2.448	20.8	23.0	23.3	23.0
60	60.95	14.97	66.90	0.8747	2.371	20.2	22.7	23.0	22.7
58	58.96	14.47	65.62	0.8740	2.294	19.7	22.3	22.7	22.4
56	56.98	13.97	64.35	0.8733	2.216	19.1	22.0	22.4	22.1
54	54.98	13.47	63.07	0.8727	2.139	18.6	21.6	22.1	21.7
52	52.99	12.98	61.80	0.8720	2.061	18.0	21.3	21.8	21.4
50	50.99	12.48	60.53	0.8713	1.984	17.4	20.9	21.4	21.0
48	48.99	11.98	59.25	0.8706	1.906	16.7	20.6	21.1	20.7
46	46.99	11.48	57.98	0.8699	1.828	16.1	20.2	20.8	20.3
44	44.98	10.98	56.70	0.8693	1.750	15.4	19.8	20.4	19.9
42	42.97	10.48	55.43	0.8686	1.672	14.7	19.5	20.1	19.6
40	40.96	9.981	54.16	0.8679	1.593	14.0	19.1	19.8	19.2
38	38.94	9.482	52.88	0.8672	1.515	13.2	18.7	19.4	18.8
36	36.92	8.983	51.61	0.8665	1.436	12.4	18.3	19.0	18.4
34	34.90	8.484	50.33	0.8659	1.358	11.5	17.9	18.7	18.0
32	32.87	7.985	49.06	0.8652	1.279	10.6	17.5	18.3	17.6
30	30.84	7.486	47.78	0.8645	1.200	9.7	17.1	17.9	17.2
28	28.81	6.987	46.51	0.8638	1.121	8.7	16.6	17.6	16.8
24	24.73	5.989	43.96	0.8625	0.9621	6.4	15.8	16.8	15.9
20	20.64	4.991	41.41	0.8611	0.8030	3.8	14.9	16.0	15.1
16	16.54	3.992	38.87	0.8597	0.6434	0.7	13.9	15.2	14.1
12	12.42	2.994	36.32	0.8584	0.4834	−2.8	13.0	14.3	13.2
8	8.30	1.996	33.77	0.8570	0.3228	−7.5	12.0	13.4	12.2
4	4.16	0.998	31.22	0.8556	0.1616	−15.3	10.9	12.5	11.2
0	0.00	0.000	28.67	0.8543	0.0000	—	9.8	11.6	10.1

29 °C DRY-BULB

Percentage saturation, μ / %	Relative humidity, ϕ /%	Value of stated parameter per kg dry air			Vapour pressure, p_v / kPa	Dew point temperature, θ_d / °C	Adiabatic saturation temperature, $\theta^\star$ / °C	Wet bulb temperature	
		Moisture content, g / (g·kg^{-1})	Specific enthalpy, h / (kJ·kg^{-1})	Specific volume, v / (m³·kg^{-1})				Screen, θ'_{sc} / °C	Sling, θ'_{sl} / °C
100	100.00	25.72	94.86	0.8908	4.005	29.0	29.0	29.0	29.0
96	96.15	24.69	92.23	0.8894	3.850	28.3	28.5	28.5	28.5
92	92.30	23.66	89.60	0.8880	3.696	27.6	27.9	28.0	27.9
88	88.43	22.63	86.98	0.8866	3.541	26.9	27.4	27.5	27.4
84	84.54	21.60	84.35	0.8852	3.386	26.1	26.8	26.9	26.8
80	80.65	20.57	81.72	0.8838	3.230	25.3	26.2	26.4	26.3
76	76.74	19.55	79.09	0.8824	3.073	24.5	25.6	25.8	25.7
72	72.82	18.52	76.47	0.8810	2.916	23.6	25.0	25.3	25.1
70	70.85	18.00	75.15	0.8803	2.837	23.2	24.7	25.0	24.8
68	68.88	17.49	73.84	0.8796	2.759	22.7	24.4	24.7	24.5
66	66.91	16.97	72.53	0.8789	2.680	22.2	24.1	24.4	24.1
64	64.94	16.46	71.21	0.8782	2.600	21.7	23.8	24.1	23.8
62	62.96	15.94	69.90	0.8775	2.521	21.2	23.4	23.8	23.5
60	60.98	15.43	68.58	0.8768	2.442	20.7	23.1	23.5	23.2
58	58.99	14.92	67.27	0.8761	2.362	20.2	22.8	23.2	22.8
56	57.01	14.40	65.96	0.8754	2.283	19.6	22.4	22.8	22.5
54	55.01	13.89	64.64	0.8747	2.203	19.1	22.1	22.5	22.1
52	53.02	13.37	63.33	0.8740	2.123	18.5	21.7	22.2	21.8
50	51.02	12.86	62.02	0.8733	2.043	17.8	21.4	21.9	21.4
48	49.02	12.34	60.70	0.8726	1.963	17.2	21.0	21.5	21.1
46	47.02	11.83	59.39	0.8719	1.883	16.6	20.6	21.2	20.7
44	45.01	11.32	58.08	0.8712	1.802	15.9	20.2	20.8	20.3
42	43.00	10.80	56.76	0.8705	1.722	15.2	19.9	20.5	20.0
40	40.98	10.29	55.45	0.8698	1.641	14.4	19.5	20.1	19.6
38	38.97	9.773	54.13	0.8691	1.560	13.6	19.1	19.8	19.2
36	36.95	9.258	52.82	0.8684	1.480	12.8	18.7	19.4	18.8
34	34.92	8.744	51.51	0.8677	1.398	12.0	18.3	19.1	18.4
32	32.90	8.230	50.19	0.8670	1.317	11.1	17.9	18.7	18.0
30	30.86	7.715	48.88	0.8662	1.236	10.1	17.4	18.3	17.6
28	28.83	7.201	47.57	0.8655	1.155	9.1	17.0	17.9	17.1
24	24.75	6.172	44.94	0.8641	0.9912	6.9	16.1	17.1	16.3
20	20.66	5.144	42.31	0.8627	0.8274	4.3	15.2	16.3	15.4
16	16.56	4.115	39.68	0.8613	0.6630	1.1	14.3	15.5	14.5
12	12.44	3.086	37.06	0.8599	0.4981	−2.4	13.3	14.6	13.5
8	8.31	2.057	34.43	0.8585	0.3326	−7.2	12.2	13.7	12.5
4	4.16	1.029	31.80	0.8571	0.1666	−14.9	11.2	12.8	11.4
0	0.00	0.000	29.18	0.8557	0.0000	—	10.1	11.9	10.4

29.5 °C DRY-BULB

Percentage saturation, μ / %	Relative humidity, ϕ /%	Value of stated parameter per kg dry air			Vapour pressure, p_v / kPa	Dew point temperature, θ_d / °C	Adiabatic saturation temperature, $\theta^\star$ / °C	Wet bulb temperature	
		Moisture content, g / (g·kg^{-1})	Specific enthalpy, h / (kJ·kg^{-1})	Specific volume, v / (m³·kg^{-1})				Screen, θ'_{sc} / °C	Sling, θ'_{sl} / °C
100	100.00	26.50	97.39	0.8933	4.122	29.5	29.5	29.5	29.5
96	96.16	25.44	94.68	0.8919	3.963	28.8	29.0	29.0	29.0
92	92.30	24.38	91.97	0.8905	3.805	28.1	28.4	28.5	28.4
88	88.44	23.32	89.27	0.8890	3.645	27.4	27.9	28.0	27.9
84	84.56	22.26	86.56	0.8876	3.485	26.6	27.3	27.4	27.3
80	80.67	21.20	83.85	0.8861	3.325	25.8	26.7	26.9	26.7
76	76.76	20.14	81.14	0.8847	3.164	25.0	26.1	26.3	26.1
72	72.84	19.08	78.43	0.8832	3.002	24.1	25.5	25.7	25.5
70	70.88	18.55	77.08	0.8825	2.922	23.7	25.2	25.4	25.2
68	68.91	18.02	75.72	0.8818	2.840	23.2	24.9	25.1	24.9
66	66.94	17.49	74.37	0.8810	2.759	22.7	24.5	24.8	24.6
64	64.97	16.96	73.01	0.8803	2.678	22.2	24.2	24.5	24.3
62	62.99	16.43	71.66	0.8796	2.596	21.7	23.9	24.2	23.9
60	61.01	15.90	70.31	0.8789	2.515	21.2	23.5	23.9	23.6
58	59.02	15.37	68.95	0.8782	2.433	20.7	23.2	23.6	23.3
56	57.04	14.84	67.60	0.8774	2.351	20.1	22.9	23.3	22.9
54	55.05	14.31	66.24	0.8767	2.269	19.5	22.5	22.9	22.6
52	53.05	13.78	64.89	0.8760	2.187	18.9	22.1	22.6	22.2
50	51.05	13.25	63.54	0.8753	2.104	18.3	21.8	22.3	21.9
48	49.05	12.72	62.18	0.8745	2.022	17.7	21.4	21.9	21.5
46	47.05	12.19	60.83	0.8738	1.939	17.0	21.0	21.6	21.1
44	45.07	11.66	59.47	0.8731	1.856	16.3	20.7	21.3	20.7
42	43.03	11.13	58.12	0.8724	1.774	15.6	20.3	20.9	20.4
40	41.01	10.60	56.76	0.8716	1.691	14.9	19.9	20.5	20.0
38	39.00	10.07	55.41	0.8709	1.607	14.1	19.5	20.2	19.6
36	36.98	9.541	54.06	0.8702	1.524	13.3	19.1	19.8	19.2
34	34.95	9.011	52.70	0.8695	1.441	12.4	18.6	19.4	18.8
32	32.92	8.481	51.35	0.8687	1.357	11.5	18.2	19.1	18.4
30	30.89	7.951	49.99	0.8680	1.273	10.6	17.8	18.7	17.9
28	28.86	7.421	48.64	0.8673	1.189	9.5	17.4	18.3	17.5
24	24.78	6.361	45.93	0.8658	1.021	7.3	16.5	17.5	16.6
20	20.68	5.301	43.22	0.8644	0.8524	4.7	15.5	16.6	15.7
16	16.57	4.240	40.51	0.8629	0.6831	1.6	14.6	15.8	14.8
12	12.45	3.180	37.80	0.8615	0.5132	−2.1	13.6	14.9	13.8
8	8.32	2.120	35.10	0.8600	0.3427	−6.8	12.5	14.0	12.8
4	4.16	1.060	32.39	0.8586	0.1717	−14.6	11.4	13.1	11.7
0	0.00	0.000	29.68	0.8571	0.0000	—	10.3	12.1	10.6

30 °C DRY-BULB

Percentage saturation, μ / %	Relative humidity, ϕ /%	Value of stated parameter per kg dry air			Vapour pressure, p_v / kPa	Dew point temperature, θ_d /°C	Adiabatic saturation temperature, $\theta\star$ /°C	Wet bulb temperature	
		Moisture content, g /(g·kg^{-1})	Specific enthalpy, h /(kJ·kg^{-1})	Specific volume, v /(m^3·kg^{-1})				Screen, θ'_{sc} /°C	Sling, θ'_{sl} /°C
100	100.00	27.31	99.98	0.8959	4.242	30.0	30.0	30.0	30.0
96	96.16	26.22	97.19	0.8944	4.079	29.3	29.5	29.5	29.5
92	92.31	25.13	94.40	0.8929	3.916	28.6	28.9	29.0	28.9
88	88.45	24.03	91.61	0.8915	3.752	27.9	28.4	28.4	28.4
84	84.57	22.94	88.81	0.8900	3.588	27.1	27.8	27.9	27.8
80	80.69	21.85	86.02	0.8885	3.423	26.3	27.2	27.3	27.2
76	76.78	20.76	83.23	0.8870	3.257	25.5	26.6	26.8	26.6
72	72.87	19.66	80.44	0.8855	3.091	24.6	26.0	26.2	26.0
70	70.91	19.12	79.04	0.8847	3.008	24.1	25.6	25.9	25.7
68	68.94	18.57	77.65	0.8840	2.924	23.7	25.3	25.6	25.4
66	66.97	18.02	76.25	0.8832	2.841	23.2	25.0	25.3	25.0
64	65.00	17.48	74.85	0.8825	2.757	22.7	24.7	25.0	24.7
62	63.02	16.93	73.46	0.8817	2.673	22.2	24.3	24.7	24.4
60	61.04	16.39	72.06	0.8810	2.589	21.7	24.0	24.4	24.0
58	59.05	15.84	70.67	0.8802	2.505	21.1	23.6	24.0	23.7
56	57.07	15.29	69.27	0.8795	2.421	20.6	23.3	23.7	23.4
54	55.08	14.75	67.87	0.8788	2.336	20.0	22.9	23.4	23.0
52	53.08	14.20	66.48	0.8780	2.252	19.4	22.6	23.0	22.6
50	51.08	13.66	65.08	0.8773	2.167	18.8	22.2	22.7	22.3
48	49.08	13.11	63.69	0.8765	2.092	18.1	21.8	22.4	21.9
46	47.08	12.56	62.29	0.8758	1.997	17.5	21.4	22.0	21.5
44	45.07	12.02	60.89	0.8750	1.912	16.8	21.1	21.7	21.2
42	43.06	11.47	59.50	0.8743	1.827	16.1	20.7	21.3	20.8
40	41.05	10.92	58.10	0.8735	1.741	15.3	20.3	20.9	20.4
38	39.03	10.38	56.71	0.8728	1.656	14.6	19.9	20.6	20.0
36	37.00	9.832	55.31	0.8720	1.570	13.7	19.4	20.2	19.6
34	34.98	9.286	53.91	0.8713	1.484	12.9	19.0	19.8	19.1
32	32.95	8.739	52.52	0.8705	1.398	12.0	18.6	19.4	18.7
30	30.92	8.193	51.12	0.8698	1.312	11.0	18.2	19.0	18.3
28	28.88	7.647	49.73	0.8690	1.225	10.0	17.7	18.6	17.9
24	24.80	6.554	46.93	0.8675	1.052	7.7	16.8	17.8	17.0
20	20.70	5.462	44.14	0.8660	0.8782	5.1	15.9	17.0	16.0
16	16.59	4.370	41.35	0.8645	0.7038	2.0	14.9	16.1	15.1
12	12.47	3.277	38.56	0.8630	0.5288	−1.7	13.8	15.2	14.1
8	8.32	2.185	35.77	0.8615	0.3531	−6.5	12.8	14.3	13.0
4	4.17	1.092	32.97	0.8600	0.1769	−14.3	11.7	13.3	11.9
0	0.00	0.000	30.18	0.8585	0.0000	—	10.5	12.3	10.8

30.5 °C DRY-BULB

Percentage saturation, μ / %	Relative humidity, ϕ /%	Value of stated parameter per kg dry air			Vapour pressure, p_v / kPa	Dew point temperature, θ_d /°C	Adiabatic saturation temperature, $\theta\star$ /°C	Wet bulb temperature	
		Moisture content, g /(g·kg^{-1})	Specific enthalpy, h /(kJ·kg^{-1})	Specific volume, v /(m^3·kg^{-1})				Screen, θ'_{sc} /°C	Sling, θ'_{sl} /°C
100	100.00	28.14	102.63	0.8985	4.365	30.5	30.5	30.5	30.5
96	96.17	27.02	99.75	0.8970	4.198	29.8	30.0	30.0	30.0
92	92.31	25.89	96.88	0.8955	4.030	29.1	29.4	29.5	29.4
88	88.46	24.76	94.00	0.8939	3.862	28.4	28.8	28.9	28.9
84	84.59	23.64	91.12	0.8924	3.693	27.6	28.3	28.4	28.3
80	80.71	22.51	88.24	0.8908	3.523	26.8	27.7	27.8	27.7
76	76.81	21.39	85.36	0.8893	3.353	26.0	27.1	27.2	27.1
72	72.89	20.26	82.49	0.8878	3.182	25.1	26.4	26.7	26.5
70	70.93	19.70	81.05	0.8870	3.096	24.6	26.1	26.4	26.1
68	68.97	19.14	79.61	0.8862	3.011	24.2	25.8	26.1	25.8
66	67.00	18.57	78.17	0.8854	2.925	23.7	25.5	25.7	25.5
64	65.03	18.01	76.73	0.8847	2.839	23.2	25.1	25.4	25.2
62	63.05	17.45	75.29	0.8839	2.752	22.7	24.8	25.1	24.8
60	61.07	16.88	73.85	0.8831	2.666	22.1	24.4	24.8	24.5
58	59.09	16.32	72.41	0.8824	2.579	21.6	24.1	24.5	24.1
56	57.10	15.76	70.98	0.8816	2.493	21.0	23.7	24.1	23.8
54	55.11	15.20	69.54	0.8808	2.406	20.5	23.4	23.8	23.4
52	53.11	14.63	68.10	0.8800	2.319	19.9	23.0	23.5	23.1
50	51.12	14.07	66.66	0.8793	2.231	19.3	22.6	23.1	22.7
48	49.12	13.51	65.22	0.8785	2.144	18.6	22.2	22.8	22.3
46	47.11	12.94	63.78	0.8777	2.057	18.0	21.9	22.4	21.9
44	45.10	12.38	62.34	0.8770	1.969	17.3	21.5	22.1	21.6
42	43.09	11.82	60.90	0.8762	1.881	16.5	21.1	21.7	21.2
40	41.08	11.26	59.46	0.8754	1.793	15.8	20.7	21.3	20.8
38	39.06	10.69	58.02	0.8746	1.705	15.0	20.2	21.0	20.4
36	37.04	10.13	56.59	0.8739	1.617	14.2	19.8	20.6	19.9
34	35.01	9.568	55.15	0.8731	1.528	13.3	19.4	20.2	19.5
32	32.98	9.005	53.71	0.8723	1.435	12.4	19.0	19.8	19.1
30	30.95	8.442	52.27	0.8716	1.351	11.4	18.5	19.4	18.7
28	28.91	7.879	50.83	0.8708	1.262	10.4	18.1	19.0	18.2
24	24.82	6.754	47.95	0.8692	1.084	8.2	17.1	18.2	17.3
20	20.72	5.628	45.07	0.8677	0.9046	5.5	16.2	17.3	16.4
16	16.61	4.502	42.40	0.8661	0.7250	2.4	15.2	16.4	15.4
12	12.48	3.377	39.32	0.8646	0.5448	−1.4	14.1	15.5	14.4
8	8.33	2.251	36.44	0.8631	0.3638	−6.2	13.0	14.5	13.3
4	4.17	1.125	33.56	0.8615	0.1823	−14.0	11.9	13.6	12.2
0	0.00	0.000	30.68	0.8600	0.0000	—	10.7	12.5	11.0

31 °C DRY-BULB

Percentage saturation, μ / %	Relative humidity, ϕ /%	Value of stated parameter per kg dry air			Vapour pressure, p_v / kPa	Dew point temperature, θ_d / °C	Adiabatic saturation temperature, $\theta\star$ / °C	Wet bulb temperature	
		Moisture content, g / (g·kg^{-1})	Specific enthalpy, h / (kJ·kg^{-1})	Specific volume, v / (m^3·kg^{-1})				Screen, θ'_{sc} / °C	Sling, θ'_{sl} / °C
100	100.00	29.00	105.3	0.9012	4.492	31.0	31.0	31.0	31.0
96	96.17	27.83	102.4	0.8996	4.320	30.3	30.5	30.5	30.5
92	92.33	26.67	99.41	0.8980	4.147	29.6	29.9	30.0	29.9
88	88.48	25.51	96.44	0.8964	3.974	28.9	29.3	29.4	29.3
84	84.61	24.35	93.48	0.8948	3.800	28.1	28.7	28.9	28.8
80	80.73	23.19	90.51	0.8932	3.626	27.3	28.1	28.3	28.2
76	76.83	22.04	87.55	0.8917	3.451	26.5	27.5	27.7	27.6
72	72.92	20.88	84.58	0.8901	3.275	25.6	26.9	27.1	26.9
70	70.96	20.30	83.10	0.8893	3.187	25.1	26.6	26.8	26.6
68	69.00	19.72	81.61	0.8885	3.099	24.6	26.2	26.5	26.3
66	67.03	19.14	80.13	0.8877	3.011	24.2	25.9	26.2	26.0
64	65.06	18.56	78.65	0.8869	2.922	23.7	25.6	25.9	25.6
62	63.08	17.98	77.16	0.8861	2.833	23.1	25.2	25.6	25.3
60	61.10	17.40	75.68	0.8853	2.744	22.6	24.9	25.2	24.9
58	59.12	16.82	74.20	0.8845	2.655	22.1	24.5	24.9	24.6
56	57.13	16.24	72.71	0.8837	2.566	21.5	24.2	24.6	24.2
54	55.14	15.66	71.23	0.8829	2.477	20.9	23.8	24.2	23.9
52	53.15	15.08	69.75	0.8821	2.387	20.3	23.4	23.9	23.5
50	51.15	14.50	68.27	0.8813	2.298	19.7	23.0	23.5	23.1
48	49.15	13.92	66.78	0.8805	2.208	19.1	22.7	23.2	22.7
46	47.15	13.34	65.30	0.8797	2.118	18.4	22.3	22.8	22.4
44	45.14	12.76	63.82	0.8789	2.027	17.7	21.9	22.5	22.0
42	43.12	12.18	62.33	0.8781	1.937	17.0	21.5	22.1	21.6
40	41.11	11.60	60.85	0.8773	1.846	16.3	21.1	21.7	21.2
38	39.09	11.02	59.37	0.8765	1.756	15.5	20.6	21.3	20.7
36	37.07	10.44	57.88	0.8757	1.665	14.6	20.2	21.0	20.3
34	35.04	9.858	56.40	0.8749	1.574	13.8	19.8	20.6	19.9
32	33.01	9.278	54.92	0.8741	1.483	12.9	19.3	20.2	19.5
30	30.97	8.698	53.45	0.8733	1.391	11.9	18.9	19.8	19.0
28	28.94	8.118	51.95	0.8725	1.300	10.9	18.4	19.3	18.6
24	24.85	6.958	48.99	0.8710	1.116	8.6	17.5	18.5	17.6
20	20.75	5.799	46.02	0.8694	0.9318	6.0	16.5	17.6	16.7
16	16.63	4.639	43.05	0.8678	0.7468	2.8	15.5	16.7	15.7
12	12.49	3.479	40.09	0.8662	0.5612	−1.0	14.4	15.8	14.6
8	8.34	2.320	37.12	0.8646	0.3748	−5.8	13.3	14.8	13.6
4	4.18	1.160	34.15	0.8630	0.1878	−13.6	12.1	13.8	12.4
0	0.00	0.000	31.19	0.8614	0.0000	—	10.9	12.8	11.2

31.5 °C DRY-BULB

Percentage saturation, μ / %	Relative humidity, ϕ /%	Value of stated parameter per kg dry air			Vapour pressure, p_v / kPa	Dew point temperature, θ_d / °C	Adiabatic saturation temperature, $\theta\star$ / °C	Wet bulb temperature	
		Moisture content, g / (g·kg^{-1})	Specific enthalpy, h / (kJ·kg^{-1})	Specific volume, v / (m^3·kg^{-1})				Screen, θ'_{sc} / °C	Sling, θ'_{sl} / °C
100	100.00	29.87	108.1	0.9039	4.621	31.5	31.5	31.5	31.5
96	96.18	28.68	105.0	0.9022	4.444	30.8	31.0	31.0	31.0
92	92.34	27.48	102.0	0.9006	4.267	30.1	30.4	30.4	30.4
88	88.49	26.29	98.94	0.8990	4.089	29.4	29.8	29.9	29.8
84	84.63	25.09	95.89	0.8973	3.911	28.6	29.2	29.3	29.2
80	80.75	23.90	92.83	0.8957	3.731	27.8	28.6	28.8	28.6
76	76.85	22.70	89.77	0.8940	3.552	26.9	28.0	28.2	28.0
72	72.95	21.51	86.72	0.8924	3.371	26.1	27.4	27.6	27.4
70	70.99	20.91	85.19	0.8916	3.280	25.6	27.0	27.3	27.1
68	69.02	20.31	83.66	0.8908	3.190	25.1	26.7	27.0	26.7
66	67.06	19.71	82.13	0.8899	3.099	24.6	26.4	26.6	26.4
64	65.09	19.12	80.60	0.8891	3.008	24.1	26.0	26.3	26.1
62	63.11	18.52	79.07	0.8883	2.917	23.6	25.7	26.0	25.7
60	61.13	17.92	77.55	0.8875	2.825	23.1	25.3	25.7	25.4
58	59.15	17.32	76.02	0.8867	2.734	22.6	25.0	25.3	25.0
56	57.17	16.73	74.49	0.8858	2.642	22.0	24.6	25.0	24.7
54	55.18	16.13	72.96	0.8850	2.550	21.4	24.2	24.7	24.3
52	53.18	15.53	71.43	0.8842	2.458	20.8	23.8	24.3	23.9
50	51.19	14.94	69.90	0.8834	2.365	20.2	23.5	24.0	23.5
48	49.18	14.34	68.38	0.8825	2.273	19.6	23.1	23.6	23.2
46	47.18	13.74	66.85	0.8817	2.180	18.9	22.7	23.2	22.8
44	45.17	13.14	65.32	0.8809	2.087	18.2	22.3	22.9	22.4
42	43.16	12.55	63.79	0.8801	1.994	17.5	21.9	22.5	22.0
40	41.14	11.95	62.26	0.8793	1.901	16.7	21.5	22.1	21.6
38	39.12	11.35	60.73	0.8784	1.808	15.9	21.0	21.7	21.1
36	37.10	10.75	59.20	0.8776	1.714	15.1	20.6	21.3	20.7
34	35.07	10.16	57.68	0.8768	1.621	14.2	20.2	20.9	20.3
32	33.04	9.559	56.15	0.8760	1.527	13.3	19.7	20.5	19.8
30	31.00	8.961	54.62	0.8751	1.433	12.3	19.3	20.1	19.4
28	28.96	8.364	53.09	0.8743	1.338	11.3	18.8	19.7	18.9
24	24.87	7.169	50.03	0.8727	1.150	9.0	17.8	18.8	18.0
20	20.77	5.974	46.98	0.8710	0.9597	6.4	16.8	18.0	17.0
16	16.65	4.780	43.92	0.8694	0.7692	3.2	15.8	17.0	16.0
12	12.51	3.584	40.86	0.8677	0.5780	−0.7	14.7	16.1	14.9
8	8.36	2.390	37.81	0.8661	0.3861	−5.5	13.6	15.1	13.8
4	4.19	1.194	34.75	0.8644	0.1934	−13.3	12.4	14.1	12.7
0	0.00	0.000	31.69	0.8628	0.0000	—	11.1	13.0	11.5

32 °C DRY-BULB

Percentage saturation, μ / %	Relative humidity, ϕ /%	Value of stated parameter per kg dry air			Vapour pressure, p_v / kPa	Dew point temperature, θ_d /°C	Adiabatic saturation temperature, $\theta^\star$ /°C	Wet bulb temperature	
		Moisture content, g / (g·kg^{-1})	Specific enthalpy, h / (kJ·kg^{-1})	Specific volume, v / (m^3·kg^{-1})				Screen, θ'_{sc} / °C	Sling, θ'_{sl} / °C
100	100.00	30.77	111.0	0.9066	4.754	32.0	32.0	32.0	32.0
96	96.18	29.54	107.8	0.9049	4.572	31.3	31.4	31.5	31.5
92	92.35	28.31	104.6	0.9032	4.390	30.6	30.9	30.9	30.9
88	88.50	27.08	101.5	0.9015	4.207	29.9	30.3	30.4	30.3
84	84.64	25.85	98.35	0.8998	4.024	29.1	29.7	29.8	29.7
80	80.77	24.62	95.20	0.8981	3.840	28.3	29.1	29.2	29.1
76	76.88	23.39	92.05	0.8965	3.655	27.4	28.5	28.7	28.5
72	72.97	22.16	88.90	0.8948	3.469	26.5	27.8	28.0	27.9
70	71.02	21.54	87.33	0.8939	3.376	26.1	27.5	27.7	27.5
68	69.05	20.92	85.75	0.8931	3.283	25.6	27.2	27.4	27.2
66	67.09	20.31	84.17	0.8922	3.189	25.1	26.8	27.1	26.9
64	65.12	19.69	82.60	0.8914	3.096	24.6	26.5	26.8	26.5
62	63.15	19.08	81.02	0.8905	3.002	24.1	26.1	26.5	26.2
60	61.17	18.46	79.45	0.8897	2.908	23.6	25.8	26.1	25.8
58	59.19	17.85	77.87	0.8888	2.814	23.0	25.4	25.8	25.5
56	57.20	17.23	76.30	0.8880	2.719	22.5	25.0	25.4	25.1
54	55.21	16.62	74.72	0.8871	2.625	21.9	24.7	25.1	24.7
52	53.22	16.00	73.15	0.8863	2.530	21.3	24.3	24.7	24.4
50	51.22	15.39	71.57	0.8854	2.435	20.7	23.9	24.4	24.0
48	49.22	14.77	70.00	0.8846	2.340	20.0	23.5	24.0	23.6
46	47.21	14.15	68.42	0.8837	2.245	19.3	23.1	23.7	23.2
44	45.21	13.54	66.85	0.8829	2.149	18.7	22.7	23.3	22.8
42	43.19	12.92	65.27	0.8820	2.053	17.9	22.3	22.9	22.4
40	41.18	12.31	63.70	0.8812	1.957	17.2	21.9	22.5	22.0
38	39.16	11.69	62.12	0.8804	1.861	16.4	21.4	22.1	21.5
36	37.13	11.08	60.55	0.8795	1.765	15.5	21.0	21.7	21.1
34	35.10	10.46	58.97	0.8787	1.669	14.7	20.5	21.3	20.7
32	33.07	9.847	57.40	0.8778	1.572	13.8	20.1	20.9	20.2
30	31.03	9.232	55.82	0.8770	1.475	12.8	19.6	20.5	19.8
28	28.99	8.616	54.25	0.8761	1.378	11.7	19.1	20.1	19.3
24	24.90	7.385	51.10	0.8744	1.183	9.5	18.2	19.2	18.3
20	20.79	6.154	47.95	0.8727	0.9884	6.8	17.2	18.3	17.3
16	16.67	4.924	44.80	0.8710	0.7923	3.6	16.1	17.3	16.3
12	12.52	3.693	41.65	0.8693	0.5954	−0.3	15.0	16.4	15.2
8	8.37	2.462	38.50	0.8676	0.3977	−5.1	13.8	15.4	14.1
4	4.19	1.231	35.35	0.8659	0.1992	−13.0	12.6	14.3	12.9
0	0.00	0.000	32.20	0.8642	0.0000	—	11.4	13.2	11.7

32.5 °C DRY-BULB

Percentage saturation, μ / %	Relative humidity, ϕ /%	Value of stated parameter per kg dry air			Vapour pressure, p_v / kPa	Dew point temperature, θ_d /°C	Adiabatic saturation temperature, $\theta^\star$ /°C	Wet bulb temperature	
		Moisture content, g / (g·kg^{-1})	Specific enthalpy, h / (kJ·kg^{-1})	Specific volume, v / (m^3·kg^{-1})				Screen, θ'_{sc} / °C	Sling, θ'_{sl} / °C
100	100.00	31.70	113.9	0.9094	4.890	32.5	32.5	32.5	32.5
96	96.19	30.43	110.6	0.9076	4.703	31.8	31.9	32.0	32.0
92	92.36	29.16	107.4	0.9059	4.516	31.1	31.4	31.4	31.4
88	88.52	27.89	104.1	0.9041	4.329	30.4	30.8	30.9	30.8
84	84.66	26.63	100.9	0.9024	4.140	29.6	30.2	30.3	30.2
80	80.79	25.36	97.62	0.9006	3.951	28.8	29.6	29.7	29.6
76	76.90	24.09	94.38	0.8989	3.761	27.9	28.9	29.1	29.0
72	73.00	22.82	91.13	0.8972	3.570	27.0	28.3	28.5	28.3
70	71.05	22.19	89.51	0.8963	3.474	26.6	28.0	28.2	28.0
68	69.08	21.55	87.88	0.8954	3.378	26.1	27.6	27.9	27.7
66	67.12	20.92	86.26	0.8945	3.282	25.6	27.3	27.6	27.3
64	65.15	20.29	84.64	0.8937	3.186	25.1	26.9	27.2	27.0
62	63.18	19.65	83.02	0.8928	3.089	24.6	26.6	26.9	26.6
60	61.20	19.02	81.39	0.8919	2.993	24.1	26.2	26.6	26.3
58	59.22	18.38	79.77	0.8910	2.896	23.5	25.8	26.2	25.9
56	57.24	17.75	78.15	0.8902	2.799	22.9	25.5	25.9	25.5
54	55.25	17.12	76.52	0.8893	2.702	22.4	25.1	25.5	25.2
52	53.25	16.48	74.90	0.8884	2.604	21.8	24.7	25.2	24.8
50	51.26	15.85	73.28	0.8875	2.506	21.1	24.3	24.8	24.4
48	49.26	15.22	71.65	0.8867	2.409	20.5	23.9	24.4	24.0
46	47.25	14.58	70.03	0.8858	2.311	19.8	23.5	24.1	23.6
44	45.24	13.95	68.41	0.8849	2.213	19.1	23.1	23.7	23.2
42	43.23	13.31	66.78	0.8840	2.114	18.4	22.7	23.3	22.8
40	41.21	12.68	65.16	0.8832	2.015	17.6	22.2	22.9	22.4
38	39.19	12.05	63.54	0.8823	1.916	16.8	21.8	22.5	21.9
36	37.16	11.41	61.92	0.8814	1.817	16.0	21.4	22.1	21.5
34	35.14	10.78	60.29	0.8805	1.718	15.1	20.9	21.7	21.0
32	33.10	10.14	58.67	0.8797	1.619	14.2	20.5	21.3	20.6
30	31.06	9.509	57.05	0.8788	1.519	13.2	20.0	20.8	20.1
28	29.02	8.875	55.42	0.8779	1.419	12.2	19.5	20.4	19.6
24	24.93	7.608	52.18	0.8762	1.219	9.9	18.5	19.5	18.7
20	20.81	6.340	48.93	0.8744	1.018	7.2	17.5	18.6	17.7
16	16.69	5.072	45.68	0.8727	0.8159	4.1	16.4	17.7	16.6
12	12.54	3.804	42.44	0.8709	0.6132	0.1	15.3	16.7	15.5
8	8.38	2.536	39.19	0.8691	0.4096	−4.8	14.1	15.6	14.4
4	4.20	1.268	35.94	0.8674	0.4096	−12.6	12.9	14.6	13.1
0	0.00	0.000	32.70	0.8656	0.0000	—	11.6	13.5	11.9

33 °C DRY-BULB

Percentage saturation, μ / %	Relative humidity, ϕ /%	Value of stated parameter per kg dry air			Vapour pressure, p_v / kPa	Dew point temperature, θ_d / °C	Adiabatic saturation temperature, $\theta\star$ / °C	Wet bulb temperature	
		Moisture content, g / (g·kg^{-1})	Specific enthalpy, h / (kJ·kg^{-1})	Specific volume, v / (m^3·kg^{-1})				Screen, θ'_{sc} / °C	Sling, θ'_{sl} / °C
100	100.00	32.65	116.8	0.9122	5.029	33.0	33.0	33.0	33.0
96	96.19	31.34	113.5	0.9104	4.838	32.3	32.4	32.5	32.4
92	92.37	30.04	110.1	0.9086	4.646	31.6	31.9	31.9	31.9
88	88.53	28.73	106.8	0.9068	4.453	30.8	31.3	31.4	31.3
84	84.68	27.43	103.4	0.9050	4.259	30.1	30.7	30.8	30.7
80	80.81	26.12	100.1	0.9032	4.064	29.3	30.1	30.2	30.1
76	76.93	24.81	96.76	0.9014	3.869	28.4	29.4	29.6	29.4
72	73.03	23.51	93.41	0.8996	3.673	27.5	28.8	29.0	28.8
70	71.08	22.85	91.74	0.8987	3.575	27.1	28.4	28.7	28.5
68	69.12	22.20	90.06	0.8978	3.476	26.6	28.1	28.3	28.1
66	67.15	21.55	88.39	0.8969	3.377	26.1	27.7	28.0	27.8
64	65.18	20.90	86.72	0.8960	3.278	25.6	27.4	27.7	27.4
62	63.21	20.24	85.05	0.8951	3.179	25.1	27.0	27.3	27.1
60	61.24	19.59	83.38	0.8942	3.080	24.5	26.7	27.0	26.7
58	59.26	18.94	81.70	0.8933	2.980	24.0	26.3	26.7	26.3
56	57.27	18.28	80.03	0.8924	2.880	23.4	25.9	26.3	26.0
54	55.28	17.63	78.36	0.8915	2.780	22.8	25.5	26.0	25.6
52	53.29	16.98	76.69	0.8906	2.680	22.2	25.1	25.6	25.2
50	51.29	16.32	75.01	0.8896	2.580	21.6	24.7	25.2	24.8
48	49.29	15.67	73.34	0.8887	2.479	21.0	24.3	24.9	24.4
46	47.29	15.02	71.67	0.8878	2.378	20.3	23.9	24.5	24.0
44	45.28	14.37	70.00	0.8869	2.277	19.6	23.5	24.1	23.6
42	43.26	13.71	68.32	0.8860	2.176	18.9	23.1	23.7	23.2
40	41.25	13.06	66.65	0.8851	2.074	18.1	22.6	23.3	22.8
38	39.23	12.41	64.98	0.8842	1.973	17.3	22.2	22.9	22.3
36	37.20	11.75	63.31	0.8833	1.871	16.5	21.8	22.5	21.9
34	35.17	11.10	61.63	0.8824	1.769	15.6	21.3	22.1	21.4
32	33.13	10.45	59.96	0.8815	1.666	14.7	20.8	21.6	21.0
30	31.10	9.795	58.29	0.8806	1.564	13.7	20.3	21.2	20.5
28	29.05	9.142	56.62	0.8797	1.461	12.6	19.9	20.8	20.0
24	24.95	7.836	53.27	0.8779	1.255	10.3	18.9	19.9	19.0
20	20.84	6.530	49.93	0.8761	1.048	7.7	17.8	18.9	18.0
16	16.71	5.224	46.58	0.8743	0.8402	4.5	16.7	18.0	16.9
12	12.56	3.918	43.24	0.8725	0.6315	0.5	15.6	17.0	15.8
8	8.39	2.612	39.89	0.8707	0.4219	−4.4	14.4	15.9	14.6
4	4.20	1.306	36.55	0.8689	0.2114	−12.3	13.1	14.8	13.4
0	0.00	0.000	32.20	0.8671	0.0000	—	11.8	13.7	12.1

33.5 °C DRY-BULB

Percentage saturation, μ / %	Relative humidity, ϕ /%	Value of stated parameter per kg dry air			Vapour pressure, p_v / kPa	Dew point temperature, θ_d / °C	Adiabatic saturation temperature, $\theta\star$ / °C	Wet bulb temperature	
		Moisture content, g / (g·kg^{-1})	Specific enthalpy, h / (kJ·kg^{-1})	Specific volume, v / (m^3·kg^{-1})				Screen, θ'_{sc} / °C	Sling, θ'_{sl} / °C
100	100.00	33.63	119.9	0.9150	5.172	33.5	33.5	33.5	33.5
96	96.20	32.28	116.4	0.9132	4.976	32.8	32.9	33.0	32.9
92	92.38	30.94	113.0	0.9113	4.778	32.1	32.4	32.4	32.4
88	88.55	29.59	109.5	0.9095	4.580	31.3	31.8	31.8	31.8
84	84.70	28.25	106.1	0.9076	4.381	30.6	31.2	31.3	31.2
80	80.84	26.90	102.6	0.9057	4.181	29.7	30.5	30.7	30.6
76	76.96	25.56	99.19	0.9039	3.980	28.9	29.9	30.1	29.9
72	73.06	24.21	95.74	0.9020	3.779	28.0	29.2	29.4	29.3
70	71.11	23.54	94.02	0.9011	3.678	27.5	28.9	29.1	28.9
68	69.15	22.87	92.29	0.9002	3.576	27.1	28.5	28.8	28.6
66	67.19	22.19	90.57	0.8992	3.475	26.6	28.2	28.5	28.2
64	65.22	21.52	88.85	0.8983	3.373	26.1	27.8	28.1	27.9
62	63.25	20.85	87.12	0.8974	3.271	25.5	27.5	27.8	27.5
60	61.27	20.18	85.40	0.8964	3.169	25.0	27.1	27.4	27.2
58	59.29	19.50	83.68	0.8955	3.067	24.5	26.7	27.1	26.8
56	57.31	18.83	81.95	0.8946	2.964	23.9	26.3	26.7	26.4
54	55.32	18.16	80.23	0.8936	2.861	23.3	26.0	26.4	26.0
52	53.33	17.49	78.51	0.8927	2.758	22.7	25.6	26.0	25.6
50	51.33	16.81	76.78	0.8918	2.655	22.1	25.2	25.6	25.2
48	49.33	16.14	75.06	0.8909	2.551	21.4	24.8	25.3	24.8
46	47.33	15.47	73.34	0.8899	2.448	20.8	24.3	24.9	24.4
44	45.32	14.80	71.61	0.8890	2.344	20.0	23.9	24.5	24.0
42	43.30	14.12	69.89	0.8881	2.240	19.3	23.5	24.1	23.6
40	41.28	13.45	68.17	0.8871	2.135	18.6	23.0	23.7	23.2
38	39.26	12.78	66.45	0.8862	2.031	17.8	22.6	23.3	22.7
36	37.23	12.11	64.72	0.8853	1.926	16.9	22.1	22.9	22.3
34	35.20	11.43	63.00	0.8843	1.821	16.0	21.7	22.4	21.8
32	33.17	10.76	61.28	0.8834	1.716	15.1	21.2	22.0	21.3
30	31.13	10.09	59.55	0.8825	1.610	14.1	20.7	21.6	20.9
28	29.08	9.416	57.83	0.8815	1.504	13.1	20.2	21.1	20.4
24	24.98	8.071	54.38	0.8797	1.292	10.8	19.2	20.2	19.4
20	20.86	6.726	50.94	0.8778	1.079	8.1	18.1	19.3	18.3
16	16.73	5.380	47.49	0.8759	0.8652	4.9	17.0	18.3	17.2
12	12.57	4.035	44.04	0.8741	0.6503	0.9	15.9	17.2	16.1
8	8.40	2.690	40.60	0.8722	0.4345	−4.1	14.6	16.2	14.9
4	4.21	1.345	37.15	0.8703	0.2177	−12.0	13.3	15.1	13.6
0	0.00	0.000	33.70	0.8685	0.0000	—	12.0	13.9	12.3

34 °C DRY-BULB

Percentage saturation, μ / %	Relative humidity, ϕ /%	Value of stated parameter per kg dry air			Vapour pressure, p_v / kPa	Dew point temperature, θ_d / °C	Adiabatic saturation temperature, $\theta^\star$ / °C	Wet bulb temperature	
		Moisture content, g / (g·kg^{-1})	Specific enthalpy, h / (kJ·kg^{-1})	Specific volume, v / (m^3·kg^{-1})				Screen, θ'_{sc} / °C	Sling, θ'_{sl} / °C
100	100.00	34.63	123.0	0.9179	5.319	34.0	34.0	34.0	34.0
96	96.20	33.25	119.4	0.9160	5.117	33.3	33.4	33.5	33.4
92	92.39	31.86	115.9	0.9141	4.914	32.6	32.9	32.9	32.9
88	88.56	30.48	112.3	0.9122	4.710	31.8	32.3	32.3	32.3
84	84.72	29.09	108.8	0.9102	4.506	31.1	31.6	31.8	31.7
80	80.86	27.71	105.2	0.9083	4.301	30.2	31.0	31.2	31.0
76	76.98	26.32	101.7	0.9064	4.094	29.4	30.4	30.5	30.4
72	73.09	24.94	98.12	0.9045	3.887	28.5	29.7	29.9	29.7
70	71.14	24.24	96.34	0.9035	3.784	28.0	29.3	29.6	29.4
68	69.18	23.55	94.57	0.9026	3.679	27.5	29.0	29.3	29.0
66	67.22	22.86	92.79	0.9016	3.575	27.1	28.6	28.9	28.7
64	65.25	22.17	91.02	0.9007	3.470	26.5	28.3	28.6	28.3
62	63.28	21.47	89.24	0.8997	3.366	26.0	27.9	28.2	28.0
60	61.31	20.78	87.47	0.8987	3.261	25.5	27.5	27.9	27.6
58	59.33	20.09	85.69	0.8978	3.155	24.9	27.2	27.5	27.2
56	57.35	19.39	83.92	0.8968	3.050	24.4	26.8	27.2	26.8
54	55.36	18.70	82.14	0.8959	2.944	23.8	26.4	26.8	26.5
52	53.37	18.01	80.37	0.8949	2.838	23.2	26.0	26.4	26.1
50	51.37	17.32	78.59	0.8939	2.732	22.5	25.6	26.1	25.7
48	49.37	16.62	76.82	0.8930	2.626	21.9	25.2	25.7	25.3
46	47.36	15.93	75.04	0.8920	2.519	21.2	24.8	25.3	24.8
44	45.35	15.24	73.27	0.8911	2.412	20.5	24.3	24.9	24.4
42	43.34	14.55	71.49	0.8901	2.305	19.8	23.9	24.5	24.0
40	41.32	13.85	69.71	0.8891	2.198	19.0	23.4	24.1	23.5
38	39.30	13.16	67.94	0.8882	2.090	18.2	23.0	23.7	23.1
36	37.27	12.47	66.16	0.8872	1.982	17.4	22.5	23.3	22.6
34	35.24	11.78	64.39	0.8863	1.874	16.5	22.1	22.8	22.2
32	33.20	11.08	62.61	0.8853	1.766	15.6	21.6	22.4	21.7
30	31.16	10.39	60.84	0.8843	1.657	14.6	21.1	21.9	21.2
28	29.12	9.697	59.06	0.8834	1.549	13.5	20.6	21.5	20.7
24	25.01	8.312	55.51	0.8814	1.330	11.2	19.5	20.6	19.7
20	20.89	6.927	51.96	0.8795	1.111	8.5	18.5	19.6	18.6
16	16.75	5.541	48.41	0.8776	0.8918	5.3	17.3	18.6	17.5
12	12.59	4.156	44.86	0.8757	0.6705	1.3	16.1	17.5	16.4
8	8.41	2.771	41.31	0.8737	0.4473	−3.7	14.9	16.4	15.1
4	4.22	1.385	37.76	0.8718	0.2241	−11.7	13.6	15.3	13.9
0	0.00	0.000	34.21	0.8699	0.0000	—	12.2	14.1	12.5

34.5 °C DRY-BULB

Percentage saturation, μ / %	Relative humidity, ϕ /%	Value of stated parameter per kg dry air			Vapour pressure, p_v / kPa	Dew point temperature, θ_d / °C	Adiabatic saturation temperature, $\theta^\star$ / °C	Wet bulb temperature	
		Moisture content, g / (g·kg^{-1})	Specific enthalpy, h / (kJ·kg^{-1})	Specific volume, v / (m^3·kg^{-1})				Screen, θ'_{sc} / °C	Sling, θ'_{sl} / °C
100	100.00	35.67	126.2	0.9208	5.468	34.5	34.5	34.5	34.5
96	96.21	34.24	122.5	0.9189	5.261	33.8	33.9	34.0	33.9
92	92.40	32.81	118.8	0.9169	5.053	33.1	33.3	33.4	33.4
88	88.58	31.39	115.2	0.9149	4.844	32.3	32.7	32.8	32.8
84	84.74	29.96	111.5	0.9129	4.634	31.5	32.1	32.2	32.1
80	80.89	28.53	107.9	0.9110	4.423	30.7	31.5	31.6	31.5
76	77.01	27.11	104.2	0.9090	4.211	29.9	30.8	31.0	30.9
72	73.12	25.68	100.6	0.9070	3.999	29.0	30.2	30.4	30.2
70	71.17	24.97	98.72	0.9060	3.892	28.5	29.8	30.0	29.9
68	69.21	24.25	96.89	0.9050	3.785	28.0	29.5	29.7	29.5
66	67.25	23.54	95.07	0.9040	3.678	27.5	29.1	29.4	29.1
64	65.29	22.83	93.24	0.9030	3.570	27.0	28.7	29.0	28.8
62	63.32	22.11	91.41	0.9021	3.463	26.5	28.4	28.7	28.4
60	61.35	21.40	89.58	0.9011	3.355	26.0	28.0	28.3	28.1
58	59.37	20.69	87.75	0.9001	3.247	25.4	27.6	28.0	27.7
56	57.39	19.97	85.92	0.8991	3.138	24.8	27.2	27.6	27.3
54	55.40	19.26	84.09	0.8981	3.029	24.3	26.8	27.2	26.9
52	53.41	18.55	82.26	0.8971	2.920	23.7	26.4	26.9	26.5
50	51.41	17.83	80.43	0.8961	2.811	23.0	26.0	26.5	26.1
48	49.41	17.12	78.61	0.8951	2.702	22.4	25.6	26.1	25.7
46	47.40	16.41	76.78	0.8941	2.592	21.7	25.2	25.7	25.3
44	45.39	15.69	74.95	0.8931	2.482	21.0	24.7	25.3	24.8
42	43.38	14.98	73.12	0.8921	2.372	20.2	24.3	24.9	24.4
40	41.36	14.27	71.29	0.8912	2.262	19.5	23.8	24.5	24.0
38	39.34	13.55	69.46	0.8902	2.151	18.7	23.4	24.1	23.5
36	37.31	12.84	67.63	0.8892	2.040	17.8	22.9	23.6	23.0
34	35.28	12.13	65.80	0.8882	1.929	16.9	22.4	23.2	22.6
32	33.24	11.41	63.97	0.8872	1.818	16.0	22.0	22.8	22.1
30	31.20	10.70	62.15	0.8862	1.706	15.0	21.5	22.3	21.6
28	29.15	9.986	60.32	0.8852	1.594	14.0	20.9	21.8	21.1
24	25.04	8.560	56.66	0.8832	1.369	11.6	19.9	20.9	20.1
20	20.92	7.133	53.00	0.8812	1.144	9.0	18.8	19.9	19.0
16	16.77	5.707	49.34	0.8793	0.9181	5.7	17.6	18.9	17.8
12	12.61	4.280	45.69	0.8773	0.6894	1.7	16.4	17.8	16.7
8	8.42	2.853	42.03	0.8753	0.4606	−3.4	15.2	16.7	15.4
4	4.22	1.427	38.37	0.8733	0.2308	−11.3	13.8	15.5	14.1
0	0.00	0.000	34.71	0.7713	0.0000	—	12.4	14.3	12.7

35 °C DRY-BULB

Percentage saturation, μ / %	Relative humidity, ϕ /%	Value of stated parameter per kg dry air			Vapour pressure, p_v / kPa	Dew point temperature, θ_d / °C	Adiabatic saturation temperature, $\theta^\star$ / °C	Wet bulb temperature	
		Moisture content, g / (g·kg^{-1})	Specific enthalpy, h / (kJ·kg^{-1})	Specific volume, v / (m^3·kg^{-1})				Screen, θ'_{sc} / °C	Sling, θ'_{sl} / °C
100	100.00	36.73	129.4	0.9238	5.622	35.0	35.0	35.0	35.0
96	96.21	35.26	125.6	0.9218	5.409	34.3	34.4	34.5	34.4
92	92.41	33.79	121.9	0.9197	5.196	33.6	33.8	33.9	33.8
88	88.60	32.32	118.1	0.9177	4.981	32.8	33.2	33.3	33.2
84	84.76	30.85	114.3	0.9157	4.765	32.0	32.6	32.7	32.6
80	80.91	29.38	110.6	0.9136	4.549	31.2	32.0	32.1	32.0
76	77.04	27.91	106.8	0.9116	4.331	30.4	31.3	31.5	31.3
72	73.15	26.44	103.0	0.9095	4.113	29.5	30.6	30.8	30.7
70	71.20	25.71	101.2	0.9085	4.003	29.0	30.3	30.5	30.3
68	69.25	24.97	99.27	0.9075	3.893	28.5	29.9	30.2	30.0
66	67.29	24.24	97.39	0.9065	3.783	28.0	29.6	29.8	29.6
64	65.33	23.51	95.50	0.9055	3.673	27.5	29.2	29.5	29.2
62	63.36	22.77	93.62	0.9044	3.562	27.0	28.8	29.1	28.9
60	61.38	22.04	91.74	0.9034	3.451	26.5	28.4	28.8	28.5
58	59.41	21.30	89.85	0.9024	3.340	25.9	28.1	28.4	28.1
56	57.42	20.57	87.97	0.9014	3.228	25.3	27.7	28.1	27.7
54	55.44	19.83	86.08	0.9004	3.117	24.7	27.3	27.7	27.3
52	53.45	19.10	84.20	0.8993	3.005	24.1	26.9	27.3	26.9
50	51.45	18.36	82.32	0.8983	2.893	23.5	26.4	26.9	26.5
48	49.45	17.63	80.43	0.8973	2.780	22.8	26.0	26.5	26.1
46	47.45	16.89	78.55	0.8963	2.667	22.2	25.6	26.1	25.7
44	45.44	16.16	76.66	0.8952	2.554	21.4	25.1	25.7	25.2
42	43.42	15.43	74.78	0.8942	2.441	20.7	24.7	25.3	24.8
40	41.40	14.69	72.90	0.8932	2.328	19.9	24.2	24.9	24.4
38	39.38	13.96	71.01	0.8922	2.214	19.1	23.8	24.5	23.9
36	37.35	13.22	69.13	0.8912	2.100	18.3	23.3	24.0	23.4
34	35.31	12.49	67.24	0.8901	1.985	17.4	22.8	23.6	22.9
32	33.27	11.75	65.36	0.8891	1.871	16.5	22.3	23.1	22.5
30	31.23	11.02	63.48	0.8881	1.756	15.5	21.8	22.7	22.0
28	29.18	10.28	61.59	0.8871	1.641	14.4	21.3	22.2	21.4
24	25.07	8.815	57.82	0.8850	1.410	12.1	20.2	21.2	20.4
20	20.94	7.346	54.06	0.8830	1.177	9.4	19.1	20.2	19.3
16	16.79	5.876	50.29	0.8809	0.9442	6.1	17.9	19.2	18.1
12	12.63	4.407	46.52	0.8789	0.7098	2.1	16.7	18.1	16.9
8	8.44	2.938	42.75	0.8768	0.4743	−3.0	15.4	17.0	15.7
4	4.23	1.469	38.98	0.8748	0.2377	−11.0	14.0	15.8	14.3
0	0.00	0.000	35.22	0.8727	0.0000	—	12.6	14.6	12.9

35.5 °C DRY-BULB

Percentage saturation, μ / %	Relative humidity, ϕ /%	Value of stated parameter per kg dry air			Vapour pressure, p_v / kPa	Dew point temperature, θ_d / °C	Adiabatic saturation temperature, $\theta^\star$ / °C	Wet bulb temperature	
		Moisture content, g / (g·kg^{-1})	Specific enthalpy, h / (kJ·kg^{-1})	Specific volume, v / (m^3·kg^{-1})				Screen, θ'_{sc} / °C	Sling, θ'_{sl} / °C
100	100.00	37.82	132.8	0.9268	5.779	35.5	35.5	35.5	35.5
96	96.22	36.31	128.9	0.9247	5.561	34.8	34.9	34.9	34.9
92	92.43	34.79	125.0	0.9226	5.342	34.1	34.3	34.4	34.3
88	88.61	33.28	121.1	0.9205	5.121	33.3	33.7	33.8	33.7
84	84.78	31.77	117.2	0.9184	4.900	32.5	33.1	33.2	33.1
80	80.94	30.26	113.3	0.9163	4.678	31.7	32.4	32.6	32.5
76	77.07	28.74	109.5	0.9142	4.454	30.9	31.8	32.0	31.8
72	73.19	27.23	105.6	0.9121	4.230	29.9	31.1	31.3	31.1
70	71.24	26.47	103.6	0.9111	4.117	29.5	30.7	31.0	30.8
68	69.28	25.72	101.7	0.9100	4.004	29.0	30.4	30.6	30.4
66	67.33	24.96	99.76	0.9090	3.891	28.5	30.0	30.3	30.1
64	65.36	24.20	97.82	0.9079	3.778	28.0	29.6	29.9	29.7
62	63.40	23.45	95.88	0.9068	3.664	27.5	29.3	29.6	29.3
60	61.42	22.69	93.94	0.9058	3.560	26.9	28.9	29.2	28.9
58	59.45	21.93	92.00	0.9047	3.436	26.4	28.5	28.9	28.6
56	57.47	21.18	90.06	0.9037	3.321	25.8	28.1	28.5	28.2
54	55.48	20.42	88.12	0.9026	3.206	25.2	27.7	28.1	27.8
52	53.49	19.67	86.18	0.9016	3.091	24.6	27.3	27.7	27.4
50	51.49	18.91	84.23	0.9005	2.976	24.0	26.9	27.3	26.9
48	49.49	18.15	82.29	0.8995	2.860	23.3	26.4	26.9	26.5
46	47.49	17.40	80.35	0.8984	2.744	22.6	26.0	26.5	26.1
44	45.48	16.64	78.41	0.8974	2.628	21.9	25.6	26.1	25.7
42	43.46	15.88	76.47	0.8963	2.512	21.2	25.1	25.7	25.2
40	41.44	15.13	74.53	0.8953	2.395	20.4	24.6	25.3	24.8
38	39.42	14.37	72.59	0.8942	2.278	19.6	24.2	24.9	24.3
36	37.39	13.62	70.65	0.8932	2.161	18.7	23.7	24.4	23.8
34	35.35	12.86	68.71	0.8921	2.043	17.8	23.2	24.0	23.3
32	33.31	12.10	66.77	0.8910	1.925	16.9	22.7	23.5	22.8
30	31.27	11.35	64.83	0.8900	1.807	15.9	22.2	23.0	22.3
28	29.22	10.59	62.89	0.8889	1.689	14.9	21.7	22.6	21.8
24	25.10	9.076	59.01	0.8868	1.451	12.5	20.6	21.6	20.7
20	20.97	7.564	55.13	0.8847	1.212	9.8	19.4	20.6	19.6
16	16.82	6.051	51.24	0.8826	0.9719	6.6	18.3	19.5	18.5
12	12.64	4.538	47.36	0.8805	0.7307	2.5	17.0	18.4	17.2
8	8.45	3.026	43.48	0.8784	0.4883	−2.7	15.7	17.2	15.9
4	4.24	1.513	39.60	0.8763	0.2448	−10.7	14.3	16.0	14.6
0	0.00	0.000	35.72	0.8742	0.0000	—	12.8	14.8	13.1

36 °C DRY-BULB

Percentage saturation, μ / %	Relative humidity, ϕ /%	Value of stated parameter per kg dry air			Vapour pressure, p_v / kPa	Dew point temperature, θ_d / °C	Adiabatic saturation temperature, $\theta^\star$ / °C	Wet bulb temperature	
		Moisture content, g / (g·kg^{-1})	Specific enthalpy, h / (kJ·kg^{-1})	Specific volume, v / (m^3·kg^{-1})				Screen, θ'_{sc} / °C	Sling, θ'_{sl} / °C
100	100.00	38.94	136.2	0.9299	5.940	36.0	36.0	36.0	36.0
96	96.23	37.38	132.2	0.9277	5.716	35.3	35.4	35.4	35.4
92	92.44	35.82	128.2	0.9256	5.491	34.6	34.8	34.9	34.8
88	88.63	34.27	124.2	0.9234	5.265	33.8	34.2	34.3	34.2
84	84.81	32.71	120.2	0.9212	5.038	33.0	33.6	33.7	33.6
80	80.96	31.15	116.2	0.9191	4.810	32.2	32.9	33.1	33.0
76	77.10	29.59	112.2	0.9169	4.580	31.3	32.3	32.4	32.3
72	73.22	28.04	108.2	0.9147	4.350	30.4	31.6	31.8	31.6
70	71.27	27.26	106.2	0.9136	4.234	30.0	31.2	31.4	31.2
68	69.32	26.48	104.2	0.9125	4.118	29.5	30.8	31.1	30.9
66	67.36	25.70	102.2	0.9115	4.002	29.0	30.5	30.5	30.5
64	65.40	24.92	100.2	0.9104	3.885	28.5	30.1	30.4	30.2
62	63.44	24.14	98.19	0.9093	3.768	28.0	29.7	30.0	29.8
60	61.46	23.59	96.19	0.9082	3.651	27.4	29.3	29.7	29.4
58	59.49	22.36	94.19	0.9071	3.534	26.9	28.9	29.3	29.0
56	57.51	21.81	92.19	0.9060	3.416	26.3	28.5	28.9	28.6
54	55.52	21.03	90.19	0.9049	3.298	25.7	28.1	28.5	28.2
52	53.53	20.25	88.19	0.9039	3.180	25.1	27.7	28.2	27.8
50	51.54	19.47	86.19	0.9028	3.061	24.4	27.3	27.8	27.4
48	49.53	18.69	84.20	0.9017	2.943	23.8	26.9	27.4	26.9
46	47.53	17.91	82.20	0.9006	2.823	23.1	26.4	27.0	26.5
44	45.52	17.13	80.20	0.8995	2.704	22.4	26.0	26.5	26.1
42	43.50	16.35	78.20	0.8984	2.584	21.6	25.5	26.1	25.6
40	41.48	15.58	76.20	0.8973	2.464	20.9	25.1	25.7	25.2
38	39.46	14.80	74.20	0.8963	2.344	20.0	24.6	25.3	24.7
36	37.43	14.02	72.20	0.8952	2.223	19.2	24.1	24.8	24.2
34	35.39	13.24	70.20	0.8941	2.102	18.3	23.6	24.3	23.7
32	33.35	12.46	68.20	0.8930	1.981	17.4	23.1	23.9	23.2
30	31.30	11.68	66.21	0.8919	1.860	16.4	22.6	23.4	22.7
28	29.25	10.90	64.21	0.8908	1.738	15.3	22.0	22.9	22.2
24	25.14	9.346	60.21	0.8886	1.493	13.0	20.9	21.9	21.1
20	21.00	7.788	56.21	0.8865	1.248	10.2	19.8	20.9	20.0
16	16.84	6.230	52.21	0.8843	1.000	7.0	18.6	19.8	18.8
12	12.66	4.673	48.22	0.8821	0.7522	2.9	17.3	18.7	17.5
8	8.46	3.115	44.22	0.8799	0.5027	−2.3	15.9	17.5	16.2
4	4.24	1.558	40.22	0.8778	0.2520	−10.4	14.5	16.3	14.8
0	0.00	0.000	36.22	0.8756	0.0000	—	13.0	15.0	13.3

36.5 °C DRY-BULB

Percentage saturation, μ / %	Relative humidity, ϕ /%	Value of stated parameter per kg dry air			Vapour pressure, p_v / kPa	Dew point temperature, θ_d / °C	Adiabatic saturation temperature, $\theta^\star$ / °C	Wet bulb temperature	
		Moisture content, g / (g·kg^{-1})	Specific enthalpy, h / (kJ·kg^{-1})	Specific volume, v / (m^3·kg^{-1})				Screen, θ'_{sc} / °C	Sling, θ'_{sl} / °C
100	100.00	40.09	139.7	0.9330	6.106	36.5	36.5	36.5	36.5
96	96.23	38.49	135.5	0.9308	5.876	35.8	35.9	35.9	35.9
92	92.45	36.88	131.4	0.9285	5.645	35.1	35.3	35.4	35.3
88	88.65	35.28	127.3	0.9263	5.412	34.3	34.7	34.8	34.7
84	84.83	33.68	123.2	0.9241	5.179	33.5	34.1	34.2	34.1
80	80.99	32.07	119.1	0.9218	4.945	32.7	33.4	33.5	33.4
76	77.13	30.47	115.0	0.9196	4.709	31.8	32.7	32.9	32.8
72	73.25	28.87	110.8	0.9174	4.472	30.9	32.0	32.2	32.1
70	71.31	28.06	108.8	0.9162	4.354	30.5	31.7	31.9	31.7
68	69.36	27.26	106.7	0.9151	4.235	30.0	31.3	31.6	31.4
66	67.40	26.46	104.7	0.9140	4.115	29.5	30.9	31.2	31.0
64	65.44	25.66	102.6	0.9129	3.996	29.0	30.6	30.8	30.6
62	63.48	24.86	100.6	0.9118	3.876	28.4	30.2	30.5	30.2
60	61.51	24.06	98.49	0.9106	3.755	27.9	29.8	30.1	29.8
58	59.53	23.25	96.43	0.9095	3.635	27.3	29.4	29.7	29.5
56	57.55	22.45	94.37	0.9084	3.514	26.8	29.0	29.4	29.1
54	55.56	21.65	92.31	0.9073	3.392	26.2	28.6	29.0	28.6
52	53.57	20.85	90.25	0.9062	3.271	25.5	28.2	28.6	28.2
50	51.58	20.05	88.19	0.9050	3.149	24.9	27.7	28.2	27.8
48	49.58	19.24	86.14	0.9039	3.027	24.2	27.3	27.8	27.4
46	47.57	18.44	84.08	0.9028	2.905	23.6	26.8	27.4	26.9
44	45.56	17.64	82.02	0.9017	2.782	22.8	26.4	27.0	26.5
42	43.55	16.84	79.96	0.9006	2.659	22.1	25.9	26.5	26.0
40	41.53	16.04	77.90	0.8994	2.535	21.3	25.5	26.1	25.6
38	39.50	15.24	75.84	0.8983	3.412	20.5	25.0	25.6	25.1
36	37.47	14.43	73.78	0.8972	2.288	19.7	24.5	25.2	24.6
34	35.43	13.63	71.72	0.8961	2.163	18.8	24.0	24.7	24.1
32	33.39	12.83	69.67	0.8950	2.039	17.8	23.5	24.3	23.6
30	31.34	12.03	67.61	0.8938	1.914	16.8	22.9	23.8	23.1
28	29.29	11.23	65.55	0.8927	1.788	15.8	22.4	23.3	22.5
24	25.17	9.622	61.43	0.8905	1.537	13.4	21.3	22.3	21.4
20	21.03	8.018	57.31	0.8882	1.284	10.7	20.1	21.2	20.3
16	16.87	6.415	53.20	0.8860	1.030	7.4	18.9	20.1	19.1
12	12.68	4.811	49.08	0.8837	0.7743	3.3	17.6	19.0	17.8
8	8.48	3.207	44.96	0.8815	0.5175	−2.0	16.2	17.8	16.5
4	4.25	1.604	40.84	0.8792	0.2594	−10.0	14.7	16.5	15.0
0	0.00	0.000	36.73	0.8770	0.0000	—	13.2	15.2	13.5

37 °C DRY-BULB

Percentage saturation, μ /%	Relative humidity, ϕ /%	Value of stated parameter per kg dry air			Vapour pressure, p_v / kPa	Dew point temperature, θ_d / °C	Adiabatic saturation temperature, $\theta^\star$ / °C	Wet bulb temperature	
		Moisture content, g /(g·kg⁻¹)	Specific enthalpy, h /(kJ·kg⁻¹)	Specific volume, v /(m³·kg⁻¹)				Screen, θ'_{sc} / °C	Sling, θ'_{sl} / °C
100	100.00	41.28	143.2	0.9362	6.274	37.0	37.0	37.0	37.0
96	96.24	39.62	139.0	0.9339	6.038	36.3	36.4	36.4	36.4
92	92.46	37.97	134.8	0.9316	5.802	35.6	35.8	35.9	35.8
88	88.67	36.32	130.5	0.9293	5.563	34.8	35.2	35.3	35.2
84	84.85	34.67	126.3	0.9270	5.324	34.0	34.5	34.6	34.6
80	81.02	33.02	122.0	0.9246	5.083	33.2	33.9	34.0	33.9
76	77.16	31.37	117.8	0.9223	4.842	32.3	33.2	33.4	33.2
72	73.29	29.72	113.6	0.9200	4.598	31.4	32.5	32.7	32.5
70	71.34	28.89	111.4	0.9189	4.476	30.9	32.1	32.4	32.2
68	69.40	28.07	109.3	0.9177	4.354	30.5	31.8	32.0	31.8
66	67.44	27.24	107.2	0.9166	4.232	30.0	31.4	31.7	31.4
64	65.48	26.42	105.1	0.9154	4.109	29.4	31.0	31.3	31.1
62	63.52	25.59	103.0	0.9143	3.985	28.9	30.6	30.9	30.7
60	61.55	24.77	100.8	0.9131	3.862	28.4	30.2	30.6	30.3
58	59.57	23.94	98.72	0.9120	3.738	27.8	29.8	30.2	29.9
56	57.59	23.11	96.60	0.9108	3.614	27.2	29.4	29.8	29.5
54	55.61	22.29	94.48	0.9096	3.489	26.6	29.0	29.4	29.1
52	53.62	21.46	92.36	0.9085	3.364	26.0	28.6	29.0	28.7
50	51.62	20.64	90.24	0.9073	3.239	25.4	28.2	28.6	28.2
48	49.62	19.81	88.12	0.9062	3.114	24.7	27.7	28.2	27.8
46	47.62	18.99	86.00	0.9050	2.988	24.0	27.3	27.8	27.4
44	45.61	18.16	83.88	0.9039	2.862	23.3	26.8	27.4	26.9
42	43.59	17.34	81.75	0.9027	2.735	22.6	26.3	26.9	26.4
40	41.57	16.51	79.63	0.9016	2.608	21.8	25.9	26.5	26.0
38	39.54	15.68	77.51	0.9004	2.481	21.0	25.4	26.0	25.5
36	37.51	14.86	75.39	0.8992	2.354	20.1	24.9	25.6	25.0
34	35.47	14.03	73.27	0.8981	2.226	19.2	24.4	25.1	24.5
32	33.43	13.21	71.15	0.8969	2.098	18.3	23.8	24.6	24.0
30	31.38	12.38	69.03	0.8958	1.969	17.3	23.3	24.1	23.4
28	29.33	11.56	66.91	0.8946	1.840	16.2	22.8	23.7	22.9
24	25.20	9.906	62.67	0.8923	1.581	13.8	21.6	22.6	21.8
20	21.06	8.255	58.43	0.8900	1.321	11.1	20.4	21.6	20.6
16	16.89	6.604	54.19	0.8877	1.060	7.8	19.2	20.4	19.4
12	12.70	4.953	49.95	0.8854	0.7970	3.7	17.9	19.3	18.1
8	8.49	3.302	45.71	0.8830	0.5327	−1.6	16.5	18.0	16.7
4	4.26	1.651	41.47	0.8807	0.2671	−9.7	15.0	16.8	15.3
0	0.00	0.000	37.23	0.8784	0.0000	—	13.4	15.4	13.7

37.5 °C DRY-BULB

Percentage saturation, μ /%	Relative humidity, ϕ /%	Value of stated parameter per kg dry air			Vapour pressure, p_v / kPa	Dew point temperature, θ_d / °C	Adiabatic saturation temperature, $\theta^\star$ / °C	Wet bulb temperature	
		Moisture content, g /(g·kg⁻¹)	Specific enthalpy, h /(kJ·kg⁻¹)	Specific volume, v /(m³·kg⁻¹)				Screen, θ'_{sc} / °C	Sling, θ'_{sl} / °C
100	100.00	42.49	146.9	0.9394	6.447	37.5	37.5	37.5	37.5
96	96.25	40.79	142.5	0.9370	6.205	36.8	36.9	36.9	36.9
92	92.48	39.09	138.2	0.9346	5.962	36.1	36.3	36.3	36.3
88	88.69	37.39	133.8	0.9323	5.718	35.3	35.7	35.8	35.7
84	84.87	35.69	129.4	0.9299	5.472	34.5	35.0	35.1	35.0
80	81.04	33.99	125.1	0.9275	5.225	33.7	34.4	34.5	34.4
76	77.19	32.29	120.7	0.9251	4.977	32.8	33.7	33.8	33.7
72	73.32	30.59	116.3	0.9227	4.727	31.9	33.0	33.2	33.0
70	71.38	29.74	114.2	0.9216	4.602	31.4	32.6	32.8	32.6
68	69.43	28.89	112.0	0.9204	4.477	30.9	32.2	32.5	32.3
66	67.48	28.04	109.8	0.9192	4.351	30.4	31.9	32.1	31.9
64	65.52	27.20	107.6	0.9180	4.225	29.9	31.5	31.8	31.5
62	63.56	26.35	105.4	0.9168	4.098	29.4	31.1	31.4	31.1
60	61.59	25.50	103.2	0.9156	3.971	28.9	30.7	31.0	30.7
58	59.62	24.65	101.1	0.9144	3.844	28.3	30.3	30.6	30.3
56	57.64	23.80	98.87	0.9132	3.716	27.7	29.9	30.2	29.9
54	55.65	22.95	96.69	0.9120	3.588	27.1	29.4	29.9	29.5
52	53.66	22.10	94.50	0.9108	3.460	26.5	29.0	29.5	29.1
50	51.67	21.25	92.32	0.9097	3.331	25.9	28.6	29.0	28.7
48	49.67	20.40	90.14	0.9085	3.202	25.2	28.1	28.6	28.2
46	47.66	19.55	87.95	0.9073	3.073	24.5	27.7	28.2	27.8
44	45.65	18.70	85.77	0.9061	2.943	23.8	27.2	27.8	27.3
42	43.64	17.85	83.59	0.9049	2.813	23.0	26.7	27.3	26.8
40	41.61	17.00	81.40	0.9037	2.683	22.2	26.3	26.9	26.4
38	39.59	16.15	79.22	0.9025	2.552	21.4	25.8	26.4	25.9
36	37.55	15.30	77.04	0.9013	2.421	20.6	25.3	26.0	25.4
34	35.52	14.45	74.85	0.9001	2.290	19.7	24.7	25.5	24.9
32	33.47	13.60	72.67	0.8989	2.158	18.7	24.2	25.0	24.3
30	31.42	12.75	70.49	0.8977	2.026	17.7	23.7	24.5	23.8
28	29.37	11.90	68.30	0.8965	1.893	16.6	23.1	24.0	23.3
24	25.24	10.20	63.93	0.8942	1.627	14.3	22.0	23.0	22.1
20	21.09	8.498	59.57	0.8918	1.360	11.5	20.8	21.9	20.9
16	16.92	6.799	55.20	0.8894	1.091	8.3	19.5	20.7	19.7
12	12.72	5.099	50.83	0.8870	0.8202	4.1	18.1	19.6	18.4
8	8.50	3.399	46.47	0.8846	0.5483	−1.3	16.7	18.3	17.0
4	4.26	1.700	42.10	0.8822	0.2749	−9.4	15.2	17.0	15.5
0	0.00	0.000	37.73	0.8798	0.0000	—	13.6	15.6	13.9

38 °C DRY-BULB

Percentage saturation, μ / %	Relative humidity, ϕ /%	Value of stated parameter per kg dry air			Vapour pressure, p_v / kPa	Dew point temperature, θ_d / °C	Adiabatic saturation temperature, $\theta^\star$ / °C	Wet bulb temperature	
		Moisture content, g / (g·kg^{-1})	Specific enthalpy, h / (kJ·kg^{-1})	Specific volume, v / (m^3·kg^{-1})				Screen, θ'_{sc} / °C	Sling, θ'_{sl} / °C
100	100.00	43.74	150.7	0.9427	6.624	38.0	38.0	38.0	38.0
96	96.25	41.99	146.2	0.9402	6.376	37.3	37.4	37.4	37.4
92	92.49	40.24	141.7	0.9378	6.127	36.6	36.8	36.8	36.8
88	88.70	38.49	137.2	0.9353	5.876	35.8	36.2	36.2	36.2
84	84.90	36.74	132.7	0.9329	5.624	35.0	35.5	35.6	35.5
80	81.07	34.99	128.2	0.9304	5.371	34.2	34.8	35.0	34.9
76	77.23	33.24	123.7	0.9279	5.116	33.3	34.2	34.3	34.2
72	73.36	31.49	119.2	0.9255	4.860	32.4	33.4	33.6	33.5
70	71.42	30.62	116.9	0.9243	4.731	31.9	33.1	33.3	33.1
68	69.47	29.74	114.7	0.9230	4.602	31.4	32.7	32.9	32.7
66	67.52	28.87	112.4	0.9218	4.473	30.9	32.3	32.6	32.4
64	65.57	28.00	110.2	0.9206	4.343	30.4	31.9	32.2	32.0
62	63.60	27.12	107.9	0.9194	4.213	29.9	31.5	31.8	31.6
60	61.64	26.25	105.7	0.9181	4.083	29.3	31.1	31.5	31.2
58	59.66	25.37	103.4	0.9169	3.952	28.8	30.7	31.1	30.8
56	57.68	24.50	101.2	0.9157	3.821	28.2	30.3	30.7	30.4
54	55.70	23.62	98.95	0.9145	3.690	27.6	29.9	30.3	30.0
52	53.71	22.75	96.70	0.9132	3.558	27.0	29.5	29.9	29.5
50	51.72	21.87	94.45	0.9120	3.426	26.3	29.0	29.5	29.1
48	49.72	21.00	92.20	0.9108	3.293	25.7	28.6	29.1	28.7
46	47.71	20.12	89.95	0.9095	3.161	25.0	28.1	28.6	28.2
44	45.70	19.25	87.70	0.9083	3.027	24.2	27.6	28.2	27.7
42	43.68	18.37	85.46	0.9071	2.894	23.5	27.2	27.7	27.3
40	41.66	17.50	83.21	0.9059	2.760	22.7	26.7	27.3	26.8
38	39.63	16.62	80.96	0.9046	2.625	21.9	26.2	26.8	26.3
36	37.60	15.75	78.71	0.9034	2.491	21.0	25.7	26.4	25.8
34	35.56	14.87	76.46	0.9022	2.356	20.1	25.1	25.9	25.3
32	33.51	14.00	74.21	0.9009	2.220	19.2	24.6	25.4	24.7
30	31.46	13.12	71.96	0.8997	2.084	18.2	24.0	24.9	24.2
28	29.41	12.25	69.72	0.8985	1.948	17.1	23.5	24.4	23.6
24	25.27	10.50	65.22	0.8960	1.674	14.7	22.3	23.3	22.5
20	21.12	8.748	60.72	0.8936	1.399	12.0	21.1	22.2	21.3
16	16.94	6.999	56.22	0.8911	1.122	8.7	19.8	21.1	20.0
12	12.74	5.249	51.73	0.8886	0.8442	4.5	18.4	19.8	18.7
8	8.52	3.499	47.23	0.8862	0.5644	−0.9	17.0	18.6	17.2
4	4.27	1.750	42.73	0.8837	0.2830	−9.0	15.4	17.2	15.7
0	0.00	0.000	38.24	0.8813	0.0000	—	13.8	15.8	14.1

38.5 °C DRY-BULB

Percentage saturation, μ / %	Relative humidity, ϕ /%	Value of stated parameter per kg dry air			Vapour pressure, p_v / kPa	Dew point temperature, θ_d / °C	Adiabatic saturation temperature, $\theta^\star$ / °C	Wet bulb temperature	
		Moisture content, g / (g·kg^{-1})	Specific enthalpy, h / (kJ·kg^{-1})	Specific volume, v / (m^3·kg^{-1})				Screen, θ'_{sc} / °C	Sling, θ'_{sl} / °C
100	100.00	45.03	154.5	0.9460	6.806	38.5	38.5	38.5	38.5
96	96.26	43.23	149.9	0.9434	6.551	37.8	37.9	37.9	37.9
92	92.50	41.42	145.2	0.9409	6.295	37.1	37.3	37.3	37.3
88	88.72	39.62	140.6	0.9384	6.038	36.3	36.7	36.7	36.7
84	84.92	37.82	136.0	0.9359	5.780	35.5	36.0	36.1	36.0
80	81.10	36.02	131.4	0.9333	5.520	34.7	35.3	35.5	35.4
76	77.26	34.22	126.7	0.9308	5.258	33.8	34.6	34.8	34.7
72	73.40	32.42	122.1	0.9283	4.995	32.9	33.9	34.1	33.9
70	71.46	31.52	119.8	0.9270	4.863	32.4	33.5	33.8	33.6
68	69.52	30.62	117.5	0.9258	4.731	31.9	33.2	33.4	33.2
66	67.57	29.72	115.2	0.9245	4.598	31.4	32.8	33.0	32.8
64	65.61	28.82	112.8	0.9232	4.465	30.9	32.4	32.7	32.4
62	63.65	27.92	110.5	0.9220	4.332	30.4	32.0	32.3	32.0
60	61.68	27.02	108.2	0.9207	4.198	29.8	31.6	31.9	31.6
58	59.71	26.12	105.9	0.9194	4.064	29.3	31.2	31.5	31.2
56	57.73	25.22	103.6	0.9182	3.929	28.7	30.8	31.1	30.8
54	55.75	24.31	101.3	0.9169	3.794	28.1	30.3	30.7	30.4
52	53.76	23.41	98.94	0.9156	3.659	27.4	29.9	30.3	30.0
50	51.76	22.51	96.62	0.9144	3.523	26.8	29.4	29.9	29.5
48	49.76	21.61	94.31	0.9131	3.387	26.1	29.0	29.5	29.1
46	47.76	20.71	91.99	0.9118	3.250	25.4	28.5	29.0	28.6
44	45.75	19.81	89.68	0.9106	3.113	24.7	28.1	28.6	28.1
42	43.73	18.91	87.36	0.9093	2.976	24.0	27.6	28.2	27.7
40	41.71	18.01	85.05	0.9080	2.838	23.2	27.1	27.7	27.2
38	39.68	17.11	82.73	0.9068	2.700	22.4	26.6	27.2	26.7
36	37.64	16.21	80.42	0.9055	2.562	21.5	26.1	26.8	26.2
34	35.60	15.31	78.10	0.9042	2.423	20.6	25.5	26.3	25.6
32	33.56	14.41	75.79	0.9030	2.284	19.6	25.0	25.8	25.1
30	31.50	13.51	73.47	0.9017	2.144	18.6	24.4	25.3	24.6
28	29.45	12.61	71.15	0.9004	2.004	17.5	23.9	24.7	24.0
24	25.31	10.81	66.52	0.8979	1.723	15.2	22.7	23.7	22.8
20	21.15	9.005	61.89	0.8954	1.440	12.4	21.4	22.5	21.6
16	16.97	7.204	57.26	0.8928	1.155	9.1	20.1	21.4	20.3
12	12.77	5.403	52.63	0.8903	0.8688	4.9	18.7	20.1	18.9
8	8.53	3.602	48.00	0.8878	0.5809	−0.6	17.2	18.8	17.5
4	4.28	1.801	43.37	0.8852	0.2913	−8.7	15.7	17.5	16.0
0	0.00	0.000	38.74	0.8827	0.0000	—	14.0	16.0	14.3

39 °C DRY-BULB

Percentage saturation, μ / %	Relative humidity, ϕ /%	Value of stated parameter per kg dry air			Vapour pressure, p_v / kPa	Dew point temperature, θ_d / °C	Adiabatic saturation temperature, $\theta^\star$ / °C	Wet bulb temperature	
		Moisture content, g / (g·kg^{-1})	Specific enthalpy, h / (kJ·kg^{-1})	Specific volume, v / (m^3·kg^{-1})				Screen, θ'_{sc} / °C	Sling, θ'_{sl} / °C
100	100.00	46.35	158.4	0.9494	6.991	39.0	39.0	39.0	39.0
96	96.27	44.49	153.7	0.9467	6.730	38.3	38.4	38.4	38.4
92	92.52	42.64	148.9	0.9441	6.468	37.6	37.8	37.8	37.8
88	88.74	40.79	144.1	0.9415	6.204	36.8	37.1	37.2	37.2
84	84.95	38.93	139.4	0.9389	5.939	36.0	36.5	36.6	36.5
80	81.13	37.08	134.6	0.9363	5.672	35.2	35.8	35.9	35.8
76	77.30	35.22	129.8	0.9337	5.404	34.3	35.1	35.3	35.1
72	73.44	33.37	125.1	0.9311	5.134	33.4	34.4	34.6	34.4
70	71.50	32.44	122.7	0.9298	4.999	32.9	34.0	34.2	34.0
68	69.56	31.52	120.3	0.9285	4.863	32.4	33.6	33.9	33.7
66	67.61	30.59	117.9	0.9272	4.727	31.9	33.2	33.5	33.3
64	65.65	29.66	115.3	0.9259	4.590	31.4	32.8	33.1	32.9
62	63.69	28.74	113.1	0.9246	4.453	30.8	32.4	32.7	32.5
60	61.73	27.81	110.8	0.9233	4.316	30.3	32.0	32.4	32.1
58	59.76	26.88	108.4	0.9220	4.178	29.7	31.6	32.0	31.7
56	57.78	25.95	106.0	0.9207	4.040	29.2	31.2	31.6	31.3
54	55.80	25.03	103.6	0.9194	3.901	28.5	30.8	31.2	30.8
52	53.81	24.10	101.2	0.9181	3.762	27.9	30.3	30.8	30.4
50	51.81	23.17	98.84	0.9168	3.622	27.3	29.9	30.3	30.0
48	49.81	22.25	94.46	0.9155	3.483	26.6	29.4	29.9	29.5
46	47.81	21.32	94.08	0.9142	3.342	25.9	29.0	29.5	29.0
44	45.80	20.39	91.69	0.9129	3.202	25.2	28.5	29.0	28.6
42	43.78	19.47	89.31	0.9116	3.061	24.4	28.0	28.6	28.1
40	41.76	18.54	86.92	0.9102	2.919	23.6	27.5	28.1	27.6
38	39.73	17.61	84.54	0.9089	2.777	22.8	27.0	27.6	27.1
36	37.69	16.68	82.16	0.9076	2.635	22.0	26.4	27.1	26.6
34	35.65	15.76	79.77	0.9063	2.492	21.0	25.9	26.7	26.0
32	33.60	14.83	77.39	0.9050	2.349	20.1	25.4	26.1	25.5
30	31.55	13.90	75.00	0.9037	2.206	19.1	24.8	25.6	24.9
28	29.49	12.98	72.62	0.9024	2.062	18.0	24.2	25.1	24.4
24	25.35	11.12	67.85	0.8998	1.772	15.6	23.0	24.0	23.2
20	21.19	9.269	63.08	0.8972	1.481	12.8	21.8	22.9	21.9
16	17.00	7.416	58.32	0.8946	1.188	9.5	20.4	21.7	20.6
12	12.79	5.562	53.55	0.8919	0.8940	5.4	19.0	20.4	19.2
8	8.55	3.708	48.78	0.8893	0.5978	−0.3	17.5	19.1	17.8
4	4.29	1.854	44.01	0.8867	0.2998	−8.4	15.9	17.7	16.2
0	0.00	0.000	39.24	0.8841	0.0000	—	14.2	16.2	14.5

39.5 °C DRY-BULB

Percentage saturation, μ / %	Relative humidity, ϕ /%	Value of stated parameter per kg dry air			Vapour pressure, p_v / kPa	Dew point temperature, θ_d / °C	Adiabatic saturation temperature, $\theta^\star$ / °C	Wet bulb temperature	
		Moisture content, g / (g·kg^{-1})	Specific enthalpy, h / (kJ·kg^{-1})	Specific volume, v / (m^3·kg^{-1})				Screen, θ'_{sc} / °C	Sling, θ'_{sl} / °C
100	100.00	47.70	162.5	0.9528	7.181	39.5	39.5	39.5	39.5
96	96.27	45.80	157.6	0.9501	6.914	38.8	38.9	38.9	38.9
92	92.53	43.89	152.7	0.9474	6.645	38.1	38.3	38.3	38.3
88	88.76	41.98	147.8	0.9447	6.374	37.3	37.6	37.7	37.6
84	84.98	40.07	142.8	0.9420	6.102	36.5	37.0	37.1	37.0
80	81.16	38.16	137.9	0.9394	5.829	35.7	36.3	35.4	36.3
76	77.33	36.25	133.0	0.9367	5.553	34.8	35.6	35.7	35.6
72	73.48	34.35	128.1	0.9340	5.276	33.9	34.9	35.0	34.9
70	71.54	33.39	125.7	0.9326	5.138	33.4	34.5	34.7	34.5
68	69.60	32.44	123.2	0.9313	4.948	32.9	34.1	34.3	34.1
66	67.65	31.48	120.8	0.9300	4.858	32.4	33.7	34.0	33.8
64	65.70	30.53	118.3	0.9286	4.718	31.9	33.3	33.6	33.4
62	63.74	29.58	115.8	0.9273	4.577	31.3	32.9	33.2	33.0
60	61.78	28.62	113.4	0.9259	4.436	30.8	32.5	32.8	32.6
58	59.81	27.67	110.9	0.9246	4.295	30.2	32.1	32.4	32.1
56	57.83	26.71	108.5	0.9232	4.153	29.6	31.6	32.0	31.7
54	55.85	25.76	106.0	0.9219	4.010	29.0	31.2	31.6	31.3
52	53.86	24.81	103.6	0.9205	3.868	28.4	30.8	31.2	30.8
50	51.86	23.85	101.1	0.9192	3.724	27.8	30.3	30.8	30.4
48	49.87	22.90	98.66	0.9179	3.581	27.1	29.9	30.3	29.9
46	47.86	21.94	96.20	0.9165	3.437	26.4	29.4	29.9	29.5
44	45.85	20.99	93.75	0.9152	3.292	25.7	28.9	29.4	29.0
42	43.83	20.04	91.30	0.9138	3.147	24.9	28.4	29.0	28.5
40	41.80	19.08	88.84	0.9125	3.002	24.1	27.9	28.5	28.0
38	39.77	18.13	86.39	0.9111	2.856	23.3	27.4	28.0	27.5
36	37.74	17.17	83.93	0.9098	2.710	22.4	26.8	27.5	27.0
34	35.70	16.22	81.48	0.9084	2.563	21.5	26.3	27.0	26.4
32	33.65	15.27	79.02	0.9071	2.416	20.5	25.7	26.5	25.9
30	31.59	14.31	76.57	0.9057	2.269	19.5	25.2	26.0	25.3
28	29.53	13.36	74.11	0.9044	2.121	18.4	24.6	25.5	24.7
24	25.39	11.45	69.20	0.9017	1.823	16.1	23.4	24.4	23.5
20	21.22	9.541	64.29	0.8990	1.524	13.3	22.1	23.2	22.3
16	17.03	7.632	59.38	0.8963	1.223	9.9	20.7	22.0	20.9
12	12.81	5.724	54.47	0.8936	0.9199	5.8	19.3	20.7	19.5
8	8.57	3.816	49.56	0.8909	0.6152	0.1	17.8	19.4	18.0
4	4.30	1.908	44.66	0.8882	0.3085	−8.1	16.1	17.9	16.4
0	0.00	0.000	39.74	0.8855	0.0000	—	14.4	16.4	14.7

40 °C DRY-BULB

Percentage saturation, μ / %	Relative humidity, ϕ /%	Value of stated parameter per kg dry air			Vapour pressure, p_v / kPa	Dew point temperature, θ_d / °C	Adiabatic saturation temperature, $\theta\star$ / °C	Wet bulb temperature	
		Moisture content, g / (g·kg^{-1})	Specific enthalpy, h / (kJ·kg^{-1})	Specific volume, v / (m³·kg^{-1})				Screen, θ'_{sc} / °C	Sling, θ'_{sl} / °C
100	100.00	49.10	166.6	0.9563	7.375	40.0	40.0	40.0	40.0
96	96.28	47.13	161.6	0.9535	7.101	39.3	39.4	39.4	39.4
92	92.54	45.17	156.5	0.9507	6.826	38.6	38.8	38.8	38.8
88	88.78	43.21	151.5	0.9480	6.548	37.8	38.1	38.2	38.1
84	85.00	41.24	146.4	0.9452	6.269	37.0	37.5	37.6	37.5
80	81.20	39.28	141.3	0.9424	5.989	36.1	36.8	36.9	36.8
76	77.37	37.31	136.3	0.9397	5.706	35.3	36.1	36.2	36.1
72	73.52	35.35	131.2	0.9369	5.422	34.3	35.3	35.5	35.4
70	71.58	34.37	128.7	0.9355	5.280	33.9	34.9	35.2	35.0
68	69.64	33.39	126.2	0.9341	5.137	33.4	34.6	34.8	34.6
66	67.70	32.40	123.7	0.9327	4.993	32.9	34.2	34.4	34.2
64	65.75	31.42	121.1	0.9314	4.849	32.4	33.8	34.0	33.8
62	63.79	30.44	118.6	0.9300	4.705	31.8	33.4	33.7	33.4
60	61.83	29.46	116.1	0.9286	4.560	31.3	32.9	33.3	33.0
58	59.86	28.48	113.5	0.9272	4.415	30.7	32.5	32.9	32.6
56	57.88	27.49	111.0	0.9258	4.269	30.1	32.1	32.5	32.2
54	55.90	26.51	108.5	0.9244	4.123	29.5	31.7	32.0	31.7
52	53.91	25.53	106.0	0.9230	3.976	28.9	31.2	31.6	31.3
50	51.92	24.55	103.4	0.9217	3.829	28.2	30.7	31.2	30.8
48	49.92	23.57	100.9	0.9203	3.682	27.6	30.3	30.8	30.4
46	47.91	22.58	98.38	0.9189	3.534	26.9	29.8	30.3	29.9
44	45.90	21.60	95.85	0.9175	3.385	26.1	29.3	29.9	29.4
42	43.88	20.62	93.32	0.9161	3.236	25.4	28.8	29.4	28.9
40	41.86	19.64	90.80	0.9147	3.087	24.6	28.3	28.9	28.4
38	39.82	18.66	88.27	0.9133	2.937	23.7	27.8	28.4	27.9
36	37.79	17.67	85.74	0.9119	2.787	22.9	27.2	27.9	27.4
34	35.74	16.69	83.21	0.9106	2.636	22.0	26.7	27.4	26.8
32	33.69	15.71	80.69	0.9092	2.485	21.0	26.1	26.9	26.3
30	31.64	14.73	78.16	0.9078	2.333	20.0	25.6	26.4	25.7
28	29.57	13.75	75.63	0.9064	2.181	18.9	25.0	25.8	25.1
24	25.43	11.78	70.58	0.9036	1.875	16.5	23.7	24.7	23.9
20	21.26	9.819	65.52	0.9008	1.568	13.7	22.4	23.5	22.6
16	17.06	7.856	60.47	0.8981	1.258	10.4	21.0	22.3	21.2
12	12.83	5.892	55.41	0.8953	0.9466	6.2	19.6	21.0	19.8
8	8.58	3.928	50.36	0.8925	0.6330	0.5	18.0	19.6	18.3
4	4.31	1.964	45.30	0.8897	0.3175	−7.7	16.3	18.2	16.6
0	0.00	0.000	40.25	0.8869	0.0000	—	14.6	16.6	14.9

41 °C DRY-BULB

Percentage saturation, μ / %	Relative humidity, ϕ /%	Value of stated parameter per kg dry air			Vapour pressure, p_v / kPa	Dew point temperature, θ_d / °C	Adiabatic saturation temperature, $\theta\star$ / °C	Wet bulb temperature	
		Moisture content, g / (g·kg^{-1})	Specific enthalpy, h / (kJ·kg^{-1})	Specific volume, v / (m³·kg^{-1})				Screen, θ'_{sc} / °C	Sling, θ'_{sl} / °C
100	100.00	52.00	175.2	0.9634	7.778	41.0	41.0	41.0	41.0
96	96.30	49.92	169.8	0.9605	7.490	40.3	40.3	40.4	40.4
92	92.57	47.84	164.5	0.9576	7.200	39.5	39.8	39.8	39.8
88	88.83	45.76	159.1	0.9546	6.909	38.8	39.1	39.2	39.1
84	85.06	43.68	153.8	0.9517	6.616	38.0	38.4	38.5	38.5
80	81.26	41.60	148.4	0.9487	6.320	37.1	37.7	37.9	37.8
76	77.44	39.52	143.0	0.9458	6.023	36.3	37.0	37.2	37.0
72	73.60	37.44	137.7	0.9429	5.725	35.3	36.3	36.5	36.3
70	71.67	36.40	135.0	0.9414	5.575	34.8	35.9	36.1	35.9
68	69.74	35.36	132.3	0.9399	5.424	34.4	35.5	35.7	35.5
66	67.79	34.32	129.7	0.9384	5.273	33.8	35.1	35.3	35.1
64	65.84	33.28	127.0	0.9370	5.121	33.3	34.7	35.0	34.7
62	63.89	32.24	124.3	0.9355	4.969	32.8	34.3	34.6	34.3
60	61.93	31.20	121.6	0.9340	4.817	32.2	33.9	34.2	33.9
58	59.96	30.16	118.9	0.9326	4.664	31.7	33.4	33.8	33.5
56	57.99	29.12	116.3	0.9311	4.510	31.1	33.0	33.4	33.1
54	56.01	28.08	113.6	0.9296	4.356	30.5	32.5	32.9	32.6
52	54.02	27.04	110.9	0.9281	4.201	29.8	32.1	32.5	32.2
50	52.03	26.00	108.2	0.9267	4.046	29.2	31.6	32.1	31.7
48	50.03	24.96	105.5	0.9252	3.891	28.5	31.1	31.6	31.2
46	48.02	23.92	102.9	0.9237	3.735	37.8	30.7	31.2	30.7
44	46.01	22.88	100.2	0.9222	3.578	27.1	30.2	30.7	30.3
42	43.99	21.84	97.51	0.9208	3.421	26.3	29.6	30.2	29.7
40	41.96	20.80	94.83	0.9193	3.264	25.5	29.1	29.7	29.2
38	39.93	19.76	92.15	0.9178	3.106	24.7	28.6	29.2	28.7
36	37.89	18.72	89.47	0.9163	2.947	23.8	28.0	28.7	28.2
34	35.84	17.68	86.79	0.9149	2.788	22.9	27.5	28.2	27.6
32	33.79	16.64	84.12	0.9134	2.628	21.9	26.9	27.7	27.0
30	31.73	15.60	81.44	0.9119	2.468	20.9	26.3	27.1	26.4
28	29.66	14.56	78.76	0.9104	2.307	19.8	25.7	26.6	25.8
24	25.51	12.48	73.40	0.9075	1.984	17.4	24.4	25.4	24.6
20	21.33	10.40	68.04	0.9045	1.659	14.6	23.1	24.2	23.3
16	17.12	8.320	62.69	0.9016	1.332	11.2	21.7	22.9	21.9
12	12.88	6.240	57.33	0.8986	1.002	7.0	20.2	21.6	20.4
8	8.62	4.160	51.97	0.8957	0.6702	1.3	18.5	20.1	18.8
4	4.32	2.080	46.61	0.8927	0.3362	−7.1	16.8	18.6	17.1
0	0.00	0.000	41.26	0.8898	0.0000	—	14.9	17.0	15.3

42 °C DRY-BULB

Percentage saturation, μ / %	Relative humidity, ϕ /%	Value of stated parameter per kg dry air			Vapour pressure, p_v / kPa	Dew point temperature, θ_d / °C	Adiabatic saturation temperature, $\theta^\star$ / °C	Wet bulb temperature	
		Moisture content, g / (g·kg^{-1})	Specific enthalpy, h / (kJ·kg^{-1})	Specific volume, v / (m^3·kg^{-1})				Screen, θ'_{sc} / °C	Sling, θ'_{sl} / °C
100	100.00	55.07	184.2	0.9709	8.199	42.0	42.0	42.0	42.0
96	96.31	52.87	178.5	0.9677	7.897	41.3	41.3	41.4	41.4
92	92.61	50.66	172.8	0.9646	7.593	40.5	40.7	40.8	40.8
88	88.87	48.46	167.2	0.9615	7.287	39.8	40.0	40.2	40.1
84	85.11	46.26	161.5	0.9584	6.978	39.0	39.4	39.5	39.4
80	81.33	44.06	155.8	0.9553	6.668	38.1	38.7	38.8	38.7
76	77.52	41.85	150.1	0.9521	6.356	37.2	38.0	38.1	38.0
72	73.69	39.65	144.5	0.9490	6.042	36.3	37.2	37.4	37.3
70	71.76	38.55	141.6	0.9474	5.884	35.8	36.8	37.0	36.9
68	69.83	37.45	138.8	0.9459	5.726	35.3	36.4	36.7	36.5
66	67.89	36.35	135.9	0.9443	5.566	34.8	36.0	36.3	36.1
64	65.95	35.24	133.1	0.9428	5.407	34.3	35.6	35.9	35.7
62	63.99	34.14	130.3	0.9412	5.247	33.8	35.2	35.5	35.3
60	62.03	33.04	127.4	0.9396	5.086	33.2	34.8	35.1	34.8
58	60.07	31.94	124.6	0.9381	4.925	32.6	34.3	34.7	34.4
56	58.10	30.84	121.7	0.9365	4.763	32.0	33.9	34.2	34.0
54	56.12	29.74	118.9	0.9349	4.601	31.4	33.4	33.8	33.5
52	54.13	28.64	116.1	0.9334	4.438	30.8	33.0	33.4	33.0
50	52.14	27.53	113.2	0.9318	4.275	30.1	32.5	32.9	32.6
48	50.14	26.43	110.4	0.9302	4.111	29.5	32.0	32.5	32.1
46	48.13	25.33	107.6	0.9287	3.946	28.7	31.5	32.0	31.6
44	46.12	24.23	104.7	0.9271	3.781	28.0	31.0	31.5	31.1
42	44.10	23.13	101.9	0.9255	3.616	27.2	30.5	31.0	30.6
40	42.07	22.03	99.03	0.9240	3.449	26.4	29.9	30.5	30.1
38	40.04	20.93	96.20	0.9224	3.283	25.6	29.4	30.0	29.5
36	38.00	19.82	93.36	0.9208	3.115	24.7	28.8	29.5	29.0
34	35.95	18.72	90.52	0.9193	2.947	23.8	28.3	29.0	28.4
32	33.89	17.62	87.68	0.9177	2.779	22.8	27.7	28.4	27.8
30	31.83	16.52	84.84	0.9161	2.610	21.8	27.1	27.9	27.2
28	29.76	15.42	82.00	0.9146	2.440	20.7	26.4	27.3	26.6
24	25.60	13.22	76.33	0.9114	2.099	18.3	25.1	26.1	25.3
20	21.41	11.01	70.65	0.9083	1.755	15.5	23.8	24.9	23.9
16	17.18	8.811	64.97	0.9052	1.409	12.1	22.3	23.5	22.5
12	12.93	6.608	59.40	0.9020	1.060	7.8	20.7	22.2	21.0
8	8.65	4.406	53.62	0.8989	0.7095	2.1	19.1	20.7	19.3
4	4.34	2.203	47.94	0.8957	0.3560	−6.4	17.2	19.1	17.6
0	0.00	0.000	42.26	0.8926	0.0000	—	15.3	17.4	15.7

43 °C DRY-BULB

Percentage saturation, μ / %	Relative humidity, ϕ /%	Value of stated parameter per kg dry air			Vapour pressure, p_v / kPa	Dew point temperature, θ_d / °C	Adiabatic saturation temperature, $\theta^\star$ / °C	Wet bulb temperature	
		Moisture content, g / (g·kg^{-1})	Specific enthalpy, h / (kJ·kg^{-1})	Specific volume, v / (m^3·kg^{-1})				Screen, θ'_{sc} / °C	Sling, θ'_{sl} / °C
100	100.00	58.30	193.7	0.9786	8.640	43.0	43.0	43.0	43.0
96	96.33	55.98	187.6	0.9752	8.322	42.3	42.3	42.4	42.4
92	92.64	53.64	181.6	0.9719	8.004	41.5	41.6	41.8	41.7
88	88.92	51.31	175.6	0.9686	7.682	40.8	40.9	41.1	41.1
84	85.18	48.98	169.6	0.9653	7.359	40.0	40.2	40.5	40.4
80	81.40	46.65	163.6	0.9620	7.033	39.1	39.7	39.8	39.7
76	77.61	44.31	157.6	0.9587	6.705	38.2	38.9	39.1	39.0
72	73.78	41.98	151.6	0.9553	6.375	37.3	38.2	38.4	38.2
70	71.86	40.82	148.5	0.9537	6.209	36.8	37.8	38.0	37.8
68	69.93	39.65	145.5	0.9520	6.042	36.3	37.4	37.6	37.4
66	68.00	38.48	142.5	0.9504	5.875	35.8	37.0	37.2	37.0
64	66.05	37.32	139.5	0.9487	5.707	35.3	36.5	36.8	36.6
62	64.10	36.15	136.5	0.9470	5.538	34.7	36.1	36.4	36.2
60	62.15	34.98	133.5	0.9454	5.369	34.2	35.7	36.0	35.7
58	60.18	33.82	130.5	0.9437	5.200	33.6	35.2	35.6	35.3
56	58.21	32.65	127.5	0.9421	5.029	33.0	34.8	35.1	34.9
54	56.24	31.49	124.5	0.9404	4.858	32.4	34.3	34.7	34.4
52	54.25	30.32	121.5	0.9387	4.687	31.7	33.9	34.3	33.9
50	52.26	29.15	118.5	0.9371	4.515	31.1	33.4	33.8	33.5
48	50.26	27.99	115.5	0.9354	4.342	30.4	32.9	33.3	33.0
46	48.25	26.82	112.4	0.9337	4.169	29.7	32.4	32.9	32.5
44	46.24	25.66	109.4	0.9321	3.995	29.0	31.9	32.4	31.9
42	44.22	24.49	106.4	0.9304	3.820	28.2	31.3	31.9	31.4
40	42.19	23.32	103.4	0.9288	3.645	27.4	30.8	31.4	30.9
38	40.15	22.16	100.4	0.9271	3.469	26.5	30.2	30.8	30.3
36	38.11	20.99	97.40	0.9254	3.292	25.7	29.6	30.3	29.8
34	36.06	19.82	94.40	0.9238	3.115	24.7	29.1	29.8	29.2
32	34.00	18.66	91.39	0.9221	2.937	23.7	28.5	29.2	28.6
30	31.93	17.49	88.39	0.9204	2.759	22.7	27.8	28.6	28.0
28	29.86	16.33	85.38	0.9188	2.580	21.6	27.2	28.1	27.3
24	25.69	13.99	79.36	0.9154	2.219	19.2	25.9	26.8	26.0
20	21.49	11.66	73.34	0.9121	1.856	16.3	24.4	25.5	24.6
16	17.25	9.329	67.33	0.9088	1.491	12.9	22.9	24.2	23.1
12	12.99	6.997	61.31	0.9055	1.122	8.7	21.3	22.7	21.5
8	8.69	4.665	55.30	0.9021	0.7509	2.9	19.6	21.2	19.8
4	4.36	2.332	49.29	0.8988	0.3769	−5.7	17.7	19.6	18.3
0	0.00	0.000	43.27	0.8954	0.0000	—	15.7	17.8	16.0

44 °C DRY-BULB

Percentage saturation, μ / %	Relative humidity, ϕ /%	Value of stated parameter per kg dry air			Vapour pressure, p_v / kPa	Dew point temperature, θ_d / °C	Adiabatic saturation temperature, $\theta\star$ / °C	Wet bulb temperature	
		Moisture content, g / (g·kg^{-1})	Specific enthalpy, h / (kJ·kg^{-1})	Specific volume, v / (m^3·kg^{-1})				Screen, θ'_{sc} / °C	Sling, θ'_{sl} / °C
100	100.00	61.73	203.6	0.9865	9.100	44.0	44.0	44.0	44.0
96	96.35	59.26	197.2	0.9830	8.768	43.3	43.3	43.4	43.4
92	92.67	56.79	190.9	0.9795	8.434	42.5	42.6	42.8	42.7
88	88.97	54.32	184.5	0.9760	8.097	41.8	41.9	42.1	42.1
84	85.24	51.85	178.1	0.9725	7.757	40.9	41.2	41.4	41.4
80	81.48	49.38	171.7	0.9689	7.415	40.1	40.4	40.8	40.7
76	77.69	46.91	165.4	0.9654	7.071	39.2	39.9	40.0	39.9
72	73.88	44.45	159.0	0.9619	6.723	38.3	39.1	39.3	39.2
70	71.96	43.21	155.8	0.9601	6.549	37.8	38.7	38.9	38.8
68	70.04	41.98	152.6	0.9584	6.374	37.3	38.3	38.5	38.4
66	68.11	40.74	149.4	0.9566	6.198	36.8	37.9	38.1	37.9
64	66.17	39.51	146.2	0.9548	6.022	36.2	37.5	37.7	37.5
62	64.22	38.27	143.1	0.9531	5.844	35.7	37.0	37.3	37.1
60	62.27	37.04	139.9	0.9513	5.666	35.1	36.6	36.9	36.7
58	60.30	35.80	136.7	0.9495	5.488	34.6	36.2	36.5	36.2
56	58.34	34.57	133.5	0.9478	5.309	34.0	35.7	36.0	35.8
54	56.36	33.33	130.3	0.9460	5.129	33.3	35.2	35.6	35.3
52	54.38	32.10	127.1	0.9443	4.949	32.7	34.7	35.1	34.8
50	52.38	30.87	123.9	0.9425	4.767	32.0	34.3	34.7	34.3
48	50.38	29.63	120.8	0.9407	4.585	31.4	33.8	34.2	33.8
46	48.38	28.40	117.6	0.9390	4.403	30.6	33.2	33.7	33.3
44	46.36	27.16	114.4	0.9372	4.219	29.9	32.7	33.2	32.8
42	44.34	25.93	111.2	0.9354	4.035	29.1	32.2	32.7	32.3
40	42.31	24.69	108.0	0.9337	3.851	28.3	31.6	32.2	31.7
38	40.27	23.46	104.8	0.9319	3.665	27.5	31.0	31.7	31.2
36	38.23	22.22	101.6	0.9301	3.479	26.6	30.5	31.1	30.6
34	36.17	20.99	98.45	0.9284	3.292	25.7	29.9	30.6	30.0
32	34.11	19.75	95.26	0.9266	3.104	24.7	29.2	30.0	29.4
30	32.04	18.52	92.07	0.9248	2.916	23.6	28.6	29.4	28.7
28	29.97	17.28	88.89	0.9231	2.727	22.5	28.0	28.8	28.1
24	25.78	14.82	82.51	0.9195	2.347	20.1	26.6	27.5	26.7
20	21.57	12.35	76.14	0.9160	1.963	17.2	25.1	26.2	25.3
16	17.33	9.877	69.77	0.9125	1.577	13.8	23.6	24.8	23.8
12	13.05	7.408	63.40	0.9089	1.187	9.5	21.9	23.3	22.1
8	8.73	4.938	57.02	0.9054	0.7946	3.7	20.1	21.7	20.4
4	4.38	2.469	50.65	0.9018	0.3989	−5.1	18.1	20.0	18.5
0	0.00	0.000	44.28	0.8983	0.0000	—	16.0	18.2	16.4

45 °C DRY-BULB

Percentage saturation, μ / %	Relative humidity, ϕ /%	Value of stated parameter per kg dry air			Vapour pressure, p_v / kPa	Dew point temperature, θ_d / °C	Adiabatic saturation temperature, $\theta\star$ / °C	Wet bulb temperature	
		Moisture content, g / (g·kg^{-1})	Specific enthalpy, h / (kJ·kg^{-1})	Specific volume, v / (m^3·kg^{-1})				Screen, θ'_{sc} / °C	Sling, θ'_{sl} / °C
100	100.00	65.34	214.1	0.9948	9.582	45.0	45.0	45.0	45.0
96	96.37	62.73	207.3	0.9911	9.234	44.3	44.3	44.4	44.4
92	92.71	60.12	200.6	0.9874	8.884	43.5	43.6	43.8	43.7
88	89.02	57.50	193.8	0.9836	8.530	42.8	42.9	43.1	43.0
84	85.31	54.89	187.0	0.9799	8.174	41.9	42.2	42.4	42.4
80	81.56	52.28	180.3	0.9761	7.815	41.1	41.4	41.7	41.6
76	77.79	49.66	173.6	0.9724	7.454	40.2	40.6	41.0	40.9
72	73.98	47.05	166.8	0.9687	7.089	39.3	40.0	40.2	40.1
70	72.07	45.74	163.4	0.9668	6.906	38.8	39.7	39.9	39.7
68	70.15	44.44	160.0	0.9649	6.722	38.3	39.3	39.5	39.3
66	68.22	43.13	156.7	0.9630	6.537	37.8	38.8	39.1	38.9
64	66.28	41.82	153.3	0.9612	6.352	37.2	38.4	38.7	38.5
62	64.34	40.51	149.9	0.9593	6.165	36.7	38.0	38.2	38.0
60	62.39	39.21	146.5	0.9574	5.978	36.1	37.5	37.8	37.6
58	60.43	37.90	143.2	0.9556	5.791	35.5	37.1	37.4	37.1
56	58.46	36.59	139.8	0.9537	5.602	34.9	36.6	36.9	36.7
54	56.49	35.29	136.4	0.9518	5.413	34.3	36.1	36.5	36.2
52	54.51	33.98	133.0	0.9499	5.223	33.7	35.6	36.0	35.7
50	52.52	32.67	129.7	0.9481	5.032	33.0	35.1	35.6	35.2
48	50.52	31.37	126.3	0.9462	4.841	32.3	34.6	35.1	34.7
46	48.51	30.06	122.9	0.9443	4.648	31.6	34.1	34.6	34.2
44	46.49	28.75	119.5	0.9424	4.455	30.9	33.6	34.1	33.7
42	44.47	27.45	116.2	0.9406	4.261	30.1	33.0	33.6	33.1
40	42.44	26.14	112.8	0.9387	4.067	29.3	32.5	33.0	32.6
38	40.40	24.83	109.4	0.9368	3.871	28.4	31.9	32.5	32.0
36	38.35	23.52	106.0	0.9349	3.675	27.5	31.3	31.9	31.4
34	36.30	22.22	102.7	0.9331	3.478	26.6	30.7	31.4	30.8
32	34.23	20.91	99.29	0.9312	3.280	25.6	30.0	30.8	30.2
30	32.16	19.60	95.91	0.9293	3.082	24.5	29.4	30.2	29.5
28	30.08	18.30	92.54	0.9274	2.882	23.4	28.7	29.5	28.9
24	25.89	15.68	85.79	0.9237	2.481	21.0	27.3	28.3	27.5
20	21.66	13.07	79.04	0.9199	2.076	18.1	25.8	26.9	26.0
16	17.40	10.46	72.29	0.9162	1.668	14.7	24.2	25.4	24.4
12	13.11	7.842	65.54	0.9124	1.256	10.3	22.5	23.9	22.7
8	8.77	5.228	58.79	0.9086	0.8417	4.5	20.6	22.2	20.9
4	4.41	2.614	52.04	0.9049	0.4221	−4.4	18.6	20.5	18.9
0	0.00	0.000	45.28	0.9011	0.0000	—	16.4	18.6	16.8

46 °C DRY-BULB

Percentage saturation, μ / %	Relative humidity, ϕ /%	Value of stated parameter per kg dry air			Vapour pressure, p_v / kPa	Dew point temperature, θ_d / °C	Adiabatic saturation temperature, $\theta^\star$ / °C	Wet bulb temperature	
		Moisture content, g / (g·kg^{-1})	Specific enthalpy, h / (kJ·kg^{-1})	Specific volume, v / (m^3·kg^{-1})				Screen, θ'_{sc} / °C	Sling, θ'_{sl} / °C
100	100.00	69.17	225.0	1.003	10.09	46.0	46.0	46.0	46.0
96	96.39	66.40	217.9	0.9995	9.722	45.3	45.3	45.4	45.4
92	92.75	63.63	210.8	0.9955	9.354	44.5	44.6	44.7	44.7
88	89.08	60.87	203.6	0.9915	8.984	43.8	43.9	44.1	44.0
84	85.37	58.10	196.4	0.9876	8.611	42.9	43.1	43.4	43.3
80	81.64	55.33	189.3	0.9836	8.235	42.1	42.3	42.7	42.6
76	77.88	52.57	182.1	0.9796	7.855	41.2	41.5	42.0	41.9
72	74.09	49.80	175.0	0.9757	7.473	40.2	40.7	41.2	41.1
70	72.18	48.42	171.4	0.9737	7.280	39.8	40.2	40.8	40.7
68	70.27	47.03	167.8	0.9717	7.087	39.3	40.0	40.4	40.3
66	68.34	45.65	164.3	0.9697	6.893	38.7	39.8	40.0	39.8
64	66.41	44.27	160.7	0.9677	6.698	38.2	39.3	39.6	39.4
62	64.47	42.88	157.1	0.9657	6.502	37.7	38.9	39.2	39.0
60	62.52	41.50	153.5	0.9637	6.306	37.1	38.5	38.7	38.5
58	60.56	40.12	150.0	0.9618	6.108	36.5	38.0	38.3	38.1
56	58.60	38.73	146.4	0.9598	5.910	35.9	37.5	37.8	37.6
54	56.63	37.35	142.8	0.9578	5.711	35.3	37.0	37.4	37.1
52	54.64	35.97	139.2	0.9558	5.511	34.6	36.5	36.9	36.6
50	52.65	34.58	135.7	0.9538	5.311	34.0	36.0	36.4	36.1
48	50.66	33.20	132.1	0.9518	5.109	33.3	35.5	35.9	35.6
46	48.65	31.82	128.5	0.9498	4.907	32.6	35.0	35.4	35.1
44	46.63	30.43	124.9	0.9478	4.703	31.8	34.4	34.9	34.5
42	44.61	29.05	121.4	0.9458	4.499	31.0	33.9	34.4	34.0
40	42.58	27.67	117.8	0.9438	4.294	30.2	33.3	33.9	33.4
38	40.53	26.28	114.2	0.9419	4.088	29.4	32.7	33.3	32.8
36	38.48	24.90	110.6	0.9399	3.882	28.5	32.1	32.7	32.2
34	36.43	23.52	107.1	0.9379	3.674	27.5	31.5	32.2	31.6
32	34.36	22.13	103.5	0.9359	3.465	26.5	30.8	31.6	31.0
30	32.28	20.75	99.92	0.9339	3.256	25.5	30.2	30.9	30.3
28	30.19	19.37	96.34	0.9319	3.045	24.3	29.5	30.3	29.6
24	25.99	16.60	89.19	0.9279	2.622	21.9	28.0	29.0	28.2
20	21.76	13.83	82.04	0.9239	2.194	19.0	26.5	27.6	26.7
16	17.48	11.07	74.89	0.9199	1.763	15.5	24.8	26.1	25.1
12	13.17	8.300	67.74	0.9159	1.328	11.2	23.1	24.5	23.3
8	8.82	5.533	60.59	0.9120	0.8895	5.3	21.1	22.8	21.4
4	4.43	2.767	53.44	0.9080	0.4467	−3.7	19.0	20.9	19.4
0	0.00	0.000	46.29	0.9040	0.0000	—	16.7	19.0	17.1

47 °C DRY-BULB

Percentage saturation, μ / %	Relative humidity, ϕ /%	Value of stated parameter per kg dry air			Vapour pressure, p_v / kPa	Dew point temperature, θ_d / °C	Adiabatic saturation temperature, $\theta^\star$ / °C	Wet bulb temperature	
		Moisture content, g / (g·kg^{-1})	Specific enthalpy, h / (kJ·kg^{-1})	Specific volume, v / (m^3·kg^{-1})				Screen, θ'_{sc} / °C	Sling, θ'_{sl} / °C
100	100.00	73.20	236.6	1.012	10.61	47.0	47.0	47.0	47.0
96	96.41	70.27	229.0	1.008	10.23	46.3	46.3	46.4	46.4
92	92.78	67.35	221.5	1.004	9.847	45.5	45.6	45.7	45.7
88	89.13	64.42	213.9	0.9998	9.459	44.7	44.9	45.1	45.0
84	85.45	61.49	206.3	0.9956	9.068	43.9	44.1	44.4	44.3
80	81.73	58.56	198.8	0.9913	8.674	43.1	43.3	43.7	43.6
76	77.98	55.63	191.2	0.9871	8.276	42.2	42.5	42.9	42.8
72	74.20	52.71	183.6	0.9829	7.875	41.2	41.6	42.2	42.0
70	72.30	51.24	179.8	0.9808	7.673	40.7	41.2	41.8	41.6
68	70.39	49.78	176.0	0.9787	7.470	40.2	40.7	41.4	41.2
66	68.47	48.31	172.2	0.9766	7.266	39.7	40.3	40.9	40.8
64	66.54	46.85	168.5	0.9745	7.061	39.2	40.0	40.5	40.3
62	64.60	45.39	164.7	0.9724	6.856	38.6	39.8	40.1	39.9
60	62.66	43.92	160.9	0.9703	6.649	38.1	39.4	39.7	39.4
58	60.70	42.46	157.1	0.9681	6.442	37.5	38.9	39.2	39.0
56	58.74	40.99	153.3	0.9660	6.234	36.9	38.4	38.8	38.5
54	56.77	39.53	149.5	0.9639	6.025	36.3	37.9	38.3	38.0
52	54.79	38.07	145.7	0.9618	5.814	35.6	37.4	37.8	37.5
50	52.80	36.60	142.0	0.9597	5.603	34.9	36.9	37.3	37.0
48	50.80	35.14	138.2	0.9576	5.391	34.2	36.4	36.8	36.5
46	48.79	33.67	134.4	0.9555	5.178	33.5	35.9	36.3	35.9
44	46.78	32.21	130.6	0.9534	4.964	32.8	35.3	35.8	35.4
42	44.75	30.75	126.8	0.9513	4.749	32.0	34.7	35.3	34.8
40	42.72	29.28	123.0	0.9491	4.534	31.2	34.1	34.7	34.3
38	40.68	27.82	119.2	0.9470	4.317	30.3	33.5	34.1	33.7
36	38.62	26.35	115.4	0.9449	4.099	29.4	32.9	33.6	33.0
34	36.56	24.89	111.7	0.9428	3.880	28.5	32.3	33.0	32.4
32	34.49	23.43	107.9	0.9407	3.660	27.5	31.6	32.3	31.8
30	32.41	21.96	104.1	0.9386	3.439	26.4	30.9	31.7	31.1
28	30.32	20.50	100.3	0.9365	3.217	25.3	30.2	31.1	30.4
24	26.11	17.57	92.74	0.9322	2.770	22.8	28.8	29.7	28.9
20	21.86	14.64	85.16	0.9280	2.319	19.9	27.2	28.3	27.4
16	17.57	11.71	77.59	0.9238	1.864	16.4	25.5	26.7	25.7
12	13.24	8.784	70.02	0.9195	1.405	12.0	23.7	25.1	23.9
8	8.87	5.856	62.44	0.9153	0.9409	6.1	21.7	23.3	21.9
4	4.45	2.928	54.87	0.9110	0.4727	−3.1	19.5	21.4	19.8
0	0.00	0.000	47.30	0.9068	0.0000	—	17.1	19.3	17.5

48 °C DRY-BULB

Percentage saturation, μ / %	Relative humidity, ϕ /%	Value of stated parameter per kg dry air			Vapour pressure, p_v / kPa	Dew point temperature, θ_d / °C	Adiabatic saturation temperature, $\theta\star$ / °C	Wet bulb temperature	
		Moisture content, g / (g·kg^{-1})	Specific enthalpy, h / (kJ·kg^{-1})	Specific volume, v / (m^3·kg^{-1})				Screen, θ'_{sc} / °C	Sling, θ'_{sl} / °C
100	100.00	77.47	248.8	1.022	11.16	48.0	48.0	48.0	48.0
96	96.43	74.37	240.8	1.017	10.76	47.3	47.4	47.4	47.4
92	92.83	71.27	232.8	1.013	10.36	46.5	46.7	46.7	46.7
88	89.19	68.17	224.7	1.008	9.956	45.7	46.0	46.1	46.0
84	85.52	65.08	216.7	1.004	9.546	44.9	45.3	45.4	45.3
80	81.82	61.98	208.7	0.9994	9.133	44.1	44.5	44.6	44.6
76	78.09	58.88	200.7	0.9949	8.716	43.2	43.8	43.9	43.8
72	74.32	55.78	192.7	0.9904	8.295	42.2	42.9	43.1	43.0
70	72.42	54.23	188.7	0.9882	8.084	41.7	42.5	42.7	42.6
68	70.51	52.68	184.6	0.9860	7.871	41.2	42.1	42.3	42.2
66	68.60	51.13	180.6	0.9837	7.657	40.7	41.7	41.9	41.7
64	66.68	49.58	176.6	0.9815	7.442	40.2	41.2	41.5	41.3
62	64.74	48.03	172.6	0.9792	7.227	39.6	40.8	41.0	40.8
60	62.80	46.48	168.6	0.9770	7.010	39.0	40.3	40.6	40.4
58	60.85	44.93	164.6	0.9748	6.792	38.5	39.8	40.1	39.9
56	58.89	43.38	160.6	0.9725	6.573	37.9	39.4	39.7	39.4
54	56.92	41.83	156.6	0.9703	6.353	37.2	38.9	39.2	38.9
52	54.94	40.28	152.6	0.9680	6.133	36.6	38.3	38.7	38.4
50	52.95	38.74	148.6	0.9658	5.911	35.9	37.8	38.2	37.9
48	50.95	37.19	144.5	0.9636	5.688	35.2	37.3	37.7	37.4
46	48.95	35.64	140.5	0.9613	5.464	34.5	36.7	37.2	36.8
44	46.93	34.09	136.5	0.9591	5.239	33.7	36.2	36.7	36.3
42	44.90	32.54	132.5	0.9568	5.012	32.9	35.6	36.1	35.7
40	42.87	30.99	128.5	0.9546	4.785	32.1	35.0	35.5	35.1
38	40.82	29.44	124.5	0.9523	4.557	31.3	34.4	35.0	34.5
36	38.77	27.89	120.5	0.9501	4.327	30.3	33.8	34.4	33.9
34	36.70	26.34	116.5	0.9479	4.097	29.4	33.1	33.8	33.2
32	34.63	24.79	112.5	0.9456	3.865	28.4	32.4	33.1	32.6
30	32.54	23.24	108.5	0.9434	3.632	27.3	31.7	32.5	31.9
28	30.45	21.69	104.4	0.9411	3.398	26.2	31.0	31.8	31.2
24	26.22	18.59	96.42	0.9366	2.927	23.7	29.5	30.4	29.7
20	21.96	15.49	88.40	0.9321	2.451	20.8	27.9	29.0	28.1
16	17.66	12.40	80.38	0.9276	1.971	17.3	26.1	27.4	26.4
12	13.31	9.296	72.36	0.9231	1.485	12.9	24.3	25.7	24.5
8	8.92	6.198	64.35	0.9186	0.9952	6.9	22.2	23.8	22.5
4	4.48	3.099	56.33	0.9141	0.5000	−2.4	19.9	21.8	20.2
0	0.00	0.000	48.31	0.9096	0.0000	—	17.4	19.7	17.8

49 °C DRY-BULB

Percentage saturation, μ / %	Relative humidity, ϕ /%	Value of stated parameter per kg dry air			Vapour pressure, p_v / kPa	Dew point temperature, θ_d / °C	Adiabatic saturation temperature, $\theta\star$ / °C	Wet bulb temperature	
		Moisture content, g / (g·kg^{-1})	Specific enthalpy, h / (kJ·kg^{-1})	Specific volume, v / (m^3·kg^{-1})				Screen, θ'_{sc} / °C	Sling, θ'_{sl} / °C
100	100.00	81.98	261.6	1.0315	11.74	49.0	49.0	49.0	49.0
96	96.45	78.70	253.1	1.0267	11.32	48.3	48.3	48.4	48.4
92	92.87	75.43	244.6	1.0220	10.90	47.5	47.7	47.7	47.7
88	89.25	72.15	236.2	1.0172	10.48	46.7	47.0	47.0	47.0
84	85.60	68.87	227.7	1.0125	10.05	45.9	46.3	46.3	46.3
80	81.92	65.59	219.2	1.0077	9.614	45.1	45.5	45.6	45.5
76	78.20	62.31	210.7	1.0030	9.177	44.2	44.7	44.9	44.8
72	74.44	59.03	202.2	0.9982	8.736	43.2	43.9	44.1	44.0
70	72.55	57.39	197.9	0.9959	8.515	42.7	43.5	43.7	43.5
68	70.65	55.75	193.7	0.9935	8.291	42.2	43.1	43.3	43.1
66	68.74	54.11	189.4	0.9911	8.067	41.7	42.6	42.8	42.7
64	66.82	52.47	185.2	0.9887	7.842	41.2	42.2	42.4	42.2
62	64.89	50.83	181.0	0.9864	7.616	40.6	41.7	42.0	41.8
60	62.95	49.19	176.7	0.9840	7.388	40.0	41.2	41.5	41.3
58	61.00	47.55	172.5	0.9816	7.159	39.4	40.8	41.1	40.8
56	59.04	45.91	168.2	0.9792	6.930	38.8	40.3	40.6	40.3
54	57.08	44.27	164.0	0.9768	6.699	38.2	39.8	40.1	39.8
52	55.10	42.63	159.7	0.9745	6.467	37.6	39.3	39.6	39.3
50	53.11	40.99	155.5	0.9721	6.233	36.9	38.7	39.1	38.8
48	51.12	39.35	151.2	0.9697	5.999	36.2	38.2	38.6	38.3
46	49.11	37.71	147.0	0.9673	5.764	35.4	37.6	38.1	37.7
44	47.09	36.07	142.7	0.9649	5.527	34.7	37.1	37.5	37.2
42	45.06	34.43	138.5	0.9626	5.289	33.9	36.5	37.0	36.6
40	43.03	32.79	134.2	0.9602	5.050	33.1	35.9	36.4	36.0
38	40.98	31.15	130.0	0.9578	4.809	32.2	35.2	35.8	35.3
36	38.92	29.51	125.7	0.9554	4.568	31.3	34.6	35.2	34.7
34	36.85	27.88	121.5	0.9530	4.325	30.3	33.9	34.6	34.1
32	34.77	26.24	117.3	0.9507	4.081	29.3	33.2	33.9	33.4
30	32.68	24.60	113.0	0.9483	3.836	28.3	32.5	33.3	32.7
28	30.58	22.96	108.8	0.9459	3.589	27.1	31.8	32.6	31.9
24	26.35	19.68	100.3	0.9411	3.092	24.6	30.3	31.2	30.4
20	22.07	16.40	91.78	0.9364	2.590	21.7	28.6	29.6	28.8
16	17.75	13.12	83.78	0.9316	2.083	18.2	26.8	28.0	27.0
12	13.38	9.838	74.79	0.9268	1.571	13.7	24.9	26.3	25.1
8	8.97	6.559	66.30	0.9220	1.053	7.7	22.7	24.4	23.0
4	4.51	3.279	57.81	0.9173	0.5290	−1.7	20.4	22.3	20.7
0	0.00	0.000	49.31	0.9125	0.0000	—	17.8	20.0	18.1

50 °C DRY-BULB

Percentage saturation, μ / %	Relative humidity, ϕ /%	Value of stated parameter per kg dry air			Vapour pressure, p_v / kPa	Dew point temperature, θ_d / °C	Adiabatic saturation temperature, $\theta^\star$ / °C	Wet bulb temperature	
		Moisture content, g /(g·kg⁻¹)	Specific enthalpy, h /(kJ·kg⁻¹)	Specific volume, v /(m³·kg⁻¹)				Screen, θ'_{sc}/ °C	Sling, θ'_{sl}/ °C
100	100.00	86.76	275.2	1.042	12.34	50.0	50.0	50.0	50.0
96	96.47	83.29	266.2	1.037	11.90	49.3	49.3	49.4	49.4
92	92.91	79.82	257.2	1.032	11.46	48.5	48.7	48.7	48.7
88	89.32	76.35	248.2	1.026	11.02	47.7	48.0	48.0	48.0
84	85.69	72.88	239.2	1.022	10.57	46.9	47.2	47.3	47.3
80	82.02	69.41	230.2	1.016	10.12	46.1	46.5	46.6	46.5
76	78.31	65.94	221.2	1.011	9.660	45.2	45.7	45.8	45.7
72	74.57	62.47	212.2	1.006	9.198	44.2	44.9	45.0	44.9
70	72.68	60.73	207.7	1.004	8.966	43.7	44.4	44.6	44.5
68	70.79	59.00	203.2	1.001	8.732	43.2	44.0	44.2	44.1
66	68.88	57.26	198.7	0.9988	8.497	42.7	43.6	43.8	43.6
64	66.97	55.53	194.2	0.9963	8.261	42.1	43.1	43.4	43.2
62	65.04	53.79	189.7	0.9937	8.023	41.6	42.7	42.9	42.7
60	63.11	52.06	185.2	0.9912	7.785	41.0	42.2	42.5	42.3
58	61.16	50.32	180.7	0.9887	7.545	40.4	41.7	42.0	41.8
56	59.21	48.58	176.2	0.9862	7.304	39.8	41.2	41.5	41.3
54	57.24	46.85	171.7	0.9836	7.061	39.2	40.7	41.0	40.8
52	55.27	45.11	167.2	0.9811	6.817	38.5	40.2	40.5	40.3
50	53.28	43.38	162.7	0.9786	6.572	37.9	39.6	40.0	39.7
48	51.28	41.64	158.2	0.9761	6.326	37.2	39.1	39.5	39.2
46	49.28	39.91	153.7	0.9735	6.079	36.4	38.5	39.0	38.6
44	47.26	38.17	149.2	0.9710	5.830	35.7	37.9	38.4	38.0
42	45.23	36.44	144.8	0.9685	5.580	34.9	37.3	37.8	37.4
40	43.19	34.70	140.3	0.9660	5.328	34.0	36.7	37.2	36.8
38	41.14	32.97	135.8	0.9634	5.075	33.2	36.1	36.7	36.2
36	39.08	31.23	131.3	0.9609	4.821	32.2	35.4	36.0	35.6
34	37.01	29.50	126.8	0.9584	4.565	31.3	34.8	35.4	34.9
32	34.93	27.76	122.3	0.9558	4.308	30.3	34.1	34.7	34.2
30	32.83	26.03	117.8	0.9533	4.050	29.2	33.3	34.1	33.5
28	30.73	24.29	113.3	0.9508	3.790	28.1	32.6	33.4	32.7
24	26.48	20.82	104.3	0.9457	3.266	25.5	31.0	31.9	31.2
20	22.19	17.35	95.29	0.9407	2.737	22.6	29.3	30.3	29.5
16	17.85	13.88	86.29	0.9356	2.202	19.0	27.5	28.7	27.7
12	13.46	10.41	77.30	0.9305	1.660	14.6	25.5	26.9	25.7
8	9.02	6.941	68.31	0.9255	1.113	8.6	23.3	24.9	23.5
4	4.54	3.470	59.31	0.9204	0.5597	−1.0	20.8	22.7	21.1
0	0.00	0.000	50.32	0.9153	0.0000	—	18.1	20.4	18.5

51 °C DRY-BULB

Percentage saturation, μ / %	Relative humidity, ϕ /%	Value of stated parameter per kg dry air			Vapour pressure, p_v / kPa	Dew point temperature, θ_d / °C	Adiabatic saturation temperature, $\theta^\star$ / °C	Wet bulb temperature	
		Moisture content, g /(g·kg⁻¹)	Specific enthalpy, h /(kJ·kg⁻¹)	Specific volume, v /(m³·kg⁻¹)				Screen, θ'_{sc}/ °C	Sling, θ'_{sl}/ °C
100	100.00	91.81	289.4	1.052	12.96	51.0	51.0	51.0	51.0
96	96.50	88.14	279.9	1.047	12.51	50.3	50.3	50.4	50.3
92	92.96	84.46	270.4	1.042	12.05	49.5	49.7	49.7	49.7
88	89.38	80.79	260.8	1.036	11.58	48.7	49.0	49.0	49.0
84	85.77	77.12	251.3	1.031	11.12	47.9	48.2	48.3	48.2
80	82.12	73.45	241.8	1.026	10.64	47.1	47.5	47.6	47.5
76	78.43	69.78	232.3	1.020	10.16	46.2	46.7	46.8	46.7
72	74.70	66.10	222.8	1.015	9.682	45.2	45.8	46.0	45.9
70	72.83	64.27	218.0	1.012	9.439	44.7	45.4	45.6	45.5
68	70.94	62.43	213.2	1.009	9.194	44.2	45.0	45.2	45.0
66	69.04	60.59	208.5	1.007	8.948	43.7	44.5	44.7	44.6
64	67.13	58.76	203.7	1.004	8.700	43.1	44.1	44.3	44.1
62	65.20	56.92	198.9	1.001	8.451	42.6	43.6	43.8	43.7
60	63.27	55.09	194.2	0.9987	8.201	42.0	43.1	43.4	43.2
58	61.33	53.25	189.4	0.9960	7.949	41.4	42.6	42.9	42.7
56	59.38	51.41	184.7	0.9933	7.696	40.8	42.1	42.4	42.2
54	57.42	49.58	179.9	0.9907	7.442	40.2	41.6	41.9	41.7
52	55.44	47.74	175.1	0.9880	7.186	39.5	41.1	41.4	41.2
50	53.46	45.90	170.4	0.9853	6.929	38.8	40.5	40.9	40.6
48	51.46	44.07	165.6	0.9826	6.670	38.1	40.0	40.4	40.1
46	49.46	42.23	160.8	0.9799	6.410	37.4	39.4	39.8	39.5
44	47.44	40.40	156.1	0.9773	6.148	36.6	38.8	39.3	38.9
42	45.41	38.56	151.3	0.9746	5.885	35.8	38.2	38.7	38.3
40	43.37	36.72	146.6	0.9719	5.621	35.0	37.6	38.1	37.7
38	41.32	34.89	141.8	0.9692	5.355	34.1	36.9	37.5	37.1
36	39.25	33.05	137.0	0.9665	5.087	33.2	36.3	36.9	36.4
34	37.18	31.22	132.3	0.9639	4.818	32.2	35.6	36.2	35.7
32	35.09	29.38	127.5	0.9612	4.548	31.2	34.9	35.6	35.0
30	32.99	27.54	122.8	0.9585	4.276	30.1	34.1	34.9	34.3
28	30.88	25.71	118.0	0.9558	4.002	29.0	33.4	34.2	33.5
24	26.62	22.03	108.5	0.9504	3.450	26.4	31.8	32.7	31.9
20	22.31	18.36	98.94	0.9451	2.892	23.5	30.0	31.1	30.2
16	17.95	14.69	89.42	0.9397	2.327	19.9	28.1	29.3	28.3
12	13.54	11.02	79.90	0.9343	1.755	15.5	26.1	27.5	26.3
8	9.08	7.345	70.37	0.9289	1.177	9.4	23.8	25.4	24.1
4	4.57	3.672	60.85	0.9235	0.5920	−0.4	21.3	23.2	21.6
0	0.00	0.000	51.33	0.9182	0.0000	—	18.4	20.8	18.8

52 °C DRY-BULB

Percentage saturation, μ / %	Relative humidity, ϕ /%	Value of stated parameter per kg dry air			Vapour pressure, p_v / kPa	Dew point temperature, θ_d / °C	Adiabatic saturation temperature, $\theta\star$ / °C	Wet bulb temperature	
		Moisture content, g / (g·kg^{-1})	Specific enthalpy, h / (kJ·kg^{-1})	Specific volume, v / (m^3·kg^{-1})				Screen, θ'_{sc} / °C	Sling, θ'_{sl} / °C
100	100.00	97.16	304.5	1.063	13.61	52.0	52.0	52.0	52.0
96	96.52	93.27	294.4	1.058	13.14	51.3	51.3	51.4	51.3
92	93.01	89.38	284.3	1.052	12.66	50.5	50.7	50.7	50.7
88	89.46	85.50	274.2	1.046	12.18	49.7	49.9	50.0	50.0
84	85.86	81.61	264.1	1.041	11.69	48.9	49.2	49.3	49.2
80	82.23	77.72	254.0	1.035	11.19	48.1	48.4	48.5	48.5
76	78.56	73.84	243.9	1.029	10.69	47.2	47.6	47.8	47.7
72	74.84	69.95	233.9	1.024	10.19	46.2	46.8	47.0	46.9
70	72.97	68.01	228.8	1.021	9.934	45.7	46.4	46.6	46.4
68	71.09	66.07	223.8	1.018	9.677	45.2	45.9	46.1	46.0
66	69.19	64.12	218.7	1.015	9.420	44.7	45.5	45.7	45.5
64	67.29	62.18	213.7	1.012	9.160	44.1	45.0	45.3	45.1
62	65.37	60.24	208.7	1.009	8.899	43.6	44.6	44.8	44.6
60	63.45	58.29	203.6	1.007	8.637	43.0	44.1	44.3	44.1
58	61.51	56.35	198.6	1.004	8.373	42.4	43.6	43.9	43.6
56	59.56	54.41	193.5	1.001	8.108	41.8	43.1	43.4	43.1
54	57.60	52.46	188.5	0.9980	7.841	41.2	42.5	42.9	42.6
52	55.63	50.52	183.4	0.9951	7.573	40.5	42.0	42.4	42.1
50	53.64	48.58	178.4	0.9923	7.303	39.8	41.5	41.8	41.6
48	51.65	46.63	173.4	0.9894	7.031	39.1	40.9	41.3	41.0
46	49.64	44.69	168.3	0.9866	6.758	38.4	40.3	40.7	40.4
44	47.62	42.75	163.3	0.9837	6.483	37.6	39.7	40.2	39.8
42	45.59	40.81	158.2	0.9809	6.207	36.8	39.1	39.6	39.2
40	43.55	38.86	153.2	0.9780	5.929	36.0	38.5	39.0	38.6
38	41.50	36.92	148.1	0.9752	5.649	35.1	37.8	38.4	37.9
36	39.43	34.98	143.1	0.9723	5.368	34.2	37.1	37.7	37.3
34	37.35	33.03	138.1	0.9695	5.085	33.2	36.4	37.1	36.6
32	35.26	31.09	133.0	0.9667	4.800	32.2	35.7	36.4	35.8
30	33.16	29.15	128.0	0.9638	4.513	31.1	35.0	35.7	35.1
28	31.04	27.20	122.9	0.9610	4.225	29.9	34.2	34.9	34.3
24	26.77	23.32	112.8	0.9553	3.644	27.4	32.5	33.4	32.7
20	22.44	19.43	102.8	0.9495	3.056	24.4	30.8	31.8	30.9
16	18.06	15.54	92.68	0.9438	2.459	20.8	28.8	30.0	29.0
12	13.63	11.66	82.59	0.9381	1.856	16.3	26.7	28.1	26.9
8	9.14	7.772	72.51	0.9324	1.245	10.2	24.3	26.0	24.6
4	4.60	3.886	62.42	0.9267	0.6263	0.3	21.7	23.7	22.0
0	0.00	0.000	52.34	0.9210	0.0000	—	18.8	21.1	19.2

53 °C DRY-BULB

Percentage saturation, μ / %	Relative humidity, ϕ /%	Value of stated parameter per kg dry air			Vapour pressure, p_v / kPa	Dew point temperature, θ_d / °C	Adiabatic saturation temperature, $\theta\star$ / °C	Wet bulb temperature	
		Moisture content, g / (g·kg^{-1})	Specific enthalpy, h / (kJ·kg^{-1})	Specific volume, v / (m^3·kg^{-1})				Screen, θ'_{sc} / °C	Sling, θ'_{sl} / °C
100	100.00	102.87	320.3	1.075	14.29	53.0	53.0	53.0	53.0
96	96.55	98.70	309.7	1.069	13.80	52.3	52.3	52.4	52.3
92	93.06	94.59	299.0	1.063	13.30	51.5	51.7	51.7	51.7
88	89.53	90.48	288.3	1.057	12.80	50.7	50.9	51.0	51.0
84	85.96	86.37	277.6	1.051	12.29	49.9	50.2	50.3	50.2
80	82.35	82.25	266.9	1.045	11.77	49.1	49.4	49.5	49.5
76	78.69	78.14	256.3	1.039	11.25	48.2	48.6	48.8	48.7
72	74.99	74.03	245.6	1.033	10.72	47.2	47.8	47.9	47.8
70	73.13	71.97	240.2	1.030	10.45	46.7	47.4	47.5	47.4
68	71.25	69.92	234.9	1.027	10.18	46.2	46.9	47.1	47.0
66	69.36	67.86	229.6	1.024	9.914	45.7	46.5	46.7	46.5
64	67.46	65.80	224.2	1.021	9.642	45.1	46.0	46.2	46.0
62	65.55	63.75	218.9	1.018	9.369	44.6	45.5	45.7	45.6
60	63.63	61.69	213.5	1.015	9.095	44.0	45.0	45.3	45.1
58	61.69	59.63	208.2	1.012	8.818	43.4	44.5	44.8	44.6
56	59.75	57.58	202.9	1.009	8.540	42.8	44.0	44.3	44.1
54	57.79	55.52	197.5	1.006	8.260	42.1	43.5	43.8	43.6
52	55.82	53.46	192.2	1.003	7.979	41.5	42.9	43.3	43.0
50	53.84	51.41	186.8	0.9995	7.695	40.8	42.4	42.7	42.5
48	51.85	49.35	181.5	0.9965	7.410	40.1	41.8	42.2	41.9
46	49.84	47.30	176.2	0.9934	7.124	39.3	41.2	41.6	41.3
44	47.82	45.24	170.8	0.9904	6.835	38.6	40.6	41.1	40.7
42	45.79	43.18	165.5	0.9874	6.545	37.8	40.0	40.5	40.1
40	43.74	41.13	160.1	0.9844	6.252	36.9	39.3	39.9	39.5
38	41.69	39.07	154.8	0.9814	5.958	36.1	38.7	39.2	38.8
36	39.62	37.01	149.5	0.9783	5.663	35.1	38.0	38.6	38.1
34	37.53	34.96	144.1	0.9753	5.365	34.2	37.3	37.9	37.4
32	35.44	32.90	138.8	0.9723	5.065	33.1	36.5	37.2	36.7
30	33.33	30.85	133.4	0.9693	4.764	32.0	35.8	36.5	35.9
28	31.21	28.79	128.1	0.9662	4.460	30.9	35.0	35.7	35.1
24	26.92	24.68	117.4	0.9602	3.848	28.3	33.3	34.2	33.5
20	22.58	20.56	106.7	0.9541	3.227	25.3	31.5	32.5	31.7
16	18.18	16.45	96.06	0.9481	2.599	21.7	29.5	30.7	29.7
12	13.72	12.34	85.38	0.9420	1.962	17.2	27.3	28.7	27.5
8	9.21	8.225	74.70	0.9360	1.316	11.1	24.9	26.5	25.2
4	4.64	4.112	64.02	0.9299	0.6625	1.1	22.2	24.1	22.5
0	0.00	0.000	53.34	0.9238	0.0000	—	19.1	21.4	19.5

54 °C DRY-BULB

Percentage saturation, μ / %	Relative humidity, ϕ /%	Value of stated parameter per kg dry air			Vapour pressure, p_v / kPa	Dew point temperature, θ_d / °C	Adiabatic saturation temperature, $\theta\star$ / °C	Wet bulb temperature	
		Moisture content, g / (g·kg^{-1})	Specific enthalpy, h / (kJ·kg^{-1})	Specific volume, v / (m³·kg^{-1})				Screen, θ'_{sc} / °C	Sling, θ'_{sl} / °C
100	100.00	108.8	337.1	1.0869	15.00	54.0	54.0	54.0	54.0
96	96.58	104.5	325.8	1.0805	14.49	53.3	53.3	53.4	53.3
92	93.11	100.1	314.5	1.0741	13.97	52.5	52.6	52.7	52.7
88	89.61	95.76	303.2	1.0678	13.44	51.7	51.9	52.0	52.0
84	86.06	91.40	291.9	1.0614	12.91	50.9	51.2	51.3	51.2
80	82.47	87.05	280.6	1.0550	12.37	50.1	50.4	50.5	50.4
76	78.83	82.70	269.2	1.0486	11.83	49.2	49.6	49.7	49.6
72	75.15	78.35	257.9	1.0422	11.27	48.2	48.8	48.9	48.8
70	73.29	76.17	252.3	1.0390	10.99	47.7	48.3	48.5	48.4
68	71.42	73.99	246.6	1.0358	10.71	47.2	47.9	48.1	47.9
66	69.54	71.82	241.0	1.0326	10.43	46.7	47.4	47.6	47.5
64	67.64	69.64	235.3	1.0294	10.16	46.1	47.0	47.2	47.0
62	65.74	67.47	229.7	1.0262	9.862	45.6	46.5	46.7	46.5
60	63.82	65.29	224.0	1.0230	9.574	45.0	46.0	46.2	46.0
58	61.89	63.11	218.4	1.0198	9.285	44.4	45.5	45.7	45.5
56	59.95	60.94	212.7	1.0166	8.993	43.8	45.0	45.2	45.0
54	57.99	58.76	207.0	1.0134	8.700	43.1	44.4	44.7	44.5
52	56.02	56.58	201.4	1.0102	8.405	42.5	43.9	44.2	44.0
50	54.04	54.41	195.7	1.0070	8.108	41.8	43.3	43.7	43.4
48	52.05	52.23	190.1	1.0038	7.809	41.1	42.7	43.1	42.8
46	50.05	50.06	184.4	1.0006	7.508	40.3	42.1	42.5	42.2
44	48.03	47.88	178.8	0.9974	7.205	39.6	41.5	42.0	41.6
42	45.99	45.70	173.1	0.9942	6.900	38.8	40.9	41.4	41.0
40	43.95	43.53	167.5	0.9909	6.593	37.9	40.2	40.7	40.4
38	41.89	41.35	161.8	0.9877	6.284	37.0	39.6	40.1	39.7
36	39.82	39.17	156.1	0.9845	5.973	36.1	38.9	39.4	39.0
34	37.73	37.00	150.5	0.9813	5.660	35.1	38.1	38.7	38.3
32	35.63	34.82	144.8	0.9781	5.345	34.1	37.4	38.0	37.5
30	33.51	32.64	139.2	0.9749	5.028	33.0	36.6	37.3	36.8
28	31.38	30.47	133.5	0.9717	4.708	31.8	35.8	36.5	36.0
24	27.08	26.12	122.2	0.9653	4.063	29.3	34.1	34.9	34.3
20	22.72	21.76	110.9	0.9588	3.409	26.2	32.2	33.2	32.4
16	18.30	17.41	99.59	0.9524	2.746	22.6	30.2	31.3	30.4
12	13.82	13.06	88.28	0.9460	2.074	18.1	27.9	29.3	28.2
8	9.28	8.705	76.97	0.9396	1.392	11.9	25.4	27.0	25.7
4	4.67	4.353	65.66	0.9331	0.7009	1.9	22.6	24.6	22.9
0	0.00	0.000	54.35	0.9267	0.0000	—	19.4	21.8	19.8

55 °C DRY-BULB

Percentage saturation, μ / %	Relative humidity, ϕ /%	Value of stated parameter per kg dry air			Vapour pressure, p_v / kPa	Dew point temperature, θ_d / °C	Adiabatic saturation temperature, $\theta\star$ / °C	Wet bulb temperature	
		Moisture content, g / (g·kg^{-1})	Specific enthalpy, h / (kJ·kg^{-1})	Specific volume, v / (m³·kg^{-1})				Screen, θ'_{sc} / °C	Sling, θ'_{sl} / °C
100	100.00	115.2	354.8	1.100	15.74	55.0	55.0	55.0	55.0
96	96.60	110.6	342.9	1.093	15.21	54.3	54.3	54.4	54.3
92	93.17	106.0	330.9	1.086	14.67	53.5	53.6	53.7	53.7
88	89.69	101.4	318.9	1.079	14.12	52.7	52.9	53.0	52.9
84	86.16	96.74	306.9	1.072	13.56	51.9	52.2	52.3	52.2
80	82.59	92.14	294.9	1.066	13.00	51.1	51.4	51.5	51.4
76	78.97	87.53	283.0	1.059	12.43	50.2	50.6	50.7	50.6
72	75.31	82.92	271.0	1.052	11.85	49.2	49.7	49.9	49.8
70	73.46	80.62	265.0	1.049	11.56	48.7	49.3	49.5	49.4
68	71.60	78.32	259.0	1.045	11.2	48.2	48.9	49.0	48.9
66	69.72	76.01	253.0	1.042	10.97	47.7	48.4	48.6	48.4
64	67.83	73.71	247.0	1.038	10.68	47.1	47.9	48.1	48.0
62	65.93	71.41	241.0	1.035	10.38	46.6	47.4	47.7	47.5
60	64.02	69.10	235.0	1.032	10.08	46.0	46.9	47.2	47.0
58	62.09	66.80	229.1	1.028	9.774	45.4	46.4	46.7	46.5
56	60.16	64.50	223.1	1.025	9.479	44.8	45.9	46.2	46.0
54	58.20	62.19	217.1	1.022	9.161	44.1	45.4	45.7	45.4
52	56.24	59.89	211.1	1.018	8.852	43.5	44.8	45.1	44.9
50	54.26	57.59	205.1	1.015	8.541	42.8	44.2	44.6	44.3
48	52.27	55.28	199.1	1.011	8.237	42.1	43.7	44.0	43.8
46	50.26	52.98	193.1	1.008	7.911	41.3	43.1	43.5	43.2
44	48.24	50.68	187.1	1.004	7.593	40.5	42.4	42.9	42.5
42	46.21	48.37	181.1	1.001	7.273	39.7	41.8	42.2	41.9
40	44.16	46.07	175.2	0.9977	6.951	38.9	41.1	41.6	41.2
38	42.10	43.76	169.2	0.9943	6.636	38.0	40.4	41.0	40.6
36	40.02	41.46	163.2	0.9909	6.300	37.1	39.7	40.3	39.9
34	37.93	39.16	157.2	0.9875	5.971	36.1	39.0	39.6	39.1
32	35.83	36.86	151.2	0.9841	5.640	35.1	38.2	38.9	38.4
30	33.71	34.55	145.2	0.9807	5.305	34.0	37.4	38.1	37.6
28	31.57	32.25	139.2	0.9773	4.979	32.8	36.6	37.4	36.8
24	27.25	27.64	127.2	0.9705	4.290	30.2	34.9	35.7	35.0
20	22.88	23.03	115.3	0.9637	3.600	27.2	33.0	34.0	33.2
16	18.43	18.43	103.3	0.9568	2.901	23.5	30.9	32.0	31.1
12	13.93	13.82	91.30	0.9500	2.192	19.0	28.6	29.9	28.8
8	9.35	9.214	79.32	0.9432	1.472	12.7	26.0	27.6	26.3
4	4.71	4.607	67.34	0.9363	0.7416	2.7	23.1	25.0	23.4
0	0.00	0.000	55.36	0.9295	0.0000	—	19.7	22.1	20.1

56 °C DRY-BULB

Percentage saturation, μ / %	Relative humidity, ϕ /%	Value of stated parameter per kg dry air			Vapour pressure, p_v / kPa	Dew point temperature, θ_d / °C	Adiabatic saturation temperature, $\theta^\star$ / °C	Wet bulb temperature	
		Moisture content, g / (g·kg⁻¹)	Specific enthalpy, h / (kJ·kg⁻¹)	Specific volume, v / (m³·kg⁻¹)				Screen, θ'_{sc} / °C	Sling, θ'_{sl} / °C
100	100.00	121.9	373.6	1.113	16.51	56.0	56.0	56.0	56.0
96	96.63	117.0	360.9	1.106	15.96	55.3	55.3	55.4	55.3
92	93.23	112.2	348.2	1.099	15.39	54.5	54.6	54.7	54.7
88	89.77	107.3	335.5	1.091	14.82	53.7	53.9	54.0	53.9
84	86.27	102.4	322.8	1.084	14.24	52.9	53.2	53.2	53.2
80	82.72	97.53	310.2	1.077	13.66	52.1	52.4	52.5	52.4
76	79.12	92.65	297.5	1.070	13.06	51.2	51.6	51.7	51.6
72	75.48	87.78	284.8	1.062	12.46	50.2	50.7	50.9	50.8
70	73.64	85.34	278.4	1.059	12.16	49.7	50.3	50.4	50.3
68	71.78	82.90	272.1	1.055	11.85	49.2	49.8	50.0	49.9
66	69.91	80.46	265.7	1.052	11.54	48.7	49.4	49.6	49.4
64	68.03	78.03	259.4	1.048	11.23	48.1	48.9	49.1	49.0
62	66.14	75.59	253.0	1.044	10.92	47.6	48.4	48.6	48.5
60	64.23	73.15	246.7	1.041	10.60	47.0	47.9	48.1	48.0
58	62.31	70.71	240.4	1.037	10.29	46.4	47.4	47.6	47.5
56	60.37	68.27	234.0	1.034	9.968	45.8	46.9	47.1	46.9
54	58.42	65.83	227.7	1.030	9.646	45.1	46.3	46.6	46.4
52	56.46	63.40	221.3	1.026	9.322	44.5	45.8	46.1	45.8
50	54.49	60.96	215.0	1.023	8.996	43.8	45.2	45.5	45.3
48	52.49	58.52	208.6	1.019	8.667	43.1	44.6	45.0	44.7
46	50.49	56.08	202.3	1.016	8.336	42.3	44.0	44.4	44.1
44	48.47	53.64	195.9	1.012	8.003	41.5	43.4	43.8	43.5
42	46.44	51.20	189.6	1.008	7.667	40.7	42.7	43.1	42.8
40	44.39	48.77	183.3	1.005	7.329	39.9	42.0	42.5	42.1
38	42.32	46.33	176.9	1.001	6.988	39.0	41.3	41.8	41.5
36	40.24	43.89	170.6	0.9976	6.644	38.1	40.6	41.2	40.7
34	38.15	41.45	164.2	0.9939	6.298	37.1	39.9	40.5	40.0
32	36.04	39.01	157.9	0.9903	5.950	36.0	39.1	39.7	39.2
30	33.91	36.57	151.5	0.9867	5.599	34.9	38.3	39.0	38.4
28	31.77	34.14	145.2	0.9831	5.245	33.8	37.5	38.2	37.6
24	27.44	29.26	132.5	0.9759	4.530	31.1	35.7	36.5	35.8
20	23.04	24.38	119.9	0.9686	3.804	28.1	33.7	34.7	33.9
16	18.57	19.51	107.1	0.9614	3.066	24.5	31.6	32.7	31.8
12	14.04	14.63	94.43	0.9541	2.317	19.9	29.2	30.6	29.4
8	9.43	9.753	81.74	0.9469	1.557	13.6	26.5	28.1	26.8
4	4.75	4.877	69.06	0.9396	0.7847	3.5	23.5	25.5	23.8
0	0.00	0.000	56.37	0.9323	0.0000	—	20.0	22.5	20.4

57 °C DRY-BULB

Percentage saturation, μ / %	Relative humidity, ϕ /%	Value of stated parameter per kg dry air			Vapour pressure, p_v / kPa	Dew point temperature, θ_d / °C	Adiabatic saturation temperature, $\theta^\star$ / °C	Wet bulb temperature	
		Moisture content, g / (g·kg⁻¹)	Specific enthalpy, h / (kJ·kg⁻¹)	Specific volume, v / (m³·kg⁻¹)				Screen, θ'_{sc} / °C	Sling, θ'_{sl} / °C
100	100.00	129.1	393.4	1.127	17.31	57.0	57.0	57.0	57.0
96	96.66	123.9	380.0	1.119	16.74	56.3	56.3	56.3	56.3
92	93.29	118.7	366.6	1.112	16.15	55.5	55.6	55.7	55.7
88	89.86	113.6	353.1	1.104	15.56	54.8	54.9	55.0	54.9
84	86.38	108.4	339.7	1.096	14.96	53.9	54.2	54.2	54.2
80	82.86	103.3	326.2	1.089	14.34	53.1	53.4	53.5	53.4
76	79.28	98.09	312.8	1.081	13.73	52.2	52.6	52.7	52.6
72	75.65	92.93	299.3	1.073	13.10	51.2	51.7	51.9	51.8
70	73.82	90.35	292.6	1.070	12.78	50.7	51.3	51.4	51.3
68	71.97	87.77	285.9	1.066	12.46	50.2	50.8	51.0	50.9
66	70.11	85.19	279.2	1.062	12.14	49.7	50.3	50.5	50.4
64	68.24	82.60	272.5	1.058	11.81	49.1	49.9	50.1	49.9
62	66.35	80.02	265.7	1.054	11.49	48.6	49.4	49.6	49.4
60	64.45	77.44	259.0	1.050	11.16	48.0	48.9	49.1	48.9
58	62.53	74.86	252.3	1.047	10.83	47.4	48.4	48.6	48.4
56	60.60	72.28	245.6	1.043	10.49	46.8	47.8	48.1	47.9
54	58.66	69.70	238.9	1.039	10.16	46.1	47.3	47.6	47.4
52	56.70	67.12	232.1	1.035	9.816	45.5	46.7	47.0	46.8
50	54.72	64.53	225.4	1.031	9.474	44.8	46.1	46.5	46.2
48	52.73	61.95	218.7	1.027	9.130	44.1	45.5	45.9	45.6
46	50.73	59.37	212.0	1.024	8.783	43.3	44.9	45.3	45.0
44	48.71	56.79	205.2	1.020	8.433	42.5	44.3	44.7	44.4
42	46.67	54.21	198.5	1.016	8.080	41.7	43.6	44.1	43.7
40	44.62	51.63	191.8	1.012	7.725	40.9	42.9	43.4	43.1
38	42.56	49.05	185.1	1.008	7.368	40.0	42.2	42.7	42.4
36	40.47	46.46	178.4	1.004	7.007	39.0	41.5	42.0	41.6
34	38.37	43.88	171.6	1.001	6.644	38.1	40.7	41.3	40.9
32	36.26	41.30	164.9	0.9967	6.277	37.0	40.0	40.6	40.1
30	34.13	38.72	158.2	0.9929	5.908	35.9	39.1	39.8	39.3
28	31.98	36.14	151.5	0.9891	5.536	34.7	38.3	39.0	38.5
24	27.63	30.98	138.0	0.9814	4.783	32.1	36.5	37.3	36.7
20	23.21	25.81	124.6	0.9737	4.018	29.1	34.5	35.4	34.7
16	18.72	20.65	111.1	0.9660	3.240	25.4	32.3	33.4	32.5
12	14.15	15.49	97.70	0.9583	2.450	20.8	29.9	31.2	30.1
8	9.51	10.33	84.26	0.9506	1.647	14.5	27.1	28.7	27.4
4	4.80	5.163	70.82	0.9429	0.8303	4.3	24.0	25.9	24.3
0	0.00	0.000	57.37	0.9352	0.0000	—	20.3	22.8	20.7

58 °C DRY-BULB

Percentage saturation, μ / %	Relative humidity, ϕ /%	Value of stated parameter per kg dry air			Vapour pressure, p_v / kPa	Dew point temperature, θ_d / °C	Adiabatic saturation temperature, $\theta^\star$ / °C	Wet bulb temperature	
		Moisture content, g / (g·kg⁻¹)	Specific enthalpy, h / (kJ·kg⁻¹)	Specific volume, v / (m³·kg⁻¹)				Screen, θ'_{sc} / °C	Sling, θ'_{sl} / °C
100	100.00	136.70	414.5	1.141	18.15	58.0	58.0	58.0	58.0
96	96.70	131.20	400.2	1.134	17.55	57.3	57.3	57.3	57.3
92	93.35	125.70	386.0	1.125	16.94	56.5	56.6	56.7	56.7
88	89.95	120.30	371.7	1.117	16.32	55.8	55.9	56.0	55.9
84	86.50	114.80	357.5	1.109	15.70	54.9	55.2	55.2	55.2
80	83.00	109.30	343.3	1.101	15.06	54.1	54.4	54.5	54.4
76	79.45	103.70	329.0	1.093	14.42	53.2	53.6	53.7	53.6
72	75.84	98.40	314.8	1.085	13.76	52.2	52.7	52.8	52.7
70	74.02	95.67	307.6	1.081	13.43	51.7	52.3	52.4	52.3
68	72.18	92.93	300.5	1.077	13.10	51.2	51.8	52.0	51.8
66	70.32	90.20	293.4	1.073	12.76	50.7	51.3	51.5	51.4
64	68.46	87.47	286.3	1.068	12.42	50.1	50.8	51.0	50.9
62	66.58	84.73	279.2	1.064	12.08	49.6	50.3	50.6	50.4
60	64.68	82.00	272.0	1.060	11.74	49.0	49.8	50.1	49.9
58	62.77	79.27	264.9	1.056	11.39	48.4	49.3	49.6	49.4
56	60.84	76.53	257.8	1.052	11.04	47.8	48.8	49.1	48.9
54	58.90	73.80	250.7	1.048	10.69	47.1	48.2	48.5	48.3
52	56.94	71.07	243.6	1.044	10.33	46.5	47.7	48.0	47.8
50	54.97	68.33	236.4	1.040	9.976	45.8	47.1	47.4	47.2
48	52.98	65.60	229.3	1.036	9.615	45.1	46.5	46.8	46.6
46	50.98	62.87	222.2	1.032	9.252	44.3	45.9	46.2	46.0
44	48.96	60.13	215.1	1.028	8.885	43.5	45.2	45.6	45.3
42	46.92	57.40	207.9	1.024	8.516	42.7	44.5	45.0	44.7
40	44.87	54.67	200.8	1.020	8.143	41.9	43.9	44.3	44.0
38	42.80	51.93	193.7	1.016	7.767	41.0	43.1	43.6	43.3
36	40.72	49.20	186.6	1.012	7.389	40.0	42.4	42.9	42.5
34	38.61	46.47	179.5	1.008	7.007	39.0	41.6	42.2	41.8
32	36.49	43.73	172.3	1.003	6.622	38.0	40.8	41.4	41.0
30	34.35	41.00	165.2	0.9993	6.234	36.9	40.0	40.7	40.2
28	32.20	38.27	158.1	0.9952	5.843	35.7	39.1	39.8	39.3
24	27.83	32.80	143.8	0.9871	5.050	33.1	37.3	38.1	37.5
20	23.39	27.33	129.6	0.9789	4.244	30.0	35.3	36.2	35.5
16	18.87	21.87	115.4	0.9707	3.424	26.3	33.0	34.1	33.2
12	14.28	16.40	101.1	0.9626	2.590	21.7	30.5	31.8	30.8
8	9.60	10.93	86.87	0.9544	1.742	15.3	27.7	29.3	28.0
4	4.84	5.467	72.62	0.9462	0.8788	5.1	24.4	26.4	24.8
0	0.00	0.000	58.38	0.9380	0.0000	—	20.6	23.1	21.1

59 °C DRY-BULB

Percentage saturation, μ / %	Relative humidity, ϕ /%	Value of stated parameter per kg dry air			Vapour pressure, p_v / kPa	Dew point temperature, θ_d / °C	Adiabatic saturation temperature, $\theta^\star$ / °C	Wet bulb temperature	
		Moisture content, g / (g·kg⁻¹)	Specific enthalpy, h / (kJ·kg⁻¹)	Specific volume, v / (m³·kg⁻¹)				Screen, θ'_{sc} / °C	Sling, θ'_{sl} / °C
100	100.00	144.7	436.8	1.157	19.02	59.0	59.0	59.0	59.0
96	96.73	138.9	421.7	1.149	18.39	58.3	58.3	58.3	58.3
92	93.41	133.2	406.6	1.140	17.76	57.5	57.6	57.7	57.7
88	90.05	127.4	391.5	1.131	17.12	56.8	56.9	57.0	56.9
84	86.62	121.6	376.4	1.123	16.47	56.0	56.2	56.2	56.2
80	83.15	115.8	361.3	1.114	15.81	55.1	55.4	55.5	55.4
76	79.62	110.0	346.2	1.105	15.14	54.2	54.6	54.7	54.6
72	76.03	104.2	331.1	1.097	14.46	53.2	53.7	53.8	53.7
70	74.22	101.3	323.6	1.092	14.11	52.7	53.2	53.4	53.3
68	72.39	98.42	316.0	1.088	13.77	52.2	52.8	52.9	52.8
66	70.54	95.53	308.5	1.084	13.41	51.7	52.3	52.5	52.4
64	68.69	92.63	300.9	1.080	13.06	51.2	51.8	52.0	51.9
62	66.81	89.74	293.4	1.075	12.70	50.6	51.3	51.5	51.4
60	64.92	86.84	285.8	1.071	12.35	50.0	50.8	51.0	50.9
58	63.02	83.95	278.3	1.066	11.98	49.4	50.3	50.5	50.4
56	61.09	81.05	270.7	1.062	11.62	48.8	49.8	50.0	49.8
54	59.16	78.16	263.2	1.058	11.25	48.2	49.2	49.5	49.3
52	57.20	75.26	255.6	1.054	10.88	47.5	48.6	48.9	48.7
50	55.23	72.37	248.1	1.049	10.50	46.8	48.0	48.4	48.1
48	53.25	69.47	240.5	1.045	10.13	46.1	47.4	47.8	47.5
46	51.25	66.58	233.0	1.041	9.745	45.3	46.8	47.2	46.9
44	49.23	63.68	225.4	1.036	9.361	44.5	46.1	46.5	46.3
42	47.19	60.79	217.9	1.032	8.973	43.7	45.5	45.9	45.6
40	45.13	57.90	210.3	1.028	8.583	42.9	44.8	45.2	44.9
38	43.06	55.00	202.8	1.023	8.189	42.0	44.1	44.5	44.2
36	40.97	52.11	195.2	1.019	7.791	41.0	43.3	43.8	43.4
34	38.86	49.21	187.7	1.015	7.390	40.0	42.5	43.1	42.7
32	36.74	46.32	180.2	1.010	6.986	39.0	41.7	42.3	41.9
30	34.59	43.42	172.6	1.006	6.578	37.9	40.9	41.5	41.0
28	32.43	40.53	165.1	1.002	6.167	36.7	40.0	40.7	40.2
24	28.04	34.74	150.0	0.9930	5.332	34.0	38.1	38.9	38.3
20	23.58	28.95	134.9	0.9843	4.484	31.0	36.0	37.0	36.2
16	19.03	23.16	119.8	0.9756	3.619	27.3	33.7	34.8	34.0
12	14.41	17.37	104.7	0.9669	2.739	22.6	31.2	32.5	31.4
8	9.69	11.58	89.58	0.9583	1.843	16.2	28.3	29.8	28.5
4	4.89	5.790	74.48	0.9496	0.9302	5.9	24.9	26.9	25.2
0	0.00	0.000	59.39	0.9409	0.0000	—	20.9	23.4	21.4

60 °C DRY-BULB

Percentage saturation, μ / %	Relative humidity, ϕ /%	Value of stated parameter per kg dry air			Vapour pressure, p_v / kPa	Dew point temperature, θ_d / °C	Adiabatic saturation temperature, $\theta\star$ / °C	Wet bulb temperature	
		Moisture content, g / (g·kg^{-1})	Specific enthalpy, h / (kJ·kg^{-1})	Specific volume, v / (m^3·kg^{-1})				Screen, θ'_{sc} / °C	Sling, θ'_{sl} / °C
100	100.00	153.3	460.4	1.173	19.92	60.0	60.0	60.0	60.0
96	96.77	147.2	444.4	1.164	19.28	59.3	59.3	59.3	59.3
92	93.48	141.1	428.4	1.155	18.62	58.6	58.6	58.7	58.7
88	90.14	134.9	412.4	1.146	17.96	57.8	57.9	58.0	57.9
84	86.75	128.8	396.4	1.137	17.28	57.0	57.2	57.2	57.2
80	83.30	122.7	380.4	1.128	16.59	56.1	56.4	56.5	56.4
76	79.80	116.5	364.4	1.118	15.90	55.2	55.6	55.7	55.6
72	76.23	110.4	348.4	1.109	15.19	54.3	54.7	54.8	54.7
70	74.43	107.3	340.4	1.105	14.83	53.8	54.2	54.4	54.3
68	72.61	104.3	332.4	1.100	14.46	53.2	53.8	53.9	53.8
66	70.78	101.2	324.4	1.096	14.10	52.7	53.3	53.5	53.4
64	68.92	98.14	316.4	1.091	13.73	52.2	52.8	53.0	52.9
62	67.06	95.06	308.4	1.086	13.36	51.6	52.3	52.5	52.4
60	65.17	91.99	300.4	1.082	12.98	51.0	51.8	52.0	51.9
58	63.28	88.93	292.4	1.077	12.60	50.4	51.3	51.5	51.4
56	61.36	85.86	284.4	1.073	12.22	49.8	50.7	51.0	50.8
54	59.43	82.79	276.4	1.068	11.84	49.2	50.2	50.4	50.3
52	57.48	79.73	268.4	1.063	11.45	48.5	49.6	49.9	49.7
50	55.51	76.66	260.4	1.059	11.06	47.8	49.0	49.3	49.1
48	53.53	73.60	252.4	1.054	10.66	47.1	48.4	48.7	48.5
46	51.52	70.53	244.4	1.050	10.26	46.3	47.8	48.1	47.9
44	49.50	67.46	236.4	1.045	9.861	45.6	47.1	47.5	47.2
42	47.47	64.40	228.4	1.041	9.455	44.7	46.4	46.8	46.5
40	45.41	61.33	220.4	1.036	9.046	43.9	45.7	46.2	45.8
38	43.34	58.26	212.4	1.031	8.632	43.0	45.0	45.5	45.1
36	41.24	55.20	204.4	1.027	8.215	42.0	44.2	44.7	44.4
34	39.13	52.13	196.4	1.022	7.795	41.0	43.4	44.0	43.6
32	37.00	49.06	188.4	1.018	7.370	40.0	42.6	43.2	42.8
30	34.84	46.00	180.4	1.013	6.941	38.9	41.8	42.4	41.9
28	32.67	42.93	172.4	1.008	6.508	37.7	40.9	41.5	41.0
24	28.27	36.80	156.4	0.9991	5.631	35.0	38.9	39.7	39.1
20	23.78	30.66	140.4	0.9899	4.737	31.9	36.8	37.8	37.0
16	19.21	24.53	124.4	0.9806	3.826	28.2	34.5	35.6	34.7
12	14.54	18.40	108.4	0.9714	2.897	23.5	31.8	33.1	32.1
8	9.79	12.27	92.40	0.9622	1.950	17.1	28.8	30.4	29.1
4	4.94	6.133	76.40	0.9529	0.9848	6.8	25.3	27.3	25.7
0	0.00	0.000	60.40	0.9437	0.0000	—	21.2	23.7	21.7

2   Properties of water and steam

2.1   Introduction

The data presented in Tables 2.1, 2.2, and 2.3 are based upon the tables prepared by the National Engineering Laboratory[1], augmented as necessary by further values obtained by interpolation from the tables of Mayhew and Rogers[2].

Other data have been published, e.g. *UK Steam Tables in SI Units*[3]. These tables differ slightly from the NEL Steam Tables. For building services applications, these variations are not significant. However, for critical applications the latest internationally agreed tables should be consulted.

The units and symbols used are as follows:

c_f Specific heat capacity ($kJ \cdot kg^{-1} \cdot K^{-1}$)

h_f Specific enthalpy (saturated liquid) ($kJ \cdot kg^{-1}$)

h_g Specific enthalpy (saturated vapour) ($kJ \cdot kg^{-1}$)

h_{fg} Specific latent heat of evaporation ($kJ \cdot kg^{-1}$)

p Absolute pressure (kPa)

p_s Absolute saturation pressure (kPa)

v Specific volume ($m^3 \cdot kg^{-1}$)

$(Pr)_f$ Prandtl number (saturated liquid)

$(Pr)_g$ Prandtl number (saturated vapour)

θ Temperature (°C)

θ_s Temperature (saturation) (°C)

μ_f Dynamic viscosity (saturated liquid) ($\mu Pa \cdot s$)

ρ Density (specific mass) ($kg \cdot m^{-3}$)

Table 2.1 lists values of saturation temperature, specific volume, specific enthalpies of saturated liquid and vapour and the specific latent heat of evaporation at round values of absolute pressure.

The values quoted were in all cases derived from NEL Table 2, except for Prandtl numbers, which were obtained by Lagrangian interpolation from Mayhew and Rogers, page 10.

Table 2.2 lists values of the saturation vapour pressure, specific heat capacity, dynamic viscosity, density (specific mass) and of the specific enthalpy and Prandtl numbers of the saturated liquid and vapour at round values of temperature.

The values quoted were derived as follows:

—   vapour pressure, density (as reciprocal of volume) and specific enthalpy from NEL Table 1.

—   specific heat capacity, dynamic viscosity and Prandtl numbers (all by Lagrangian interpolation) from Mayhew and Rogers, page 10.

Table 2.3 lists values of specific enthalpy for superheated steam at round values of absolute pressure for a restricted range of final temperatures.

The values quoted were in all cases derived from NEL Table 3.

References

1   *Steam Tables 1964* (Edinburgh: National Engineering Laboratory/Her Majesty's Stationery Office) (1964)

2   Mayhew Y R and Rogers G F C *Thermodynamics and transport properties of fluids* (Oxford: Blackwell) (1989)

3   *UK Steam Tables in SI units* (Oxford: Butterworth-Heinemann) (1970)

Table 2.1 Properties of saturated steam

Absolute pressure, p / kPa	Temperature, θ_s / °C	Specific enthalpy			Specific volume, v / $(m^3 \cdot kg^{-1})$	Specific heat capacity of vapour, c_f / $(kJ \cdot kg^{-1} \cdot K^{-1})$	Prandtl number, $(Pr)_g$	Absolute pressure, p / kPa
		In saturated liquid, h_f / $(kJ \cdot kg^{-1})$	Latent heat of evaporation, h_{fg} / $(kJ \cdot kg^{-1})$	In saturated vapour, h_g / $(kJ \cdot kg^{-1})$				
1	6.98	29.3	2484.3	2513.6	129.205	1.86	1.03	1
2	17.51	73.5	2459.5	2533.0	67.010	1.87	1.03	2
4	28.98	121.4	2432.4	2553.9	34.805	1.88	1.02	4
6	36.18	151.5	2415.3	2566.8	23.742	1.88	1.02	6
8	41.53	173.9	2402.5	2576.4	18.104	1.89	1.02	8
10	45.83	191.8	2392.2	2584.1	14.673	1.89	1.03	10
20	60.09	251.5	2357.7	2609.1	7.648	1.91	1.03	20
30	69.13	289.3	2335.4	2624.8	5.228	1.93	1.03	30
40	75.89	317.7	2318.6	2636.3	3.992	1.94	1.03	40
50	81.35	340.6	2304.9	2645.4	3.239	1.95	1.04	50
60	85.95	359.9	2293.2	2653.1	2.731	1.96	1.04	60
70	89.96	376.8	2282.9	2659.7	2.364	1.97	1.04	70
80	83.51	391.7	2273.7	2665.4	2.087	1.98	1.04	80
90	96.71	405.2	2265.4	2670.6	1.869	1.99	1.04	90
100	99.63	417.5	2257.7	2675.2	1.694	2.01	1.04	100
110	102.32	428.8	2250.6	2679.5	1.549	2.02	1.05	110
120	104.81	439.3	2244.0	2683.3	1.428	2.03	1.05	120
130	107.13	449.2	2237.8	2686.9	1.325	2.04	1.05	130
140	109.32	458.4	2231.9	2690.3	1.237	2.05	1.05	140
150	111.37	367.5	2226.3	2693.4	1.159	2.05	1.05	150
160	113.32	475.4	2221.0	2696.4	1.091	2.06	1.06	160
170	115.17	483.2	2215.9	2699.1	1.031	2.07	1.06	170
180	116.93	490.7	2211.1	2701.8	0.977	2.07	1.06	180
190	118.62	497.9	2206.4	2704.2	0.929	2.08	1.06	190
200	120.23	504.7	2201.9	2706.6	0.886	2.09	1.06	200
210	121.78	511.3	2197.6	2708.9	0.846	2.10	1.06	210
220	123.27	517.6	2193.4	2711.0	0.810	2.11	1.07	220
230	124.71	523.7	2189.3	2713.1	0.777	2.12	1.07	230
240	126.09	529.6	2185.4	2715.0	0.747	2.13	1.07	240
250	127.43	535.4	2181.6	2716.9	0.719	2.13	1.07	250
260	128.73	540.9	2177.8	2718.7	0.693	2.14	1.07	260
270	129.99	546.2	2174.2	2720.5	0.669	2.15	1.08	270
280	131.21	551.5	2170.7	2722.2	0.646	2.16	1.08	280
290	132.39	556.5	2167.3	2723.8	0.625	2.16	1.08	290
300	133.54	561.4	2163.9	2725.4	0.606	2.17	1.08	300
310	134.66	566.2	2160.6	2726.9	0.587	2.18	1.09	310
320	135.76	570.9	2157.4	2728.4	0.570	2.19	1.09	320
330	136.82	575.5	2154.3	2729.8	0.554	2.20	1.09	330
340	137.86	579.9	2151.2	2731.1	0.539	2.20	1.09	340
350	138.88	584.3	2148.2	2732.5	0.524	2.21	1.10	350
360	139.87	588.5	2145.2	2733.8	0.510	2.21	1.10	360
370	140.84	592.7	2142.3	2735.0	0.497	2.22	1.10	370
380	141.79	596.8	2139.5	2736.3	0.485	2.22	1.10	380
390	142.72	600.8	2136.7	2737.5	0.473	2.23	1.11	390
400	143.63	604.7	2133.9	2738.6	0.462	2.24	1.11	400
410	144.52	608.5	2131.2	2739.8	0.452	2.24	1.11	410
420	145.39	612.3	2128.6	2740.9	0.442	2.25	1.11	420
430	146.25	616.0	2125.9	2741.9	0.432	2.26	1.11	430
440	147.09	619.6	2123.4	2743.0	0.423	2.27	1.12	440
450	147.92	623.2	2120.8	2744.0	0.414	2.28	1.12	450
460	148.73	626.7	2118.2	2745.0	0.405	2.28	1.12	460
470	149.53	630.1	2115.8	2746.0	0.397	2.29	1.13	470
480	150.31	633.5	2113.4	2746.9	0.389	2.29	1.13	480
490	151.09	636.8	2111.0	2747.8	0.382	2.30	1.13	490
500	151.85	640.1	2108.6	2748.7	0.375	2.31	1.13	500

Table 2.1 Properties of saturated steam — *continued*

Absolute pressure, p / kPa	Temperature, θ_s / °C	Specific enthalpy			Specific volume, v / (m³·kg⁻¹)	Specific heat capacity of vapour, c_f / (kJ·kg⁻¹·K⁻¹)	Prandtl number, $(Pr)_g$	Absolute pressure, p / kPa
		In saturated liquid, h_f / (kJ·kg⁻¹)	Latent heat of evaporation, h_{fg} / (kJ·kg⁻¹)	In saturated vapour, h_g / (kJ·kg⁻¹)				
520	153.33	646.5	2104.0	2750.5	0.361	2.32	1.13	520
540	154.77	652.8	2099.4	2752.2	0.349	2.33	1.14	540
560	156.16	658.8	2095.0	2753.8	0.337	2.34	1.14	560
580	157.52	664.7	2090.7	2755.4	0.326	2.35	1.14	580
600	158.84	670.4	2086.4	2756.8	0.316	2.37	1.14	600
620	160.12	676.0	2082.3	2758.3	0.306	2.38	1.15	620
640	161.38	681.5	2078.2	2759.9	0.297	2.39	1.15	640
660	162.60	686.8	2074.2	2761.0	0.288	2.40	1.16	660
680	163.79	692.0	2070.3	2762.3	0.280	2.41	1.16	680
700	164.96	697.1	2066.4	2763.5	0.273	2.43	1.16	700
720	166.10	702.0	2062.7	2764.7	0.266	2.44	1.17	720
740	167.21	706.9	2058.9	2765.8	0.259	2.45	1.17	740
760	168.30	711.7	2055.3	2767.0	0.252	2.47	1.17	760
780	169.37	716.4	2051.7	2768.0	0.246	2.48	1.18	780
800	170.41	720.9	2048.2	2769.1	0.240	2.49	1.18	800
820	171.44	725.4	2044.7	2770.1	0.235	2.51	1.18	820
840	172.45	729.8	2041.2	2771.1	0.229	2.52	1.19	840
860	173.43	734.2	2037.8	2772.0	0.224	2.53	1.19	860
880	174.40	738.4	2034.5	2772.9	0.220	2.55	1.20	880
900	175.36	742.6	2031.2	2773.8	0.215	2.56	1.21	900
920	176.29	746.8	2028.0	2774.7	0.210	2.57	1.21	920
940	177.21	750.8	2024.7	2775.6	0.206	2.58	1.21	940
960	178.12	754.8	2021.6	2776.4	0.202	2.60	1.22	960
980	179.01	758.7	2018.4	2777.2	0.198	2.61	1.22	980
1000	179.88	762.6	2015.3	2777.9	0.194	2.62	1.23	1000
1100	184.06	781.1	2000.4	2781.5	0.177	2.67	1.25	1100
1200	187.96	798.4	1986.2	2784.6	0.163	2.71	1.26	1200
1300	191.60	814.7	1972.6	2787.3	0.151	2.76	1.27	1300
1400	195.04	830.0	1959.6	2789.7	0.141	2.81	1.29	1400
1500	198.28	844.6	1947.1	2791.8	0.132	2.86	1.30	1500
1600	201.37	858.5	1935.1	2793.6	0.124	2.91	1.31	1600
1700	204.30	871.8	1923.4	2795.2	0.117	2.96	1.33	1700
1800	207.10	884.5	1912.1	2796.6	0.110	3.01	1.35	1800
1900	209.79	896.8	1901.1	2797.8	0.105	3.07	1.36	1900
2000	212.37	908.6	1890.4	2798.9	0.100	3.13	1.37	2000
2200	217.24	930.0	1869.7	2800.6	0.091	3.19	1.39	2200
2400	221.78	951.9	1850.0	2801.9	0.083	3.25	1.41	2400
2600	226.03	971.7	1831.0	2802.7	0.077	3.36	1.43	2600
2800	230.04	990.5	1812.7	2903.2	0.071	3.45	1.44	2800
3000	233.84	1008.3	1795.0	2803.4	0.067	3.53	1.46	3000
3200	237.44	1025.4	1777.9	2803.3	0.062	3.60	1.49	3200
3400	240.88	1041.8	1761.2	2803.0	0.059	3.68	1.53	3400
3600	244.16	1057.6	1744.9	2802.4	0.055	3.77	1.57	3600
3800	247.31	1072.7	1728.9	2802.1	0.052	3.86	1.59	3800
4000	250.33	1087.4	1713.4	2801.7	0.050	3.94	1.60	4000

Table 2.2 Properties of water at saturation

Temperature, θ_s / °C	Absolute vapour pressure, p_s / kPa	Specific heat capacity, c_f / (kJ·kg^{-1}·K^{-1})	Dynamic viscosity, μ_f / (μPa·s)	Density, ρ / (kg·m^{-3})	Specific enthalpy of liquid, h_f / (kJ·kg^{-1})	Prandtl number, $(Pr)_g$	Temperature, θ_s / °C
0.01	0.61	4.2100	1782	999.8	0.00	13.61	0.01
1	0.66	4.2096	1724	999.8	4.17	13.11	1
2	0.71	4.2088	1669	999.9	8.39	12.64	2
3	0.76	4.2075	1616	999.9	12.60	12.18	3
4	0.81	4.2059	1565	999.9	16.80	11.75	4
5	0.87	4.2040	1517	999.9	21.01	11.33	5
6	0.93	4.2019	1471	999.9	25.21	10.93	6
7	1.00	4.1997	1427	999.9	29.41	10.55	7
8	1.07	4.1974	1385	999.8	33.61	10.19	8
9	1.15	4.1952	1344	999.7	37.81	9.85	9
10	1.23	4.1930	1306	999.7	42.00	9.52	10
11	1.31	4.1913	1269	999.6	46.19	9.21	11
12	1.40	4.1897	1234	999.4	50.38	8.92	12
13	1.50	4.1883	1201	999.3	54.57	8.64	13
14	1.60	4.1871	1169	999.2	58.75	8.37	14
15	1.70	4.1860	1138	999.0	62.94	8.12	15
16	1.82	4.1852	1108	998.9	67.13	7.88	16
17	1.94	4.1845	1080	998.7	71.31	7.64	17
18	2.06	4.1839	1053	998.6	75.49	7.42	18
19	2.20	4.1834	1027	998.4	79.68	7.20	19
20	2.34	4.1830	1002	998.2	83.86	7.00	20
21	2.49	4.1826	978	997.9	88.04	6.81	21
22	2.64	4.1821	955	997.7	92.23	6.62	22
23	2.81	4.1817	932	997.5	96.41	6.44	23
24	2.98	4.1814	911	997.2	100.59	6.27	24
25	3.17	4.1810	890	997.0	104.77	6.11	25
26	3.36	4.1806	870	996.7	108.95	5.95	26
27	3.56	4.1801	851	996.5	113.13	5.80	27
28	3.78	4.1797	833	996.2	117.31	5.66	28
29	4.00	4.1794	815	995.9	121.49	5.52	29
30	4.24	4.1790	798	995.6	125.67	5.39	30
31	4.49	4.1787	781	995.3	129.85	5.26	31
32	4.75	4.1784	765	995.0	134.03	5.14	32
33	5.01	4.1782	749	994.6	138.20	5.02	33
34	5.32	4.1781	734	994.3	142.38	4.91	34
35	5.62	4.1780	719	994.0	146.56	4.80	35
36	5.94	4.1781	705	993.6	150.74	4.69	36
37	6.27	4.1782	692	993.3	154.92	4.59	37
38	6.62	4.1784	678	993.0	159.09	4.49	38
39	6.99	4.1787	666	992.6	163.27	4.39	39
40	7.38	4.1790	653	992.2	167.45	4.30	40
41	7.78	4.1794	641	991.8	171.63	4.21	41
42	8.20	4.1798	629	991.4	175.81	4.13	42
43	8.64	4.1802	618	991.0	179.99	4.05	43
44	9.10	4.1806	606	990.6	184.17	3.97	44
45	9.58	4.1810	596	990.2	188.35	3.89	45
46	10.09	4.1812	586	989.8	192.53	3.81	46
47	10.61	4.1815	576	989.3	196.71	3.74	47
48	11.16	4.1817	566	988.9	200.90	3.67	48
49	11.74	4.1818	556	988.5	205.08	3.60	49
50	12.33	4.1820	547	988.0	209.26	3.53	50
51	12.96	4.1822	538	987.6	213.44	3.47	51
52	13.61	4.1823	529	987.2	217.62	3.40	52
53	14.29	4.1825	521	986.7	221.81	3.35	53
54	15.00	4.1828	512	986.2	225.99	3.29	54

Table 2.2 Properties of water at saturation — *continued*

Temperature, θ_s / °C	Absolute vapour pressure, p_s / kPa	Specific heat capacity, c_f / (kJ·kg^{-1}·K^{-1})	Dynamic viscosity, μ_f/(μPa·s)	Density, ρ / (kg·m^{-3})	Specific enthalpy of liquid, h_f / (kJ·kg^{-1})	Prandtl number, $(Pr)_g$	Temperature, θ_s / °C
55	15.74	4.1830	504	985.7	230.17	3.23	55
56	16.51	4.1833	496	985.2	234.35	3.17	56
57	17.31	4.1837	489	984.7	238.54	3.12	57
58	18.15	4.1841	481	984.3	242.72	3.06	58
59	19.02	4.1845	474	983.7	246.81	3.01	59
60	19.92	4.1850	467	983.2	251.09	2.96	60
61	20.86	4.1856	460	982.7	255.27	2.91	61
62	21.84	4.1861	453	982.1	259.46	2.87	62
63	22.85	4.1867	447	981.6	263.65	2.82	63
64	23.91	4.1874	440	981.1	267.83	2.78	64
65	25.01	4.1880	434	980.5	272.02	2.74	65
66	26.15	4.1886	428	979.9	276.21	2.70	66
67	27.33	4.1892	422	979.4	280.40	2.66	67
68	28.56	4.1898	416	978.9	284.59	2.62	68
69	29.84	4.1904	410	978.3	288.78	2.58	69
70	31.16	4.1910	404	977.7	292.97	2.54	70
71	32.53	4.1916	399	977.1	297.16	2.50	71
72	33.96	4.1921	394	976.6	301.35	2.47	72
73	35.43	4.1927	388	976.0	305.54	2.43	73
74	36.96	4.1934	383	975.4	309.74	2.39	74
75	38.55	4.1940	378	974.9	313.93	2.36	75
76	40.19	4.1947	373	974.3	318.12	2.33	76
77	41.89	4.1955	369	973.6	322.32	2.30	77
78	43.65	4.1962	364	973.1	326.52	2.27	78
79	45.47	4.1971	359	972.5	330.71	2.24	79
80	47.36	4.1980	355	971.8	334.91	2.21	80
81	49.31	4.1990	350	971.2	339.11	2.18	81
82	51.33	4.1999	346	970.6	343.31	2.15	82
83	53.42	4.2009	342	969.9	347.51	2.12	83
84	55.57	4.2020	338	969.3	351.71	2.10	84
85	57.80	4.2030	334	968.6	355.91	2.07	85
86	60.11	4.2040	330	968.0	360.11	2.05	86
87	62.49	4.2050	326	967.3	364.32	2.02	87
88	64.95	4.2060	322	966.7	368.52	2.00	88
89	67.49	4.2070	318	966.0	372.73	1.97	89
90	70.11	4.2080	314	965.3	376.94	1.95	90
91	72.82	4.2090	311	964.7	381.15	1.93	91
92	75.61	4.2099	307	964.0	385.36	1.90	92
93	78.49	4.2109	304	963.3	389.57	1.88	93
94	81.46	4.2120	300	962.7	393.78	1.85	94
95	84.53	4.2130	297	961.9	397.99	1.83	95
96	87.69	4.2141	294	961.2	402.30	1.81	96
97	90.94	4.2153	291	960.5	406.42	1.79	97
98	94.30	4.2165	287	959.8	410.63	1.77	98
99	97.76	4.2177	284	959.1	414.84	1.76	99
100	101.33	4.2190	281	958.3	419.06	1.74	100
102	108.78	4.2217	275	956.9	427.50	1.70	102
104	116.68	4.2246	269	955.5	435.95	1.67	104
106	125.04	4.2274	264	954.0	444.40	1.63	106
108	133.90	4.2302	259	952.6	452.86	1.60	108
110	143.26	4.2330	253	951.0	461.32	1.57	110
112	153.16	4.2357	248	949.5	469.79	1.54	112
114	163.61	4.2386	243	948.0	478.26	1.51	114
116	174.64	4.2414	239	946.3	486.74	1.48	116
118	186.28	4.2445	234	944.7	495.20	1.45	118

Table 2.2 Properties of water at saturation — *continued*

Temperature, θ_s / °C	Absolute vapour pressure, p_s / kPa	Specific heat capacity, c_f / (kJ·kg^{-1}·K^{-1})	Dynamic viscosity, μ_f /(μPa·s)	Density, ρ / (kg·m^{-3})	Specific enthalpy of liquid, h_f / (kJ·kg^{-1})	Prandtl number, $(Pr)_g$	Temperature, θ_s / °C
120	198.53	4.2480	230	943.1	503.70	1.42	120
122	211.44	4.2527	226	941.5	512.20	1.40	122
124	225.03	4.2576	223	939.9	520.70	1.38	124
126	239.32	4.2621	219	938.3	529.20	1.36	126
128	254.34	4.2661	216	936.5	537.80	1.34	128
130	270.12	4.2700	212	934.8	546.30	1.32	130
132	286.68	4.2740	209	933.1	554.90	1.30	132
134	304.05	4.2780	206	931.4	563.40	1.28	134
136	322.27	4.2820	202	929.6	572.00	1.26	136
138	341.36	4.2860	199	927.9	580.50	1.25	138
140	361.36	4.2900	196	926.1	589.10	1.23	140
142	382.28	4.2934	193	924.3	597.70	1.21	142
144	404.18	4.2975	191	922.5	606.30	1.20	144
146	427.07	4.3029	189	920.6	614.90	1.18	146
148	450.99	4.3102	187	918.8	623.50	1.17	148
150	475.97	4.3200	185	916.9	632.20	1.17	150
152	502.05	4.3250	183	915.1	640.80	1.16	152
154	529.26	4.3320	181	913.2	649.40	1.15	154
156	557.64	4.3380	178	911.2	658.10	1.13	156
158	587.23	4.3440	176	909.3	666.80	1.12	158
160	618.05	4.3500	174	907.4	675.50	1.11	160
162	650.14	4.3557	172	905.4	684.20	1.10	162
164	683.55	4.3614	170	903.4	692.90	1.09	164
166	718.31	4.3674	167	901.5	701.60	1.07	166
168	754.45	4.3735	165	899.4	710.40	1.06	168
170	792.03	4.3800	163	897.3	719.1	1.05	170
172	831.07	4.3875	161	895.3	727.9	1.04	172
174	871.61	4.3954	159	893.3	736.7	1.03	174
176	913.71	4.4034	157	891.2	745.5	1.02	176
178	957.39	4.4117	155	889.1	754.3	1.01	178
180	1002.7	4.4200	153	886.9	763.1	1.00	180
182	1049.7	4.4277	151	884.8	772.0	0.99	182
184	1098.4	4.4354	150	882.6	780.8	0.99	184
186	1148.9	4.4434	148	880.4	789.7	0.98	186
188	1201.1	4.4515	146	879.7	798.6	0.98	188
190	1255.2	4.4600	145	876.0	807.5	0.97	190
192	1311.2	4.4695	144	873.8	816.4	0.96	192
194	1369.2	4.4794	142	781.5	825.4	0.96	194
196	1429.1	4.4894	141	869.3	834.4	0.95	196
198	1491.0	4.4997	139	867.0	843.4	0.95	198
200	1555.1	4.5100	138	864.7	852.4	0.94	200
205	1724.5	4.5337	134	858.8	875.0	0.92	205
210	1908.0	4.5600	131	852.8	897.7	0.91	210
215	2106.3	4.5937	128	846.6	920.6	0.90	215
220	2320.1	4.6300	125	840.3	943.7	0.90	220
225	2550.4	4.6644	122	833.9	966.9	0.90	225
230	2797.0	4.7000	120	827.3	990.3	0.89	230
235	3063.5	4.7387	118	820.6	1013.8	0.89	235
240	3348.0	4.7800	115	813.6	1037.6	0.88	240
245	3652.4	4.8231	112	806.5	1061.6	0.87	245
250	3977.6	4.8700	110	799.2	1085.8	0.87	250

Table 2.3 Enthalpy of superheated steam

Enthalpy of superheated steam (/ $kJ \cdot kg^{-1}$) for stated final steam temperature / °C

Absolute pressure, p / kPa	Saturation temperature, θ_s / °C	100	120	140	160	180	200	220	240	260	280	300	320	340	360	380	400
100	99.6	2676	2717	2757	2797	2836	2876	2915	2955	2995	3034	3075	3115	3155	3196	3237	3278
120	104.8		2715	2755	2796	2835	2875	2914	2954	2994	3034	3074	3114	3155	3196	3237	3278
140	109.3		2713	2754	2794	2834	2874	2914	2953	2993	3033	3074	3114	3155	3195	3236	3278
160	113.3		2711	2752	2793	2833	2873	2913	2953	2993	3033	3073	3114	3154	3195	3236	3277
180	116.9		2708	2751	2792	2832	2872	2912	2952	2992	3032	3073	3113	3154	3195	3236	3277
200	120.2			2749	2790	2831	2871	2911	2951	2992	3032	3072	3113	3153	3194	3235	3277
220	123.3			2747	2789	2830	2870	2911	2951	2991	3031	3072	3112	3153	3194	3235	3276
240	126.1			2745	2787	2829	2969	2910	2950	2990	3031	3071	3112	3153	3194	3235	3276
260	128.7			2743	2786	2827	2868	2909	2949	2990	3030	3071	3111	3152	3193	3234	3276
280	131.2			2742	2785	2826	2867	2908	2949	2989	3030	3070	3111	3152	3193	3234	3275
300	133.5			2740	2783	2825	2866	2907	2948	2988	3029	3070	3110	3151	3192	3234	3275
340	137.9			2736	2780	2823	2865	2906	2947	2987	3028	3069	3110	3151	3192	3233	3274
380	141.8				2777	2820	2863	2904	2945	2986	3027	3068	3109	3150	3191	3232	3274
420	145.4				2774	2818	2861	2902	2944	2985	3026	3067	3108	3149	3190	3232	3273
460	148.7				2771	2816	2859	2901	2942	2984	3025	3066	3107	3148	3189	3231	3273
500	151.8				2768	2813	2857	2899	2941	2982	3024	3065	3106	3147	3189	3230	3272
600	158.8				2759	2807	2851	2895	2937	2979	3021	3062	3104	3145	3187	3229	3270
700	165.0					2800	2846	2890	2933	2976	3018	3060	3102	3143	3185	3227	3269
800	170.4					2793	2840	2886	2930	2973	3015	3057	3099	3141	3183	3225	3267
900	175.4					2785	2835	2881	2926	2969	3012	3055	3097	3139	3181	3223	3266
1000	179.9					2778	2829	2876	2922	2966	3009	3052	3095	3137	3179	3222	3264
1200	188.0						2817	2867	2914	2959	3003	3047	3090	3133	3176	3218	3261
1400	195.0						2803	2856	2905	2952	2997	3042	3085	3129	3172	3215	3257
1600	201.4							2846	2897	2945	2991	3036	3081	3124	3168	3211	3254
1800	207.1							2834	2888	2937	2985	3031	3076	3120	3164	3207	3251
2000	212.4							2822	2878	2930	2978	3025	3071	3116	3160	3204	3248
2500	223.9								2853	2909	2961	3011	3058	3105	3150	3195	3239
3000	233.8								2825	2888	2943	2995	3045	3093	3140	3185	3231
3500	242.5									2864	2925	2980	3031	3081	3129	3176	3222
4000	250.3									2838	2904	2963	3017	3069	3118	3166	3214
4500	257.4									2809	2883	2946	3003	3056	3107	3156	3205
5000	263.9										2859	2927	2988	3043	3096	3146	3196
6000	275.6										2806	2887	2955	3016	3072	3126	3177
7000	285.8											2841	2919	2987	3048	3104	3158
8000	295.0											2787	2880	2955	3021	3082	3139
9000	303.3												2835	2921	2993	3058	3118
10000	311.0												2784	2884	2964	3033	3097

3 Heat transfer

3.1 Introduction

This chapter of CIBSE Guide C is concerned with heat transfer. It is divided into a theoretical part and a practical part. The theoretical part provides a number of basic equations and discussion for convection, conduction and radiation together with a brief review of mass transfer. This part is not exhaustive and for a detailed treatment of the subject, the references cited at the end of the section should be consulted.

The practical part is intended for reference in dealing with common heat transfer problems related to the built environment. This is structured as: external environment; internal environment; human body. This part concludes with a treatment of components and equipment. For particular products, the manufacturer's data should be consulted. Example calculations are provided where appropriate to aid understanding and application.

In view of the number of equations, the notation is given at the start so as to provide a point of reference for the section.

3.1.1 Notation

A Area (m^2)

A_c Cross-sectional area (m^2)

A_i, A_j Area for surface i or j (m^2)

A_s Heated or cooled surface area (m^2)

A_{si} Inside surface area (m^2)

A_{so} Outside surface area (m^2)

A_1 Area of surface 1, etc. (m^2)

C A constant (specified in text)

C_{max} Fluid heat capacity rate (greater) (W·K^{-1})

C_{min} Fluid heat capacity rate (smaller) (W·K^{-1})

D Characteristic plate dimension (m)

E Emissivity factor (dimensionless)

E_{bi} Emissive power for surface i (W·m^{-2})

F View factor (or form factor or angle factor)

F_{ij} View factor of surface j with respect to surface i

F_{p-N} Mean view factor between a person and a room surface (see Figures 3.3–3.7)

F_r Radiation exchange factor for two surfaces (dimensionless)

F_{12} View factor of surface 2 with respect to surface 1

Gr Grashof number ($= \gamma g \rho^2 D^3 \Delta\theta / \mu^2$)

H Height of vertical rectangular enclosure (m)

I Intensity of solar radiation (W·m^{-2})

I_{clo} Thermal resistance of clothing (clo)

$\mathcal{J}_i, \mathcal{J}_j$ Radiosity for surfaces i and j respectively (W·m^{-2})

L Length of cylinder, pipe, etc. (m)

M Mass flow rate (kg·s^{-1})

N Number of surfaces within the enclosure

NTU   Number of exchanger heat transfer units

Nu Nusselt number ($= h D / \lambda$)

P Perimeter (m)

Pr Prandtl number ($= c_p \mu / \lambda$)

R Thermal resistance (m^2·K·W^{-1})

R_a Thermal resistance of air gap (m^2·K·W^{-1})

Ra Rayleigh number ($= Gr\cdot Pr$)

R_e Thermal resistance of earth (m^2·K·W^{-1})

Re Reynolds number ($= \rho v D / \mu$)

R_n	Thermal resistance of insulation ($m^2{\cdot}K{\cdot}W^{-1}$)	h_{cn}	Convective heat transfer coefficient for natural convection at internal surfaces ($W{\cdot}m^{-2}{\cdot}K^{-1}$)
R_{se}	External surface resistance ($m^2{\cdot}K{\cdot}W^{-1}$)	h_{co}	Outside surface convective heat transfer coefficient ($W{\cdot}m^{-2}{\cdot}K^{-1}$)
R_1	Thermal resistance of element 1, etc. ($m^2{\cdot}K{\cdot}W^{-1}$)		
T	Absolute temperature (K)	h_{fg}	Latent heat of evaporation of water ($kJ{\cdot}kg^{-1}$) ($= 2450\ kJ{\cdot}kg^{-1}$ at 20 °C)
T_a	Absolute temperature of air (K)		
T_{fs}	Absolute temperature of fictitious surface (given by an area and emissivity-weighted average of other surfaces) (K)	h_r	Radiative heat transfer coefficient ($W{\cdot}m^{-2}{\cdot}K^{-1}$)
		h_{si}	Inside surface heat transfer coefficient (or film coefficient) ($W{\cdot}m^{-2}{\cdot}K^{-1}$)
T_i	Absolute surface temperature for surface i (K)	h_{so}	Outside surface heat transfer coefficient (or film coefficient) ($W{\cdot}m^{-2}{\cdot}K^{-1}$)
T_r	Absolute mean radiant temperature (K)		
T_{rs}	Absolute mean radiant temperature of the sky (K) ($= 253 + \theta_a$)	l	Length (m)
		m	Burial depth (m)
T_s	Absolute temperature of heat emitting/absorbing surface (K)	n	An index (specified in text)
		p_{sw}	Saturated vapour pressure at water surface (kPa)
T_{sw}	Absolute temperature of water surface (K)	p_v	Vapour pressure of moisture in air remote from water surface (kPa)
T_1	Absolute temperature of surface 1, etc. (K)		
U	Overall thermal transmittance ($W{\cdot}m^{-2}{\cdot}K^{-1}$)	q_v	Volume flow rate ($m^3{\cdot}s^{-1}$)
U_c	Thermal transmittance of clean surfaces ($W{\cdot}m^{-2}{\cdot}K^{-1}$)	r	Radius (m)
		r_i	Inside radius (m)
U_t	Thermal transmittance of water tank ($W{\cdot}m^{-2}{\cdot}K^{-1}$)	r_o	Outside radius (m)
W	Rate of water evaporation ($kg{\cdot}m^{-2}{\cdot}s^{-1}$)	r_1	Radius of surface 1, etc. (m)
Z	Heat capacity rate ratio	x	Thickness (m)
a	Length (m)	x_n	Thickness of insulation (m)
a_1	Length of side 1, etc. (m)	x_w	Wall thickness (m)
b	Width (m)	x_{zi}	Inside fouling substance thickness (m)
c	Velocity ($m{\cdot}s^{-1}$)	x_{zo}	Outside fouling substance thickness (m)
c_{as}	Air velocity at water surface ($m{\cdot}s^{-1}$)	x_1	Thickness of element 1, etc. (m)
c_{ar}	Air velocity in room ($m{\cdot}s^{-1}$)	$\Delta\theta$	Temperature difference (K)
c_p	Specific heat capacity at constant pressure ($kJ{\cdot}kg^{-1}{\cdot}K^{-1}$)	$\Delta\theta_{ca}$	Difference between clothing and air temperatures (K)
c_s	Surface wind speed ($m{\cdot}s^{-1}$)	$\Delta\theta_l$	Logarithmic mean temperature difference (K)
d	Diameter (m)	$\Delta\theta_m$	Change in temperature per unit length ($K{\cdot}m^{-1}$)
d_h	Hydraulic mean (equivalent) diameter (m)	$\Delta\theta_{tg}$	Greatest terminal temperature difference (K)
d_i	Inside diameter (m)	$\Delta\theta_{sa}$	Surface to air temperature difference (K)
d_{ic}	Inside diameter of casing (m)	$\Delta\theta_{ts}$	Smallest terminal temperature difference (K)
d_{i1}	Inside diameter of element 1, etc. (m)	$\Delta\theta_\lambda$	Temperature difference between opposite surfaces of a solid with thermal conductivity λ (K)
d_o	Outside diameter (m)		
d_{on}	Outside diameter of insulation (m)	Φ	Actual rate of heat transfer (for a heat exchanger) (W)
d_{op}	Outside diameter of pipe (m)		
d_{o1}	Outside diameter of element 1, etc. (m)	Φ_c	Rate of convective heat transfer by a heated or cooled surface (W)
f	A function (specified in text)		
f_{cl}	Clothing area factor (ratio of clothed to unclothed body surface area)	Φ_i	Net rate of heat transfer by radiation to surface i (W)
g	Acceleration due to gravity ($m{\cdot}s^{-2}$) ($= 9.81\ m{\cdot}s^{-2}$)	Φ_{max}	Maximum possible rate of heat transfer (for a heat exchanger) (W)
h	Heat transfer coefficient ($W{\cdot}m^{-2}{\cdot}K^{-1}$)	Φ_r	Rate of radiant heat transfer by a heated or cooled surface (W)
h_c	Convective heat transfer coefficient ($W{\cdot}m^{-2}{\cdot}K^{-1}$)		
h_{ci}	Inside surface convective heat transfer coefficient ($W{\cdot}m^{-2}{\cdot}K^{-1}$)	Φ_t	Total rate of heat transfer by a heated or cooled surface (W)

α	Angle (degrees)
γ	Coefficient of cubical expansion (K^{-1})
ε	Emissivity
ε_i	Emissivity of surface i
ε_w	Emissivity of water
ε_1	Emissivity of surface 1, etc.
η	Heat exchanger effectiveness
θ	Celsius temperature (°C)
θ_a	Air temperature (°C)
θ_c	Casing temperature (°C)
θ_{cfi}	Cold fluid inlet temperature (°C)
θ_{cfo}	Cold fluid outlet temperature (°C)
θ_{cl}	Clothing surface temperature (°C)
θ_d	Temperature at down stream end of pipe or duct section (°C)
θ_e	Ground temperature (°C)
θ_f	Free stream fluid temperature (°C)
θ_{fs}	Area weighted average fictitious surface temperature (°C)
θ_{hfi}	Hot fluid inlet temperature (°C)
θ_{hfo}	Hot fluid outlet temperature (°C)
θ_{hi}	Shell inlet temperature (°C)
θ_{ho}	Shell outlet temperature (°C)
θ_i	Inside temperature (°C)
θ_j	Surface temperature of each of the surfaces comprising the fictitious surface (°C)
θ_m	Mean of the inlet and outlet fluid temperatures in a tube (°C)
θ_n	Insulation temperature (°C)
θ_o	Outside temperature (°C)
θ_s	Surface temperature (°C)
θ_{si}	Inside surface temperature (°C)
θ_{so}	Outside surface temperature (°C)
θ_{s1}	Temperature of surface 1, etc. (°C)
θ_{ti}	Tube inlet temperature (°C)
θ_{to}	Tube outlet temperature (°C)
θ_u	Temperature at upstream end of pipe or duct section (°C)
θ_w	Water temperature (°C)
θ_{sw}	Water surface temperature (°C)
λ	Thermal conductivity ($W \cdot m^{-1} \cdot K^{-1}$)
λ_e	Thermal conductivity of earth ($W \cdot m^{-1} \cdot K^{-1}$)
λ_n	Thermal conductivity of insulation ($W \cdot m^{-1} \cdot K^{-1}$)
λ_w	Thermal conductivity of wall ($W \cdot m^{-1} \cdot K^{-1}$)
λ_{zi}	Inside surface thermal conductivity of fouling substance ($W \cdot m^{-1} \cdot K^{-1}$)
λ_{zo}	Outside surface thermal conductivity of fouling substance ($W \cdot m^{-1} \cdot K^{-1}$)

$\lambda^\star$	Pipe friction coefficient (see chapter 4)
μ	Dynamic viscosity (Pa·s)
ν	Kinematic viscosity ($m^2 \cdot s^{-1}$)
ξ	Layer thickness (m)
ρ	Density ($kg \cdot m^{-3}$)
σ	Stefan-Boltzmann constant ($W \cdot m^{-2} \cdot K^{-4}$) ($= 5.67 \times 10^{-8}\ W \cdot m^{-2} \cdot K^{-4}$)
ϕ	Heat exchange per unit area ($W \cdot m^{-2}$)
ϕ_c	Convective heat exchange per unit area ($W \cdot m^{-2}$)
ϕ_{cd}	Conductive heat exchange per unit area ($W \cdot m^{-2}$)
ϕ_e	Evaporative heat exchange per unit area ($W \cdot m^{-2}$)
ϕ_{hb}	Heat loss by convection per unit area of the human body ($W \cdot m^{-2}$)
ϕ_r	Radiative heat exchange per unit area ($W \cdot m^{-2}$)

3.2 Heat transfer principles

The mechanisms of heat transfer are convection, conduction, radiation and mass transfer. Theoretical and experimental work has led to the development of many equations that express the magnitude of heat transfer by these modes. Some of the commonly used equations are given in this chapter of CIBSE Guide C, but a wider range of heat transfer equations, especially those for particular applications, may be found in some of the many references given at the end of the chapter.

3.2.1 Convection

Convection is a mode of heat transfer between a moving fluid and a solid, liquid or gas. Convection can be free or forced. Free convection is the movement of a fluid primarily due to buoyancy forces. Forced convection is the movement of a fluid due primarily to external means, i.e. a mechanical pump or a pressure difference induced by a fan, for example. Many complications can arise due to the following reasons:

(a) The flow can be laminar (having smooth and orderly streamlines) or turbulent (having irregularly interwoven streamlines) or separated (having a reversed flow along the fluid boundary, as with cylinders in cross flow with vortex shedding). There is a transitional state between laminar and turbulent flow.

(b) There is a boundary layer between the fluid and the other medium.

(c) At the base of the boundary layer the fluid is stationary with respect to the other medium. This means that there is a thin layer in which only conduction and mass transfer can take place.

(d) For heat to be transferred within any substance, a temperature gradient must exist. In a fluid, therefore, there are density gradients which cause buoyancy forces.

The remainder of this section is structured as follows. Empirical correlations (in the form of dimensionless numbers) are presented for the conditions of free and forced convection and for a range of common situations. These situations are classified as being either external flows (over surfaces) or internal flows (inside enclosures). In both cases the flow regimes can be either laminar or turbulent. For each situation, guidance is given regarding its particular characteristics and the use of the appropriate equation.

The following equations can be used for heating or cooling applications provided that no phase change (e.g. condensation or evaporation) occurs since, for most practical purposes, the theoretical differences between heating and cooling are usually negligible. The equations are valid (strictly) only for ideal fluids, i.e. with non-variable property values, and for incompressible flow. Table 3.1[1] gives typical values of the convection coefficients for various situations.

If the fluid property values change significantly over the temperature range investigated, account can be taken of them by using values at some mean temperature[2].

Table 3.1 Typical convection coefficients, h_c, for different modes of convection (reproduced from *Engineering Thermodynamics, Work and Heat Transfer* by G F C Rogers and Y R Mayhew by permission of Pearson Education Ltd. ©Longman Group UK Ltd.)

Mode	Coefficient / $W \cdot m^{-2} \cdot K^{-1}$
Forced convection:	
— gases and dry vapours	10 to 10^3
— liquids	10^2 to 10^4
— liquid metals	5×10^3 to 4×10^4
Free convection:	
— gases and dry vapours	0.5 to 10^3
— liquids	50 to 3×10^3
Condensation:	
— filmwise	5×10^2 to 3×10^4
— dropwise	2×10^4 to 5×10^5
Boiling	5×10^2 to 2×10^4

3.2.1.1   Free convection over surfaces

Table 3.2 presents correlations for the average Nu number for free convection over various geometries for a range of Ra numbers. The appropriate characteristic length is also given. The flow regime is determined by calculating the Ra number for a particular situation; note that the power of the Ra number is usually 0.25 for laminar flow and 0.33 for turbulent flow. All fluid properties are evaluated at the average of the surface temperature (θ_s) and the free stream fluid temperature (θ_f).

3.2.1.2   Free convection inside enclosures

Table 3.3 presents correlations for the average Nu number for free convection within enclosures of various geometries for a range of Ra numbers. Here, the term 'enclosures' refers to cavities such as those found in walls, double glazed windows or solar collectors etc. The characteristic length is the distance between the hot and cold surfaces. All fluid properties are evaluated at the average of the hot and cold surface temperatures.

3.2.1.3   Forced convection over flat plates

For laminar flow over an entire horizontal flat surface, the average Nu number, based on plate length D, over the entire plate is given by:

$$Nu_D = 0.664 \, Re_D^{1/2} \, Pr^{1/3} \qquad (3.27)$$

for $Pr \geq 0.6$ and $Re_D < 5 \times 10^5$.

For turbulent flow over an entire horizontal flat surface, the average Nu number, based on plate length D, over the entire plate is given by:

$$Nu_D = 0.037 \, Re_D^{4/5} \, Pr^{1/3} \qquad (3.28)$$

for $0.6 \leq Pr \leq 60$ and $5 \times 10^5 \leq Re_D \leq 10^7$.

Equations 3.27 and 3.28 are restricted to the condition of uniform surface temperature over a smooth plate[3]. However, for other conditions, including uniform heat flux over a plate, unheated sections, combinations of laminar and turbulent flows, entry region effects and evaluation of local Nu numbers, the reader should consult references 3 and 4. Note that fluid properties are evaluated at the average of the surface temperature (θ_s) and the free stream fluid temperature (θ_f).

3.2.1.4   Cross flow

Table 3.4 presents correlations for the average Nu number for forced convection over circular and non-circular smooth cylinders and surfaces in cross flow for a range of Re numbers. The characteristic length is also shown. All fluid properties are evaluated at the average of the surface temperature (θ_s) and the free stream fluid temperature (θ_f).

3.2.1.5   Forced convection inside enclosures (tubes)

Table 3.5 presents correlations for the average Nu number for forced convection, fully developed, laminar flow inside tubes of circular and non-circular cross-sections. Laminar flow in tubes occurs for $Re_D < 2300$. Values of Nu numbers are given for the following thermal conditions at the surface of the tube:

(a)   *Constant surface temperature*: a typical situation for which this condition is applicable would be when a phase change process takes place at the outer surface of the tube (such as condensation or evaporation).

(b)   *Constant heat flux*: a typical example would be when the tube is subjected to uniform heating such as from an electric element.

For turbulent flow within circular and non-circular tubes and ducts, the following correlation can be used:

$$Nu_D = 0.023 \, Re_D^{4/5} \, Pr^n \qquad (3.41)$$

where $n = 0.4$ for heating ($\theta_s > \theta_m$) and 0.3 for cooling ($\theta_s < \theta_m$), where θ_m is the mean fluid temperature, evaluated as the average of the inlet and outlet fluid temperatures of the tube:

$$\theta_m = (\theta_{ti} + \theta_{to}) / 2 \qquad (3.42)$$

Table 3.2 Empirical correlations for the average Nusselt number for free convection over surfaces (adapted from *Introduction to Thermodynamics and Heat Transfer* by Y A Cengel (1997) by permission of The McGraw-Hill Companies)

Geometry	Characteristic length	Ra range	Nusselt number, Nu	
Vertical plate	D	10^4–10^9	$Nu = 0.59\, Ra^{1/4}$	(3.1)
		10^9–10^{13}	$Nu = 0.1\, Ra^{1/3}$	(3.2)
		Entire range	$Nu = \left(0.825 + \dfrac{0.387\, Ra^{1/6}}{[1 + (0.492\,/\,Pr)^{9/16}]^{8/27}}\right)^2$	(3.3)
			(complex but more accurate)	
Inclined plate	D		Use vertical plate equations as a first degree of approximation	
			Replace g with $g\cos\theta$ in the formula for Gr, see page 3-1, for $Ra < 10^9$	
Horizontal plate (surface area $= A$ and perimeter $= P$)	A/P			
(a) Upper surface of a hot plate or lower surface of a cold plate		10^4–10^7	$Nu = 0.54\, Ra^{1/4}$	(3.4)
		10^7–10^{11}	$Nu = 0.15\, Ra^{1/3}$	(3.5)
(b) Lower surface of a hot plate or upper surface of a cold plate		10^5–10^{11}	$Nu = 0.27\, Ra^{1/4}$	(3.6)
Vertical cylinder	D		A vertical cylinder can be treated as a vertical plate when:	
			$d \geq \dfrac{35\, D}{Gr^{1/4}}$	(3.7)
Horizontal cylinder	d	10^5–10^{12}	$Nu = \left(0.6 + \dfrac{0.387\, Ra^{1/6}}{[1 + (0.559\,/\,Pr)^{9/16}]^{8/27}}\right)^2$	(3.8)
Sphere	$\pi d/2$	$Ra \leq 10^{11}$ $Pr \geq 0.7$	$Nu = 2 + \dfrac{0.589\, Ra^{1/4}}{[1 + (0.469\,/\,Pr)^{9/16}]^{4/9}}$	(3.9)

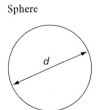

Table 3.3 Empirical correlations for the average Nusselt number for free convection in enclosures (the characteristic length D is as indicated on the respective diagram) (adapted from *Introduction to Thermodynamics and Heat Transfer* by Y A Cengel (1997) by permission of The McGraw-Hill Companies)

Geometry	Fluid	H/D	Pr range	Ra range	Nusselt number, Nu	
Vertical rectangular or cylindrical enclosure	Gas or liquid	—	—	< 2000	$Nu = 1$	(3.10)
	Gas	11–42	0.5–2	(2×10^3)–(2×10^5)	$Nu = 0.197\, Ra^{1/4}\left(\dfrac{H}{D}\right)^{-1/9}$	(3.11)
		11–42	0.5–2	(2×10^5)–10^7	$Nu = 0.073\, Ra^{1/3}\left(\dfrac{H}{D}\right)^{-1/9}$	(3.12)
	Liquid	10–40	1–20 000	10^4–10^7	$Nu = 0.42\, Pr^{0.012}\, Ra^{1/4}\left(\dfrac{H}{D}\right)^{-0.3}$	(3.13)
		1–40	1–20	10^6–10^9	$Nu = 0.046\, Ra^{1/3}$	(3.14)
Inclined rectangular enclosure					Use the correlations for vertical enclosures as a first degree approximation for $a \le 20°$ by replacing g with $g \cos \theta$ in the formula for Ra, see page 3-1.	
Horizontal rectangular enclosure (hot surface at the top)	Gas or liquid	—	—	—	$Nu = 1$	(3.15)
Horizontal rectangular enclosure (hot surface at the bottom)	Gas or liquid	—	—	< 1700	$Nu = 1$	(3.16)
	Gas	—	0.5–2	(1.7×10^3)–(7×10^3)	$Nu = 0.059\, Ra^{0.4}$	(3.17)
		—	0.5–2	(7×10^3)–(3.2×10^5)	$Nu = 0.212\, Ra^{1/4}$	(3.18)
		—	0.5–2	$> 3.2 \times 10^5$	$Nu = 0.061\, Ra^{1/3}$	(3.19)
	Liquid	—	1–5000	(1.7×10^3)–(6×10^3)	$Nu = 0.012\, Ra^{0.6}$	(3.20)
		—	1–5000	(6×10^3)–(3.7×10^4)	$Nu = 0.375\, Ra^{0.2}$	(3.21)
		—	1–20	(3.7×10^4)–10^8	$Nu = 0.13\, Ra^{0.3}$	(3.22)
		—	1–20	$> 10^8$	$Nu = 0.057\, Ra^{1/3}$	(3.23)
Concentric horizontal cylinders	Gas or liquid	—	1–5000	(6.3×10^3)–10^6	$Nu = 0.11\, Ra^{0.29}$	(3.24)
		—	1–5000	10^6–10^8	$Nu = 0.40\, Ra^{0.20}$	(3.25)
Concentric spheres	Gas or liquid	—	0.7–4000	10^2–10^9	$Nu = 0.228\, Ra^{0.226}$	(3.26)

Table 3.4 Empirical correlations for the average Nusselt number for forced convection over circular and non-circular cylinders in cross flow[5,6] (adapted from *Introduction to Thermodynamics and Heat Transfer* by Y A Cengel (1997) by permission of The McGraw-Hill Companies)

Cross section	Fluid	Re range	Nusselt number, Nu	
Circle	Gas or liquid	0.4–4	$Nu = 0.989\,Re^{0.33}\,Pr^{1/3}$	(3.29)
		4–40	$Nu = 0.911\,Re^{0.385}\,Pr^{1/3}$	(3.30)
		40–4000	$Nu = 0.683\,Re^{0.466}\,Pr^{1/3}$	(3.31)
		4000–40 000	$Nu = 0.193\,Re^{0.618}\,Pr^{1/3}$	(3.32)
		40 000–400 000	$Nu = 0.027\,Re^{0.805}\,Pr^{1/3}$	(3.33)
Square	Gas	5000–100 000	$Nu = 0.102\,Re^{0.675}\,Pr^{1/3}$	(3.34)
Square (tilted 45°)	Gas	5000–100 000	$Nu = 0.246\,Re^{0.588}\,Pr^{1/3}$	(3.35)
Hexagon	Gas	5000–100 000	$Nu = 0.153\,Re^{0.638}\,Pr^{1/3}$	(3.36)
Hexagon (tilted 45°)	Gas	5000–19 500	$Nu = 0.160\,Re^{0.638}\,Pr^{1/3}$	(3.37)
		19 500–100 000	$Nu = 0.0385\,Re^{0.782}\,Pr^{1/3}$	(3.38)
Vertical plate	Gas	4000–15 000	$Nu = 0.228\,Re^{0.731}\,Pr^{1/3}$	(3.39)
Ellipse	Gas	2500–15 000	$Nu = 0.248\,Re^{0.612}\,Pr^{1/3}$	(3.40)

Table 3.5 Nusselt numbers for fully developed laminar flow in tubes of various cross sections (hydraulic diameter $d_h = 4A_c/P$) (adapted from *Introduction to Thermodynamics and Heat Transfer* by Y A Cengel (1997) by permission of The McGraw-Hill Companies)

Cross section of tube	a/b or $a°$	Nusselt number, Nu	
		θ_s = const.	Φ_t = const.
Circle	—	3.66	4.36
Hexagon	—	3.35	4.00
Square	1	2.98	3.61
Rectangle	1	2.98	3.61
	2	3.39	4.12
	3	3.96	4.79
	4	4.44	5.33
	6	5.14	6.05
	8	5.60	6.49
	∞	7.54	8.24
Ellipse	1	3.66	4.36
	2	3.74	4.56
	4	3.79	4.88
	8	3.72	5.09
	16	3.65	5.18
Triangle	10°	1.61	2.45
	30°	2.26	2.91
	60°	2.47	3.11
	90°	2.34	2.98
	120°	2.00	2.68

Equation 3.41 is known as the Dittus-Boelter equation, and has been confirmed by experiment[4] to be valid for the range $0.7 \leq Pr \leq 160$, and for $Re_D > 10000$.

Flow in tubes is considered to be turbulent for $Re > 3000$ and laminar for $Re < 2000$.

Another expression has been proposed[7] to cover the range of Re_D for the transitional and turbulent regimes:

$$Nu_D = \frac{(\lambda^*/8)\,(Re_D - 1000)\,Pr}{1 + 12.7\,(\lambda^*/8)^{1/2}\,(Pr^{2/3} - 1)} \qquad (3.43)$$

where λ^* is the friction coefficient.

Equation 3.43 is valid for the range $0.5 < Pr < 2000$, and $2300 < Re_D < 5 \times 10^6$.

Friction coefficients may be obtained from chapter 4, equation 4.5.

3.2.2   Conduction

Conduction is the transfer of heat within substances from positions of higher temperature to positions of lower temperature. Within all substances, except metals, conduction is primarily due to molecular movements although internal radiation can be significant. Within metals, most heat is transferred by free electrons[1].

The following equations assume that heat is transferred steadily, one dimensionally, and that materials are homogeneous and isotropic. These equations can be used for heating or cooling applications and are based on Fourier's Law:

$$\Phi = -\lambda A \, \frac{\mathrm{d}\theta}{\mathrm{d}x} \tag{3.44}$$

where λ is the thermal conductivity (W·m⁻¹·K⁻¹).

In practice, it is usually necessary to consider heat transfer by conduction in two or three dimensions in order to obtain the temperature distribution throughout the medium of interest. To do this, it is necessary to solve the Fourier conduction equation in its two- or three-dimensional form. This can be achieved either analytically (using the method of separation of variables), graphically (using the flux plotting method), or numerically (using the finite difference technique). For details of these methods see reference 4.

Non-steady state or transient heat transfer occurs in situations where the boundary conditions are varying with respect to time. In these instances, the methods stated above can be used to solve the transient or non-steady state conduction equation in one, two or three dimensions as required[4]. References 8 and 9 also contain methods for solving such heat transfer problems. The availability of powerful computers together with software for simulating the dynamic thermal behaviour of buildings and systems has meant that the numerical method is the most commonly used for producing practical solutions.

Chapter 5 of CIBSE Guide A[10] describes a number of procedures that can be used for structural problems.

Complications arise when heat is conducted through porous materials; this is because they are rarely dry, so that there are transient periods at the end and beginning of heat transfer during which moisture is also transferred. Eventually, equilibrium states are reached, though sometimes only after many months. Chapter 3 of CIBSE Guide A[10] deals with the problem of moisture content in more detail.

3.2.2.1   Conduction through flat structures

For single layer flat structures and for pipes and curved structures of large radii, the heat transfer rate is given by:

$$\Phi = \frac{\lambda \, (\theta_{\mathrm{so}} - \theta_{\mathrm{si}}) \, A}{x} \tag{3.45}$$

where x is the thickness of the element (m).

For multi-layered structures or pipes having large radii:

$$\Phi = \frac{A}{R} (\theta_{\mathrm{so}} - \theta_{\mathrm{si}}) \tag{3.46}$$

where:

$$R = \frac{x_1}{\lambda_1} + \frac{x_2}{\lambda_2} + \cdots \tag{3.47}$$

These equations are valid for steady state conditions, i.e. when the rate of heat transfer is constant with respect to time, and in the direction of the temperature gradient.

Table 3.6 Error in approximating a cylinder to a flat surface

$\dfrac{r + \xi}{r}$	Error / %
1.2	10
1.1	5
1.05	3
1.025	1.3
1.0125	0.8

Note: r is the radius of cylinder and ξ is the thickness of the layer

The criterion which describes whether the radii of curved structures are large is:

$$\frac{r + \xi}{r} \approx 1 \tag{3.48}$$

Table 3.6 gives percentage errors introduced to the value of the heat transfer rate by using the above formulae for various ratios of actual structure radii.

3.2.2.2   Conduction through cylindrical structures

For a single element:

$$\Phi = \frac{2 \, \pi \, \lambda \, L \, (\theta_{\mathrm{so}} - \theta_{\mathrm{si}})}{\ln \left(\dfrac{d_{\mathrm{o}}}{d_{\mathrm{i}}} \right)} \tag{3.49}$$

For multi-layered structures:

$$\Phi = \frac{2 \, \pi \, L \, (\theta_{\mathrm{so}} - \theta_{\mathrm{si}})}{R_1 + R_2 + \cdots} \tag{3.50}$$

where:

$$R_1 = \frac{x}{\lambda_1} \ln \left(\frac{d_{\mathrm{o}1}}{d_{\mathrm{i}1}} \right), \text{ etc.} \tag{3.51}$$

3.2.2.3   Heat flow through structures by conduction and convection

The effects of convection from the surfaces of structures can be included in the above formulae by the addition of surface convective heat transfer coefficients. For multi-layered flat structures or structures with large radii of curvature with convective heat transfer on both exposed surfaces, the heat transfer rate is given by:

$$\Phi = \frac{A \, (\theta_{\mathrm{i}} - \theta_{\mathrm{o}})}{R_1 + R_2 + \ldots + \dfrac{1}{h_{\mathrm{ci}}} + \dfrac{1}{h_{\mathrm{co}}}} \tag{3.52}$$

where:

$$R_1 = \frac{x}{\lambda_1} \qquad (3.53)$$

For multi-layered cylindrical structures:

$$\Phi = \frac{2 \pi L (\theta_i - \theta_o)}{R_1 + R_2 + \ldots + \dfrac{2}{h_{ci} d_i} + \dfrac{2}{h_{co} d_o}} \qquad (3.54)$$

where:

$$R_1 = \frac{x}{\lambda_1} \ln \left(\frac{d_{o1}}{d_{i1}} \right), \text{etc.} \qquad (3.55)$$

For structures having continuous air spaces, the resistance of the air space, which takes account of radiative, convective, and conductive heat transfer can also be included in the above equations, see chapter 3 of CIBSE Guide A[10].

3.2.3 Radiation

Radiation, in the context of heating, is the emission, from a source, of electromagnetic waves having wavelengths between those of visible light and those of radio waves. Radiation heat transfer is governed by the Stefan-Boltzmann law for black bodies which can be written:

$$\phi = \sigma T^4 \qquad (3.56)$$

A black body is defined as one which absorbs totally all radiation falling onto its surface. A grey body has a surface which absorbs all wavelengths equally but does not absorb all the radiation. Emissivity is defined as the ratio of the total emissive power of a body to the total emissive power of a black body at the same temperature. Some values of emissivity are given in Tables 3.7, 3.8 and 3.9.

Equations for black body radiation are simple, but in practice black body radiation does not often occur. Most of the following equations assume that the reflective, emissive and absorptive properties of the surfaces remain constant with wavelength, i.e. grey body radiation is assumed, though these equations are also valid for black body radiation. Unless otherwise stated, all equations require that reflections are non-specular, i.e. have no directional properties.

For problems involving surfaces which are so placed that a significant proportion of the radiation emitted by one surface does not fall upon the other surface, or escapes from between the surfaces, or for problems involving enclosures with varying surface temperatures, then the following equations can be modified. These terms will include view factors (otherwise known as form factors or angle factors), which are functions of the geometry of the surfaces only, and are a measure of the proportion of the field of view of one surface which is occupied by the other surface. Table 3.10 and Figure 3.1 contain view factors for some of the more common geometries. References 11, 12, and 13 contain further work and examples of view factors. A comprehensive catalogue of view factor relations may be found in reference 14.

It can be shown that the relation between the view factors for two surfaces is:

$$F_{12} A_1 = F_{21} A_2 \qquad (3.57)$$

and that the heat exchange between two black body finite areas is given by:

$$\Phi = A_1 \sigma F_{12} (T_1^4 - T_2^4) \qquad (3.58)$$

$$\Phi = A_2 \sigma F_{21} (T_1^4 - T_2^4) \qquad (3.59)$$

3.2.3.1 Radiation between parallel flat surfaces

For surfaces so placed that negligible radiation escapes from between them, the heat exchange for grey body radiation is given by[1]:

$$\Phi = \sigma \varepsilon_{12} A_1 (T_1^4 - T_2^4) \qquad (3.60)$$

where:

$$\varepsilon_{12} = \frac{\varepsilon_1 \varepsilon_2}{\varepsilon_1 + \varepsilon_2 - \varepsilon_1 \varepsilon_2} \qquad (3.61)$$

for $A_1 = A_2$.

3.2.3.2 Radiation between concentric curved surfaces

The following equation is valid for grey body radiation with or without a specular reflection, assuming negligible edge losses:

$$\phi = \sigma \varepsilon_{12} (T_1^4 - T_2^4) \qquad (3.62)$$

where:

$$\varepsilon_{12} = \frac{1}{\varepsilon_1} + \frac{A_1}{A_2} \left(\frac{1}{\varepsilon_2} - 1 \right) \qquad (3.63)$$

for $A_1 < A_2$.

Note that:

$$\Phi = \phi A_1 \qquad (3.64)$$

3.2.3.3 Radiation between small surfaces well separated

For surfaces which are small compared with their distance apart, the amount of radiation reflected back to the radiating surface from the other surface is negligible. The heat exchange for grey bodies is given by:

$$\Phi = \sigma \varepsilon_1 \varepsilon_2 F_{12} A_1 (T_1^4 - T_2^4) \qquad (3.65)$$

Table 3.7 Absorptivity and emissivity: impermeable materials

Material	Condition (where known)	Absorptivity	Emissivity
Aluminium	Polished	0.10–0.40	0.03–0.06
	Dull/rough polish	0.40–0.65	0.18–0.30
	Anodised	—	0.72
Aluminium surfaced roofing		—	0.216
Asphalt	Newly laid	0.91–0.93	—
	Weathered	0.82–0.89	—
	Block	0.85–0.98	0.90–0.98
Asphalt pavement		0.852–0.928	—
Bitumen/felt roofing		0.86–0.89	0.91
Bitumen pavement		0.86–0.89	0.90–0.98
Brass	Polished	0.30–0.50	0.03–0.05
	Dull	0.40–0.065	0.20–0.30
	Anodised	—	0.59–0.61
Bronze		0.34	—
Copper	Polished	0.18–0.50	0.02–0.05
	Dull	0.40–0.065	0.20–0.30
	Anodised	0.64	0.60
Glass	Normal	⋆	0.88
	Hemispherical	⋆	0.84
Iron	Unoxidised	—	0.05
	Bright/polished	0.40–0.65	0.20–0.377
	Oxidised	—	0.736–0.74
	Red rusted	—	0.61–0.65
	Heavily rusted	0.737	0.85–0.94
Iron, cast	Unoxidised/polished	—	0.21–0.24
	Oxidised	—	0.64–0.78
	Strongly oxidised	—	0.95
Iron, galvanised	New	0.64–0.66	0.22–0.28
	Old/very dirty	0.89–0.92	0.89
Lead	Unoxidised	—	0.05–0.075
	Old/oxidised	0.77–0.79	0.28–0.281
Rubber	Hard/glossy	—	0.945
	Grey/rough	—	0.859
Steel	Unoxidised/polished/stainless	0.20	0.074–0.097
	Oxidised	0.20	0.79–0.82
Tin	Highly polished/unoxidised	0.10–0.40	0.043–0.084
Paint:			
— aluminium		0.30–0.55	0.27–0.67
— zinc		0.30	0.95
Polyvinylchloride (pvc)		—	0.90–0.92
Tile	Light colour	0.3–0.5	0.85–0.95
Varnish		—	0.80–0.98
Zinc	Polished	0.55	0.045–0.053
	Oxidised	0.05	0.11–0.25

⋆ See manufacturers' data

3.3.2.4 Radiation between an enclosure and a contained surface

For a comparatively small area within an enclosure, it is possible to assume that the enclosure behaves like a black body. This is because negligible radiation from the enclosed body will be reflected back to it from the enclosure. Hence $F_{12} = 1$ and $\varepsilon_2 = 1$ so:

$$\Phi = \sigma \varepsilon_1 A_1 (T_1^4 - T_2^4) \qquad (3.66)$$

Surface 1 has the smaller area and this equation is valid for grey body radiation.

3.2.3.5 Equivalent radiative heat transfer coefficient

Very often it is useful to have a heat transfer coefficient for radiation heat exchange such that:

$$\Phi = f h_r A_1 (\theta_{s1} - \theta_{s2}) \qquad (3.67)$$

The function $f = f(\varepsilon_{12}, F_{12})$ is extremely complex unless either the radiation is black body (in which case $\varepsilon_{12} = 1$) or the radiation is independent of the geometry (in which case $F_{12} = F_{21} = 1$).

Table 3.8 Absorptivity and emissivity: inorganic, porous materials

Material	Condition (where known)	Absorptivity	Emissivity
Asbestos:			
— board		—	0.96
— paper		—	0.93–0.94
— cloth		—	0.90
— cement	New	0.61	0.95–0.96
	Very dirty	0.83	0.95–0.96
Brick	Glazed/light	0.25–0.36	0.85–0.95
	Light	0.36–0.62	0.85–0.95
	Dark	0.63–0.89	0.85–0.95
Cement mortar, screed		0.73	0.93
Clay tiles	Red, brown	0.60–0.69	0.85–0.95
	Purple/dark	0.81–0.82	0.85–0.95
Concrete		0.65–0.80	0.85–0.95
— tile		0.65–0.80	0.85–0.95
— block		0.56–0.69	0.94
Plaster		0.30–0.50	0.91
Stone:			
— granite (red)		0.55	0.90–0.93
— limestone		0.33–0.53	0.90–0.93
— marble		0.44–0.592	0.90–0.93
— quartz		—	0.90
— sandstone		0.54–0.76	0.90–0.93
— slate		0.79–0.93	0.85–0.98

Table 3.9 Absorptivity and emissivity: hygroscopic materials

Material	Condition (where known)	Absorptivity	Emissivity
Paper	—		0.091–0.94
— white, bond		0.25–0.28	—
Cloth:			
— cotton, black		0.67–0.98	—
— cotton, deep blue		0.82–0.83	—
— cotton, red		0.562	—
— wool, black		0.75–0.88	—
— felt, black		0.775–0.861	—
— fabric (unspecified)		—	0.89–0.92
Wood:			
— beach		—	0.94
— oak		—	0.89–0.90
— spruce		—	0.82
— walnut		—	0.83

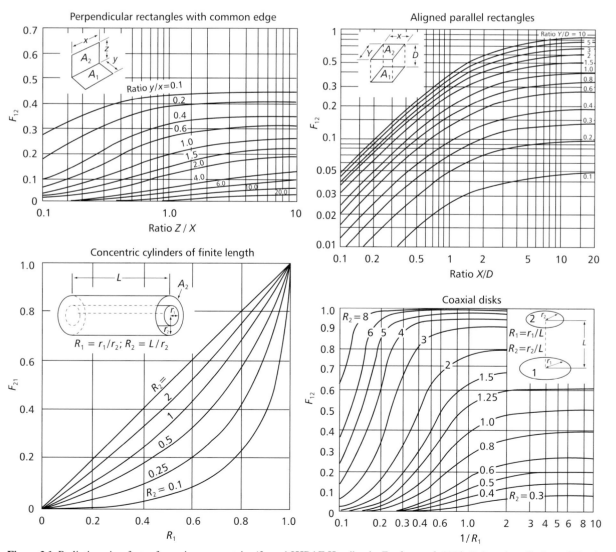

Figure 3.1 Radiation view factor for various geometries (from ASHRAE Handbook: *Fundamentals* 2005. © American Society of Heating, Refrigerating and Air-Conditioning Engineers Inc. (www.ashrae.org))

Table 3.10 View factors

Configuration	View factor
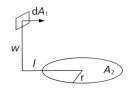	$F_{12} = \dfrac{w}{2\,l}\left\{\dfrac{\left(\dfrac{w}{l}\right)^2 + \left(\dfrac{r}{l}\right)^2 + 1}{\left[\left(\left(\dfrac{w}{l}\right)^2 + \left(\dfrac{r}{l}\right)^2 + 1\right)^2 - 4\left(\dfrac{r}{l}\right)^2\right]^{0.5}} - 1\right\}$
	$F_{12} = \dfrac{1}{2}\left\{1 - \dfrac{\left(\dfrac{w}{y}\right)^2 + \left(\dfrac{r}{y}\right)^2 + 1}{\left[\left(\left(\dfrac{w}{y}\right)^2 + \left(\dfrac{r}{y}\right)^2 + 1\right)^2 - 4\left(\dfrac{r}{y}\right)^2\right]^{0.5}}\right\}$
	$F_{12} = \sin^2 \lambda \cos \theta$
	$F_{12} = \dfrac{1}{2\,\pi}\left\{\left[\dfrac{y}{(w^2 + y^2)^{0.5}}\arctan\dfrac{z}{(w^2 + y^2)^{0.5}}\right] + \left[\dfrac{z}{(w^2 + z^2)^{0.5}}\arctan\dfrac{y}{(w^2 + z^2)^{0.5}}\right]\right\} = F_{\mathrm{p}}$
	$F_{12} = \dfrac{1}{2\,\pi}\left\{\arctan\dfrac{z}{w} - \left[\dfrac{w}{(w^2 + y^2)^{0.5}}\arctan\dfrac{z}{(w^2 + y^2)^{0.5}}\right]\right\} = F_{\mathrm{N}}$
	$F_{12} = F_{\mathrm{p}}\cos\psi + F_{\mathrm{N}}\sin\psi$
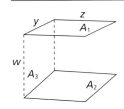	$F_{12} = \dfrac{1}{2}\left\{\dfrac{r^2 + w^2 + l^2}{l^2} - \left[\left(\dfrac{r^2 + w^2 + l^2}{l^2}\right)^2 - \dfrac{4\,r^2}{l^2}\right]^{0.5}\right\}$
	$F_{12} = \dfrac{2}{\pi\,y\,z}\left\{\left[y\,(w^2 + z^2)^{0.5}\arctan\dfrac{y}{(w^2 + z^2)^{0.5}}\right] + \left[z\,(w^2 + y^2)^{0.5}\arctan\dfrac{z}{(w^2 + y^2)^{0.5}}\right]\right.$ $\left. - \left[w\,y\arctan\dfrac{y}{w}\right] - \left[w\,z\arctan\dfrac{z}{w}\right] - \left[\dfrac{w^2}{2}\ln\dfrac{w^2\,(w^2 + y^2 + z^2)}{(y^2 + w^2)(w^2 + z^2)}\right]\right\}$ $F_{32} = \dfrac{1}{\pi}\left\{\left[\arctan\dfrac{y}{w}\right] + \left[\dfrac{z}{w}\arctan\dfrac{y}{z}\right] - \left[\dfrac{(w^2 + z^2)^{0.5}}{w}\arctan\dfrac{y}{(w^2 + z^2)^{0.5}}\right]\right.$ $+ \left[\dfrac{w}{4\,y}\ln\dfrac{w^2\,(w^2 + y^2 + z^2)}{(w^2 + z^2)(w^2 + y^2)}\right] + \left[\dfrac{z^2}{4\,w\,y}\ln\dfrac{z^2\,(w^2 + y^2 + z^2)}{(y^2 + z^2)(w^2 + z^2)}\right]$ $\left. - \left[\dfrac{y}{4\,w}\ln\dfrac{y^2\,(w^2 + y^2 + z^2)}{(y^2 + z^2)(w^2 + y^2)}\right]\right\}$
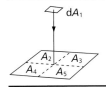	$F_{1(2+3+4+5)} = F_{12} + F_{13} + F_{14} + F_{15}$

Notes: (1) the arrowhead indicates the direction of the normal to the radiating element; (2) in some configurations a particular distance has been taken as unity, since view factors are independent of the scale.

Table 3.11 Values of radiative heat transfer coefficient h_r

θ_1 / °C	\multicolumn{11}{c}{Values of h_r (/ W·m⁻²·K⁻¹) for stated values of θ_2 (/ °C)}										
	−40	−20	0	5	10	15	20	25	30	40	50
−10	3.5	3.9	4.4	4.5	4.6	4.8	4.9	5.0	5.2	5.5	5.8
−5	3.6	4.0	4.5	4.6	4.8	4.9	5.0	5.2	5.3	5.6	5.9
0	3.7	4.1	4.6	4.7	4.9	5.0	5.2	5.3	5.4	5.7	6.0
5	3.8	4.3	4.7	4.9	5.0	5.1	5.3	5.4	5.6	5.9	6.2
10	3.9	4.4	4.9	5.0	5.1	5.3	5.4	5.6	5.7	6.0	6.3
15	4.1	4.5	5.0	5.1	5.3	5.4	5.6	5.7	5.9	6.2	6.5
20	4.2	4.6	5.2	5.3	5.4	5.6	5.7	5.9	6.0	6.3	6.6
25	4.3	4.8	5.3	5.4	5.6	5.7	5.9	6.0	6.2	6.5	6.8
30	4.4	4.9	5.4	5.6	5.7	5.9	6.0	6.2	6.3	6.6	7.0
40	4.7	5.2	5.7	5.9	6.0	6.2	6.3	6.5	6.6	7.0	7.3
50	5.0	5.5	6.0	6.2	6.3	6.5	6.6	6.8	7.0	7.3	7.6
60	5.3	5.8	6.4	6.5	6.7	6.8	7.0	7.1	7.3	7.7	8.0
70	5.6	6.1	6.7	6.9	7.0	7.2	7.3	7.5	7.7	8.0	8.4
80	5.9	6.5	7.1	7.2	7.4	7.5	7.7	7.9	8.1	8.4	8.8
90	6.3	6.8	7.4	7.6	7.8	7.9	8.1	8.3	8.4	8.8	9.2

Hence, for black body radiation, equation 3.67 can be simplified to:

$$\Phi = F_{12}\, h_r\, A_1\, (\theta_{s1} - \theta_{s2}) \qquad (3.68)$$

or, for grey body radiation (with $F_{12} = 1$):

$$\Phi = \varepsilon_{12}\, h_r\, A_1\, (\theta_{s1} - \theta_{s2}) \qquad (3.69)$$

It can be shown that:

$$h_r = \sigma (T_1 + T_2)\, (T_1^2 + T_2^2) \qquad (3.70)$$

Table 3.11 gives values of h_r for various values of surface temperature.

When $T_1 = T_2$ then:

$$h_r = 4\, \sigma\, T^3 \qquad (3.71)$$

3.2.4 Mass transfer

Mass transfer can be described as the diffusion of one substance into another. Most commonly, a liquid vapourises into, or condenses from, a gas with an accompanying variation of vapour concentration, i.e. partial pressure, within the gas. This variation occurs within a boundary layer.

In buildings and building services systems, the most common examples of mass transfer are condensation, humidification and evaporation. These examples can all take place within air conditioning equipment and cooling towers but the first and last examples often occur within structures, such as during the drying out period of buildings and condensation on walls and windows. For these examples, the previous heat transfer equations are not applicable.

Calculations for most mass transfer problems are quite complex although generally the equations follow the form of the convection heat transfer equations.

A detailed treatment of mass transfer is beyond the scope of this section. For a general introduction to mass transfer the reader is referred to references 2, 4, 15 and 16. Reference 1 contains data and procedures involving mixtures (as well as most other aspects of thermodynamics) and reference 17 has a section that covers the simple aspects of water sprays.

3.3 Heat transfer practice

3.3.1 External environment

At the external surfaces of buildings, heat transfer takes place via the processes of convection and radiation. While radiation heat loss is a function of surface temperature and emissivity, convection heat loss is more complex, being a function of a number of variables such as wind speed and direction, flow regime and surface roughness. This makes difficult the accurate determination of heat transfer at a building surface.

3.3.1.1 Radiative exchange at external surfaces

The longwave radiation exchange at the external surface of a building is dependent upon the difference between the incoming longwave radiation from the external environment (sky, other buildings and the ground) and the outgoing longwave radiation emitted from the surface of the building in question. Normally, calculation of the radiative exchange is simplified by the use of linear expressions, rather than retaining the fourth power temperature term. This linearisation is produced by the introduction of a longwave radiation heat transfer coefficient, h_r. In order to determine a value for h_r, certain approximations are necessary. One approximation is the assumption that the external environment radiates as a black body at external air temperature; the other approximation is that the surrounding external environment can be assigned a view factor of unity. This leads to a value for the radiation component $(E \times h_r)$ of 4.0 W·m⁻²·K⁻¹, where the emissivity factor (E) is the product of the view factor and the emissivity of the building surface[18].

3.3.1.2 Convective exchange at external surfaces

For design purposes, the exposure of buildings has been classified into three categories based on near-surface wind speeds: 'sheltered', 'normal' and 'severe' exposure (see CIBSE Guide A[10], section 3.3.9.4). These exposure levels correspond to wind speeds at roof surfaces of 1.0, 3.0 and 9.0 m.s^{-1}, respectively; at wall surfaces, the corresponding near-surface wind speeds are 0.7, 2.0 and 6.0 m.s^{-1}, respectively.

Wind speed at the surface c_s and the convection coefficient h_c at the external surface have to date been correlated using the following expression derived from wind tunnel studies[19]:

$$h_c = 5.8 + 4.1 c_s \tag{3.72}$$

This equation has been assumed to be valid for all external wind speeds.

Use of this correlation with the wind speeds given above leads to the design values of external surface resistance, R_{se}, based on the following relation:

$$R_{se} = 1 / (h_c + E h_r) \tag{3.73}$$

These values for R_{se} are given in Table 3.9 of CIBSE Guide A[10], for the three levels of exposure. In recent years, however, a number of experiments to measure h_c at the external surface of actual buildings have been made. These results are discussed below.

3.3.1.3 Full-scale external measurements

Reference 20 presents a review of full-scale measurements for h_c at building external surfaces, and has suggested the following combined correlation for use by designers for the case of 'normal' exposure:

$$h_c = 16.7 c_s^{0.5} \tag{3.74}$$

for h_c in W·m^{-2}·K^{-1} and c_s in m·s^{-1} up to a surface wind speed of 3.5 m·s^{-1}. Substituting a value for c_s of 2.0 m·s^{-1} leads to a value for h_c of 23.6 W·m^{-2}·K^{-1} and a corresponding modified value of the external surface resistance R_{se} for normal exposure of 0.04 m^2·K·W^{-1}.

3.3.2 Internal environment

3.3.2.1 Internal surface convection coefficients

There have been several studies of internal surface convection coefficients[21–24], showing that a range of variation exists in the measured values. Reference 21 presents correlations that give typical values for convective heat transfer coefficients at heated wall, floor and ceiling surfaces of a room-sized test enclosure; the correlations were expressed in terms of a hydraulic diameter d_h, and a temperature difference $\Delta\theta_{sa}$, as follows.

For a heated wall:

$$h_{cn} = \frac{1.823}{d_h^{0.121}} (\Delta\theta_{sa})^{0.293} \tag{3.75}$$

For a heated floor:

$$h_{cn} = \frac{2.175}{d_h^{0.076}} (\Delta\theta_{sa})^{0.308} \tag{3.76}$$

For a heated ceiling:

$$h_{cn} = \frac{0.704}{d_h^{0.601}} (\Delta\theta_{sa})^{0.133} \tag{3.77}$$

Here, $\Delta\theta_{sa}$ was the difference between the surface and air temperatures (measured at 0.1 m from the surface for wall and floor and at the centre of the enclosure for the case of the ceiling); $\Delta\theta_{sa}$ values ranged between 5 and 25 K. In these expressions, the value for d_h was evaluated as $4 A_s/P$.

Note that values for the internal surface resistance R_{si} can be estimated from a knowledge of appropriate convective and radiative heat transfer coefficients. Values are given in Table 3.10 of CIBSE Guide A[10].

3.3.2.2 Radiation exchange between internal surfaces

For a multi-surface enclosure of N surfaces, each with area $A_1, A_2 \ldots A_N$ and with emissivities of $\varepsilon_1, \varepsilon_2 \ldots \varepsilon_N$, respectively, the following equations can be used, based on radiosity formulation methods (see, for example, any standard heat transfer text), to determine the net rate of heat exchange by radiation to each surface:

$$\Phi_i = \frac{\varepsilon_i A_i (E_{bi} - \mathcal{J}_i)}{(1 - \varepsilon_i)} \tag{3.78}$$

and:

$$\frac{\varepsilon_i A_i (E_{bi} - \mathcal{J}_i)}{(1 - \varepsilon_i)} = \sum_{j=1}^{N} (\mathcal{J}_i - \mathcal{J}_j)(A_i F_{ij}) \tag{3.79}$$

For N surfaces, equation 3.79 results in a set of N linear equations with unknowns $\mathcal{J}_1, \mathcal{J}_2 \ldots \mathcal{J}_N$. For the surface '$i$' at a known surface temperature T_i, knowledge of the value for $\mathcal{J}_i$ permits calculation of the net rate of heat transfer by radiation, q_i, to the surface 'i' by use of equation (3.79).

If the surface 'i' is considered to be a black body of known temperature T_i, then its radiosity $\mathcal{J}_i$ is equal to its emissive power E_{bi}, that is:

$$E_{bi} = \mathcal{J}_i = \sigma T_i^4 \tag{3.80}$$

and the net rate of heat transfer by radiation to the black surface 'i' can be determined from the following expression:

$$\Phi_i = \sum_{j=1}^{N} (\mathcal{J}_i - \mathcal{J}_j)(A_i F_{ij}) \tag{3.81}$$

To calculate the rate of radiation exchange between surfaces within the multi-surface enclosure, the following rules of view factor algebra must be applied:

(a) Reciprocity rule:

$$A_i F_{ij} = A_j F_{ji} \qquad (3.82)$$

(b) Summation rule:

$$\sum_{j=1}^{N} F_{ij} = 1 \qquad (3.83)$$

Values of view factors for some of the more commonly encountered geometries are given in Table 3.10 or Figure 3.1. From a knowledge of view factors and known values of radiosities, for all surfaces, the net rate of heat transfer by radiation to each surface can be determined using equation 3.78.

Example 3.1

A cuboidal room is 6 m long, 4 m wide and 3 m high. It contains a chilled ceiling of surface temperature 18 °C, and a floor of surface temperature 22 °C; each of its four walls is at a surface temperature of 25 °C. Determine the net rate of heat transfer by radiation to the ceiling and to the floor, assuming that the walls act as a black body surface, and that the emissivities of the ceiling and the floor are 0.9 and 0.85, respectively.

The ceiling is treated as surface 1, the floor as surface 2, and all the four walls can be treated as a single surface, surface 3. Figure 3.2 illustrates the arrangement:

Using equation 3.79, calculate the radiosities $\mathcal{J}_1$ and $\mathcal{J}_2$ for surfaces 1 and 2, respectively:

For surface 1 ($i = 1$):

$$\frac{\varepsilon_1 A_1}{(1 - \varepsilon_1)} (E_{b1} - \mathcal{J}_1) = \sum_{j=1}^{3} (\mathcal{J}_1 - \mathcal{J}_j)(A_1 F_{1j}) \qquad (3.84)$$

but:

$$\sum_{j=1}^{3} (\mathcal{J}_1 - \mathcal{J}_j)(A_1 F_{ij}) = (\mathcal{J}_1 - \mathcal{J}_1)(A_1 F_{11})$$
$$+ (\mathcal{J}_1 - \mathcal{J}_2)(A_1 F_{12})$$
$$+ (\mathcal{J}_1 - \mathcal{J}_3)(A_1 F_{13}) \qquad (3.85)$$

Therefore:

$$\frac{\varepsilon_1 A_1}{(1 - \varepsilon_1)} (E_{b1} - \mathcal{J}_1) = (\mathcal{J}_1 - \mathcal{J}_2)(A_1 F_{12})$$
$$+ (\mathcal{J}_1 - \mathcal{J}_3)(A_1 F_{13}) \qquad (3.86)$$

Similarly, for surface 2 ($i = 2$):

$$\frac{\varepsilon_2 A_2}{(1 - \varepsilon_2)} (E_{b2} - \mathcal{J}_2) = (\mathcal{J}_2 - \mathcal{J}_1)(A_2 F_{21})$$
$$+ (\mathcal{J}_2 - \mathcal{J}_3)(A_2 F_{23}) \qquad (3.87)$$

Surface 3 is assumed to be a black body surface, therefore, from equation 3.80:

$$\mathcal{J}_3 = \sigma T_3^4 \qquad (3.88)$$

The view factors are then evaluated as follows.

F_{12} (parallel plates) is 0.34, found from Table 3.10, or from a suitable chart of view factors for various geometries, as given in Figure 3.1[25].

From equation 3.83:

$$F_{11} + F_{12} + F_{13} = 1 \qquad (3.89)$$

But $F_{11} = 0$ for a flat surface, so:

$$F_{13} = 1 - F_{12} \qquad (3.90)$$

Therefore, $F_{13} = 1 - 0.34 = 0.66$.

Similarly, $F_{23} = 0.66$.

The value for F_{21} can be found from equation 3.82:

$$A_1 F_{12} = A_2 F_{21} \qquad (3.91)$$

In this case, $A_1 = A_2$, and so $F_{21} = F_{12} = 0.34$.

Equations 3.86 and 3.87 can now be solved (using matrix inversion, for example) for $\mathcal{J}_1$ and $\mathcal{J}_2$, since values for all other terms are now known. In situations where there are a large number of 'grey' surfaces, necessitating the calculation of $\mathcal{J}$-values, a solution can be obtained from matrix inversion or from the use of a suitable computer program.

Solution gives:

$$\mathcal{J}_1 = 410.06 \text{ W·m}^{-2}$$

$$\mathcal{J}_2 = 430.17 \text{ W·m}^{-2}$$

$$\mathcal{J}_3 = 447.14 \text{ W·m}^{-2}$$

Finally, the values for the rates of heat transfer by radiation to each surface, Φ_1, Φ_2 and Φ_3 can now be evaluated from equations 3.78 and 3.79, giving:

$$\Phi_1 = \frac{\varepsilon_1 A_1}{(1 - \varepsilon_1)} (E_{bi} - \mathcal{J}_1) \qquad (3.92)$$

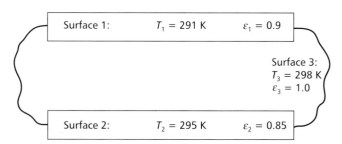

Surface 1: $T_1 = 291$ K $\quad \varepsilon_1 = 0.9$

Surface 3: $T_3 = 298$ K $\quad \varepsilon_3 = 1.0$

Surface 2: $T_2 = 295$ K $\quad \varepsilon_2 = 0.85$

Figure 3.2 Example 3.1: illustration of room as a 3-surface enclosure

Hence:

$$\Phi_1 = \frac{0.9 \times 6 \times 4}{(1 - 0.9)} (5.67 \times 10^{-8} \times 291^4 - 410.06)$$

$$= -749.9 \text{ W}$$

Similarly, $\Phi_2 = -103.3$ W, and $\Phi_3 = 854.1$ W.

Thus, the ceiling removes radiant heat at a rate of 749.9 W, while the floor removes 103.3 W.

To check the results, the total rate of heat removal by the ceiling plus the floor should equal the total rate of heat supplied by the four walls, that is:

$$749.9 + 103.3 = 853.2 \text{ W}$$

The agreement is within rounding error.

3.3.2.3 Simplified technique for rooms

The multi-surface enclosure can be simplified by treating it as a two-surface approximation[26]. Here, the radiant exchange in the room is modelled by assuming that one surface (the heated or cooled surface) radiates to a single fictitious surface (made up of the other surfaces in the room, which are considered to be at a similar temperature and emissivity to one another). View factors do not need to be determined in the case of a two-surface enclosure. This simplification leads to the following equation:

$$\Phi_r = \sigma F_r A_s (T_s^4 - T_{fs}^4) \qquad (3.93)$$

where Φ_r is the rate of radiant heat transfer exchanged by the heated (or cooled) surface of area A_s at temperature T_s (K), and T_{fs} is the area-weighted and emissivity-weighted average temperature of the other surfaces in the room (K); F_r is a radiation exchange factor for two surfaces and takes a value of 0.87 for most rooms in which the emissivities of the surfaces can be regarded as approximately 0.9 (see reference 27). For this situation, reference 22 shows that equation 3.93 can be expressed as:

$$\Phi_r = 5 \times 10^{-8} A_s [(\theta_s + 273)^4 - (\theta_{fs} + 273)^4]$$

$$\qquad (3.94)$$

where θ_s is the temperature (°C) of the heated or cooled surface; the term θ_{fs} is the area-weighted average surface temperature (°C) for the fictitious surface, given by:

$$\theta_{fs} = \left(\sum_{j=1}^{N} (A_j \, \theta_j) / \sum_{j=1}^{N} A_j ; i \neq j \right) \qquad (3.95)$$

(that is, when the emissivities of those surfaces comprising the fictitious surface are nearly equal). Here, θ_j is the temperature in °C of a surface making up the fictitious surface.

Equation 3.94 can be used by designers to estimate the rate of heat removal by radiation by a heated or cooled surface as a function of the temperature of the surface and of θ_{fs}.

Example 3.2

Estimate the rate of heat removal by radiation by the chilled ceiling of Example 3.1 for the same room conditions, but using the simplified technique for rooms.

Calculate θ_{fs} for the four walls and floor using equation 3.95:

$$\theta_{fs} = \frac{[((2 \times 3 \times 6) + (2 \times 3 \times 4)) \times 25] + [(6 \times 4) \times 22]}{(2 \times 3 \times 6) + (2 \times 3 \times 4) + (6 \times 4)}$$

$$= 24.14 \,°C$$

The rate of heat removal by radiation ϕ_r by the chilled ceiling can now be estimated using equation 3.94:

$$\Phi_r = 5 \times 10^{-8} \times (6 \times 4) [(18 + 273)^4 - (24.14 + 273)^4]$$

$$= -749.6 \text{ W}$$

In addition, a radiative heat transfer coefficient h_r can be determined using the following linear expression:

$$\Phi_r = h_r A_s (\theta_s - \theta_{fs}) \qquad (3.96)$$

For the ceiling of Example 3.2, the value for h_r is 5.1 W·m^{-2}·K^{-1}; this is a typical value for indoor conditions (see Table 3.7 of CIBSE Guide A[10]).

3.3.2.4 Combined convective and radiative heat transfer in enclosures

The total rate of heat exchange at a surface in an enclosure can be determined by adding the convective and radiative components discussed in the previous sections:

$$\Phi_t = \Phi_c + \Phi_r \qquad (3.97)$$

where Φ_c is given by:

$$\Phi_c = h_c A_s (\theta_s - \theta_a) \qquad (3.98)$$

Values for h_c are dependent upon conditions, but could be evaluated, as h_{cn}, for example, from equations 3.75, 3.76 or 3.77, as appropriate. The term Φ_r can be evaluated from equation 3.94 when the simplified technique is adopted; alternatively, Φ_i replaces Φ_r for that surface in equation 3.97, where Φ_i is evaluated from equation 3.78.

3.3.3 Human body heat transfer

3.3.1 Occupied enclosures

The presence of a human body in an enclosure can be treated as the addition of a further surface which exchanges heat by convection and by radiation with the surroundings. Such a treatment can be of relevance to the estimation of room thermal loads (see chapter 6 of CIBSE Guide A[10]), and to the determination of human thermal comfort (see chapter 1 of CIBSE Guide A[10]). Here, correlations for natural (free) and for forced convection for a human body are given, together with view factors for use in estimation of radiant exchange.

3.3.3.2 Human heat exchange by convection

The rate of heat transfer per unit area by convection, ϕ_{hb}, between the human body surface and its surroundings is given by:

$$\phi_{hb} = f_{cl}\, h_c\, (\theta_{cl} - \theta_a) \qquad (3.99)$$

where f_{cl} is the clothing area factor, given by[28]:

$$f_{cl} \approx 1 + 0.15\, I_{clo} \qquad (3.100)$$

where I_{clo} is the thermal resistance of clothing (clo).

Values for h_c for natural or for forced convection can be determined from a suitable correlation equation. Table 3.12 (after reference 29) summarises some of the existing correlations available.

Table 3.12 Human body convection coefficients

h_c / W·m^{-2}·K^{-1}	Reference	Remarks
Natural convection:		
3.0	Nishi and Gagge (1977)[30]	Still body in still air
2.38 $\Delta\theta_{ca}^{0.25}$	Neilsen and Pedersen (1952)[31]	Used in Fanger's equation[28]
4.0	Rapp (1973)[32]	Recommended (by McIntyre)[29] for sedentary people
Forced convection:		
8.3 $v_r^{0.6}$	Mitchell (1974)[33]	Best average
12.1 $\sqrt{v_r}$	Winslow *et al.* (1937)[34]	Used in Fanger's equation[28]
8.3 $\sqrt{v_r}$	Kerslake (1972)[35]	Recommended (by McIntyre)[29]

3.3.3.3 Human heat exchange by radiation

This can be treated using the radiosity technique as described above (section 3.3.2.2). Here, the human body is regarded as an additional surface for radiant exchange. Human body view factors for use in the technique are given in reference 36, and are reproduced here with permission (Figures 3.3 to 3.6).

Example 3.3 (adapted from reference 28)

Determine the view factors between a seated person (of known position but unknown orientation) and the surrounding surfaces of the room as shown in Figure 3.7 (upper figure).

Each surface of the room is divided into rectangles as shown in Figure 3.7 (lower figures). The view factors pertaining to each rectangle can then be determined graphically from Figures 3.3 and 3.4, or analytically from the equations in Table 3.13. The results are given in Table

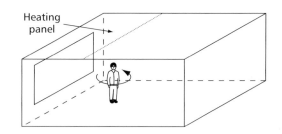

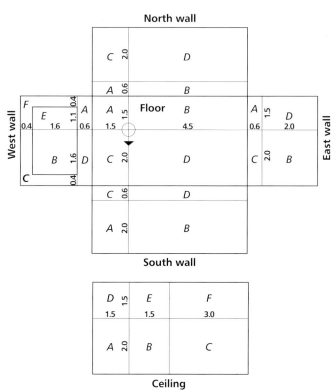

Figure 3.7 Example 3.3: room dimensions and person placement (adapted from reference 28)

3.14. As a check on the calculations, the sum of all the view factors between the person and the surrounding surfaces should equal unity.

Note that once the view factors have been determined, the rate of heat exchange by radiation between a person and the room surroundings can be calculated using the radiosity approach as illustrated in Example 3.1. Here, the person can be regarded as an additional 'surface' within the enclosure.

Table 3.13 Example 3.3: parameters for calculation of view factors

View factor = $F'_{max}\,(1 - e^{-(a'/c')/\tau})\,(1 - e^{-(b'/c')/\beta})$

where: $\tau = A' + B'\,(a'/c');\ \beta = C' + D'\,(b'/c') + E'\,(a'/c')$

Configuration	Parameter value					
	F'_{max}	A'	B'	C'	D'	E'
Seated person (Fig. 3.3); vertical surfaces (wall, window)	0.118	1.216	0.169	0.717	0.087	0.052
Seated person (Fig. 3.4); horizontal surfaces (floor, ceiling)	0.116	1.396	0.130	0.951	0.080	0.055
Standing person (Fig. 3.5); Vertical surfaces (wall, window)	0.120	1.242	0.167	0.616	0.082	0.051
Standing person (Fig. 3.6); horizontal surfaces (floor, ceiling)	0.116	1.595	0.128	1.226	0.046	0.044

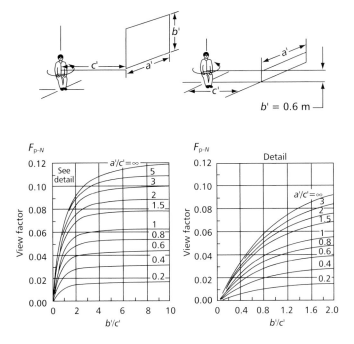

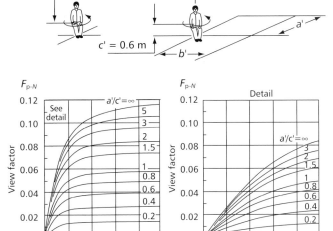

Example

$a' = 4$ m; $b' = 3$ m; $c' = 5$ m;
$b'/c' = 0.6$; $a'/c' = 0.8$; $F_{p-N} = 0.029$

Figure 3.3 Mean value of view factor between a seated person and a vertical rectangle (above or below his centre) when the person is rotated around a vertical axis. (To be used when the location but not the orientation of the person is known.) (Reproduced from BS EN ISO 7726 by permission of the British Standards Institution.)

Example

$a' = 3$ m; $b' = 6$ m; $c' = 2$ m;
$b'/c' = 3.0$; $a'/c' = 1.5$; $F_{p-N} = 0.067$

Figure 3.4 Mean value of view factor between a seated person and a horizontal rectangle (on the ceiling or floor) when the person is rotated around a vertical axis. (To be used when the location but not the orientation of the person is known.) (Reproduced from BS EN ISO 7726 by permission of the British Standards Institution.)

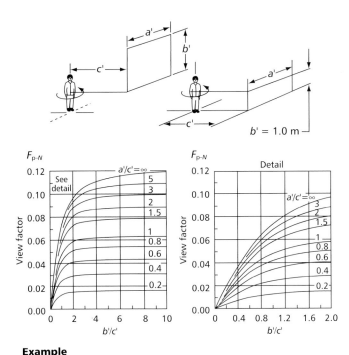

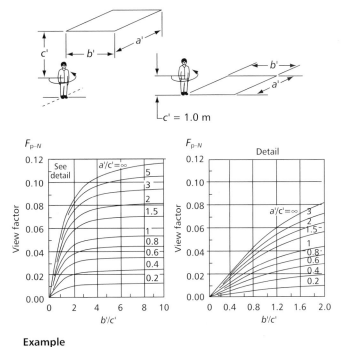

Example

$a' = 4.5$ m; $b' = 2.0$ m; $c' = 3.0$ m;
$b'/c' = 0.67$; $a'/c' = 1.5$; $F_{p-N} = 0.047$

Figure 3.5 Mean value of view factor between a standing person and a vertical rectangle (above or below his centre) when the person is rotated around a vertical axis. (To be used when the location but not the orientation of the person is known.) (Reproduced from BS EN ISO 7726 by permission of the British Standards Institution.)

Example

$a' = 1.0$ m; $b' = 15$ m; $c' = 1.5$ m;
$b'/c' = 10$; $a'/c' = 0.67$; $F_{p-N} = 0.039$

Figure 3.6 Mean value of view factor between a standing person and a horizontal rectangle (on the ceiling or floor) when the person is rotated around a vertical axis. (To be used when the location but not the orientation of the person is known.) (Reproduced from BS EN ISO 7726 by permission of the British Standards Institution.)

Table 3.14 Example 3.3: calculation of view factors (adapted from reference 28)

Surface	View factor equation	Component	Dimension ratios		Component value	View factor
			(b'/c')	(a'/c')		
North wall (Figure 3.3)	$F_{P-ABCD} = F_{P-A} + F_{P-B} + F_{P-C} + F_{P-D}$					
		F_{P-A}	0.40	1.0	0.024	
		F_{P-B}	0.40	3.0	0.033	
		F_{P-C}	1.3	1.0	0.033	
		F_{P-D}	1.3	3.0	0.072	
		F_{P-ABCD}	—	—	—	0.179
East wall (Figure 3.3)	$F_{P-ABCD} = F_{P-A} + F_{P-B} + F_{P-C} + F_{P-D}$					
		F_{P-A}	0.13	0.33	0.004	
		F_{P-B}	0.44	0.44	0.015	
		F_{P-C}	0.13	0.44	0.005	
		F_{P-D}	0.44	0.33	0.011	
		F_{P-ABCD}	—	—	—	0.035
South wall (Figure 3.3)	$F_{P-ABCD} = F_{P-A} + F_{P-B} + F_{P-C} + F_{P-D}$					
		F_{P-A}	1.0	0.75	0.037	
		F_{P-B}	1.0	2.3	0.060	
		F_{P-C}	0.30	0.75	0.015	
		F_{P-D}	0.30	2.3	0.024	
		F_{P-ABCD}	—	—	—	0.136
West wall (Figure 3.3)						
(a) Window	$F_{P-BE} = F_{P-B} + F_{P-E}$					
		F_{P-B}	1.1	1.1	0.049	
		F_{P-E}	1.1	0.73	0.038	
		F_{P-BE}	—	—	0.087	
(b) Rest of the wall	$F_{P-ACDF} = F_{P-A} + F_{P-C}F_{P-D} + F_{P-F}$					
	$= F_{P-A} + F_{P-BC} - F_{P-B} + F_{P-D} + F_{P-EF} - F_{P-E}$					
	$= F_{P-A} + F_{P-BC} + F_{P-D} + F_{P-EF} - F_{P-BE}$					
		F_{P-A}	0.40	1.0	0.024	
		F_{P-BC}	1.3	1.3	0.057	
		F_{P-D}	0.40	1.3	0.026	
		F_{P-EF}	1.3	1.0	0.050	
		F_{P-BE}	—	—	0.087	
		F_{P-ACDF}	—	—	—	0.070
Floor (Figure 3.4)	$F_{P-ABCD} = F_{P-A} + F_{P-B} + F_{P-C} + F_{P-D}$					
		F_{P-A}	2.5	2.5	0.078	
		F_{P-B}	2.5	7.5	0.090	
		F_{P-C}	3.3	2.5	0.082	
		F_{P-D}	3.3	7.5	0.095	
		F_{P-ABCD}	—	—	—	0.345
Ceiling (Figure 3.4)						
(a) Heating panel	$F_{P-ABDE} = F_{P-A} + F_{P-B} + F_{P-D} + F_{P-E}$					
		F_{P-A}	1.0	0.75	0.030	
		F_{P-B}	1.0	0.75	0.030	
		F_{P-D}	0.75	0.75	0.025	
		F_{P-E}	0.75	0.75	0.025	
		F_{P-ABDE}	—	—	—	0.110
(b) Rest of the ceiling	$F_{P-CF} = F_{P-C} + F_{P-F}$					
	$= F_{P-BC} - F_{P-B} + F_{P-EF} - F_{P-E}$					
		F_{P-BC}	1.0	2.3	0.051	
		F_{P-B}	1.0	0.75	0.030	
		F_{P-EF}	0.75	2.3	0.042	
		F_{P-E}	0.75	0.75	0.025	
		F_{P-CF}	—	—	—	0.038
		$F_{person-all\ surfaces}$	—	—	—	1.000

3.3.3.4 Total human heat exchange with surroundings

Sections 3.3.3.2 and 3.3.3.3 deal with heat transfer between a human body and its surroundings by convection and by radiation only. However, the total heat exchange includes not only convective and radiative components, but also heat exchange by evaporation, respiration and conduction. For a treatment of these, refer to chapter 1 of CIBSE Guide A[(10)] or to references 25 or 37.

3.3.4 Equipment and components

3.3.4.1 Plane surfaces

Tables 3.15 and 3.16 (pages 3-22 and 3-23) give the heat emission/absorption from freely exposed plane surfaces to air. They have been prepared from the following equations.

Radiation (from equation 3.60):

$$\phi_r = 5.67 \times 10^{-8} \, \varepsilon \, (T_s^4 - T_r^4) \tag{3.101}$$

Convection (laminar flow from equation 3.6):

$$\phi_c = 0.64 \frac{(\theta_s - \theta_f)^{1.25}}{D^{0.25}} \tag{3.102}$$

Convection (turbulent flow from equation 3.5):

$$\phi_c = 1.7 \, (\theta_s - \theta_f)^{1.33} \tag{3.103}$$

Hence, for room applications and taking $D = 1$ m, equations 3.102 and 3.103 can be put in the general form:

$$\phi_c = C \, (T_s - T_a)^n \tag{3.104}$$

The values of C and n for particular arrangements are given in Table 3.17.

The radiation and convection emissions are shown separately in Tables 3.15 and 3.16 since there may be significant differences between the mean radiant temperature of the enclosure and the air temperature within it. Absorption by the surfaces is shown by negative values of emission.

The radiation equation (equation 3.101) is strictly true only for a panel of comparatively small area relative to the rest of the room area.

In practice, the convection emission applies to draught-free conditions and appreciable increases in heat transfer occur if air movement is present[(10)]. Table 3.18 gives some indication of the effect of air velocity on heat transfer.

3.3.4.2 Bare pipes

The heat emissions per metre run of horizontal steel and copper pipes are given in Tables 3.19, 3.20 and 3.21 (pages 3-24 to 3-26). Absorption by the surfaces is shown by negative values of emission. These tables have been prepared using equation 3.102 and for convection:

$$\phi_c = \frac{\lambda}{d_{op}} Nu \, \Delta t \tag{3.105}$$

For horizontal pipes in air, free convection, laminar flow, and $Gr < 10^8$, the following equation can be used:

$$Nu = 0.53 \, (Gr \, Pr)^{0.25} \tag{3.106}$$

Hence, equation 3.104 becomes:

$$\phi_c = 1.35 \left[\frac{T_s - T_a}{d_{op}} \right]^{0.25} (T_s - T_a) \tag{3.107}$$

The emission per metre run may then be found from:

$$\Phi / l = \pi \, d_{op} \, (\phi_r + \phi_c) \tag{3.108}$$

Tables 3.19, 3.20 and 3.21 assume that both the ambient temperature and the mean radiant temperature are equal to 20 °C. It is also assumed that the external surface of the pipe is at the same temperature as the fluid contained within it.

In practice, for a given temperature difference, a change in air temperature or mean radiant temperature of ±5 °C introduces an error of about 2% while a change of ±10 °C gives an error of about 5%.

Heat emission/absorption under site conditions may vary from the tabulated data since:

(a)   draught-free surroundings may not occur in practice; Table 3.22 gives some indication of the effect on heat transfer

(b)   the actual surface emissivity may differ from those used in preparing the tables; emissivities for other materials and surface finishes are given in Tables 3.7, 3.8 and 3.9

(c)   British Standards[(38,40,41)] permit tolerances in pipe diameters from the mean values used in preparing the tables.

Considerations (b) and (c) may lead to the actual heat emission of a given pipe varying by a further 10% from the tabulated figure.

All these aspects should be taken into consideration in system design and an appropriate allowance made according to circumstances.

Vertical pipes

Pipes set in a vertical position have a heat emission/absorption which differs from that arising from horizontal fixing due to the variation in the thickness of the boundary layer of air about the pipe surface. Correction factors quoted in Table 3.23 are for use in conjunction with the data listed in Tables 3.19, 3.20 and 3.21.

Table 3.15 Heat emission from plane surfaces by radiation (based on equation 3.101)

Surface temp. /°C	Heat emission (/W·m⁻²) for stated surface emissivity and enclosure mean radiant temperature (/°C)																				
	Surface emissivity = 0.3							Surface emissivity = 0.6							Surface emissivity = 0.9						
	10	12.5	15	17.5	20	22.5	25	10	12.5	15	17.5	20	22.5	25	10	12.5	15	17.5	20	22.5	25
5	−7.5	−11	−15	−20	−24	−28	−33	−15	−23	−31	−39	−48	−56	−65	−23	−34	−46	−59	−71	−84	−98
10	0	−3.9	−7.9	−12	−16	−21	−25	0	−7.8	−16	−24	−33	−41	−50	0	−12	−24	−36	−49	−62	−75
15	7.9	4.0	0	−4.1	−8.3	−13	−17	16	8.0	0	−8.2	−17	−25	−34	24	12	0	−12	−25	−38	−51
20	16	12	8.3	4.2	0	−4.3	−8.8	33	25	17	8.4	0	−8.7	−18	49	37	25	13	0	−13	−26
30	34	30	26	22	18	14	9.2	69	61	53	44	36	27	18	103	91	79	67	54	41	28
40	54	50	46	42	38	34	29	108	100	92	84	76	67	58	162	151	139	126	114	101	87
50	76	72	68	64	60	55	51	152	144	136	128	120	111	102	228	216	204	192	179	166	153
60	100	96	92	88	84	79	75	200	192	184	176	168	159	150	300	288	276	264	251	238	225
70	126	122	118	114	110	106	101	253	245	237	229	220	211	203	379	367	355	343	330	317	304
80	155	151	147	143	139	134	130	310	302	294	286	278	269	260	465	453	441	429	416	403	390
90	186	182	178	174	170	166	161	372	365	357	348	340	331	322	559	547	535	523	510	497	484
100	220	216	212	208	204	200	195	440	432	424	416	408	399	390	660	649	637	624	612	599	585
120	297	293	289	285	280	276	272	593	586	577	569	561	552	543	890	878	866	854	841	828	815
140	386	382	378	374	370	365	361	772	764	756	747	739	730	721	1160	1150	1130	1120	1110	1100	1080
160	489	485	481	477	473	468	464	978	970	962	954	945	936	928	1470	1450	1440	1430	1420	1400	1390
180	607	603	599	595	591	587	582	1210	1210	1200	1190	1180	1170	1160	1820	1810	1800	1790	1770	1760	1750
200	742	738	734	730	726	722	717	1480	1480	1470	1460	1450	1440	1430	2230	2220	2200	2190	2180	2170	2150
220	896	892	888	884	879	875	871	1790	1780	1780	1770	1760	1750	1740	2690	2680	2660	2650	2640	2630	2610
240	1070	1070	1060	1060	1050	1050	1040	2140	2130	2120	2110	2110	2100	2090	3210	3200	3180	3170	3160	3150	3130
260	1260	1260	1260	1250	1250	1240	1240	2530	2520	2510	2500	2490	2490	2480	3790	3780	3770	3760	3740	3730	3720
280	1480	1480	1470	1470	1470	1460	1460	2960	2960	2950	2940	2930	2920	2910	4440	4430	4420	4410	4400	4380	4370
300	1720	1720	1720	1710	1710	1700	1700	3450	3440	3430	3430	3420	3410	3400	5170	5160	5150	5140	5120	5110	5100
320	1990	1990	1990	1980	1980	1970	1970	3990	3980	3970	3960	3960	3950	3940	5980	5970	5960	5950	5930	5920	5910
340	2290	2290	2280	2280	2280	2270	2270	4590	4580	4570	4560	4550	4540	4540	6880	6870	6850	6840	6830	6820	6800
360	2620	2620	2610	2610	2610	2600	2600	5240	5240	5230	5220	5210	5200	5190	7870	7850	7840	7830	7820	7800	7790
380	2980	2980	2980	2970	2970	2960	2960	5970	5960	5950	5940	5930	5930	5920	8950	8940	8930	8920	8900	8890	8880
400	3380	3380	3370	3370	3360	3360	3360	6760	6750	6740	6740	6730	6720	6710	10100	10100	10100	10100	10100	10100	10100

Note: values above 1000 rounded to nearest 10, values above 10 000 rounded to nearest 100

Table 3.16 Heat emission from plane surfaces by free convection (based on equation 3.104 and Table 3.17)

Heat emission (/ W·m⁻²) for stated surface emissivity and enclosure mean radiant temperature (/°C)

Surface temp. /°C	Surface emissivity = 0.3							Surface emissivity = 0.6							Surface emissivity = 0.9						
	10	12.5	15	17.5	20	22.5	25	10	12.5	15	17.5	20	22.5	25	10	12.5	15	17.5	20	22.5	25
5	-14	-25	-36	-49	-62	-77	-91	-12	-20	-30	-40	-51	-63	-75	-4.8	-7.9	-11	-15	-19	-23	-27
10	0	-5.8	-14	-25	-36	-49	-62	0	-4.7	-12	-20	-30	-40	-51	0	-2.0	-4.8	-7.9	-11	-15	-19
15	4.8	2.0	0	-5.8	-14	-25	-36	12	4.7	0	-4.7	-12	-20	-30	14	5.8	0	-2.0	-4.8	-7.9	-11
20	11	7.9	4.8	2.0	0	-5.8	-14	30	20	12	4.7	0	-4.7	-12	36	25	14	5.8	0	-2.0	-4.8
30	27	23	19	15	11	7.9	4.8	75	63	51	40	30	20	12	91	77	62	49	36	25	14
40	45	40	36	31	27	23	19	129	115	101	88	75	63	51	157	140	123	107	91	77	62
50	64	59	54	50	45	40	36	189	174	158	144	129	115	101	230	211	192	174	157	140	123
60	85	80	75	69	64	59	54	255	238	221	205	189	174	158	309	289	269	249	230	211	192
70	107	101	96	90	85	80	75	324	307	289	272	255	238	221	394	372	351	330	309	289	269
80	130	124	118	112	107	101	96	398	379	361	342	324	307	289	484	461	438	416	394	372	351
90	153	147	141	135	130	124	118	476	456	436	417	398	379	361	578	554	530	507	484	461	438
100	177	171	165	159	153	147	141	556	536	516	495	476	456	436	675	651	626	602	578	554	530
120	228	222	215	209	202	196	190	726	705	683	661	640	619	598	882	856	829	803	777	751	726
140	281	274	267	261	254	248	241	907	884	861	838	816	793	771	1100	1070	1050	1020	990	963	936
160	336	329	322	315	308	301	295	1100	1070	1050	1020	1000	977	954	1330	1300	1270	1240	1220	1190	1160
180	393	386	378	371	364	357	350	1300	1270	1250	1220	1200	1170	1150	1570	1540	1510	1480	1450	1420	1390
200	451	444	437	429	422	415	407	1500	1480	1450	1420	1400	1370	1350	1820	1790	1760	1730	1700	1670	1640
220	512	504	496	489	481	474	466	1720	1690	1660	1640	1610	1580	1560	2080	2050	2020	1990	1950	1920	1890
240	573	565	558	550	542	535	527	1940	1910	1880	1850	1830	1800	1770	2350	2320	2280	2250	2220	2180	2150
260	636	628	620	612	605	597	589	2160	2140	2110	2080	2050	2020	1990	2630	2590	2560	2520	2490	2460	2420
280	700	692	684	676	668	660	652	2400	2370	2340	2310	2280	2250	2220	2910	2880	2840	2800	2770	2730	2700
300	766	758	749	741	733	725	717	2640	2610	2580	2550	2520	2490	2460	3200	3170	3130	3090	3060	3020	2980
320	832	824	816	807	799	791	782	2880	2850	2820	2790	2760	2730	2700	3500	3460	3420	3390	3350	3310	3280
340	900	892	883	875	866	858	849	3130	3100	3070	3040	3010	2970	2940	3800	3760	3730	3690	3650	3610	3570
360	969	960	952	943	934	926	917	3390	3350	3320	3290	3260	3230	3190	4110	4070	4030	4000	3960	3920	3880
380	1040	1030	1020	1010	1000	995	986	3650	3610	3580	3550	3520	3480	3450	4430	4390	4350	4310	4270	4230	4190
400	1110	1100	1090	1080	1070	1060	1060	3910	3880	3840	3810	3780	3740	3710	4750	4710	4670	4630	4590	4550	4510

Note: values above 1000 rounded to nearest 10, values above 10 000 rounded to nearest 100

Table 3.17 Values of coefficients in equation 3.104

Situation	C	n
Warm or cold vertical planes	1.4	1.33
Warm horizontal planes facing up	1.7	1.33
Cold horizontal planes facing down	1.7	1.33
Warm horizontal planes facing down	0.64	1.25
Cold horizontal planes facing up	0.64	1.25

Table 3.18 Effect of air velocity on convective heat transfer from plane surfaces

Velocity / m·s^{-1}	Multiplying factor
0	1
0.5	1.3
1.0	1.7
2.0	2.4
3.0	3.1

Table 3.19 Heat emission from single horizontal steel pipes ($\varepsilon = 0.95$) freely exposed in surroundings at 20 °C

Temp. diff. between surface and surroundings / K	Heat emission (/ W·m^{-1}) for stated pipe nominal size* and outside diameter†, d_{op} (/ mm)															
	*15	20	25	32	40	50	65	80	100	125	150	200	250	300	350	400
	†21.3	26.9	33.7	42.4	48.3	60.3	76.1	88.9	114.3	139.7	168.3	219.1	273.0	323.9	355.6	406.4
−15	−12	−15	−18	−22	−24	−29	−36	−41	−52	−62	−71	−92	−112	−130	−142	−160
−10	−7.7	−9.4	−11	−14	−16	−19	−23	−27	−33	−40	−46	−60	−73	−85	−92	−104
−5	−3.5	−4.3	−5.3	−6.5	−7.3	−8.9	−11	−13	−16	−19	−22	−28	−35	−40	−44	−50
0	0	0	0	0	0	0	0	0	0	0	0	0	0	0	0	0
5	3.6	4.5	5.5	6.7	7.5	9.1	11	13	16	19	23	29	36	42	46	52
10	8.1	9.8	12	15	16	20	25	28	35	42	49	63	77	90	98	111
15	13	16	19	23	26	32	39	45	56	67	78	100	123	143	156	176
20	18	22	27	33	37	45	55	63	78	94	109	140	171	199	217	245
25	24	29	35	43	48	58	71	81	102	122	141	182	221	258	281	317
30	29	36	44	53	60	72	88	101	126	151	175	226	275	320	349	393
35	35	43	53	64	72	87	106	122	152	182	211	272	331	385	419	473
40	42	51	62	75	84	102	125	143	179	214	248	319	389	453	493	556
45	48	59	71	87	98	118	145	166	207	247	287	369	449	524	570	642
50	55	67	81	99	111	135	165	189	236	281	327	421	512	597	649	732
55	62	75	92	112	125	152	186	213	266	317	368	474	577	673	732	825
60	69	84	102	125	140	169	207	238	297	354	411	529	644	751	817	921
65	77	93	114	138	155	188	230	263	329	392	456	586	714	832	905	1020
70	84	103	125	152	170	206	253	290	362	432	502	646	786	916	997	1120
75	92	112	137	167	186	226	277	317	396	473	549	706	860	1000	1090	1230
80	100	122	149	181	203	246	301	345	431	515	598	769	937	1090	1190	1340
100	135	164	200	244	273	331	406	466	582	695	808	1040	1270	1480	1610	1820
120	173	211	257	314	352	427	523	600	750	897	1040	1340	1640	1910	2080	2350
140	215	262	320	391	438	532	653	750	937	1120	1310	1680	2050	2400	2610	2950
160	261	318	389	476	534	648	796	915	1140	1370	1600	2060	2520	2940	3200	3620
180	311	380	465	569	638	776	954	1100	1370	1650	1920	2480	3030	3540	3860	4360
200	366	447	547	670	753	916	1130	1300	1620	1950	2270	2940	3600	4200	4580	5180
220	425	520	637	781	878	1070	1320	1510	1900	2280	2660	3450	4220	4930	5380	6090
240	490	600	735	902	1010	1240	1520	1750	2200	2650	3090	4000	4900	5740	6260	7080
260	560	686	842	1030	1160	1420	1750	2010	2530	3040	3550	4610	5650	6620	7220	8180
280	635	780	957	1180	1320	1620	2000	2300	2890	3480	4060	5280	6470	7590	8280	9380
300	717	881	1080	1330	1500	1830	2260	2610	3280	3950	4620	6010	7370	8650	9440	10 700
320	806	990	1220	1500	1690	2060	2550	2940	3710	4470	5230	6800	8350	9800	10 700	12 100

* Nominal pipe sizes are to BS EN 10255: 2004[38] and BS EN 545: 2006[39]
† Outside diameters are to BS EN 10220: 2002[40]

Multiple banks of pipes

Where horizontal pipes are arranged one above another at close pitch, the heat emission is reduced overall owing to a cumulative interference with the convection output. Table 3.24 lists correction factors which illustrate the reduction in single pipe emission.

Effect of proximity of walls

Where pipes are installed near to cold external walls, the emission by radiation is likely to increase and that by convection to remain unchanged. With internal walls, there may be a reduction in radiation and a slight increase in convection. These variations are, however, probably appreciably smaller than variations in emission due to draughts, etc.

Finned surfaces

Owing to the wide variation in geometrical arrangement and fin efficiency, it is impractical to give any formulae for heat emission by forced or free convection from such surfaces. References should be made to manufacturers' catalogues and to other test data, etc.[2,42–46].

Table 3.20 Heat emission from single horizontal copper pipes ($\varepsilon = 0.5$) freely exposed in surroundings at 20 °C

Temp. diff. between surface and surroundings / K	Heat emission (/ W·m^{-1}) for stated pipe nominal size*														
	*8	10	12	15	18	22	28	35	42	54	66.7	76.1	108	133	159
−15	−4.3	−5.2	−6.0	−7.2	−8.4	−9.9	−12	−14	−17	−21	−25	−28	−37	−44	−51
−10	−2.7	−3.2	−3.8	−4.5	−5.2	−6.2	−7.5	−9.1	−11	−13	−16	−17	−23	−28	−33
−5	−1.2	−1.4	−1.7	−2.0	−2.3	−2.8	−3.4	−4.1	−4.8	−5.9	−7.1	−7.9	−11	−13	−15
0	0	0	0	0	0	0	0	0	0	0	0	0	0	0	0
5	1.2	1.5	1.7	2.0	2.4	2.8	3.5	4.2	4.9	6.0	7.2	8.1	11	13	15
10	2.8	3.3	3.9	4.6	5.4	6.4	7.8	9.4	11	14	16	18	24	29	34
15	4.5	5.4	6.3	7.5	8.8	10	13	15	18	22	26	29	39	47	55
20	6.4	7.7	8.9	11	12	15	18	21	25	31	37	41	55	66	77
25	8.4	10	12	14	16	19	23	28	33	40	48	54	72	86	100
30	10	13	15	17	20	24	29	35	41	50	60	67	90	107	125
35	13	15	18	21	24	29	35	42	49	61	72	81	109	130	151
40	15	18	21	25	29	34	42	50	58	72	85	95	128	153	178
45	17	21	24	29	33	39	48	58	67	83	99	110	148	177	205
50	20	24	27	33	38	45	55	66	77	94	112	126	169	201	234
55	22	27	31	37	43	51	62	74	86	106	127	142	190	227	264
60	25	30	34	41	48	56	69	83	96	119	141	158	212	253	294
65	27	33	38	46	53	62	76	92	107	131	156	175	235	280	326
70	30	36	42	50	58	69	84	101	117	144	172	192	258	308	358
75	33	39	46	55	64	75	91	110	128	158	188	210	282	337	392
80	36	43	50	60	69	81	99	120	139	171	204	229	307	366	426
100	48	57	66	80	92	109	133	160	186	230	274	306	412	492	572
120	61	73	84	101	118	139	170	204	238	293	350	392	527	630	733
140	74	89	104	125	145	171	209	252	294	363	433	485	653	781	910
160	89	107	125	150	174	206	252	304	354	438	523	586	790	945	1100
180	105	126	147	177	206	244	298	360	419	519	620	695	938	1120	1310
200	122	147	171	206	240	284	347	420	490	606	726	814	1100	1320	1540
220	140	169	196	237	276	327	400	484	565	701	839	941	1270	1530	1780
240	160	192	224	270	315	373	457	553	646	802	961	1080	1460	1760	2050
260	180	217	253	305	356	422	518	627	734	911	1090	1230	1660	2000	2340
280	202	243	284	342	400	475	583	707	827	1030	1230	1390	1880	2270	2650
300	225	271	316	382	447	531	653	792	927	1150	1390	1560	2120	2550	2990
320	249	301	351	425	497	590	727	882	1030	1290	1550	1740	2370	2860	3350

* Nominal pipe sizes are to BS EN 1057: 2006[41]

3.3.4.3 Insulated pipes

If the external surface temperature of insulation concentric to a pipe is known, then the theoretical heat emission may be calculated in the same way as for an exposed pipe. In practice, however, it is the surface temperature of the pipe itself which can be more readily ascertained so that an equation relating the temperature difference between this and ambient air is more useful. The main variables are the thermal conductivity of the insulation material, its thickness and the nature of the final surface finish. The data are, therefore, given per unit area of pipe.

The heat exchange from insulated pipes is given by:

$$\phi = U \left(\theta_s - \theta_a\right) \tag{3.109}$$

or, more conveniently, per metre run of pipe by:

$$\Phi / l = \pi \, d_{op} \left(\theta_s - \theta_a\right) \tag{3.110}$$

where the overall thermal transmittance is given by:

$$U = \frac{1}{R_n + \dfrac{d_{op}}{h_{so} \, d_{on}}} \tag{3.111}$$

and where the thermal resistance of the insulation is given by:

$$R = \frac{d_{op}}{2 \, k_n} \ln\left(\frac{d_{on}}{d_{op}}\right) \tag{3.112}$$

The surface temperature of the exterior of the insulation is a function of the value assumed for the surface heat transfer coefficient (see Table 3.25) and may be calculated from:

$$\theta_n = \frac{\phi \, d_{op}}{h_{so} \, d_{on}} + \theta_a \tag{3.113}$$

$$= \frac{(\Phi / l)}{\pi \, h_{so} \, d_{on}} + \theta_a \tag{3.114}$$

Outside surface heat transfer coefficient, h_{so}

Values for the outside heat transfer coefficient (h_{so}) appropriate to normal finishes are recommended in BS 5422[47] where they are defined as giving 'reasonable approximations to the surface temperature of insulation fully exposed in still air and not influenced by other external sources of heat, including sunshine'. Table 3.25 gives these values and also those for moving air.

Table 3.21 Heat emission from single horizontal copper pipes ($\varepsilon = 0.95$) freely exposed in surroundings at 20 °C

Temp. diff. between surface and surroundings / K	Heat emission (/ W·m^{-1}) for stated pipe nominal size*														
	*8	10	12	15	18	22	28	35	42	54	66.7	76.1	108	133	159
−15	−5.2	−6.3	−7.4	−8.9	−10	−12	−15	−18	−22	−27	−32	−36	−49	−59	−69
−10	−3.3	−4.0	−4.7	−5.7	−6.6	−7.9	−9.7	−12	−14	−17	−21	−23	−32	−38	−45
−5	−1.5	−1.8	−2.1	−2.6	−3.1	−3.6	−4.5	−5.5	−6.4	−8.0	−9.7	−11	−15	−18	−21
0	0	0	0	0	0	0	0	0	0	0	0	0	0	0	0
5	1.5	1.9	2.2	2.7	3.1	3.7	4.6	5.6	6.6	8.3	10	11	15	19	22
10	3.5	4.2	4.9	5.9	6.9	8.3	10	12	15	18	22	25	34	41	48
15	5.6	6.7	7.9	9.5	11	13	16	20	23	29	35	39	53	64	76
20	7.8	9.4	11	13	16	19	23	28	32	40	49	55	75	90	105
25	10	12	14	17	20	24	30	36	42	53	63	71	97	117	137
30	13	15	18	22	25	30	37	45	53	66	79	89	120	145	170
35	15	19	22	26	31	36	45	54	63	79	95	107	145	175	204
40	18	22	25	31	36	43	53	64	75	93	112	125	171	205	240
45	21	25	29	36	42	49	61	74	86	107	129	145	197	237	278
50	24	29	34	41	47	56	69	84	98	122	147	165	225	270	317
55	27	32	38	46	53	63	78	95	111	138	166	186	253	305	357
60	30	36	42	51	60	71	87	106	124	154	185	208	283	340	399
65	33	40	47	57	66	78	97	117	137	171	205	230	313	377	442
70	37	44	51	62	73	86	106	129	151	188	225	253	345	415	486
75	40	48	56	68	79	94	116	141	165	205	247	277	377	454	532
80	43	52	61	74	86	103	126	153	179	223	268	302	411	494	579
100	58	70	82	99	116	138	170	206	242	301	362	407	554	668	783
120	75	90	105	127	149	177	218	265	311	387	466	525	715	862	1010
140	92	112	131	158	185	220	272	330	387	483	581	655	893	1080	1260
160	112	135	158	192	224	267	330	401	471	588	709	798	1090	1320	1550
180	133	161	188	228	267	319	394	479	563	704	848	956	1310	1580	1860
200	155	188	221	268	314	375	464	565	664	830	1000	1130	1550	1870	2200
220	180	218	256	311	365	436	539	658	774	969	1170	1320	1810	2190	2580
240	207	251	294	358	420	502	622	759	893	1120	1350	1530	2100	2540	2990
260	235	286	336	409	480	574	712	869	1020	1280	1550	1750	2410	2920	3440
280	266	324	380	463	545	652	809	989	1170	1460	1770	2000	2750	3340	3930
300	299	364	428	522	615	736	914	1120	1320	1660	2010	2270	3130	3790	4470
320	335	408	480	586	690	827	1030	1260	1480	1870	2260	2560	3530	4290	5060

* Nominal pipe sizes are to BS EN 1057: 2006[41]

Table 3.22 Effect of air velocity on heat transfer

Emissivity of surfaces	Correction factor to be applied to Tables 3.19, 3.20 and 3.21 for stated air velocity (/ m·s^{-1})			
	0	0.5	1.0	2.0
0.5 (dull metal)	1.0	1.05	1.15	1.25
0.95	1.0	1.04	1.12	1.20

Table 3.24 Correction factors for multiple banks of pipes (horizontal, one above another at close pitch)

Number of pipes in bank	Emission from each pipe as a fraction of the theoretical single pipe value
2	0.95
4	0.85
6	0.75
8	0.65

Table 3.23 Correction factors for heat emission/absorption from vertical pipes

Nominal pipe size / mm	Correction factor for Tables 3.19, 3.20 and 3.18
8	0.72
10	0.74
15	0.76
20	0.79
25	0.82
32	0.84
40	0.86
50	0.88
65	0.90
80	0.92
100	0.95
125	0.97
150	0.99
200	1.03
250	1.05
300	1.07

Table 3.25 Outside surface heat transfer coefficients (h_{so}) for insulated surfaces at various wind speeds

Wind speed / m·s⁻¹	Surface coefficient, h_{so} (/ W·m⁻²·K⁻¹) for stated surface emissivity		
	High ($\varepsilon \geq 0.9$)	Medium ($0.2 < \varepsilon < 0.9$)	Low ($\varepsilon < 0.2$)
Still air	10.0	8.0	5.7
1	13.5	11.5	9.0
2	16.5	14.5	12.5
3	20.0	18.0	15.5
5	26.0	24.0	22.0
10	40.0	38.0	36.0

If the average wind speed is unknown, it is recommended[47] that the following values be assumed:

— sheltered situations: wind speed = 1 m·s⁻¹

— normal situations: wind speed = 3 m·s⁻¹

— exposed situations: wind speed = 10 m·s⁻¹

Thermal conductivity of insulation

Thermal conductivities (λ) for commonly used insulating materials are shown in Figure 3.8. These values are derived from chapter 3 of CIBSE Guide A[10] and reference 48. The insulating effect of a hard setting finish is insignificant and may be neglected in the calculations.

Tabulated data

Table 3.26 gives heat emission or absorption per degree temperature difference between the pipe surface and the ambient air using equation 3.110; here, thermal conductivities of 0.025, 0.040, 0.055 and 0.070 W·m⁻¹·K⁻¹ are selected as examples covering the range of values encountered in thermal heating practice, together with a value of 10 W·m⁻²·K⁻¹ for the surface coefficient. From a practical

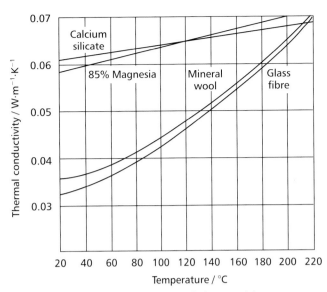

Figure 3.8 Thermal conductivities of insulating materials

point of view, heat transfer under site conditions may vary from the tabulated data for the following reasons:

(a) Draught-free surroundings may not occur in practice; Table 3.22 may be used to assess the effect of air velocity on heat transfer.

(b) For brighter surface finishes than those tabulated, the heat emission will be reduced, the amount of the reduction varying according to the surface area, i.e. the pipe size and the insulation thickness. With a bright metallic finish, e.g. aluminium, the reduction in emission will be about 8 per cent. For dull metallic finishes the reduction will be about 4 per cent. Such reductions in heat emissions lead to an increase in outside surface temperature of insulation and sheathing.

(c) Damp insulation will also have an important effect on emission and can increase losses up to fivefold on installations which have the appearance of being satisfactory.

Table 3.26 Heat emission or absorption from insulated pipes per unit length and per unit temperature difference

Nominal pipe size	Heat emission or absorption from insulated pipework per unit temperature difference (/ W·m⁻¹ K⁻¹) for stated thermal conductivity of insulation (/ W·m⁻¹ K⁻¹) and thickness of insulation (/ mm)																			
	0.025					0.040					0.055					0.070				
	12.5	19	25	38	50	12.5	19	25	38	50	12.5	19	25	38	50	12.5	19	25	38	50
15	0.18	0.14	0.12	0.10	0.09	0.27	0.22	0.19	0.16	0.14	0.34	0.29	0.25	0.21	0.19	0.41	0.35	0.31	0.27	0.24
20	0.21	0.16	0.14	0.11	0.10	0.31	0.25	0.22	0.18	0.16	0.40	0.33	0.29	0.24	0.21	0.47	0.40	0.36	0.30	0.26
25	0.25	0.19	0.16	0.13	0.11	0.36	0.29	0.25	0.20	0.18	0.47	0.38	0.33	0.27	0.24	0.56	0.46	0.41	0.34	0.30
32	0.29	0.22	0.19	0.15	0.13	0.43	0.34	0.29	0.23	0.20	0.55	0.45	0.39	0.31	0.27	0.66	0.54	0.47	0.38	0.34
40	0.32	0.25	0.21	0.16	0.14	0.48	0.37	0.32	0.25	0.21	0.61	0.49	0.42	0.33	0.29	0.72	0.59	0.52	0.42	0.36
50	0.39	0.29	0.24	0.18	0.16	0.57	0.44	0.37	0.29	0.24	0.73	0.58	0.49	0.39	0.33	0.86	0.70	0.60	0.48	0.41
65	0.47	0.35	0.29	0.22	0.18	0.69	0.55	0.44	0.34	0.28	0.88	0.69	0.58	0.45	0.38	1.04	0.83	0.71	0.56	0.48
80	0.54	0.40	0.33	0.24	0.20	0.79	0.60	0.50	0.38	0.32	1.0	0.78	0.66	0.50	0.43	1.19	0.94	0.80	0.63	0.53
100	0.67	0.49	0.40	0.29	0.24	0.98	0.74	0.61	0.45	0.38	1.25	0.96	0.80	0.61	0.51	1.47	1.16	0.98	0.75	0.63
125	0.81	0.58	0.47	0.34	0.28	1.18	0.88	0.72	0.53	0.44	1.49	1.14	0.95	0.71	0.59	1.76	1.38	1.16	0.88	0.73
150	0.96	0.69	0.55	0.40	0.32	1.37	1.02	0.83	0.61	0.50	1.74	1.32	1.09	0.81	0.67	2.05	1.59	1.33	1.01	0.84
200	1.22	0.88	0.70	0.50	0.40	1.78	1.32	1.07	0.77	0.63	2.26	1.70	1.40	1.03	0.84	2.66	2.05	1.71	1.27	1.05
250	1.50	1.07	0.86	0.60	0.48	2.19	1.61	1.30	0.94	0.75	2.77	2.09	1.71	1.25	1.01	3.27	2.51	2.08	1.54	1.26
300	1.77	1.26	1.00	0.70	0.56	2.58	1.89	1.52	1.09	0.87	3.26	2.44	2.00	1.45	1.17	3.84	2.94	2.48	1.79	1.46

Note: the pipes sizes are to BS EN 10255: 2004[38] and BS EN 545: 2006[39]. It is assumed that the outside surface of the insulation has been painted, is in still air at 20 °C and h_{so} = 10 W·m⁻²·K⁻¹

The corrections given for vertical pipes, multiple banks of pipes and the effect of the proximity of walls in the section on bare pipes are applicable to insulated pipes.

Thicknesses of insulation

Minimum thicknesses of insulation for the prevention of freezing or condensation are given in BS 5422[47] for a range of applications and conditions. These include refrigeration, chilled and cold water supplies in industrial and commercial applications, central heating, air conditioning and direct hot water supply installations in both non-domestic and domestic applications.

In some circumstances it is important to relate the thickness of insulation to the financial cost involved. This can be addressed by introducing the concept of the 'economic thickness of insulation'. According to BS 5422[47], the 'economic thickness' is defined as the thickness of insulation that gives a minimum total cost over a chosen evaluation period.

The costs to be considered are:

(a)   the cost of heat lost from the insulated surfaces during the evaluation period

(b)   the cost of the insulation system during the evaluation period.

Methods of calculating these costs and hence the economic thicknesses of insulation for the applications stated above are given in BS 5422[47], to which the reader is referred.

Temperature changes in insulated pipes

In a piping system, the heat gains or losses of the fluid can be significant, especially when passing through an untreated space. The temperature change in the fluid passing through a pipe is given by:

$$\Delta\theta = \theta_u - \theta_d = \frac{\theta_u - \theta_a}{0.5 + f} \qquad (3.115)$$

where:

$$f = \frac{M c_p \times 10^3}{\pi l d_{op} U} \qquad (3.116)$$

For water, $c_p = 4.19$ kJ·kg^{-1}·K^{-1} and the loss per metre run is approximately:

$$\Delta\theta_m = \frac{U (\theta_u - \theta_a) d_{op}}{1330 M} \qquad (3.117)$$

Equation 3.117 is illustrated in Figure 3.9 for various values of overall transmittance. The U-values for various thermal conductivities, thicknesses of insulation and pipe sizes may be found by dividing the values in Table 3.26 by πd_{op} or by using equation 3.111.

3.3.4.4   Buried pipes

The heat emission from underground piping, whether buried in ducts, pressure-tight casings, insulating materials *in situ* or laid directly in the earth, varies from that of the insulated pipe exposed freely to ambient air; this is the result of the additional insulating effect of the air gap within the duct or outer pipe, where present, and that of the earth cover. Equation 3.110 may be adapted to each of these cases with sufficient accuracy for practical purposes, bearing in mind the thermal resistance of the air gap is not greatly significant and that of the earth cover

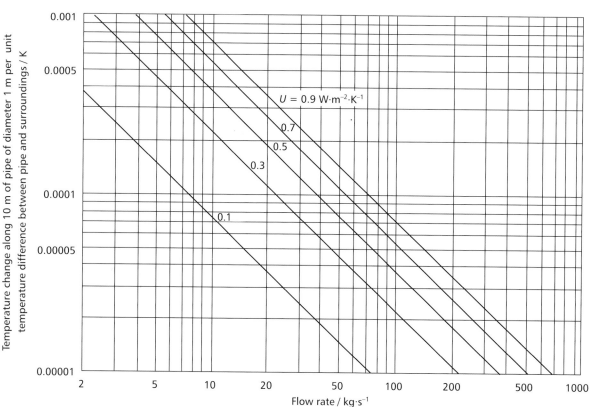

Figure 3.9 Temperature change along insulated pipes in air

will vary dependent upon its wetness. BS 4508[49] describes methods for the determination of heat losses.

The heat loss per metre run of buried pipe is given by the following expression:

$$\Phi / l = \pi\, d_{op}\, U\, (\theta_s + \theta_e) \qquad (3.118)$$

where the overall thermal transmittance is given by:

$$U = \frac{1}{R_n + R_a + R_e} \qquad (3.119)$$

The thermal resistance of the insulation is given by:

$$R_n = \frac{d_{op}}{2\,\lambda_n} \ln\!\left(\frac{d_{on}}{d_{op}}\right) \qquad (3.120)$$

The thermal resistance of the air gap is given by:

$$R_a = \frac{d_{op}}{h_{so}\, d_{on}} + \frac{d_{op}}{h_{si}\, d_{ic}} \qquad (3.121)$$

The thermal resistance of the earth cover is given by:

$$R_e = \frac{d_{op}}{2\,\lambda_e} \ln\!\left(\!\left(\frac{2\,m}{d_{ic}}\right)\!\left\{1 + \left[1 - \left(\frac{d_{ic}}{2\,m}\right)^2\right]\right\}\!\right)^{0.5} \qquad (3.122)$$

If the burial depth m is greater than $2\,d_{on}$, then equation 3.122 reduces to approximately:

$$R_e = \frac{d_{op}}{2\,\lambda_e} \ln\!\left(\frac{4\,m}{d_{ic}}\right) \qquad (3.123)$$

If there is no air gap, d_{ic} equals d_{on}.

The outside surface temperature of the insulation or pressure tight casing is often an important factor and may be calculated from:

$$\theta_c = \theta_s - R_n\,(\theta_s - \theta_e)\,U \qquad (3.124)$$

The overall thermal transmittance required to prevent the fluid temperature falling below a specified value over a given distance may be calculated from:

$$U = \frac{M\, c_p \ln\!\left(\dfrac{\theta_{s_1} - \theta_e}{\theta_{s_2} - \theta_e}\right)}{\pi\, d_{op}\, l} \qquad (3.125)$$

In equations 3.118 to 3.125, it is assumed that the surface temperature of the pipe is equal to the fluid temperature and that the thermal resistances of the pressure tight casing and the surface of the ground are negligible.

Twin pipe arrangements

Underground flow and return mains are often run together in a pressure tight casing or concrete duct as illustrated in Figure 3.10. The following method of heat

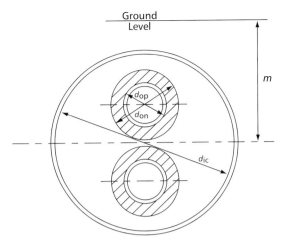

Figure 3.10 Twin pipe underground mains

loss calculation gives answers agreeing closely with field test results:

(a)   Use equation 3.118 to calculate the heat losses from the flow pipe assuming it to be alone in the centre of a large casing.

(b)   Repeat this procedure for the return pipe.

(c)   Add (a) and (b) to give the total loss.

If the duct is of rectangular cross-section (dimension a_1 by a_2) then the equivalent diameter should be used, given by:

$$d_h = \frac{2\, a_1\, a_2}{a_1 + a_2} \qquad (3.126)$$

Thermal conductivity of insulation

The values shown in Figure 3.8 are for dry insulants. If the insulation becomes wet, a considerable increase in the thermal conductivity may be expected. Thoroughly saturated insulation may approach the thermal conductivity of water (approximately 0.6 W·m⁻¹·K⁻¹). If evaporation occurs, the heat loss will be even greater.

Thermal resistance of air space

Although an air space around an encased insulated pipe is essential for the detection of leaks and for the drainage and drying of wet insulation, it has only a small insulation value compared with normal dry insulants. A typical value for resistance of the air space (R_a) would be in the order of 0.06 m²·K⁻¹·W⁻¹.

Thermal conductivity of earth cover

The depth of the earth cover, the physical properties of the soil including the porosity and permeability and the external temperature of the casing are all factors affecting the thermal conductivity of the earth. Table 3.27 lists typical values of thermal conductivity for various soils (λ_e)[50].

Ground ambient temperature

Table 3.28 lists mean values of ground ambient temperature (θ_e) for various parts of the UK, measured at a depth of one metre.

Table 3.27 Thermal conductivity of soils, λ_e

Soil description	Summer		Winter	
	Moisture content / %	Thermal conductivity / W·m⁻¹·K⁻¹	Moisture content / %	Thermal conductivity / W·m⁻¹·K⁻¹
Pea ballast	2.3	0.7	11.8	1.8
Poorly graded sand: (one predominant particle size)	2.4	0.5	7.7	1.6
Well graded sand	9.3	0.9	21.8	2.1
Sand/clay mixture (~20%)	15.0	0.9	33.0	1.9
Ditto (if under impervious cover, e.g. paving)	—	—	—	1.3*
Predominantly clay	26.3	0.8	33.7	1.5
Chalk	18.2	0.9	30.4	1.2
Mean values	<12%	0.7	>25%	1.7

*Areas in the order of 10^3 to 10^4 m²

Table 3.28 Ground ambient temperature θ_e at the depth of 1 m

Region	Mean ground temp. / °C	
	Summer	Winter
South of England and South Wales	18	8
Northern Ireland, North Wales and East Midlands	17	7
Central Midlands, North West England and Scotland	16	6
North East England and Scotland	15	5

1 °C should be added to the above values for built-up areas

Tabulated data

Owing to the number of variables involved, tables of heat emissions are not presented. However, for convenience, values of $\ln (d_{on}/d_{op})$ and $\ln (4\,m/d_{ic})$ are listed in Tables 3.29 and 3.30 for different thicknesses of insulation and burial depths.

The following practical considerations should be taken into account.

(a) To use theoretical figures based on dry insulation could sometimes lead to technical or economic failures except in those systems that are pressure-tight to at least 200 kPa and the insulation is capable of being dried out to its original thermal and physical condition.

(b) Damp insulation conditions are frequently observed and measurement of heat losses, even on installations which appear satisfactory, have shown that they can be several times greater than theoretical figures and of the same order as bare pipes in dry soils. Flooded ducts and wet soil will result in excessive heat losses.

(c) The thermal conductivity of the soil makes a relatively small contribution to the overall heat loss from a well-insulated pipe. Therefore, where the type and state of the earth cover are not known, the mean value may be used without undue error.

(d) There are now many proprietary underground piping systems available and reference should be made to manufacturers' literature.

Cross conduction between pipes

Where flow and return pipes at different temperatures are close together, heat will flow between them. Whilst this is not a heat loss, it amounts to an extra pump load on the system involving extra running costs. For example, an increase of only 3% in the mass flow rate to maintain flow temperature would result in 10% extra pumping costs. Insulation systems which can positively ensure an adequate degree of insulation between flow and return will therefore show an additional economic benefit.

3.3.4.5　　Air ducts

In an air duct system heat gains or losses of the ducted air can be significant, especially when passing through an untreated space in a supply system. This also has the effect of reducing the heating or cooling capacity of the air. The heat emission or absorption from air ducts is given by:

$$\Phi = U A \,\Delta\theta \tag{3.127}$$

or more conveniently per metre run of duct:

Table 3.29 Solutions of $\ln (d_{on}/d_{op})$ for steel pipe

Nominal pipe size / mm	Value of $\ln (d_{on}/d_{op})$ for stated thickness of insulation / mm						
	12.5	19	25	38	50	75	100
15	0.77	1.0	1.2	1.5	1.7	2.1	2.3
20	0.66	0.88	1.1	1.3	1.6	1.9	2.1
25	0.55	0.75	0.91	1.2	1.4	1.7	1.9
32	0.46	0.64	0.78	1.0	1.2	1.5	1.7
40	0.42	0.58	0.71	0.94	1.1	1.4	1.6
50	0.35	0.49	0.60	0.82	0.98	1.2	1.5
65	0.28	0.41	0.51	0.69	0.84	1.1	1.3
80	0.25	0.36	0.45	0.62	0.75	0.99	1.2
100	0.20	0.29	0.36	0.51	0.63	0.84	1.0
125	0.16	0.24	0.31	0.43	0.54	0.73	0.89
150	0.14	0.21	0.26	0.38	0.47	0.65	0.79
200	0.11	0.16	0.21	0.30	0.38	0.52	0.65
250	0.088	0.13	0.17	0.25	0.31	0.44	0.55
300	0.074	0.11	0.14	0.21	0.27	0.38	0.48
350	0.068	0.10	0.13	0.19	0.25	0.35	0.45
400	0.060	0.089	0.12	0.17	0.22	0.31	0.40

Table 3.30 Solutions of $\ln (4\,m/d_{ic})$

Nominal pipe size / mm	Value of $\ln (4\,m/d_{ic})$ for stated burial depth / mm					
	0.5	1.0	1.5	2.0	2.5	3.0
50	3.7	4.4	4.8	5.1	5.3	5.5
75	3.3	4.0	4.4	4.7	4.9	5.1
100	3.0	3.7	4.1	4.4	4.6	4.8
125	2.8	3.5	3.9	4.2	4.4	4.6
150	2.6	3.3	3.7	4.0	4.2	4.4
175	2.4	3.1	3.5	3.8	4.1	4.2
200	2.3	3.0	3.4	3.7	3.9	4.1
225	2.2	2.9	3.3	3.6	3.8	4.0
250	2.1	2.8	3.2	3.5	3.7	3.9
275	2.0	2.7	3.1	3.4	3.6	3.8
300	1.9	2.6	3.0	3.3	3.5	3.7

$$\Phi / l = U P \left[\frac{(\theta_u + \theta_d)}{2} - \theta_a \right] \qquad (3.128)$$

The temperature change in a ducted air stream is given by:

$$\theta_u - \theta_d = \frac{\theta_u - \theta_a}{0.5 + f} \qquad (3.129)$$

where:

$$f = \frac{c_p \, d_h \, \rho \, c \times 10^3}{4 \, U \, l} \qquad (3.130)$$

The hydraulic mean (equivalent) diameter is found from equation 3.126 or from the following equation:

$$d_h = 4 \, A_c / P \qquad (3.131)$$

For air at 20 °C, $\rho = 1.2$ kg·m^{-3} and $c_p = 1.02$ kJ·kg^{-1}·K^{-1}, the temperature change per metre is:

$$\Delta \theta_m = \frac{U (\theta_u - \theta_a)}{306 \, d_h \, c} \qquad (3.132)$$

This relationship is illustrated in Figure 3.11 for various thicknesses of insulation, where a thermal conductivity of 0.045 W·m^{-1}·K^{-1} has been used. Figure 3.12 relates the change in temperature to air volume flow for various air velocities and for 25 mm of insulation.

Overall thermal transmittance

In this context, the overall thermal transmittance is given by:

$$U = \frac{1}{\dfrac{1}{h_{si}} + \dfrac{l_n}{k_n} + \dfrac{1}{h_{so}}} \qquad (3.133)$$

Table 3.31 lists values of U for various thicknesses and thermal conductivities of insulation.

Inside surface heat transfer coefficient

The internal surface heat transfer coefficient (h_{si}) is a function of the Reynolds number as shown by equation 3.41. The value for h_{si} can be determined from equation 3.41, applied for the appropriate conditions.

Table 3.31 U-values for insulated air ducts

Thermal conductivity of insulation / W·m^{-1}·K^{-1}	U-value (/ W·m^{-2}·K^{-1}) for given thickness of insulation (/ mm)			
	25	50	75	100
0.025	0.89	0.47	0.32	0.24
0.03	1.04	0.56	0.38	0.29
0.035	1.19	0.64	0.44	0.34
0.04	1.33	0.73	0.50	0.38
0.045	1.47	0.81	0.56	0.43
0.05	1.60	0.89	0.61	0.47
0.055	1.72	0.97	0.67	0.51
0.06	1.84	1.04	0.73	0.56
0.07	2.07	1.19	0.83	0.64
0.08	2.28	1.33	0.94	0.73

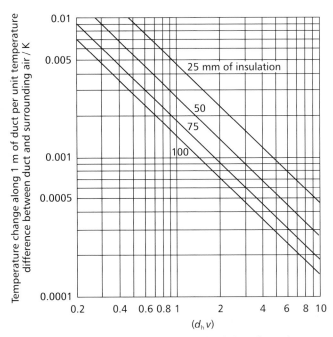

Figure 3.11 Temperature change along insulated ducts for various thicknesses of insulation

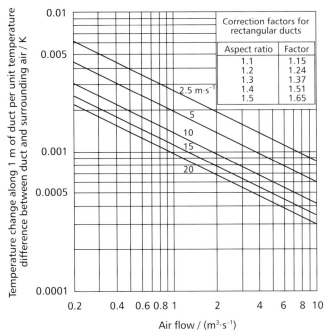

Figure 3.12 Temperature change along insulated ducts for various air flow velocities (for 25 mm of insulation)

Outside surface heat transfer coefficient

A typical value for the outside surface heat transfer coefficient (h_{so}) is 10 W·m^{-2}·K^{-1} but this value may well be lower if the duct is in close proximity to its surroundings. Values for other conditions may be obtained from Table 3.25.

Practical considerations

As the temperature difference in equation 3.132 is expressed in terms of the initial temperature difference rather than the mean temperature difference, some error will be introduced if the value of the length of ductwork chosen for calculation is too large. The smaller the value of $d_h \times v$, the larger the error. A maximum length of 10 m is recommended. It may be noted from Figure 3.11 that as the value of $d_h \times v$ falls below 1.5, the rate of temperature drop in ducts with 50 mm or less of insulation increases considerably. It is usually not practical to keep the value above this by changing d_h or v, so extra insulation should be considered.

3.3.4.6 Heat exchangers

A heat exchanger transfers heat from one fluid to another by conduction, radiation or convection or by a combination of these. The two fluids can stay as liquids or gases or they can change from one state to the other as, for example, in evaporators and condensers. The commonest arrangement is for the two fluids to flow in separate channels with heat exchange between them and without change of state. This arrangement is discussed below.

The basic equation for heat transfer between the two fluids separated by a solid surface is:

$$\Phi = U A \, \Delta\theta_\lambda \tag{3.134}$$

Overall heat transfer coefficient

The overall heat transfer coefficient between two separated fluids can be calculated from:

$$U = \frac{1}{\dfrac{1}{h_{so}} + \dfrac{l_{zo}}{\lambda_{zo}} + \dfrac{l_w}{\lambda_w} + \dfrac{l_{zi}}{\lambda_{zi}} + \dfrac{1}{h_{si}}} \tag{3.135}$$

The overall heat transfer coefficient for thin-walled tubes is:

$$U = \frac{1}{\dfrac{1}{h_{so}} + \dfrac{l_{zo}}{\lambda_{zo}} + \dfrac{l_w}{\lambda_w} + \left(\dfrac{l_{zi}}{\lambda_{zi}} \times \dfrac{A_{so}}{A_{si}}\right) + \left(\dfrac{1}{h_{si}} \times \dfrac{A_{so}}{A_{si}}\right)} \tag{3.136}$$

In the case of clean tube surfaces and neglecting the tube wall resistance, equation 3.136 simplifies to:

$$U_c = \frac{1}{\dfrac{1}{h_{so}} + \left(\dfrac{1}{h_{si}} \times \dfrac{A_{so}}{A_{si}}\right)} \tag{3.137}$$

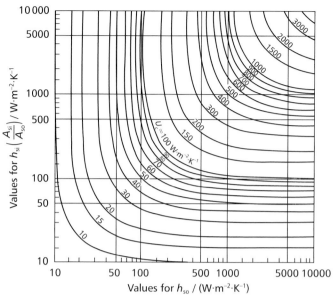

Figure 3.13 Values of U_c

or more conveniently:

$$U_c = \frac{h_{so} \, h_{si} \, \dfrac{A_{si}}{A_{so}}}{h_{so} + h_{si} \, \dfrac{A_{si}}{A_{so}}} \tag{3.138}$$

Values for U_c can be obtained from Figure 3.13.

Values of h_{si} for water flow through tubes and h_{so} for forced water flow over tubes are shown in Tables 3.32 and 3.33. Values for l_{zo}/λ_{zo} and l_{zi}/λ_{zi} (fouling resistances) are usually determined by experience although the values given in Table 3.34 provide a guide[51]. The fouling resistance can be a significant proportion of the total resistance and hence should be taken into account in heat exchanger design.

For heat transfer calculations in shell and tube heat exchangers, it is necessary to determine values for the surface heat transfer coefficients for particular flow configurations:

(a)   For forced convection flow inside tubes, use can be made of equation 3.41 or 3.43.

Table 3.32 Convective film coefficient (h_{si}) for turbulent water flow through straight plain tubes

Tube inside diameter / mm	Inside film coefficient (/ W·m⁻²·K⁻¹) for a water temperature of 75 °C and stated water velocities (/ m·s⁻¹)								
	0.2	0.4	0.6	0.8	1.0	1.5	2	3	4
20	1760	3060	4240	5340	6380	8820	11 100	15 400	19 300
25	1680	2930	4060	5110	6100	8440	10 600	14 700	18 500
32	1600	2790	3860	4860	5810	8040	10 100	14 000	17 600
40	1530	2670	3690	4650	5560	7680	9620	13 400	16 800
50	1470	2550	3540	4450	5320	7350	9260	12 800	16 100
80	1330	2320	3210	4050	4830	6690	8420	11 600	14 700
100	1280	2220	3080	3870	4630	6400	8050	11 100	14 000

Correction factors for other water temperatures

Temperature / °C	10	25	50	100	150	200			
Multiplying factor	0.65	0.65	0.84	1.11	1.34	1.37			

Table 3.33 Convective film coefficient, h_{so}, for turbulent water flow over straight plain tubes

Tube outside diameter / mm	Outside film coefficient (/ W·m⁻²·K⁻¹) for a water temperature of 75 °C and stated water velocities (/ m·s⁻¹)					
	0.1	0.2	0.3	0.4	0.5	0.6
20	2120	3100	3880	4540	5130	5680
25	1920	2810	3510	4110	4650	5140
32	1720	2520	3150	3680	4170	—
40	1550	2270	2840	3320	—	—
50	1400	2050	2570	—	—	—

Correction factors for other water temperatures

Temperature / °C	10	25	50	100	150	200
Multiplying factor	0.70	0.79	0.85	1.10	1.21	1.25

(b) For free or forced correction flow outside single tubes, refer to Tables 3.2 and 3.4, respectively.

(c) For forced convection flow outside tube bundles, details can be found in reference 4.

Logarithmic mean temperature difference

The logarithmic mean temperature difference can be calculated from:

$$\Delta\theta_1 = \frac{\Delta\theta_{tg} - \Delta\theta_{ts}}{\ln\left(\dfrac{\Delta\theta_{tg}}{\Delta\theta_{ts}}\right)} \qquad (3.139)$$

Equation 3.139 is not solvable if $\Delta\theta_{tg}$ and $\Delta\theta_{ts}$ are equal. In this case, and when the ratio $\Delta\theta_{tg}/\Delta\theta_{ts}$ is close to unity, $\Delta\theta_{tl}$ can be taken as the arithmetic mean value of $\Delta\theta_{tg}$ and $\Delta\theta_{ts}$. Values of $\Delta\theta_1$ can be obtained directly from Figure 3.14. Here, the term 'terminal' temperature difference refers to the temperature difference between hot and cold fluid streams at a given end of the heat exchanger. The use of the logarithmic mean temperature difference in equation 3.134 is strictly correct only for constant U, constant specific heat capacity and parallel or counterflow arrangements under steady state conditions.

For multipass shell and tube heat exchangers, a correction factor should be applied to the logarithmic mean temper-

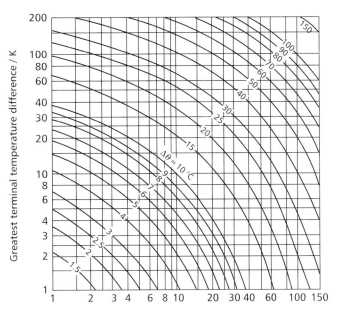

Figure 3.14 Values of logarithmic mean temperature difference

ature difference. Typical values of this factor are given in Figures 3.15 and 3.16 and more detailed information can be obtained from references 51 to 54.

Effectiveness — NTU method

The logarithmic mean temperature difference method[54] is convenient for calculating the heat transfer rates in heat exchangers when terminal temperatures are known. More commonly, however, the terminal temperatures are unknown, rendering impractical the adoption of the logarithmic mean temperature difference method. In this situation, the alternative 'effectiveness-NTU' method can be used[54]. This method is based upon three dimensionless parameters:

$$\eta = \frac{\text{actual rate of heat transfer, } \Phi}{\text{maximum possible rate of heat transfer, } \Phi_{max}}$$

(3.140)

Table 3.34 Fouling resistances, l_z/λ_z

Type of water	Fouling resistances (/ m⁻²·K⁻¹·W⁻¹) for stated temperatures and water velocities			
	Heating medium ≤ 120 °C; water ≤ 50 °C		Heating medium 120–200 °C; water > 50 °C	
	≤ 1 m·s⁻¹	> 1 m·s⁻¹	≤ 1 m·s⁻¹	> 1 m·s⁻¹
Sea water	0.0001	0.0001	0.0002	0.0002
Brackish water	0.0004	0.0002	0.0005	0.0004
Cooling tower make-up water:				
— treated	0.0002	0.0002	0.0004	0.0004
— untreated	0.0005	0.0005	0.0009	0.0007
Well water	0.0002	0.0002	0.0004	0.0004
River water:				
— clean	0.0004	0.0002	0.0005	0.0004
— polluted	0.0014	0.0011	0.0018	0.0014
Boiler blowdown	0.0004	0.0004	0.0004	0.0004
Boiler feedwater (treated)	0.0002	0.0001	0.0002	0.0002

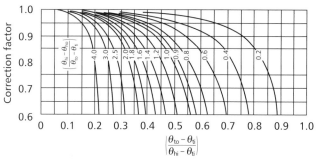

Figure 3.15 Correction factors for assessing mean temperature difference of multipass heat exchangers (one shell pass, two or more tube passes)

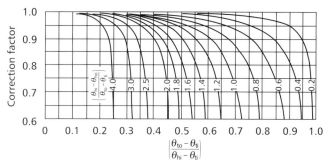

Figure 3.16 Correction factors for assessing mean temperature difference of multipass heat exchangers (two shell pass, four or more tube passes)

$$\text{NTU} = \frac{A\,U}{C_{\min}} \tag{3.141}$$

and:

$$Z = \frac{C_{\min}}{C_{\max}} \tag{3.142}$$

where η is the heat exchanger effectiveness, NTU is the number of heat exchanger heat transfer units, Z is the heat capacity rate ratio, $C_{\min}$ and $C_{\max}$ are the smaller and greater, respectively, of the fluid heat capacity rates, i.e:

$$C_{(\min, \max)} = M\,c_{p} \tag{3.143}$$

The maximum possible heat transfer rate $\Phi_{\max}$ is given by:

$$\Phi_{\max} = C_{\min}\,(\theta_{\text{hfi}} - \theta_{\text{cfi}}) \tag{3.144}$$

where θ_{hfi} and θ_{cfi} are the inlet temperatures of the hot and cold fluids, respectively. From a knowledge of these temperatures, together with values for $C_{\min}$ and η, the actual heat transfer rate of the heat exchanger can be determined from equation 3.140. Note that fluid inlet temperatures and mass flow rates are commonly known in a given application. The heat exchanger effectiveness η is a function of NTU, Z and heat exchanger configuration.

For the parallel flow configuration:

$$\eta = \frac{1 - \exp[-\text{NTU}\,(1 + Z)]}{1 + Z} \tag{3.145}$$

For the counterflow configuration:

$$\eta = \frac{1 - \exp[-\text{NTU}\,(1 + Z)]}{1 - Z\exp[-\text{NTU}\,(1 - Z)]} \tag{3.146}$$

Note that for the case where one fluid remains at a constant temperature throughout the heat exchanger (i.e. a change in phase occurs, as in condensers and evaporators in refrigeration), Z becomes zero. For any heat exchanger configuration where Z is zero, the heat exchanger effectiveness is:

$$\eta = 1 - e^{-\text{NTU}} \tag{3.147}$$

References 11 and 55 give relationships for η, NTU and Z for other configurations.

Example 3.4

Hot oil enters a counterflow heat exchanger at a mass flow rate of 2.0 kg·s⁻¹ with an inlet temperature of 150 °C and an outlet temperature of 45 °C. The hot oil is being cooled by water that enters at a temperature of 20 °C and at a mass flow rate of 1.8 kg·s⁻¹. The diameter of the heat exchanger inner tube is 0.025 m and its length is 10.0 m. Determine the overall heat transfer coefficient, U, of this heat exchanger using (*a*) the logarithmic mean temperature method (LMTD), and (*b*) the effectiveness-NTU method.

Data: specific heat capacity of oil = 2.1 kJ·kg⁻¹·K⁻¹, specific heat capacity of water = 4.2 kJ·kg⁻¹·K⁻¹.

(*a*)   LMTD method

The actual rate of heat transfer from the hot fluid (oil) is:

$$\Phi = M\,c_{p}\,(\theta_{\text{hfi}} - \theta_{\text{hfo}}) \tag{3.148}$$

$$= 2.0 \times 2.1\,(150 - 45) = 441\text{ kW}$$

The outlet temperature of the cold fluid (water) is:

$$\theta_{\text{cfo}} = \theta_{\text{cfi}} + (\Phi / M\,c_{p}) \tag{3.149}$$

$$= 20 + (441/(1.8 \times 4.2)) = 78.3\text{ °C}$$

Now that the outlet temperatures of both fluids are known, the LMTD method can be used to determine the overall heat transfer coefficient.

The greatest terminal temperature difference, $\Delta\theta_{\text{tg}}$, is:

$$\Delta\theta_{\text{tg}} = \theta_{\text{hfi}} - \theta_{\text{cfo}} \tag{3.150}$$

$$= 150 - 78.3 = 71.7\text{ °C}$$

The smallest terminal temperature difference, $\Delta\theta_{\text{ts}}$, is:

$$\Delta\theta_{\text{ts}} = \theta_{\text{hfo}} - \theta_{\text{cfi}} \tag{3.151}$$

$$= 45 - 20 = 25\text{ °C}$$

The logarithmic mean temperature difference, $\Delta\theta_{\text{l}}$, can then be determined either graphically from Figure 3.14 or analytically from equation 3.139 giving:

$$\Delta\theta_{\text{l}} = \frac{(71.7 - 25)}{\ln(71.7/25)} = 44.3\text{ °C}$$

The overall heat transfer coefficient, U, is then given by:

$$U = \Phi / A\,\Delta\theta_{\text{l}} \tag{3.152}$$

$$= 441/(\pi \times 0.025 \times 10 \times 44.3) = 12.7\text{ kW·m}^{-2}\text{·K}^{-1}$$

(b)   Effectiveness — NTU method

The heat capacity rate of the hot fluid (oil) is:

$$M c_p = 2.0 \times 2.1 = 4.2 \text{ kW·K}^{-1}$$

Similarly, the heat capacity rate of the cold fluid (water) is:

$$M c_p = 1.8 \times 4.2 = 7.56 \text{ kW·K}^{-1}$$

The heat capacity rate ratio, Z, from equation 3.142 is:

$$Z = 4.2 / 7.56 = 0.56$$

The maximum possible heat transfer rate, Φ_{max}, is given by equation 3.144:

$$\Phi_{max} = 4.2 (150 - 20) = 546 \text{ kW}$$

The actual rate of heat transfer from the hot fluid (oil) from equation 3.149 is:

$$\Phi = 2.0 \times 2.1 (150 - 45) = 441 \text{ kW}$$

The heat exchanger effectiveness, η, is given by equation 3.141:

$$\eta = 441 / 546 = 0.81$$

For the counterflow configuration, equation 3.146 can be rearranged to give:

$$\text{NTU} = \frac{1}{(Z-1)} \ln \left(\frac{\eta - 1}{\eta Z - 1} \right) \qquad (3.153)$$

$$= \frac{1}{0.56 - 1} \ln \left(\frac{0.81 - 1}{(0.81 \times 0.56) \times 1} \right) = 2.4$$

From equation 3.141, the overall heat transfer coefficient, U, can be calculated to give:

$$U = (2.4 \times 4.2) / (\pi \times 0.025 \times 10)$$

$$= 12.8 \text{ kW·m}^{-2}\text{·K}^{-1}$$

3.3.4.6   Evaporators and condensers

For heat exchangers where one or both of the fluids undergoes a change of state, the fundamental equations are complex. They depend on the mode of boiling and condensing and this, in turn, depends on the fluid conditions and mechanical design of the heat exchanger. Information on the design of heat exchangers for boiling and condensing is given in references 5 and 56.

3.3.4.7   Open water surfaces

Heat transfer from open water surfaces takes place by:

(a)   evaporation, i.e. conversion of part of the water to vapour and the transfer of the vapour through diffusion and convection (Φ_e)

(b)   convection to, and from, the air in contact with the surface (Φ_c).

(c)   Radiation to, and from, the surface (Φ_r).

(d)   Conduction to, and from, the surrounds (Φ_{cd}).

The actual part which each component contributes to the total heat transfer depends on prevailing conditions. In the case of indoor pools and tanks, this will normally depend on the environment provided by the heating and ventilating installation.

In the case of outdoor pools, reservoirs, cooling ponds, etc., it will depend on the prevailing weather conditions and hence the time of the year. During the hottest part of summer up to 90% or more of the total heat transfer from the water is by evaporation. In winter, at low air temperature, the surface evaporation is reduced to approximately 50% of the total, and convection increases proportionally.

Heat transfer by radiation can be an important factor in the performance of outdoor cooling ponds where solar radiation can seriously reduce the cooling effect. Conversely, solar radiation can contribute to the heating of outdoor swimming pools.

Conduction between the water and the surrounds when the containing walls are sunk in the ground is generally small, even when heating up or cooling down, because of the large masses involved. The mass of earth surrounding the pool eventually warms up to a temperature close to that of the water and acts as a stabiliser because of its large thermal capacity.

Where the containing walls are surrounded by air, conduction can be significant but is still small in relation to the total heat transfer.

The total heat loss rate from unit area of an open water surface, in W·m^{-2}, can be expressed as:

$$\Sigma \Phi = \Phi_e + \Phi_c + \Phi_r + \Phi_{cd} \qquad (3.154)$$

where:

$$\Phi_e = (91.5 + 77.6 \, c_a) (p_{sw} - p_v) \qquad (3.155)$$

$$\Phi_c = 3.18 \, c_a^{0.8} (\theta_{sw} - \theta_a) \qquad (3.156)$$

$$\Phi_r = 5.67 \times 10^{-8} \, \varepsilon_w (T_{sw}^{\,4} - T_{rs}^{\,4}) - I \qquad (3.157)$$

$$\Phi_{cd} = U_t (\theta_{sw} - \theta_a) \qquad (3.158)$$

Values of Φ_e are given in Figure 3.17 and values of convective heat transfer coefficient for estimation of Φ_c are given in Figure 3.18. Where the tank walls and floor are surrounded by a large mass, Φ_{cd} is generally negligible. The emissivity of water can be taken as 0.96 and radiation gains, for the UK, are given in Table 3.35[57].

The mass rate of evaporation from an open water surface is:

$$W = \frac{\Phi_e}{h_{fg} \times 10^3} \qquad (3.159)$$

The mean radiant absolute temperature of the sky can be approximated as:

$$T_{rs} = 253 + \theta_a \qquad (3.160)$$

(i.e. 20 K below the air temperature).

Table 3.35 Radiation gains to outside pools and reservoirs in the UK

Period	Daily gain / MJ·m^{-2}	Average duration of radiation gain / h	Average intensity / W·m^{-2}	Average night loss rate / W·m^{-2}	Night loss / MJ·m^{-2}	Net radiation gain per 24-hours / MJ·m^{-2}
May–September	13.8	16	240	50	1.4	12.4
January–December	8.4	14	167	41	1.5	6.9

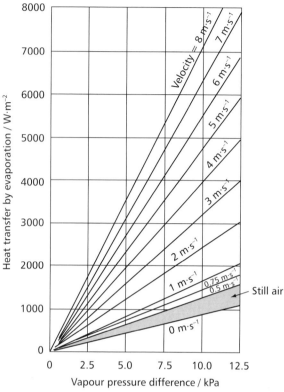

Figure 3.17 Values of evaporative heat transfer

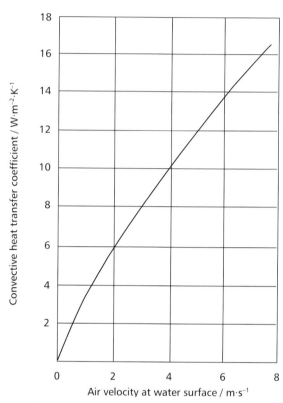

Figure 3.18 Values of convective heat transfer

Assumptions for water temperature values must be made in order to solve these equations. If there is an artificial heat source and this is thermostatically controlled to maintain the water at a constant temperature, no problem exists. In the case of a cooling pond the outlet temperature should be used.

If there is no artificial heat source, an equilibrium state is reached when the rate of heat loss by evaporation equals the rates of heat gain by convection plus radiation and conduction, i.e.:

$$\Phi_e = \Phi_c + \Phi_r + \Phi_{cd} \qquad (3.161)$$

If Φ_r and Φ_{cd} are approximately zero, then the water temperature will approach the wet bulb temperature of the air.

The heat transfer by evaporation is based on empirical data. Various references give results covering a fairly wide range. Many of the experiments that have been carried out have been based on relatively small surface areas and errors are probably introduced when extrapolating to larger areas. The equation given appears to give reasonable results in practice.

3.3.4.8   Building components

The thermal performance of building components (e.g. walls, windows, doors, shutters, etc.) is evaluated for design purposes using standardised procedures. This is

necessary because of the variability of conditions that can be encountered in practice. For example, for the purpose of Building Regulations, U-values (thermal transmittances) are calculated for conditions of steady state heat transfer and on the basis of standardised heat transfer coefficients. The reader is therefore referred to references 58–64 which cover in more detail the measurement, simulation or calculation of parameters, such as U-values, in accordance with accepted standards.

For example, windows (glazing and framework) can have a significant influence upon the internal environment of a building. In this respect, the thermal, acoustic, solar and daylight performances of windows are important and need to be evaluated in an integrated manner. With respect to glazing only, such factors have been investigated for a number of configurations[65], and the reader is referred to the latter reference. For double glazed windows, factors such as temperature distribution of the inner glazing, condensation occurrence and the influence of framework are discussed in reference 66. For further information on overall window performance, refer to the standards cited above.

References

1   Rogers G F C and Mayhew Y R *Engineering Thermodynamics, Work and Heat Transfer* 4th edn. (London: Longman) (1992)

2   Eckert E R G and Drake R M *Heat and Mass Transfer* (London: McGraw-Hill) (1959)

3   Cengel, Y A, *Introduction to Thermodynamics and Heat Transfer*, (New York, NY: McGraw-Hill) (1997)

4   Incropera F P and De Witt D P *Fundamentals of Heat and Mass Transfer* 3rd edn. (New York: Wiley) (1990)

5   Jakob M *Heat Transfer* Vol. 1 (New York, NY: Wiley) (1949)

6   Zhukauskas A 'Heat transfer from tubes in cross flow', in Hartnett J P and Irvine T F Jr. (eds.) *Advances in Heat Transfer*, Vol. 8 (New York NY: Academic Press) (1972)

7   Gnielinski V 'New equations for heat and mass transfer in turbulent pipe and channel flow' *Int. Chemical Engineering* **16**(2) 359 (1976)

8   Kreith F and Bohm M S *Principles of Heat Transfer* 5th edn. (West) (1993).

9   Holman J P *Heat Transfer* 7th edn. (New York, NY: McGraw-Hill) (1992)

10   *Environmental design* CIBSE Guide A (London: Chartered Institution of Building Services Engineers) (2006)

11   McAdams W H *Heat Transmission* (New York, NY: McGraw-Hill) (1954)

12   Moon P H *Scientific Basis of Illuminating Engineering* (New York, NY: McGraw-Hill) (1936)

13   Hamilton D C and Morgan W R *Radiant interchange configuration factors* NACA Technical Note 2536 (Washington DC: National Advisory Council on Aeronautics) (1952)

14   Siegel R and Howell J R *Thermal Radiation Heat Transfer* 3rd edn. (New York, NY: Hemisphere Publishing Corporation) (1992)

15   Kays W M and Crawford M E *Convective Heat and Mass Transfer* 3rd edn. (New York, NY: McGraw-Hill) (1993)

16   Mills A F *Basic Heat and Mass Transfer* 2nd edn. (Englewood Cliffs, NJ: Prentice Hall) (1999)

17   Threlkeld J L *Thermal Environmental Engineering* 2nd edn. (Englewood Cliffs, NJ: Prentice Hall) (1970)

18   Rowley F B, Algren A B and Blackshaw J L 'Effects of Air Velocities on Surface Coefficients' *ASHVE Trans.* **36** 426–446 (1930)

19   Jürges W 'Der Wärmeubergang an einem ebenen Wand (Heat transfer at a plane wall)' *Beizh. Z Giesundh. Ing. Ser.* **1**(19) (1924)

20   Loveday D L and Taki A H 'Outside surface resistance: proposed new value for building design', *Proc. CIBSE A: Building Serv. Eng. Res. Technol.* **19**(1) 23–29 (1998)

21   Awbi H B and Hatton A 'Natural Convection from Heated Room Surfaces', *Energy and Buildings* **30**(3) (1999)

22   Min T C, Schutrum L F, Parmelee G V and Vouris J D, 'Natural convection and radiation in a panel heated room', *ASHVE Trans.* **62** 337 (1956)

23   Alamdari F and Hammond G P 'Improved correlations for buoyancy-driven convection in rooms', *Building Serv. Eng. Res. Technol.* **4** 106–112 (1983)

24   Khalifa A J N and Marshall R H 'Validation of heat transfer coefficients on interior building surfaces using a real-sized indoor test cell' *Int. J. Heat and Mass Transfer* **33** 2219–2236 (1990)

25   *Fundamentals* ASHRAE Handbook (Atlanta, GA: American Society of Heating, Refrigerating and Air-conditioning Engineers) (2005)

26   Walton G N 'A new algorithm for radiant interchange in room load calculations' *ASHRAE Trans.* **2** 190–208 (1980)

27   *HVAC Systems and Equipment* ASHRAE Handbook (Atlanta, GA: American Society of Heating, Refrigerating and Air-conditioning Engineers) (2004)

28   Fanger P O *Thermal Comfort Analysis and Applications in Environmental Engineering* (Copenhagen: Danish Technical Press) (1970)

29   McIntyre D A *Indoor Climate* (London: Applied Science Publishers) (1980)

30   Nishi Y and Gagge A P 'Effective temperature scale useful for hyperbaric environments', *Aviation, Space and Environmental Medicine* **48** 97–107 (1977)

31   Neilson M and Pedersen L 'Studies on the heat loss by radiation and convection from the clothed human body', *Gita Psychologica Scandinavia* **27** 272–294 (1952)

32   Rapp G M 'Convective heat transfer and convective coefficients of nude man, cylinders and spheres at low air velocities', *ASHRAE Trans.* **79**(1) 75–87 (1973)

33   Mitchell D 'Convective Heat Loss from Man and Other Animals' in Monteith I L and Mount L E (eds.) *Heat Loss from Animals and Man* (London: Butterworth) (1974)

34   Winslow C E A, Herrington L P and Gagge A P 'Physiological Reactions of the Human Body to Varying Environmental Temperatures' *American J. of Physiology* **120**(1) 1–22 (1937)

35   Kerslake D McK *The Stress of Hot Environments* (Cambridge: Cambridge University Press) (1972)

36   BS EN ISO 7726: 2001: *Ergonomics of the thermal environment. Instruments for measuring physical quantities* (London: British Standards Institution) (2001)

37   Parsons K C *Human Thermal Environments* (London: Taylor and Francis) (1993)

38   BS EN 10255: 2004: *Non-alloy steel tubes suitable for welding or threading. Technical delivery conditions* (London: British Standards Institution) (2004)

39   BS EN 545: 2006: *Ductile iron pipes, fittings, accessories and their joints for water pipelines. Requirements and test methods* (London: British Standards Institution) (2006)

40   BS EN 10220: 2002: *Seamless and welded steel tubes. Dimensions and masses per unit length* (London: British Standards Institution) (2002)

41   BS EN 1057: 2006: *Copper and copper alloys. Seamless, round copper tubes for water and gas in sanitary and heating applications* (London: British Standards Institution) (2006)

42   Gardner K A 'Efficiency of extended surface', *Trans. ASME*, **67**(8) 621 (November 1945)

43   Schneider R J *Conduction Heat Transfer* (Addison-Wesley) (1955)

44   Norris R H and Spofford W A 'High performance fins for heat transfer' *Trans. ASME* **64** 489 (1942)

45   Joyce T F 'Optimisation and design of fin-tube heat exchangers *JIHVE* (**35**) 8 (April 1967)

46   Peach J 'Radiators and other convectors' *JIHVE* **39** 239 (February 1972) and *JIHVE* **40** 85 (July 1972)

47   BS 5422: 2001: *Method for specifying thermal insulating materials on pipes, ductwork and equipment (in the temperature range –40 °C to +700 °C)* (London: British Standards Institution) (2001)

48   BS 3958: *Thermal insulation materials* (London: British Standards Institution) (1972–1986)

49   BS 4508: *Thermally insulated underground pipelines* (2 parts) (London: British Standards Institution) (1977, 1986)

50   Mochlinski K and Gosland L *Field evidence on soil properties affecting cable ratings* ERA 70–88 (Electrical Research Association) (1970)

51   *Standards of the Tubular Exchanger Manufacturers Association* 8th edn. (New York, NY: Tubular Exchanger Manufacturers Association) (1998)

52   Smith D M 'Mean temperature difference in cross flow' *Engineering* **138** 479 and 606 (1934)

53   Bowman R A, Mueller A C and Nagle W M 'Mean temperature difference in design' *Trans. ASME* 283 (May 1940)

54   Cengel Y A *Heat Transfer: A Practical Approach* (New York, NY: McGraw-Hill) (1998)

55   Kays W M and London A L *Compact Heat Exchangers* 3rd edn. (New York, NY: McGraw-Hill) (1984)

56   Kern D Q *Process Heat Transfer* (New York, NY: McGraw-Hill) (1950)

57   Holt J S C *Some Aspects of Swimming Pool Design* HVRA Technical Note No. 10 (Bracknell: Heating and Ventilating Research Association) (1962)

58   BS 874: *Methods for determining thermal insulating properties with definitions of thermal insulating terms. Tests for thermal transmittance and conductance*: Part 3.1: 1987: *Guarded hot-box method*; Part 3.2: 1990: *Calibrated hot-box method* (London: British Standards Institution) (1987, 1990)

59   BS 6993: *Thermal and radiometric properties of glazing*: Part 1: 1989: *Method for calculation of the steady state U-value (thermal transmittance)*; Part 2: 1990: *Method for direct measurement of U-value (thermal transmittance)* (London: British Standards Institution) (1989, 1990)

60   BS EN 673: 1998: *Glass in building. Determination of thermal transmittance (U- value). Calculation method* (London: British Standards Institution) (1998)

61   BS EN 12412: 2003: *Thermal performance of windows, doors and shutters. Determination of thermal transmittance by hot box method* (2 parts) (London: British Standards Institution) (2003)

62   BS EN ISO 10077: *Thermal performance of windows, doors and shutters. Calculation of thermal transmittance*: Part 1: 2006: *General*; Part 2: 2003: *Numerical method for frames* (London: British Standards Institution) (2006, 2003)

63   BS EN ISO 6946: 1997: *Building components and building elements. Thermal resistance and thermal transmittance. Calculation method* (London: British Standards Institution) (1997)

64   BS EN ISO 10211: *Thermal bridges in building construction; heat flows and surface temperatures*: Part 1: 1996: *General calculation methods* (London: British Standards Institution) (1996)

65   Muneer T and Han B 'Multiple glazed windows: design charts' *Proc. CIBSE A: Building Serv. Eng. Res. Technol.* **17**(4) 223–229 (1996)

66   Muneer T, Abodahab N and Gilchrist A 'Combined conduction, convection and radiation heat transfer model for double-glazed windows' *Proc. CIBSE A: Building Serv. Eng. Res. Technol.* **18**(4) 183–191 (1997)

4 Flow of fluids in pipes and ducts

4.1 Introduction

4.1.1 New to the 2007 edition

At the time of publication of the previous (2001) edition of this Guide, the report of a major European Research Programme[1] on more than 500 different ductwork components was not available. Data from this report for the most important items are simplified for inclusion in the present edition. Some data in the 2001 edition have been amended in the light of this recent and comprehensive research. Furthermore the European Research Programme was the first to test each component comprehensively at a variety of air speeds (i.e. Reynolds numbers). Where possible therefore, data on Reynolds number effects have now been added, as the effect is not negligible. Being now more certain that values of the pressure loss factor (ζ) depend upon Reynolds number and size, this renders much earlier research work inadequate. Thus data from Idelchik[2], on which the 2001 edition leaned heavily, must now be viewed with circumspection.

The method for calculating the pressure drop along pipes and ducts is now much simplified. Hitherto, only cumbersome iterative methods were possible, therefore many pages of pre-calculated values were provided. Since a much simpler, but still accurate equation is now available (equation 4.5), pipe sizing can be carried out directly on a simple spreadsheet for any temperature and indeed for any fluid. The CD-ROM that accompanies this Guide contains Microsoft® Excel spreadsheets for pipe and duct sizing. Pre-calculated pressure-drop tables are therefore no longer needed, and such tables have been omitted from this edition of Guide C. However, for those wishing to use the familiar pipe sizing tables, these may be generated using the spreadsheet provided. Similar tables may also be generated for duct sizing.

Every effort has been made to present data in a consistent manner, to spare the user the perplexity which has troubled the author. Even new research data have been found to contain many irregularities. Such contradictory data have been 'massaged', and such values are printed in italics.

For the correct selection of pumps and fans, and the sizing of pipes/ducts on a life-cycle cost-effective basis, it is essential that calculated predictions of pressure loss should be reasonably accurate. The range of data provided has been extended to enable this. This Guide is intended for everyday use. Complex as some of these data might appear to be, it is nevertheless often the result of simplifications in an effort to produce guidance which is at the same time both easy to use and of acceptable accuracy.

Two versions of the Moody chart have been in circulation, one using a factor $4f$ and another f or λ. In 2001, the CIBSE adopted λ to be in harmony with British hydraulics engineers and international practice. The new chart has the appropriate version of the D'Arcy equation printed on it to avoid any chance of misuse. Nevertheless, with personal computers now so widespread, numerical calculations are preferred to the more difficult and inaccurate graphical method.

4.2 Notation

A Cross-section area of duct (m^2)

A_c Clear area of mesh screen (m^2)

C_α Correction factor for bends of angle α, relative to $\alpha = 90°$

C_{cp} Interaction factor for components in close proximity

C_{Re}　Correction factor for Reynolds number effect, relative to $Re = 2 \times 10^5$

C_1　Correction factor

K　Capacity (sometimes called 'flow capacity') (litre·h^{-1}·bar$^{-0.5}$ or m^3·s^{-1}·Pa$^{-0.5}$)

P　Perimeter (mm)

P_f　Fan power (W)

R　Gas constant (kJ·kg^{-1}·K^{-1})

Re　Reynolds number

T　Temperature (absolute) (K)

V　Volume (m^3)

Z　Pressure factor for compressible flow (steam and air) (kPa$^{1.929}$)

c　Velocity (m·s^{-1})

c_p　Specific thermal capacity (at constant pressure) (kJ·kg^{-1}·K^{-1})

d　Diameter (m or mm)

d_e　Equivalent diameter (mm)

d_{ec}　Equivalent diameter at position of combined flow (tees) (mm)

d_h　Hydraulic diameter (= 4 × hydraulic mean radius) (mm)

g　Gravitational acceleration (= 9.807) (m·s^{-2})

h　Breadth of rectangular duct (perpendicular to the turning plane for bends) (mm)

k　Equivalent roughness (mm)

l　Length (m or mm)

n　Number of damper blades

p　Pressure (Pa)

p_v　Velocity pressure (= $\frac{1}{2} \rho c^2$) (Pa)

q_v　Volume flow (m^3·s^{-1} or litre·s^{-1})

q_m　Mass flow (kg·s^{-1})

q_c　Combined flow at tees

q_b　Branch flow at tees

q_s　Minor flow in the straight of a tee

r　Mean radius of a bend (mm)

r_i　Inner radius of a bend (mm)

r_o　Outer radius of a bend (mm)

v　Specific volume (m^3·kg^{-1})

w　Width of rectangular duct (in the turning plane for bends) (mm)

x　Distance between blades of louvres (mm)

z　Height or head of liquid (m or mm)

Δp　Pressure difference (Pa)

Δp_b　Pressure difference, buoyancy (Pa)

Δp_f　Drop in total pressure, caused by friction (Pa)

α　Angle turned by a bend (degrees)

β　Angle of a branch tee (degrees)

γ　Included angle of contraction or expansion (degrees)

δ　Thickness of orifice plate (mm)

ε　Pipe wall thickness (mm)

ζ　Pressure loss factor

η　Dynamic viscosity (kg·m^{-1}·s^{-1})

θ　Temperature (°C)

λ　Friction coefficient

λ_c　Friction coefficient for a circular duct

λ_r　Friction coefficient for a rectangular duct

v　Kinematic viscosity (m^2·s^{-1})

ρ　Density (kg·m^{-3})

Suffices for tees

b　Branch

c　Combined flow

s　Single flow along straight path (not combined)

4.3　Fluid flow in straight pipes and ducts

4.3.1　General

This section gives the basic principles for predicting the pressure drop in pipes and ducts.

The D'Arcy equation for pressure loss due to friction may be given as:

$$\Delta p = \lambda \frac{l}{d} \, {}^1\!/_2 \, \rho \, c^2 \tag{4.1}$$

The friction factor, λ, may be obtained mathematically or from the Moody chart, Figure 4.1, and depends upon the values of Reynolds number, Re, and relative roughness, where:

$$Re = \frac{\rho \, c \, d}{\eta} = \frac{c \, d}{v} \tag{4.2}$$

and:

relative roughness = k / d.

Values of roughness k are given in Table 4.1.

Values of internal diameters of pipes, d, are given in Tables 4.2, 4.3 and 4.4. For copper pipes (Table 4.3), the sizes listed are the preferred sizes given in BS EN 1057: 2006[9]. Although manufacturers may not as yet supply the entire range, they may be manufacturing other sizes as a transitional arrangement. CEN has defined the recommended dimensions as a first step towards rationalisation. It is aiming for not more than three wall thicknesses for any diameter, and to have a restricted number of diameters. Three categories of pipe are given: R220 (annealed), R250

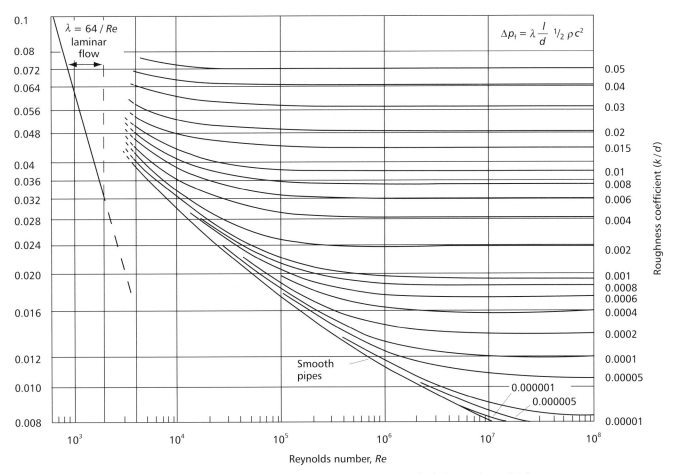

Figure 4.1 Moody chart: variation of friction coefficient (λ) with Reynolds number (Re) and relative roughness (k/d)

(half hard) and R290 (hard). Specification involves two numbers: e.g. 28 × 1.2 means that the outside diameter is 28 mm and the wall thickness is 1.2 mm.

For pipes of PVC-U, grey Imperial (inch) pipes are still available. The internal diameters given in Table 4.4 were obtained from Annex B of BS EN 1452-2: 1999[10].

Values of ρ, η, and ν for some fluids are given in Appendix 4.A1.

4.3.2 Laminar flow

Laminar flow occurs for values of Reynolds number less than 2000. This is most unlikely to occur for water flow or air flow, but is very likely for more viscous fluids such as oil. Rather than use Figure 4.1, the value of λ is more easily obtained from the Poisseuille equation:

For $Re < 2000$:

$$\lambda = \frac{64}{Re} \tag{4.3}$$

With increasing velocity, Re increases and λ is seen to decrease. Nevertheless when substituted into equation 4.1, it will be found that the pressure drop increases with increasing velocity. With laminar flow, the pressure drop is directly proportional to velocity. This type of flow sometimes occurs for air passing through HEPA filters where the air passageways are particularly small, and with liquids of high viscosity.

Surface roughness of the duct or pipe is found to have no effect.

4.3.3 Turbulent flow

This occurs for values of Re greater than 3000. Since air flow in ducts is more likely to have a Reynolds number in the region of 100 000 (i.e. 10^5), it is clear that air flow is almost invariably turbulent. Water flow is also likely to be turbulent.

It will be seen from Figure 4.1 that the friction coefficient depends upon values of both Reynolds number and relative roughness, k/d. The family of curves on the chart was generated from the following equation, developed by Colebrook–White, which may be used directly instead of using the chart:

$$\frac{1}{\sqrt{\lambda}} = -2 \log \left(\frac{2.51}{Re \sqrt{\lambda}} + \frac{k/d}{3.7} \right) \tag{4.4}$$

Note that the square of the above equation might appear more elegant, but the essential negative sign would thereby be lost. It is $\sqrt{\lambda}$ that is needed for the iteration.

The Colebrook–White equation, (equation 4.4), gives values of λ which are some 2 to 4 per cent greater than others and so can be considered to include a small margin of safety[2]. The Moody chart was constructed using this equation.

Several texts give abbreviated forms of equation 4.4 for particularly smooth pipes and for high values of Re. It is

Table 4.1 Values of equivalent roughness, k, for various pipe and duct materials

Type of material	Condition	Roughness, k / mm	Source
Seamless copper, brass, lead	Commercially smooth	0.0015–0.0100	Idelchik[2]
Cast iron	New	0.25–1.00	Idelchik[2]
	Corroded	1.00–1.25	Idelchik[2]
	With appreciable deposits	2.0–4.0	Idelchik[2]
	Heavily corroded	up to 3.0	Idelchik[2]
Steel pipe, seamless	New	0.02–0.10	Idelchik[2]
	Old but cleaned	0.04	Idelchik[2]
	Moderately corroded	0.4	Idelchik[2]
	Water pipelines, used	1.2–1.5	Idelchik[2]
	Encrusted	0.8–0.9	Lamont[3]
	Poor condition	> 5.0	Idelchik[2]
Steel pipe, welded	New	0.04–1.0	Idelchik[2]
	With small deposits	1.5	Idelchik[2]
	With appreciable deposits	2.0–4.0	Idelchik[2]
	Poor condition	> 5.0	Idelchik[2]
Steel pipe, galvanised	Bright galvanisation, new	0.07–0.10	Idelchik[2]
	Ordinary galvanisation	0.10–0.15	Idelchik[2]
Steel duct, galvanised	Longitudinal seams	0.05–0.10	ASHRAE[4]
	Spiral seams	0.06–0.12	ASHRAE[4]
Coated steel	Glass enamel	0.001–0.01	Idelchik[2]
	Asphalt	0.12–0.30	Idelchik[2]
Glass		0.0015–0.010	Idelchik[2]
Brick	Fair-faced brickwork	1.5–7.5	Schneider[5]
	Rough	3.5–40	Schneider[5]
Plaster	New	0.05–0.15	Idelchik[2]
Concrete pipes	New	0.25–0.34	Idelchik[2]
	Carefully smoothed	0.5	Idelchik[2]
	Brushed, air-placed	2.3	Idelchik[2]
	Non-smoothed, air-placed	3.0–6.0	Idelchik[2]
Polymers:			
— PVC-U	New	0.0015–0.010★	Schneider[5]
— poly-butylene (PB)		0.0015–0.010	Schneider[5]
— poly-ethylene (PE-X)		0.0015–0.010	Schneider[5]
— ABS		0.007★	
Aluminium		0.05	ASHRAE[4]
Flexible duct	Fully extended	1.0–4.6	ASHRAE[4]
Fibrous glass duct	Spray coated	4.5	ASHRAE[4]
Rock tunnels	Blast-hewed, little jointing	100–140	Idelchik[2]
	Roughly cut, highly uneven surface	500–1500	Idelchik[2]

★ No original source has been found for the surface roughness of PVC-U or ABS, their values being generally assumed to be identical to that of PB and PE-X. The values of $k = 0.007$ mm quoted above are merely those used by manufacturers in their calculations of pressure drop. In this range, the surface is so 'smooth' that the value chosen has little effect on the pressure drop calculation.

considered safer not to risk making false assumptions with the consequential risk of using an inappropriate equation.

Since λ appears on both sides of equation 4.4, values can only be obtained iteratively. Altshul was the first to derive an equation to give λ directly. Since then, Haaland[14] has provided an even more useful equation:

$$\frac{1}{\sqrt{\lambda}} = -1.8 \log \left[\frac{6.9}{Re} + \left(\frac{k/d}{3.71} \right)^{1.11} \right] \qquad (4.5)$$

The Haaland equation (equation 4.5) is found to have a narrower band of accuracy over the entire turbulent zone of the Moody diagram. Relative to the Colebrook-White equation, the Haaland equation gives values which differ by no more than ± 1.5%. In the light of this, the use of equation 4.5 is recommended.

Example

Calculation of λ, for copper pipe R290 76.1 × 1.5, having $d_i = 73.1$ mm; $k = 0.0015$ mm, $Re = 2.16 \times 10^5$

$$\frac{1}{\sqrt{\lambda}} = -1.8 \log \left[\frac{6.9}{Re} + \left(\frac{k/d}{3.71} \right)^{1.11} \right]$$

$$\frac{1}{\sqrt{\lambda}} = -1.8 \log \left[\frac{6.9}{2.16 \times 10^5} + \left(\frac{0.0015 \div 73.1}{3.71} \right)^{1.11} \right]$$

$$= -1.8 \log \left[31.94 \times 10^{-6} + 1.4605 \times 10^{-6} \right]$$

$$= 8.057$$

$$\lambda = 0.01540$$

Table 4.2 Internal diameters of steel and iron pipes

Nominal pipe size	Non-alloy steel (BS EN 10255)			Ductile iron (BS EN 545)			Seamless and welded steel 'Series 1' (BS EN 10220)*		
	Specified outside diameter / mm	Inside diameter / mm		Nominal outside diameter / mm	Inside diameter / mm		Outside diameter / mm	Wall thickness / mm	Inside diameter / mm
		'Medium'	'Heavy'		'Class 40'	'Type K9'			
6	10.2	6.2	5.0	—	—	—	10.2	1.4	7.4
8	13.5	9.0	7.8	—	—	—	13.5	1.6	10.3
10	17.2	12.5	11.3	—	—	—	17.2	1.8	13.6
15	21.3	16.2	15.0	—	—	—	21.3	2.0	17.3
20	26.9	21.7	20.5	—	—	—	26.9	2.3	29.1
25	33.7	27.4	25.8	—	—	—	33.7	2.3	22.3
32	42.4	36.1	34.5	—	—	—	42.4	2.3	37.8
40	48.3	42.0	40.4	56	46.4	44.0	48.3	2.6	43.1
50	60.3	53.1	51.3	66	56.4	54.0	60.3	2.6	55.1
60	—	—	—	77	67.4	65.0	76.1	2.6	70.9
65	76.1	68.8	67.0	82	72.4	70.0	—	—	—
80	88.9	80.8	78.8	98	88.4	86.0	88.9	2.6	83.7
100	114.3	105.1	103.3	118	108.4	106.0	114.3	2.9	108.5
125	139.7	129.7	128.9	144	134.4	132.0	139.7	3.2	133.3
150	165.1	155.2	154.4	170	160.0	158.0	168.3	3.2	161.9
200	—	—	—	222	211.2	209.4	219.1	3.6	211.9
250	—	—	—	274	262.4	260.4	273.0	3.6	265.8
300	—	—	—	326	313.6	311.6	323.9	4.0	315.9
350	—	—	—	378	364.0	362.6	355.6	4.0	347.6
400	—	—	—	429	413.4	412.8	406.4	4.0	398.4
450	—	—	—	480	—	462.8	457.0	4.5	448.0
500	—	—	—	532	—	514.0	508.0	4.5	499.0
600	—	—	—	635	—	615.2	610.0	4.5	601.0
700	—	—	—	738	—	716.4	711.0	5.0	701.0
800	—	—	—	842	—	818.6	813.0	5.0	803.0
900	—	—	—	945	—	919.8	914.0	5.0	904.0
1000	—	—	—	1048	—	1021.0	1016.0	5.0	1006.0
1100	—	—	—	1152	—	1123.2	1067.0	5.4	1056.2
1200	—	—	—	1255	—	1224.4	1118.0	5.4	1107.2
1400	—	—	—	1462	—	1427.8	1219.0	5.4	1208.2
1500	—	—	—	1565	—	1529.0	1422.0	5.6	1410.8
1600	—	—	—	1668	—	1630.2	1626.0	6.3	1613.4
1800	—	—	—	1875	—	1833.6	—	—	—
2000	—	—	—	2082	—	2037.0	—	—	—

* BS EN 10220 quotes such a wide range of possible sizes for large steel pipes that the values given should only be regarded as typical.

Table 4.3 Wall thickness and internal diameters of copper pipes (BS EN 1057[9]) (The pipes tabulated are those marked 'R' in BS EN 1057 but all might not be readily available in the UK.)

Nominal pipe size / mm	Combinations of nominal wall thickness, ε (/ mm), and mean internal diameter, d_i (/ mm)									
	ε	d_i	ε	d_i	ε	d_i	ε	d_i	ε	d_i
6	0.6	4.8	0.8	4.4	1.0	4.0	—	—	—	—
8	0.6	6.8	0.8	6.4	1.0	6.0	—	—	—	—
10	0.6	8.8	0.7	8.6	0.8	8.4	1.0	8.0	—	—
12	0.6	10.8	0.7	10.6	0.8	10.4	1.0	10.0	—	—
15	0.7	13.6	0.8	13.4	1.0	13.0	—	—	—	—
16	1.0	14.0	—	—	—	—	—	—	—	—
18	0.8	16.4	1.0	16.0	—	—	—	—	—	—
22	0.9	20.2	1.0	20.0	1.1	19.8	1.2	19.6	1.5	19.0
28	0.9	26.2	1.0	26.0	1.2	25.6	1.5	25.0	—	—
35	1.0	33.0	1.2	32.6	1.5	32.0	—	—	—	—
42	1.0	40.0	1.2	39.6	1.5	39.0	—	—	—	—
54	1.0	52.0	1.2	51.6	1.5	51.0	2.0	50.0	—	—
66.7	1.2	64.3	2.0	62.7	—	—	—	—	—	—
76.1	1.5	73.1	2.0	72.1	—	—	—	—	—	—
88.9	2.0	84.9	—	—	—	—	—	—	—	—
108	1.5	105	2.5	103	—	—	—	—	—	—
133	1.5	130	3.0	127	—	—	—	—	—	—
159	2.0	155	3.0	153	—	—	—	—	—	—
219	3.0	210	—	—	—	—	—	—	—	—
267	3.0	261	—	—	—	—	—	—	—	—

Table 4.4 Internal diameters of polymer pipes

Nom. outside diam. / mm	PVC-U (BS EN 1452-2[10])								Nom. outside diam. / inch	PVC-U (Annex B) (Imperial)		
	Nom. internal diameter / mm									Nom. internal diameter / mm		
	PN 6	PN 8	PN 10	PN 12.5	PN 16	PN 20	—	—		PN 8	PN 12	PN 15
12	—	—	—	—	—	9.0			3/8	—	—	14.2
16	—	—	—	—	—	13.0			1/2	—	—	18.0
20	—	—	—	—	17.0	16.2			3/4	—	—	23.0
25	—	—	—	22.0	21.2	20.4			1	—	—	29.2
32	—	29.0	28.8	28.2	27.2	26.2			1 1/4	—	37.9	36.9
40	37.0	36.8	36.2	35.2	34.0	32.6			1 1/2	—	43.3	42.1
50	46.8	46.0	45.2	44.0	42.6	40.8			2	55.4	54.2	52.6
63	59.0	58.0	57.0	55.4	53.6	51.4			3	81.9	79.7	77.5
75	70.4	69.2	67.8	66.0	63.8	61.4			4	105.3	102.3	99.7
90	84.4	83.0	81.4	79.2	76.6	73.6			6	155.1	150.7	146.7

Nom. outside diam. / mm	PN 6	PN 7.5	PN 8	PN 10	PN 12.5	PN 16	PN 20	PN 25	Nom. outside diam. / inch	PN 8	PN 12	PN 15
110	104.6	103.6	103.2	101.6	99.4	96.8	93.8	90.0	8	203.5	198.5	187.7
125	118.8	117.6	117.2	115.4	113.0	110.2	106.6	102.2	10	253.6	247.4	235.6
140	133.0	131.8	131.4	129.2	126.6	123.4	119.4	114.6	12	300.9	293.5	277.1
160	152.0	150.6	150.2	147.6	144.6	141.0	136.4	130.8	16	377.4	368.4	—
180	171.2	169.4	169.0	166.2	162.8	158.6	153.4	147.2	18	424.6	414.4	—
200	190.2	188.2	187.6	184.6	180.8	176.2	170.6	163.6	20	471.8	—	—
225	214.0	211.8	211.2	207.8	203.4	198.2	187.8	—	24	566.2	—	—
250	237.6	235.4	234.6	230.8	226.2	220.4	213.2	—				
280	266.2	263.6	262.8	258.6	253.2	246.8	238.8	—				
315	299.6	296.6	295.6	290.8	285.0	277.6	268.6	—				
355	337.6	334.2	333.2	327.8	321.2	312.8	302.8	—				
400	380.4	376.6	375.4	369.4	361.8	352.6	341.2	—				
450	428.0	423.6	422.4	415.6	407.0	396.6	383.8	—				
500	475.4	470.8	469.4	461.8	452.2	440.6	426.4	—				
560	532.6	527.2	525.6	517.2	506.6	—	—	—				
630	599.2	593.2	591.4	581.8	570.0	—	—	—				
710	675.2	668.6	666.4	655.6	—	—	—	—				
800	760.8	753.4	751.0	738.8	—	—	—	—				
900	856.0	847.4	844.8	—	—	—	—	—				
1000	951.0	941.6	938.8	—	—	—	—	—				

Nom. outside diam. / mm	PB and PE-X (BS 7291[11]/BS EN 1057[9])	Nom. outside diam. / mm	PB and PE-X (BS 7291[11]/BS ISO 4065[12])	Nom. outside diam. / mm	PN	ABS (BS 2782-11[13]/BS ISO 4065[12])
	Nom. int. diam. / mm		Nom. int. diam. / mm			Nom. int. diam. / mm
0	6.7	10	6.8	16	10	13.0
12	8.7	12	8.8	20	10	16.8
15	11.7	16	12.3	25	10	21.2
18	14.2	20	16.0	32	10	27.8
22	17.7	25	20.2	40	10	34.6
28	22.5	32	26.0	50	10	43.2
35	28.3			63	10	54.6
				75	10	65.0
				90	10	78.0
			PB	110	10	95.4
		40	32.0	125	10	108.6
		50	40.2	140	10	121.4
		63	50.8	160	10	139.0
		75	60.6	200	10	173.6
		90	72.6	225	10	195.4
		110	88.8	250	10	217.8
				315	8	273.4

Note: PVC-U = unplasticized polyvinyl chloride; PB = polybutene; PE-X = cross-linked polyethylene; ABS = acrylonitrile butadiene styrene

4.3.4   Unpredictable flow

In the region $2000 < Re < 3000$ the flow may be laminar or turbulent depending upon upstream conditions. The nature of the flow may even be unstable and oscillate between laminar and turbulent. Applying caution in pressure drop estimates, it would appear prudent to base calculations on turbulent flow in this region.

4.3.5   Flexible steel-reinforced smooth rubber hoses

As these hoses are usually used under pressure, the internal diameter will extend slightly with pressure. For instance, a nominal internal diameter of 50 mm may extend to 55 mm at a pressure of 150 kPa. If these dimensional changes are known they should be included in the calculation using equation 4.1.

Since lengths are not likely to be great, only a few guidance figures are given in Table 4.5, taken from Idelchik[2] at a pressure of 150 kPa.

Table 4.5 Values of λ for flexible rubber hose (from Idelchik[2])

Nominal diameter / mm	d / mm	λ
25	25	0.051–0.057
32	32.2	0.053–0.066
38	40.5	0.072–0.090
50	55	0.083–0.094
65	67.4	0.085–0.100

4.3.6   Non-circular ducts

The basic equation given in section 4.3.1 (equation 4.1) needs to be rewritten in terms of hydraulic mean diameter instead of diameter, where hydraulic mean diameter d_h is given by:

$$d_h = \frac{4A}{P} \tag{4.6}$$

where A is the cross-sectional area (m^2) and P is the perimeter of the duct (m). (For a circular duct the hydraulic diameter d_h is equal to the actual diameter d.)

Then:

$$\Delta p = \lambda \frac{l}{d_h} \tfrac{1}{2} \rho c^2 \tag{4.7}$$

For airflow through ducts, improved equations for 'equivalent diameter' are given in section 4.8.

4.3.7   Head and head loss

An alternative method of presenting pressure and pressure loss of liquids (but not of gases) is in terms of an imaginary column of the liquid with standard atmospheric pressure acting on the free surface. Technically this height or 'head' would also depend on the temperature of the liquid.

The equivalent head and head loss are then given by:

$$\Delta z = \frac{\Delta p}{\rho g} \tag{4.8}$$

It should be noted that several pump manufacturers quote 'pump head' or 'delivery pressure' when meaning the increased head or pressure of the outlet compared with the inlet.

4.3.8   Buoyancy

Natural circulation may occur whenever there are density differences in a circuit and a vertical height. Fan or pump pressures will usually render the buoyancy effect negligible. However, in the absence of a pump or fan, natural circulation will take place. This is sometimes called a 'thermosyphon'.

The pumping pressure difference due to buoyancy is given by the following formula where the densities ρ_c and ρ_h of the cold and hot parts of the fluid are the average of the downward and upward flowing parts of the circuit respectively. Note that it is only the vertical height, z, which is significant, not the length of pipe:

$$\Delta p = g z (\rho_c - \rho_h) \tag{4.9}$$

4.3.9   Pressure measurements

With air flow, where pressure measurements are small, it has been common practice to use manometers and to quote the pressure in a height of the manometer fluid. Care should be taken in the case of liquid flow where the density of the manometer fluid, ρ_m, may be of the same order of magnitude as that of the flowing fluid, ρ. The equation to be used is:

$$\Delta p = g z (\rho_m - \rho) \tag{4.10}$$

4.4   Components and fittings

4.4.1   Pressure loss factor, ζ

To obtain the extra pressure loss due to the installation of any fitting, data are generally presented in terms of a pressure loss factor, ζ. The data obtained experimentally are complex but a simplified collection of the data is available in sections 4.9 and 4.10. Whether for liquids in pipes, or gases in ducts, the same fundamental equation applies:

$$\Delta p = \zeta \tfrac{1}{2} \rho c^2 \tag{4.11}$$

In particular it should be noted that where velocity changes occur due either to changes in section or flow splitting in tees, there may be instances where the static pressure increases despite a loss in total pressure due to friction. Δp is always the 'drop in total pressure':

$$\Delta p = (p_1 + \tfrac{1}{2} \rho c_1^2) - (p_2 + \tfrac{1}{2} \rho c_2^2) \tag{4.12}$$

4.4.2   Capacity, K

Most valve manufacturers and damper manufacturers quote the performance of their components in terms of capacity, K, defined in the following relationship:

$$q_v = K \sqrt{\Delta p} \qquad (4.13)$$

This implies that K has units, usually of $m^3 \cdot h^{-1} \cdot bar^{-0.5}$ for liquids, or $m^3 \cdot s^{-1} \cdot Pa^{-0.5}$ for gases. Some manufacturers may quote values of K with different units so care is needed.

There is a relation between K and ζ, but it is not really necessary to convert one to the other. Pressure drops are more simply calculated separately for those components for which K is given.

K is also useful when dealing with the authority of a valve, and in the prediction of flows in complex circuits. Further information can be obtained from Appendix 4.A3.

4.5   Water flow in pipes

4.5.1   Pipe sizing: desirable velocities

There are no rules concerning pipe sizing. The most cost effective will be the design based on life-cycle costing including the pumping costs. The smaller the pipework, the greater the pumping power and energy consumption. Increasing the pipe diameter by one size can have a large effect in decreasing pumping power: smaller friction pressure drops of the basic circuit will require smaller pressure drops through control valves, for the same value of valve authority. The optimum sizing from the point of view of life-cycle costing must consider the length of the system, the capital cost, the mean pressure drop, the running time at full and partial flow, the efficiency of the pump–motor combination, and anticipated electrical tariffs (i.e. 'on-peak' or 'off-peak' operation).

To give a starting point in selecting pipe sizes, rule of thumb water velocities are reproduced from BSRIA[15] (1995) in Table 4.6. An alternative starting point might be to consider a typical pressure drop per unit length of $360 \ Pa \cdot m^{-1}$[15] or $250 \ Pa \cdot m^{-1}$[4], but this is arbitrary. Ultimately, sizing ought to be based on life-cycle costing.

Table 4.6 Typical water velocities for pipework (BSRIA[15])

Situation/diameter	Velocity / $m \cdot s^{-1}$	Total pressure drop / kPa
Small bore	<1.0	—
Diam. 15 to 50 mm	0.75–1.15	—
Diam. > 50 mm	1.25–3.0	—
Heating/cooling coils	0.5–1.5	28

4.5.2   Noise

With small pipes, excessive velocities can lead to noise generation where, with hot water, cavitation may occur at elbows, valves, pumps and especially orifice plates. Some information has been provided by Ball and Webster[16], and Rogers[17]. In this respect larger pipes should be able to tolerate higher velocities without a noise problem. Similarly higher velocities are possible with polymer piping due to the noise absorption effect of such piping.

Noise problems are more likely to occur if entrained air is not separated and vented. Arrangements should be made so that this is achieved easily. An upstand and air vent at the top of each vertical run of pipe is recommended; during pump-off periods, entrained air will separate out into the higher position. This will simultaneously reduce corrosion by eliminating oxygen as soon as possible.

4.5.3   Allowances for ageing

Corrosion and scaling of the internal diameter of pipework will occur with age depending on the chemical composition of the water. This will increase the surface roughness of the pipe and decrease the internal diameter, both of which will increase the friction pressure drop. No firm recommendation can be made on the allowance to be made. A large allowance is more justifiable with small diameter pipes. Open systems will suffer more than closed systems. ASHRAE[4] reports others finding an increase of 15 to 20% in the friction factor λ, compared with new pipework. This was for closed systems. For open systems, there could be a 75% increase. ASHRAE also reports that work of the Plastic Plastic Pipe Institute (1971) shows that there is little corrosion with plastic pipe.

4.5.4   Water hammer

Large pressures can arise when the fluid flow is stopped abruptly by the sudden closure of a valve. This pressure wave then reverberates within the pipework. The magnitude of the pressure wave is in proportion to the momentum of the flowing fluid and thus to its velocity.

4.5.5   Water expansion

Between a heating system being cold (usually under the 'fill' situation), and warm under the design running condition, the water contained in the system will expand. The expansion, as a percentage, has been calculated with reference to a cold situation of 4 °C using:

$$\frac{\Delta V}{V_4} = \left(\frac{\rho_4}{\rho} - 1 \right) \qquad (4.14)$$

The volumetric expansion of the pipework may be deduced from the volumetric expansion of the water, if desired. Values of the density of water are given in Table 4.7. Pre-calculated values for the expansion of water are given in Table 4.8.

4.5.6   Buoyancy; thermosyphon

In any closed system, when one vertical section of the pipework is at a different temperature from another, a pressure difference will exist and create a driving pressure difference so as to cause a natural thermosyphon. Using equation 4.9, some pre-calculated values for hot water are given in Table 4.9.

Table 4.7 Properties of water: density, dynamic and kinematic viscosity

Temperature θ / °C	Density ρ / kg·m^{-3}	Dynamic viscosity η / 10^{-6} kg·m^{-1}·s^{-1}	Kinematic viscosity ν / 10^{-6} m^2·s^{-1}
0.001	999.8	1752	1.7524
4	1000.0	1551	1.5510
10	999.7	1300	1.3004
20	999.8	1002	1.0022
30	995.6	797	0.8005
40	992.2	651	0.6561
50	988.0	544	0.5506
60	983.2	463	0.4709
70	977.8	400	0.4091
80	971.8	351	0.3612
90	965.3	311	0.3222
100	958.4	279	0.2911
110	950.6	252	0.2651
120	943.4	230	0.2438
130	934.6	211	0.2258
140	925.9	195	0.2106
150	916.6	181	0.1975
160	907.4	169	0.1862
170	897.7	158	0.1760
180	886.5	149	0.1681
190	875.6	141	0.1610
200	864.3	134	0.1550

Table 4.8 Percentage expansion of water at different temperatures, relative to the volume at 4 °C

Temp. / °C	Expansion / %	Temp. / °C	Expansion / %
40	0.786	130	7.00
50	1.21	140	8.00
60	1.71	150	9.10
70	2.27	160	10.2
80	2.90	170	11.4
90	3.63	180	12.8
100	4.34	190	14.2
110	5.20	200	15.7
120	6.00		

4.5.7 Pipe-sizing

Until recently, the best curve-fit for pressure drop data was the equation of Colebrook-White (equation 4.4), an equation which could only be solved iteratively. Therefore, earlier editions of CIBSE Guide C provided many tables of pressure-loss data for water at two tempera-

tures. Since the much simpler, but still accurate, equation of Haaland (equation 4.5) is now available, pipe sizing can be carried out directly on a simple spreadsheet for any temperature and, indeed, for any fluid. A Microsoft® Excel spreadsheet is provided on the CD-ROM that accompanies this Guide. This enables fluid velocities, pressure losses and velocity pressures to be calculated for water and water–glycol mixtures at various temperatures in pipes of various materials and sizes. The mathematical steps required for the spreadsheet calculations are given in Appendix 4.A2, (based on section 4.3), where a worked example is also given. Pre-calculated pressure-drop tables are therefore no longer needed. However, the spreadsheet also enables such tables to be produced, if desired.

Traditionally the tables were given for just two water temperatures, 10 °C and 75 °C. In the interests of boiler efficiency which, especially with condensing boilers, improves with lower water temperatures, designers should not choose 75 °C merely because such data had previously been given in CIBSE Guide C.

It should be noted that, particularly for small pipes, the flow is sometimes in the laminar regime, $Re < 2000$. For $Re > 3000$ the flow is almost invariably turbulent. In the intermediate zone, the flow may be either laminar or turbulent depending upon upstream conditions. This is sometimes referred to as the 'transition zone' though in reality the flow does not change gradually from one form to the other, but may 'flip-flop' and oscillate between the two conditions. Thus in the zone $2000 < Re < 3000$ the pressure drop conditions are impossible to predict.

4.5.8 Pipework fittings; water flow

Since in the course of the simple calculation of the previous section, the value of $1/2 \rho c^2$ is available, the calculation of the extra pressure drop due to components is easily obtained using equation 4.11 with appropriate values of ζ.

Nevertheless some values of the velocity pressure ($1/2 \rho c^2$) of water are given in Table 4.10, but these are valid only for water at 10 °C.

The values of velocity pressure in Table 4.10 may be corrected for different temperatures by dividing by the density of water at 10 °C (= 999.7 kg·m^{-3}) and multiplying by the density at the required temperature.

Table 4.9 The thermosyphon driving pressure for a gravity hot water system, Δp_b, using equation 4.9

Flow temp. / °C	Circulating pressure (/ Pa per metre height) for stated flow–return temperature difference / K										
	2	4	6	8	10	12	14	16	18	20	22
40	7.37	14.4	21.2	27.6	33.7	39.5	44.9	49.9	54.6	58.8	62.7
45	8.07	15.9	23.4	30.6	37.5	44.1	50.4	56.3	61.9	67.1	72.0
50	8.73	17.2	25.4	33.3	41.0	48.4	55.4	62.2	68.6	74.7	80.5
55	9.36	18.5	27.3	35.9	44.3	52.3	60.2	67.7	74.9	81.8	88.4
60	9.95	19.7	29.1	38.4	47.4	56.1	64.6	72.8	80.7	88.4	95.7
65	10.5	20.8	30.9	40.7	50.3	59.7	68.8	77.6	86.2	94.6	103
70	11.1	21.9	32.6	43.0	53.1	63.1	72.8	82.3	91.5	101	109
75	11.6	23.0	34.2	45.1	55.9	66.4	76.7	86.8	96.6	106	116
80	12.1	24.0	35.8	47.3	58.5	69.6	80.5	91.1	102	112	122
85	12.6	25.1	37.3	49.3	61.1	72.7	84.1	95.3	106	117	128
90	13.1	26.0	38.7	51.3	63.6	75.7	87.6	99.3	111	122	133
95	13.5	26.9	40.1	53.1	65.9	78.5	91.0	103	115	127	139

Table 4.10 Velocity pressures, p_v ($= \frac{1}{2} \rho c^2$), for water at 10 °C

c / m·s⁻¹	p_v / Pa	c / m·s⁻¹	p_v / Pa
0.01	0.049 99	0.85	361.152
0.02	0.199 95	0.9	404.891
0.03	0.449 88	0.95	451.128
0.04	0.799 78	1	499.865
0.05	1.249 66	1.1	604.837
0.06	1.799 51	1.2	719.806
0.07	2.449 34	1.3	844.772
0.08	3.199 14	1.4	979.735
0.09	4.048 91	1.5	1124.69
0.10	4.999	1.6	1279.65
0.15	11.247	1.7	1444.61
0.25	31.242	1.8	1619.56
0.30	44.988	1.9	1804.51
0.35	61.233	2	1999.46
0.40	79.978	2.5	3124.2
0.45	101.223	3	4498.8
0.50	124.966	3.5	6123.3
0.55	151.209	4	7997.8
0.6	179.951	4.5	10 122.3
0.65	211.193	5	12 496.6
0.7	244.934	5.5	15 120.9
0.75	281.174	6	17 995.1
0.8	319.914	6.5	21 119.3

Values of ζ for pipework are to be found in sections 4.9 and 4.10. Since the additional pressure drop caused by a fitting is largely due to the internal friction of the fluid suffering an abrupt change of direction, rusting and scaling have traditionally been considered not to have a significant effect on pressure drop. However, for elbows, the values of ζ are found to vary considerably with diameter, which implies that surface effects are significant. An allowance for ageing is therefore needed.

4.6   Flow of steam in pipes

Due to the considerable variation in steam conditions which may be encountered, and the fact that the steam conditions themselves (notably temperature and pressure) do not remain constant as the steam flows along the pipe, this is a very complex subject. Advice of specialists ought to be sought.

Some property data are is given in Appendix 4.A4. It should be remembered that density varies with temperature.

4.7   Natural gas in pipes

Natural gas is a mixture of many gases; a mixture which depends on the geographical source of the gas. In the UK, natural gas consists predominantly of methane. It should be noted that gases are highly compressible and that the density therefore varies considerably with pressure and temperature. Although the viscosity varies little with pressure, that too varies with temperature. Thus pressure drops are therefore best obtained by direct calculation using the method explained in section 4.3. Although section 4.3 assumes incompressible flow (ρ = constant), the method may be used with reasonable accuracy so long

as the drop in pressure along the pipe does not exceed 10% of the initial (absolute) inlet pressure.

Some data are given in Appendix 4.A1. It should be remembered that the density varies considerably with pressure.

4.8   Air flow in ducts

4.8.1   Duct sizing: desirable velocities

The are no rules concerning duct sizing. The most cost effective will be the design based on life-cycle costing including the fan running costs. The smaller the duct-work, the greater the fan power and energy consumption. Increasing the duct size can have a large effect in decreasing fan power: smaller friction pressure drops of the basic circuit will require smaller pressure drops through control dampers, for the same value of control authority thus leading to a further saving. The optimum sizing from the point of view of life-cycle costing must consider the length of the system, the capital cost, the mean pressure drop, the running time at full and partial flow, the efficiency of the fan–motor combination and anticipated electrical tariffs (i.e. 'on-peak', 'off-peak' operation).

To provide a starting point in selecting duct sizes, rule of thumb air velocities are reproduced from BSRIA[15] in Table 4.11. An alternative starting point might be to consider a typical pressure drop per unit length of 1 Pa·m⁻¹ for low velocity systems and 8 Pa·m⁻¹ for high velocity systems[15]. Typical air velocities for air handling and other components are given in Table 4.12[4,18].

Table 4.11 Typical air velocities for ductwork[4,15]

System type	Velocity / m·s⁻¹	Maximum pressure drop per unit length / Pa·m⁻¹	Total pressure drop / kPa
Low velocity	3–6	1	0.900 (supply) 0.400 (extract)
High velocity	7.5–15	8	1.5–2.0 (supply)

Table 4.12 Typical air velocities (face velocities) for air handling units and other components[4,18]

Situation	Velocity / m·s⁻¹	Pressure drop / Pa
Heating system	2.5–4 (through face area)	50–125
Cooling system	1.5–2.5 (through face area)	60–180
Inlet louvres	2.5 (through free area)	35 max[4]
Extract louvres	2.5 (through free area)	60 max[4]
Filters[4]:		
— flat panel	As duct	—
— pleated	< 3.8	—
— HEPA	1.3	—
— moving curtain viscous	2.5	—
— moving curtain dry	1.0	—
— electronic, ionising	0.8–1.8	—

4.8.2 Noise

The major source of duct-generated noise is caused by the vortices created in diffusers, grilles, fittings and the fan itself. Higher air velocities will create more noise. The ductwork and sharp elbows can have an attenuating effect especially of the higher frequencies. Frequently a noise problem may be due to noise from one zone being able to be propagated to another either via grilles and the ductwork, or by 'break-in' to the ductwork itself or 'break-out'. For detailed consideration, see CIBSE Guide B[19], chapter 5.

4.8.3 Pressure drop for circular ducts

The pressure drop per unit length can be calculated for any duct material, and for any air condition using the pressure loss factor λ, as explained in section 4.3.

Repeating the D'Arcy equation for pressure loss due to friction (equation 4.1):

$$\Delta p = \lambda \frac{l}{d} \, {}^1\!/_2 \, \rho \, c^2$$

Useful property values for air are given in Table 4.13, and in Appendix 4.A1.

Table 4.13 Some properties of air at a relative humidity of 50% and at a pressure of 1.013 25 bar

Temperature, θ / °C	Density, ρ / kg·m^{-3}	Dynamic viscosity, η / 10^{-6} kg·m^{-1}·s^{-1}	Specific heat capacity, c_p / kJ·kg^{-1}·K^{-1}
0	1.29	17.15	1.006
5	1.27	17.39	1.009
10	1.24	17.63	1.011
15	1.22	17.88	1.014
20	1.20	18.12	1.018
25	1.18	18.36	1.022
30	1.16	18.55	1.030
35	1.14	18.78	1.039
40	1.11	19.01	1.050

Note that values of density, being the reciprocal of the specific volume, are best obtained from the psychrometric chart which covers any value of humidity.

The variation of density with pressure can be obtained using a value ρ_0 from Table 4.13 or from the psychrometric chart, and the ideal gas equation:

$$\rho = \rho_0 \left(\frac{p}{1.01325} \right) \qquad (4.15)$$

where p is pressure (bar).

Values of viscosity and specific thermal capacity do not vary significantly with pressure.

4.8.4 Pre-calculated values of pressure drop for circular ducts

Until recently, the best curve-fit for pressure drop data was the equation of Colebrook-White (equation 4.4), which could only be solved by iteration. To help with duct-sizing, a chart is provided (Figure 4.2), but this is valid only for one condition of air, see (a) below. However, since the much simpler, but still accurate, equation of Haaland (equation 4.5) is now available, duct-sizing can be carried out directly on a simple spreadsheet for any temperature and air density. The mathematical steps required for the spreadsheet calculations are given in Appendix 4.A2, (based on section 4.3), where a worked example is included. A Microsoft® Excel spreadsheet is provided on the CD-ROM that accompanies this Guide. This enables air velocities, pressure losses and velocity pressures to be calculated at various temperatures in various types and sizes of duct. The spreadsheet also enables duct sizing tables to be produced, if desired.

The chart (Figure 4.2) was produced using values for the appropriate variables as follows:

(a)   air at 20 °C, 101.325 kPa, 43% saturation

(b)   density, $\rho = 1.200$ kg·m^{-3}

(c)   viscosity, $\eta = 18.2 \times 10^{-6}$ kg·m^{-1}·s^{-1}

(d)   roughness, $k = 0.15$ mm (longitudinal seams).

Compared with values from equation 4.5 (for $k = 0.075$ mm, from Table 4.1), the chart gives slightly greater pressure drops, reading +1.5% high, over much of the chart. There is some evidence that small ducts give greater pressure drops than expected, the suspicion being that the connections play a relatively larger role. Such work as has been done to investigate this was inconclusive.

For air at a temperature other than 20 °C, the pressure loss read from the chart may be corrected by use of the following expression, where T must be in kelvins:

$$\Delta p = \Delta p_{20} \left(\frac{293}{T} \right)^{0.86} \qquad (4.16)$$

4.8.5 Spirally wound ductwork

Table 4.14 illustrates the small extra pressure drop incurred by using spirally wound galvanized ductwork instead of ductwork with longitudinal seams. This comparison was made using $k = 0.09$ mm for spirally wound and $k = 0.075$ mm for longitudinal seamed ductwork.

Table 4.14 Additional pressure drop (%) incurred by using spirally wound galvanized ductwork rather than longitudinal seamed ductwork

Diameter, d / mm	Additional pressure drop for spirally wound ductwork (/ %) for stated value of pressure drop (longitudinal seam) / Pa·m^{-1}									
	0.1	0.2	0.5	1	2	5	10	20	50	100
200	0.4	0.5	0.8	1.1	1.3	1.8	2.1	2.5	2.9	3.21
500	0.6	0.7	1.0	1.3	1.6	2.1	2.4	2.6	3.0	—
1000	0.7	0.9	1.2	1.5	1.8	2.2	2.5	2.7	—	—
2000	0.8	1.1	1.4	1.7	2.1	2.3	2.6	—	—	—

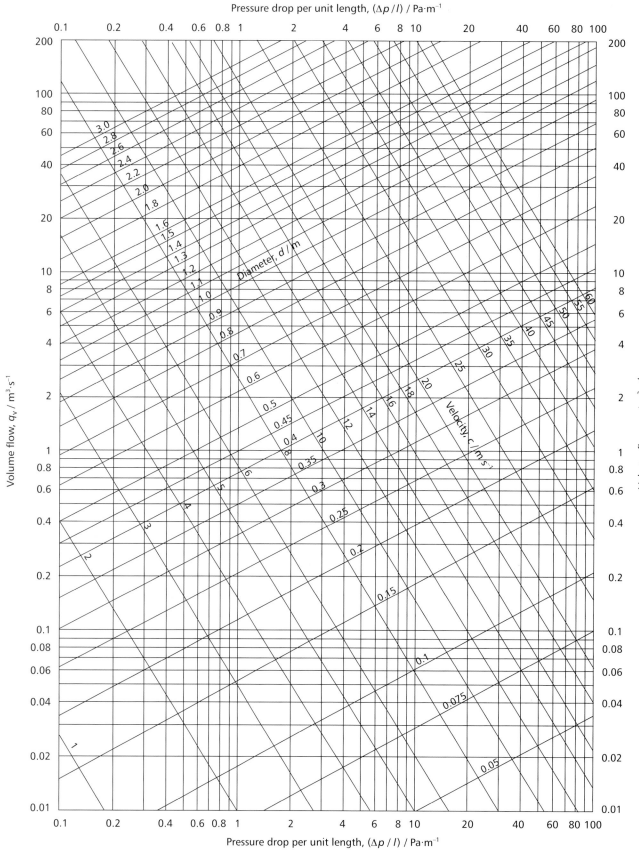

Figure 4.2 Pressure drop for air in galvanised circular ducts (ρ = 1.2 kg·m^{-3}; T = 293 K)

When the spiral is additionally swaged for stiffness, a further pressure drop can be expected but no data are available.

4.8.6   Ducts of other materials

Using the values for surface roughness given in Table 4.1, and Haaland's equation (equation 4.5) a duct friction factor λ is easily obtained for any material.

4.8.7   Flexible ductwork

The use of flexible ductwork for making final connections to supply diffusers is very convenient. However such ductwork produces pressure drops much greater than those for the equivalent smooth galvanised steel ductwork.

Flexible ductwork naturally has an equivalent roughness which is appreciably more than for galvanised steel ductwork (1.0–4.6 mm, compared to 0.15 mm, see Table 4.1). This alone causes a much greater pressure drop. If the flexible duct is not fully extended then, according to ASHRAE[4], if the length is only 70% of the extended length, the pressure loss can be greater by a factor of 4.

Thus, when using flexible ductwork, it is recommended that:

—   lengths should be kept as short as possible

—   it should be almost fully extended.

Based on a worst case of roughness $k = 4.6$ mm, and extended to only 70% of full length, Table 4.15 has been derived as guidance to give the multiplying factor to be applied to the equivalent rigid circular galvanised duct.

Table 4.15 Correction factors to be applied to the pressure drop of a rigid duct (obtained from Figure 4.2) for flexible duct having a roughness of 4.6 mm and extended to only 70% of full length (from ASHRAE[4])

Velocity, c / m·s⁻¹	Correction factor for flexible duct of stated diameter, d / mm		
	100	200	500
2.5	6.70	7.47	8.3
4.5	7.35	8.05	8.7
6.0	7.66	8.21	8.9

4.8.8   Non-circular ducts

4.8.8.1   Direct calculation

For ducts of non-circular cross section, the use of equation 4.1 necessitates the use of a value for a 'diameter' characteristic of the non-circular duct. For this, hydraulic mean diameter has traditionally been used, defined by:

$$d_h = \frac{4A}{P} \quad (4.17)$$

where A is the cross-sectional area (m²) and P is the perimeter (m²) of the duct. (For a circular duct the hydraulic diameter d_h is equal to the actual diameter d.)

The pressure loss is then given by:

$$\Delta p = \lambda \frac{l}{d_h} \, {}^1/_2 \, \rho \, c^2 \quad (4.18)$$

To obtain a value of λ, the Haaland equation (4.5) should be used. For this the hydraulic diameter d_h should be used for obtaining relative roughness k/d and Re. The use of equation 4.18 then gives the pressure drop for any condition of air and duct material. A worked example is illustrated in Appendix 4.A2.2.

The concept of using hydraulic diameter is nevertheless fundamentally flawed. The flow in a circular duct is totally symmetrical about the axis, giving identical fluid velocities close to all parts of the duct surface; this does not exist within non-circular ducts. For ductwork having particularly sharp apex angles, it has been shown that the use of equation 4.17 does not give a good correlation.

4.8.8.2   Manual method using charts and tables

Prior to the use of the Haaland equation, values of λ could only be obtained by iteration; a process so tedious that engineers preferred to use pre-calculated tables or charts to obtain the pressure drop along a duct, even though these were for only one condition of air, one ductwork material, and only for circular ducts. To enable the use of these charts for non-circular ducts, the concept of an 'equivalent diameter' (d_e) was conceived, relating to an equivalent circular duct. Since most design problems have as their starting point a desired volume flow q_v, the most convenient form of equivalent diameter is that which will give the same pressure drop per unit length and for the same volume flow.

When hydraulic diameter is used in conjunction with equation 4.18 to determine a circular equivalent for a non-circular duct, to give the same pressure drop for the same volume flow, the following equation is easily derived:

$$d_e = 1.453 \frac{A^{0.6}}{P^{0.2}} \quad (4.19)$$

There is nothing empirical about this equation. Its validity rests solely on an assumed validity for hydraulic mean diameter.

Once the equivalent diameter has been obtained, using equation 4.19, it may be used in conjunction with pre-calculated tables for a circular duct, or with Figure 4.2. Care must be taken to use such circular duct data only with the same volume flow q_v.

Rectangular ducts

Huebscher[20] carried out tests on a square duct and a rectangular duct (of aspect ratio $w/h = 8$), for a wide range of velocities. His results, recently re-analysed by CIBSE, are not sufficiently reliable to prove the validity of using hydraulic diameter in the above equation 4.18, nor did they provide an alternative. The direct calculation approach should therefore be used as explained above.

Table 4.16 Equivalent diameters for rectangular ductwork, to give the same pressure drop for the same volume flow, surface roughness and friction coefficient λ; calculated from equation 4.19

Equivalent-diameter formula (shown in box in the lower-left of the table):

$$d_e = \frac{1.453\,A^{0.6}}{P^{0.2}}$$

In the table below, the columns are the 20 physical positions of the printed grid. For each row, values to the **right** of the staircase correspond to the top-axis widths $w = 100 \ldots 900$; values to the **left** of the staircase (upper-left region) correspond to the bottom-axis widths $w = 950 \ldots 2500$ (see second header at foot).

Dimen. of side, h	100	125	150	175	200	225	250	300	350	400	450	500	550	600	650	700	750	800	850	900	Dimen. of side, h
100	110	123	134	145	154	163	171	185	199	211	222	232	242	251	260	268	276	284	291	298	100
125	347	138	151	162	173	183	192	209	225	238	251	263	275	285	295	305	314	323	331	339	125
150	386	394	165	178	190	201	212	231	248	264	278	291	304	316	327	338	348	358	368	377	150
175	421	430	440	193	206	218	230	251	269	287	302	317	331	344	357	369	380	391	401	411	175
200	454	464	474	484	220	234	246	269	289	308	325	341	356	371	384	397	409	421	433	444	200
225	485	496	507	517	527	248	261	286	308	328	346	364	380	395	410	424	437	450	462	474	225
250	515	527	538	549	560	570	275	301	325	346	366	385	402	419	434	449	463	477	490	503	250
300	570	583	596	608	620	632	643	330	357	381	403	424	443	462	479	496	512	527	542	556	300
350	620	635	649	662	676	689	701	713	385	412	436	459	481	501	520	539	556	573	589	605	350
400	667	682	698	713	727	741	755	768	794	440	467	492	515	537	558	578	597	616	633	650	400
450	710	727	744	760	776	791	805	820	848	874	496	522	547	571	594	615	636	655	674	693	450
500	751	770	787	804	821	837	853	868	898	927	954	551	577	603	627	650	672	693	713	732	500
550	790	809	828	846	864	881	898	915	946	976	1005	1033	606	632	658	682	706	728	749	770	550
600	827	847	867	887	905	923	941	958	992	1024	1054	1084	1112	661	688	713	738	761	784	806	600
650	862	884	905	925	944	964	982	1000	1035	1069	1101	1132	1162	1191	716	743	768	793	817	840	650
700	896	918	940	961	982	1002	1022	1041	1077	1112	1146	1179	1210	1240	1269	771	798	824	849	873	700
750	928	952	974	997	1018	1039	1059	1079	1118	1154	1189	1223	1256	1287	1318	1347	826	853	879	904	750
800	959	984	1007	1030	1053	1075	1096	1116	1156	1195	1231	1266	1300	1333	1365	1396	1425	881	908	934	800
850	989	1015	1039	1063	1086	1109	1131	1152	1194	1234	1272	1308	1343	1378	1410	1442	1473	1503	936	963	850
900	1018	1044	1070	1095	1119	1142	1165	1187	1230	1271	1311	1349	1385	1420	1455	1488	1520	1551	1581	991	900
950	1046	1073	1100	1125	1150	1174	1198	1221	1265	1308	1349	1388	1426	1462	1497	1532	1565	1597	1629	1659	950
1000		1101	1128	1155	1180	1205	1230	1253	1299	1343	1385	1426	1465	1503	1539	1574	1609	1642	1675	1706	1000
1050			1156	1183	1210	1236	1261	1285	1332	1378	1421	1463	1503	1542	1580	1616	1651	1686	1719	1752	1050
1100				1211	1238	1265	1291	1316	1365	1411	1456	1499	1540	1580	1619	1657	1693	1728	1763	1796	1100
1150					1266	1294	1320	1346	1396	1444	1490	1534	1576	1618	1657	1696	1733	1770	1805	1840	1150
1200						1321	1349	1375	1426	1476	1523	1568	1612	1654	1695	1735	1773	1810	1847	1882	1200
1250							1376	1404	1456	1507	1555	1601	1646	1690	1732	1772	1812	1850	1887	1924	1250
1300								1432	1485	1537	1586	1634	1680	1724	1767	1809	1850	1889	1927	1964	1300
1400									1542	1596	1647	1697	1745	1792	1837	1880	1923	1964	2004	2043	1400
1500										1652	1706	1758	1808	1856	1903	1949	1993	2036	2078	2119	1500
1600											1762	1816	1868	1919	1967	2015	2061	2106	2149	2191	1600
1700												1872	1926	1978	2029	2078	2126	2172	2218	2262	1700
1800													1982	2036	2089	2140	2189	2237	2284	2330	1800
1900														2092	2146	2199	2250	2300	2348	2395	1900
2000															2202	2257	2309	2361	2411	2459	2000
2100																2312	2367	2420	2471	2521	2100
2200																	2423	2477	2530	2581	2200
2300																		2533	2587	2640	2300
2400																			2643	2697	2400
2500																				2753	2500

Foot axis (bottom header, Dimension of side of duct, w):

Dimen. of side, h	950	1000	1050	1100	1150	1200	1250	1300	1400	1500	1600	1700	1800	1900	2000	2100	2200	2300	2400	2500	Dimen. of side, h

For those wishing to use a manual graphical approach, the concept of circular duct equivalent is useful. Hubscher has sometimes been credited with an equation which is erroneous and should not be used. Table 4.16 was obtained using equation 4.19, and gives pre-calculated values of equivalent diameter for rectangular ductwork of preferred sizes.

Flat-oval spirally wound ducts

Heyt and Diaz[21] carried out tests on several flat-oval ducts having a range of aspect ratios w/h from 2.0 to 4.2 for a wide range of velocities. Their results, recently re-analysed by CIBSE, are not sufficiently reliable to prove the validity of using hydraulic diameter in the above equation 4.18, nor did they provide an alternative. The direct calculation approach should therefore be used as explained above.

For those wishing to use a manual graphical approach, the concept of circular duct equivalent is useful. Heyt and Diaz[21] have sometimes been credited with an equation which is erroneous and should not be used. Table 4.17 gives values of perimeter P and area A. The pre-calculated values of d_e given in Table 4.18 have been obtained using equation 4.19.

Table 4.17 Areas and perimeters for flat-oval ductwork; the dimensions are those of the preferred sizes of ductwork[22]

Dimension	Area, A (/ mm²), for stated width, w (/ mm), and height, h / mm											Perimeter, P / mm
	75	100	125	150	200	250	300	350	400	450	500	
w	320											720
A	22793											
w	360	350	330	320								808
A	25793	32854	37897	43171								
w	400	390	370	360								888
A	28793	36854	42897	49171								
w	440	430	410	400								968
A	31793	40854	47897	55171								
w	480	470	450	440								1048
A	34793	44854	52897	61171								
w	520	505	490	480								1126
A	37793	48354	57897	67171								
w		545	530	520								1206
A		52354	62897	73171								
w				555	525							1280
A				78421	96416							
w				635	605	580						1442
A				90421	112416	131587						
w				715	690	660	630					1604
A				102241	129416	151587	169686					
w				800	770	740	710	685	655			1767
A				115171	145416	171587	193686	213461	227664			
w				880	845	825	790	765	735	705	680	1927
A				127171	160416	192837	217686	241461	259664	273793	286350	
w				960	930	900	875	845	815	785	755	2067
A				139171	177416	211587	243186	269461	291664	309793	323850	
w				1040	1010	985	955	925	895	865	835	2249
A				151171	193416	232837	267186	297461	323664	345793	363850	
w				1120	1090	1065	1035	1005	975	945	915	2409
A				163171	209416	252837	291186	325461	355664	381793	403850	
w				1200	1170	1145	1115	1085	1055	1025	1000	2570
A				175171	225416	272837	315186	353461	387664	417793	446350	
w					1335	1305	1275	1245	1215	1190	1160	2892
A					258416	312837	363186	409461	451664	492043	526350	
w						1465	1435	1405	1375	1350	1320	3211
A						352837	411186	465461	515664	564043	606350	
w						1625	1595	1570	1540	1510	1480	3535
A						392837	459186	523211	581664	636043	686350	
w						1785	1760	1730	1700	1670	1640	3856
A						432837	508686	579211	645664	708043	766350	

Table 4.18 Equivalent diameters for flat-oval ductwork to give the same pressure drop for the same volume flow, surface roughness and friction coefficient λ; values of d_e have been obtained using equation 4.19; the dimensions are those of the preferred sizes of ductwork[22]

Dimension	Equivalent diameter, d_e (/ mm) for stated width, w (/ mm), and height, h / mm											Perimeter, P / mm
	75	100	125	150	200	250	300	350	400	450	500	
w	320											720
d_e	160											
w	360	350	330	320								808
d_e	169	195	213	230								
w	400	390	370	360								888
d_e	177	205	225	244								
w	440	430	410	400								968
d_e	185	215	236	257								
w	480	470	450	440								1048
d_e	192	223	247	269								
w	520	505	490	480								1126
d_e	199	230	257	281								
w		545	530	520								1206
d_e		238	266	291								
w				555	525							1280
d_e				300	340							
w				635	605	580						1442
d_e				319	364	400						
w				715	690	660	630					1604
d_e				337	388	426	456					
w				800	770	740	710	685	655			1767
d_e				354	408	450	484	513	534			
w				880	845	825	790	765	735	705	680	1927
d_e				370	425	475	510	543	567	586	602	
w				960	930	900	875	845	815	785	755	2067
d_e				384	444	494	537	571	599	621	638	
w				1040	1010	985	955	925	895	865	835	2249
d_e				398	461	515	560	597	628	653	674	
w				1120	1090	1065	1035	1005	975	945	915	2409
d_e				411	477	534	581	621	655	684	707	
w				1200	1170	1145	1115	1085	1055	1025	1000	2570
d_e				423	492	552	602	645	681	713	741	
w					1335	1305	1275	1245	1215	1190	1160	2892
d_e					522	585	640	688	729	768	799	
w						1465	1435	1405	1375	1350	1320	3211
d_e						616	675	727	773	816	852	
w						1625	1595	1570	1540	1510	1480	3535
d_e						644	708	765	815	860	901	
w						1785	1760	1730	1700	1670	1640	3856
d_e						671	739	799	853	902	946	

$$d_e = \frac{1.453\, A^{0.6}}{P^{0.2}}$$

4.8.9 Components and fittings

Whether for liquids in pipes or gasses in ducts, the same fundamental equation applies:

$$\Delta p_f = \zeta \tfrac{1}{2} \rho c^2 \qquad (4.23)$$

Data for ζ for ductwork components are given in sections 4.9 and 4.11.

Values of $\tfrac{1}{2}\rho c^2$ for air at 20 °C, normal atmospheric pressure, and 50% saturation are given in Table 4.19. Values of $\tfrac{1}{2}\rho c^2$ are easily calculated for other conditions.

Table 4.19 Velocity pressure, p_v ($= \tfrac{1}{2}\rho c^2$), for air having a density $\rho = 1.20$ kg·m^{-3}; this is the case at 20 °C, 50% saturation and pressure of 101.325 bar

Velocity c / m·s^{-1}	Velocity pressure, p_v (/ Pa), for stated velocity, c / m.s^{-1}									
	0.0	0.1	0.2	0.3	0.4	0.5	0.6	0.7	0.8	0.9
0	0.00	0.01	0.02	0.05	0.10	0.15	0.22	0.29	0.38	0.49
1	0.60	0.73	0.86	1.01	1.18	1.35	1.54	1.73	1.94	2.17
2	2.40	2.65	2.90	3.17	3.46	3.75	4.06	4.37	4.70	5.05
3	5.40	5.77	6.14	6.53	6.94	7.35	7.78	8.21	8.66	9.13
4	9.60	10.09	10.58	11.09	11.62	12.15	12.70	13.25	13.82	14.41
5	15.00	15.61	16.22	16.85	17.50	18.15	18.82	19.49	20.18	20.89
6	21.60	22.33	23.06	23.81	24.58	25.35	26.14	26.93	27.74	28.57
7	29.40	30.25	31.10	31.97	32.86	33.75	34.66	35.57	36.50	37.45
8	38.40	39.37	40.34	41.33	42.34	43.35	44.38	45.41	46.46	47.53
9	48.60	49.69	50.78	51.89	53.02	54.15	55.30	56.45	57.62	58.81
10	60.00	61.21	62.42	63.65	64.90	66.15	67.42	68.69	69.98	71.29
11	72.60	73.93	75.26	76.61	77.98	79.35	80.74	82.13	83.54	84.97
12	86.40	87.85	89.30	90.77	92.26	93.75	95.26	96.77	98.30	99.85
13	101.40	102.97	104.54	106.13	107.74	109.35	110.98	112.61	114.26	115.93
14	117.60	119.29	120.98	122.69	124.42	126.15	127.90	129.65	131.42	133.21
15	135.00	136.81	138.62	140.45	142.30	144.15	146.02	147.89	149.78	151.69
16	153.60	155.53	157.46	159.41	161.38	163.35	165.34	167.33	169.34	171.37
17	173.40	175.45	177.50	179.57	181.66	183.75	185.86	187.97	109.10	192.25
18	194.40	196.57	198.74	200.93	203.14	205.35	207.58	209.81	212.06	214.33
19	216.60	218.89	221.18	223.49	225.82	228.15	230.50	232.85	235.22	237.61
20	240.00	242.41	244.82	247.25	249.70	252.15	254.62	257.09	259.58	262.09
21	264.60	367.13	269.66	272.21	274.78	277.35	279.94	282.53	285.14	287.77
22	290.40	293.05	295.70	298.37	301.06	303.75	306.46	309.17	311.90	413.65
23	317.40	320.17	322.94	325.73	328.54	331.35	334.18	337.01	339.86	342.73
24	345.60	348.49	351.38	354.29	357.22	360.15	363.10	366.05	369.02	372.01
25	375.00	378.01	381.02	384.05	387.10	390.15	393.22	396.29	399.38	402.49
26	405.60	408.73	411.86	415.01	418.18	421.35	424.54	427.37	430.94	434.17
27	437.40	440.65	443.90	447.17	450.46	453.75	457.06	460.37	463.70	467.05
28	470.40	473.77	477.14	480.53	483.94	487.35	490.78	494.21	497.66	501.13
29	504.60	508.09	511.58	515.09	518.62	522.15	525.70	529.25	532.82	536.41
30	540.00	543.61	547.22	550.85	554.50	558.15	561.82	565.49	569.18	572.89
31	576.60	580.33	584.06	587.81	591.58	595.35	599.14	602.93	606.74	610.57
32	614.40	618.25	622.10	625.97	629.86	633.75	637.66	641.57	645.50	649.45
33	653.40	657.37	661.34	665.33	669.34	673.35	677.38	681.41	685.46	689.53
34	693.60	697.69	701.78	705.89	710.02	714.15	718.30	722.45	726.62	730.81
35	735.00	739.21	743.42	747.65	751.90	756.15	760.42	764.69	768.98	773.29
36	777.60	781.93	786.26	790.61	794.98	799.35	803.74	808.13	812.54	816.97
37	821.40	825.85	830.30	834.77	839.26	843.75	848.26	852.77	857.30	861.85
38	866.40	870.97	875.54	880.13	884.74	889.35	893.98	898.61	903.26	907.93
39	912.60	917.29	921.98	926.69	931.42	936.15	940.90	945.65	950.42	955.21
40	960.00	964.81	969.62	974.45	979.30	984.15	989.02	993.78	998.78	1003.69

4.9   Pressure loss factors

An extensive review of pressure loss factors has been undertaken. Many sources give conflicting information, much derived from research results of many years ago. The data presented here are those that are considered most reliable.

In the light of modern research, much older data, where values of ζ for ductwork components using air had been derived from tests using water[23], are now known to be inappropriate. With few exceptions most published data on pressure loss factors historically gave just single values for a component, irrespective of size or of fluid velocity. It has been known for some time[24] that the values of ζ for elbows in ductwork vary with the air velocity, but the data have been so sparse that this has not been considered in design guides. It is now known that such variation with velocity exists also for pipework components. More recently it has been possible to include research data showing the variation with size.

The pressure loss due to the insertion of a component such as an elbow is predominantly due to the vortices created downstream. Practical measurements close to the component would therefore be highly unrepeatable, and therefore unreliable. Experimental measurements of pressure are therefore made well upstream and downstream of the disturbance (i.e. 20 diameters upstream/downstream). The results are always quoted as the 'extra pressure drop due to the insertion of the component'.

The pressure drop calculated for a component is always to be added to the pressure drop of the full length of the pipework or ducting (unless otherwise stated).

If the distance between one component and another (entries and exits included) is less than 20 diameters, there is an interaction between the components. Thus the pressure drop could be more or less than the calculated figure depending on the type of component and the type of flow disturbances created, especially by the upstream component.

The predominant source of friction pressure drop has traditionally been attributed to the flow separation and vortices downstream of an elbow or bend. However, with pipework in particular, surface effects play an important part, the pressure drop being very dependent upon the surface roughness and shape of the inner surface. Thus it is found that the values of ζ depend upon the diameter and the material. Since even a small change in the internal shape of a pipe fitting can cause an appreciable difference in friction effects, it is clear that for small diameters, the pressure loss factor could also be manufacturer-dependent. This applies principally to elbows of pipework, (see Miller[25] and Rahmeyer[26,27]) but also to elbows of ductwork[1,28].

With tees, the predominant friction pressure drop is due to the turbulence created by the mixing or separation of flows. In the past it was convenient to consider that surface effects would not play such an important part with tees and that therefore the values of ζ might not vary with diameter. This would appear doubtful in the light of recent work by Rahmeyer[29,30] on tees in pipework. There is an indication that larger diameter tees give smaller values of ζ but the effect is easily swamped by manufacturing details.

It had previously been assumed that any possible variation with diameter would not apply to ductwork components due to the larger diameters. Recent work carried out by the European project[1] and by the United McGill Corporation[28] on circular ductwork, shows this not to be the case. For bends in ductwork, ζ is strongly diameter-dependent. Work done on rectangular bends by Madison and Parker[31] showed that size effects are appreciable for square bends of long radius and for those having a low aspect ratio (h/w).

Smith and Jones[32], testing flat oval tees, found ζ to be slightly smaller for tees of larger size. Despite the breadth of work carried out by the European project[1] on ductwork components, and although several combinations of sizes were tested, no simple test was carried out to confirm the general assumption that, with tees, the size has no significant effect. Nevertheless, interpolation to obtain values of ζ for other tee geometries does permit a direct comparison. Size is seen to play a part, which is far from negligible. Larger tees give smaller values of ζ.

With tees, there are three flows and three velocity pressures. The use of the velocity pressure of the combined flow is sometimes queried by engineers; one wonders whether the use of branch velocity pressures for branch pressure loss might seem clearer (some but not all texts treat it this way). However, if branch velocity pressures were used, the value of the appropriate ζ would result in very large variations. Therefore, to avoid any confusion, all the pressure loss coefficients are quoted in relation to the velocity pressure of the combined flow.

Where possible, the most recent research results have been included in sections 4.10 and 4.11. It is expected that as more research is carried out, the data and advice given in this Guide will be amended. Similarly as computational fluid dynamics (CFD) modelling improves to the point where it agrees with reliable experimental data, it may one day be possible to extrapolate its use to those components which have not yet been physically tested.

4.10   Pressure loss factors for pipework components

For elbows there is considerable evidence that values of ζ vary with diameter. Rahmeyer[27] has shown that ζ can vary appreciably with velocity (Re). For tees there is little such evidence. Previously it had been considered that with tees, the predominant friction pressure drop was due to the turbulence created by the mixing or separation of flows. It was convenient therefore to consider that surface effects would not play such an important part with tees and that therefore their values of ζ might not vary with diameter. In his tests on PVC-U tees, Rahmeyer[33] found larger diameter tees to give slightly lower values of ζ but that the effect could be considerably swamped by the internal details of the design. He also found considerable variation in the values of ζ for tees of 100 mm diameter from five different manufacturers. This confirms that the internal surface roughness and form play a significant part, even for tees.

The guidance given on ageing allowances when using water (see section 4.5.3) should be applied to fittings as well as to straight pipes.

4.10.1 Elbows and bends

4.10.1.1 Laminar flow

As with the friction factor λ for straight pipes, the pressure loss factor ζ for elbows/bends is found to be much higher in the laminar flow regime. This fact, generally overlooked, is important since pipes may often carry fluids of high viscosity which results in laminar flow.

Using Idelchik[2], to quote a simplistic value of ζ for laminar flow ($Re < 1000$), suggests that:

— $\zeta = 2.30$ could be taken for smooth elbows (laminar)

— $\zeta = 2.35$ could be taken for rough elbows (laminar).

It is interesting to note that in the laminar flow regime neither relative roughness nor pipe diameter have any great effect on the value of ζ.

4.10.1.2 Turbulent flow

Since the primary cause of friction pressure drop around elbows and tees is internal fluid friction resulting from the change of direction, it is sometimes considered that surface roughness will play little part. However, Idelchik[2] and Miller[25] show that surface roughness, particularly at the inner wall, does indeed have a very significant effect on the pressure loss created by bends. The effect is less for sharp elbows for which flow separation is the greatest

factor. Since surface roughness plays a part, ζ will depend on the material. However there are no comprehensive data on this effect. The guidance given on ageing allowances when using water (see section 4.5.3), should therefore be applied to fittings as well as to straight pipes

The upstream joint causes a discontinuity equivalent to increasing the effective roughness substantially. Comparing values from ASHRAE[4] and Miller[25], the type of upstream fitting has an effect on the pressure drop: in descending order of friction, screwed joints give most, welded and soldered joints less, while smooth joints give least friction[34].

Miller[25] showed that even a very slight rounding of the inside part of an elbow has an appreciable effect on the value of ζ. Thus we can expect that the value of ζ to vary with the form and thus depend on the manufacturer. Rahmeyer[26,27,35] included in his tests samples from five, sometimes six different manufacturers, and several components from each. The spread of results is considerable.

Recent research by Rahmeyer[27] shows that fluid velocity also has a considerable effect on the value of ζ. The tests were all carried out using water at 16 °C, ($v = 0.1208 \times 10^{-5}$ m$^2 \cdot$s^{-1}). These most recent data are given in Table 4.20 and show the variation of ζ with diameter and velocity. The PVC-U elbows tested were all proprietary sharp elbows, except one where the 90° bend was made up of two 45° elbows glued together. This fabrication results in a bend of increased r/d, the effect of which is a reduction in the values of ζ far greater than any adverse effect from the discontinuity of the glued joint. Table 4.21 gives more comprehensive data, and shows the variation of ζ with size.

Table 4.20 Elbows: values of ζ varying with velocity; (a) screwed joint, malleable iron, (b) welded joint, forged steel, (c) and (d) PVC-U (derived from Rahmeyer[26,27,35])

Type and material	Diameter, d / mm	Velocity, c / m·s^{-1}								
		0.5	1	1.5	2	2.5	3	3.5	4	5
Short radius ($r/d = 1.0$):										
(a) Screwed joint, malleable iron	50	0.52	0.58	0.63	0.66	0.68	0.71	0.72	—	—
(b) Welded joint, forged steel	100	0.41	0.38	0.36	0.35	0.34	0.33	0.33	—	—
Long radius ($r/d = 1.5$):										
(b) Welded joint, forged steel	100	0.28	0.26	0.25	0.25	0.24	0.24	0.24	0.23	0.23
	300*	*0.18*	*0.16*	*0.15*	*0.15*	*0.14*	*0.14*	*0.14*	*0.13*	*0.13*
	400	0.15	0.13	0.12	0.12	0.12	0.11	0.11	0.11	0.11
	500	0.13	0.12	0.11	0.11	0.12	0.10	0.10	0.10	0.10
	600	0.11	0.10	0.10	0.10	0.09	0.09	0.09	0.08	0.08

	Diameter†, d / mm	Velocity, c / m·s^{-1}								
		0.85	1	1.5	2	3	4	5	6	7.5
Sharp inner edge ($r/d = 0.5$):										
(c) PVC-U	51	1.077	1.490	0.990	0.976	0.956	0.938	0.925	0.914	0.901
	102	0.978	0.955	0.914	0.902	0.886	0.873	0.863	0.855	0.844
	153*	*0.887*	*0.869*	*0.835*	*0.826*	*0.815*	*0.805*	*0.797*	*0.789*	—
	204	0.794	0.782	0.759	0.753	0.745	0.738	0.732	0.727	—
Glued 45° elbows giving 90° bend ($r/d \approx 1.0$):										
(d) PVC-U	204	0.462	0.448	0.419	0.412	0.402	0.394	0.387	0.382	—

* Experimental readings for this size were unreliable. Figures in italics were obtained by interpolation, and should be considered as 'best advice' only.

† 51 mm = nominal 2-inch, 102 mm = nominal 4-inch, 153 mm = nominal 6-inch, 204 mm = nominal 8-inch.

Note: accuracy: (a) ±22% for d = 50 mm; (b) ±10% for d = 400 mm and 500 mm; (c) ±1.3% for d = 51–204 mm

Table 4.21 Elbows: values of ζ varying with diameter (derived from ASHRAE[4] and Miller[25])

Type	Diameter, d / mm								
	10	15	20	25	32	40	50	75	100
(a) Elbows:									
— screwed fitting[4]★	2.5	2.1	1.7	1.5	1.3	1.2	1.0	0.82	0.70
— rough, sharp inner edge[25]	1.56	1.45	1.35	1.3	1.24	1.18	1.15	1.10	1.10
— smooth radiused inner[25]	1.10	0.93	0.75	0.8	0.75	0.72	0.70	0.70	0.70
(b) Bends:									
— screwed fitting[4]†	—	—	0.92	0.78	0.65	0.54	0.42	0.33	0.24
— smooth, $r/d > 1.5$[25]	0.57	0.53	0.49	0.46	0.43	0.42	0.40	0.40	0.40

★ Accuracy ± 40% for $d < 50$ mm, ± 20% for $d > 50$ mm; † accuracy ± 25%

4.10.2 Elbows in close proximity

See Figure 4.3. When components are in close proximity, the flow disturbance created by the first will interact with the second. The pressure drop will not then be the same as for the two components in isolation. Table 4.22 contains values for a 'coefficient of close proximity', C_{cp} to be used in the following equations.

For two components:

$$\Delta p = C_{cp}\, 2\, \zeta_1\, \tfrac{1}{2}\, \rho\, c^2 \qquad (4.24)$$

For three components:

$$\Delta p = C_{cp}\, 3\, \zeta_1\, \tfrac{1}{2}\, \rho\, c^2 \qquad (4.25)$$

where ζ_1 is the pressure loss coefficient for one of the components in isolation.

4.10.3 Expanding and contracting elbows

See Figure 4.4 and Tables 4.23 and 4.24. Values of ζ are to be used with the velocity pressure at the smallest dimension.

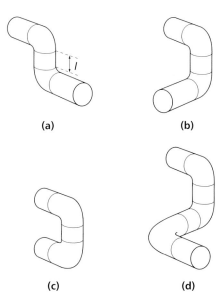

(a)   (b)

(c)   (d)

Figure 4.3 Elbows in close proximity; configurations for Table 4.22: (a) two elbows in same plane, (b) two elbows in different planes, (c) two elbows in same plane ('U'), (d) three elbows (swing)

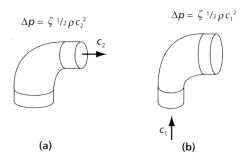

$$\Delta p = \zeta\, \tfrac{1}{2}\rho\, c_2^2 \qquad\qquad \Delta p = \zeta\, \tfrac{1}{2}\rho\, c_1^2$$

(a)   (b)

Figure 4.4 (a) Contracting elbow, (b) expanding elbow

Table 4.22 Elbows in close proximity: values of correction factor C_{cp} (Rahmeyer[36]; ASHRAE *Transactions* **108** (1) 2002. © American Society of Heating, Refrigerating and Air-Conditioning Engineers Inc. (www.ashrae.org))

Configuration (see Figure 4.3)	Ratio of separation to diameter, l/d							
	0	1	2	3	4	5	10	20
Diameter, $d = 51$ mm ('2-inch'):								
(a) Two elbows in plane	0.90	0.88	0.86	0.89	0.88	0.88	1.00	1.01
(b) Two elbows out of plane	0.87	0.88	0.88	0.85	0.87	0.88	0.97	1.00
(c) Two elbows in plane ('U')	0.60	0.65	0.70	0.72	0.77	0.83	1.00	1.00
(d) Three elbows (swing)	0.70	0.72	0.74	0.72	0.75	0.77	0.99	0.99
Diameter, $d = 102$ mm ('4-inch'):								
(a) Two elbows in plane	0.95	0.93	0.90	0.90	0.92	0.94	0.98	1.00
(b) Two elbows out of plane	0.73	0.79	0.86	0.85	0.88	0.90	0.97	0.99
(c) Two elbows in plane ('U')	0.82	0.86	0.71	0.85	0.89	0.93	0.97	0.99
(d) Three elbows (swing)	0.86	0.87	0.87	0.87	0.88	0.90	0.95	0.99

Table 4.23 Contracting elbows: values of ζ varying with velocity; the value of ζ is with reference to the downstream velocity pressure[18]

Type and diameter, d	Area ratio A_2/A_1	Velocity, c_2 / m·s^{-1}					
		1	2	3	4	5	6
Screwed joint, 50 mm > 37 mm	0.548	0.237	0.250	0.268	0.274	0.280	0.286
welded joint 100 mm > 76 mm	0.578	0.230	0.192	0.173	0.159	0.146	0.137

Note: the 50 mm fitting is of malleable iron, contracting round the elbow from 50 mm to 37 mm; the 100 mm fitting is of forged steel, contracting round the elbow from 100 mm to 76 mm. Both are of long radius.

Table 4.24 Expanding elbows: values of ζ varying with velocity; the value of ζ is with reference to the upstream velocity pressure[26]

Type and diameter, d	Area ratio A_2/A_1	Velocity, c_1 / m·s^{-1}						
		0.5	1	1.5	2	2.5	3	3.5
Screwed joint, 37 mm < 50 mm	1.83	0.662	0.61	0.521	0.55	0.532	0.521	0.508
welded joint 76 mm < 100 mm	1.73	0.285	0.276	0.272	0.269	0.267	0.265	0.263

Note: the 37 mm fitting is of malleable iron, expanding round the elbow from 37 mm to 50 mm; the 76 mm fitting is of forged steel, expanding round the elbow from 76 mm to 100 mm. Both are of long radius.

4.10.4 Gradual changes of section

See Figure 4.5 and Tables 4.25 and 4.26. Values of ζ are to be used with the velocity pressure at the smallest dimension.

4.10.4.1 Contractions

Rahmeyer[26,27,35] tested contractions of two types, the results of which are reproduced in Table 4.25. The smaller size, with screw threads, gave the highest values of ζ. It is

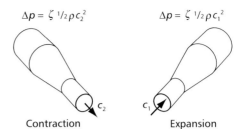

$$\Delta p = \zeta \, \tfrac{1}{2}\rho c_2^2 \qquad \Delta p = \zeta \, \tfrac{1}{2}\rho c_1^2$$

Contraction   Expansion

Figure 4.5 Gradual changes of section

not known how much of this is due to the smaller size, and how much due to the screwed joint, as both are known to increase the value of ζ.

4.10.4.2 Expansions

Rahmeyer[26,27,35] tested expansions of two types, the results of which are reproduced in Table 4.26. The smaller size, with screwed joints, gave the highest values of ζ. It is not known how much of this is due to the smaller size, and how much due to the screwed joint, as both are known to increase the value of ζ.

4.10.5 Abrupt changes of section

See Figure 4.6 and Table 4.27. Values of ζ are to be used with the velocity pressure at the smallest dimension.

4.10.5.1 Sudden contractions

There will be a range when flow is in the laminar range upstream of the contraction, whilst turbulent downstream. In the intermediate zone, it is anticipated that the disturbance of the sudden contraction will trigger downstream turbulence at $Re_2 < 3 \times 10^3$, possibly as low as $Re_2 = 2 \times 10^3$, see Figure 4.1.

Table 4.25 Contractions: values of ζ (derived from Rahmeyer[26,27,35])

Type and diameters	Area ratio A_2/A_1	Velocity, c_2 / m·s^{-1}						
		0.5	1	2	3	4	5	7
(a) Screwed joint, malleable iron: — 50 mm > 37 mm	0.548	0.45	0.34	0.20	0.14	0.11	0.09	—
(b) Welded joint, forged steel: — 100 mm > 75 mm	0.562	0.17	0.14	0.09	0.05	0.04	0.04	—
(c) PVC-U: — 150 mm > 100 mm	0.444	0.18	0.16	0.13	0.11	0.10	0.10	0.10

Note: spread between items of different manufacturers: (a) $\Delta\zeta = \pm 0.020$, $\pm 22\%$ at $c_2 = 2$ m·s^{-1}; (b) $\Delta\zeta = \pm 0.022$, $\pm 55\%$ at $c_2 = 4$ m·s^{-1}; (c) $\Delta\zeta = \pm 0.028$, $\pm 27\%$ at $c_2 = 5$ m·s^{-1}

Table 4.26 Expansions: values of ζ (derived from Rahmeyer[26,27,35])

Type and diameters	Area ratio A_2/A_1	Velocity, c_1 / m·s^{-1}						
		0.3	0.5	1	1.5	2	2.5	3	3.7
(a) Screwed joint, malleable iron: — 37 mm < 50 mm	1.83	0.25	0.21	0.17	0.15	0.14	0.13	0.12	0.12
(b) Welded joint, forged steel: — 75 mm < 100 mm	1.78	0.14	0.13	0.13	0.12	0.11	0.11	0.11	0.11
(c) Wrought steel, butt-welded: — 254 mm < 305 mm	1.44	$\zeta = 0.111$ for 0.5 m·s^{-1} < c < 6 m·s^{-1}							
— 305 mm < 406 mm	1.78	$\zeta = 0.075$ for 0.5 m·s^{-1} < c < 6 m·s^{-1}							
— 406 mm < 508 mm	1.56	$\zeta = 0.022$ for 0.5 m·s^{-1} < c < 6 m·s^{-1}							
— 508 mm < 610 mm	1.44	$\zeta = 0.020$ for 0.5 m·s^{-1} < c < 6 m·s^{-1}							

Note: accuracy: (a) $\pm 14\%$; (b) $\pm 13\%$

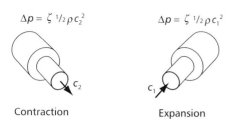

$$\Delta p = \zeta \tfrac{1}{2} \rho c_2^2 \qquad\qquad \Delta p = \zeta \tfrac{1}{2} \rho c_1^2$$

Contraction   Expansion

Figure 4.6 (a) Sudden contraction, (b) sudden expansion

For flow in the laminar regime, values of ζ are appreciably larger than for turbulent flow[2]. The value varies considerably with Reynolds number in a very non-linear manner; e.g. for a value of $Re = 10$, $\zeta < 4.9$, referring to the velocity pressure at the smaller dimension.

For turbulent flow, the Idelchik data suggest that for $Re > 10^5$, variation of ζ with Re is trivial and the following equation has been found to fit best the available data for $Re > 10^4$:

$$\zeta = 0.5 \left(1 - \frac{A_2}{A_1} \right)^{0.75} \qquad (4.26)$$

However, this equation takes no account of size effects and Reynolds number effects, which are in evidence for the more recent data of Table 4.25 for gradual contractions. Standard pipe fittings would normally have a more rounded transition and give a slightly lower pressure drop than the values given in Table 4.27.

4.10.5.2   Sudden enlargements

The Borda–Carnot equation may be used for $Re > 10^4$:

$$\zeta = 0.5 \left(1 - \frac{A_1}{A_2} \right)^{2} \qquad (4.27)$$

However this equation takes no account of size effects and Reynolds Number effects which are in evidence for the more recent data of Table 4.26 for gradual expansions. Standard pipe fittings would normally have a more rounded transition and give a slightly lower pressure drop.

4.10.5.3   Sudden entry/exit of a pipe to/from a vessel

For a sudden entry to a pipe from a vessel, $\zeta = 0.5$.

For a sudden exit from a pipe into vessel, $\zeta = 1.0$

4.10.6   Tees

See Figures 4.7 to 4.9 and Tables 4.28 to 4.34.

Although for elbows there is considerable evidence that values of ζ vary with diameter, there is no clear evidence that this is also the case for tees. It once seemed reasonable to suppose that in tees, the fluid turbulence dominates to the total exclusion of surface effects and relative roughness (k/d). Rahmeyer[27] tested equal tees of 50 and 100 mm diameter, but not of identical form or connection. No firm data are therefore available on the effect of size.

Note that all values of ζ must be used with the velocity pressure of the combined flow.

4.10.6.1   Notes on the information as presented

The only recent data are for tees made of PVC-U and steel. Similarly the only joints mentioned are either screwed or welded. No data are available concerning either smooth joints or tees of copper, either of which might be expected to give lower values of ζ.

The most recently obtained values are those of Rahmeyer[29,30,33]. From analysis of his results the values given in Tables 4.28 to 4.34 were derived. He tested only for reduced values of $d_s/d_c = 0.74$ and 1.0, and for branch ratios of $d_b/d_c = 0.74$ and 1.0. Where identical geometries permit comparisons, the Rahmeyer data give consistently lower values of ζ than those of Idelchik[2]. Being more recent, CIBSE is inclined to favour the former values.

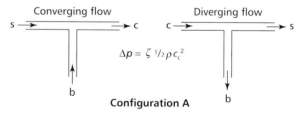

Converging flow   Diverging flow

$$\Delta p = \zeta \tfrac{1}{2} \rho c_c^2$$

Configuration A

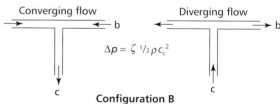

Converging flow   Diverging flow

$$\Delta p = \zeta \tfrac{1}{2} \rho c_c^2$$

Configuration B

Figure 4.7 Equal tees: configurations (Tables 4.28 to 4.30)

Table 4.27 Abrupt contraction: values of ζ; for $Re_2 < 10^4$ (from diagram 4-10 of Idelchik[2])

Area ratio, A_2/A_1	Reynolds number, Re_2									
	40	50	100	200	500	1000	2000	4000	5000	10 000
0.1	2.00	1.80	1.30	1.04	0.82	0.64	0.50	*0.80*	*0.75*	0.50
0.2	1.84	1.62	1.20	0.95	0.70	0.50	0.40	*0.60*	0.60	0.40
0.3	1.70	1.50	1.10	0.85	0.60	0.44	0.30	0.55	0.55	0.35
0.4	1.60	1.40	1.00	0.78	0.50	0.35	0.25	0.45	0.50	0.30
0.5	1.46	1.30	0.90	0.65	0.42	0.30	0.20	0.40	0.42	0.25
0.6	1.35	1.20	0.80	0.56	0.35	0.24	0.15	0.35	0.35	0.20

Note: figures in italics are for conditions where, although turbulent flow occurs downstream of the contraction, laminar conditions occur upstream.

4.10.6.2 Tees: laminar flow

In the laminar region, ζ is sensibly constant for flow to or from a branch, being rather higher than for turbulent flow.

Summarised from Idelchik[2] it could be said that for $Re < 2000$:

— for laminar flow, converging flow branch: $\zeta = 2.5$

— laminar flow, diverging flow branch: $\zeta = 3.4$

Surprisingly, compared with turbulent flow, it is the pressure loss factor for the straight flow across the tee which is said to be most complex. Idelchik gives very complex relationships depending on the relative branch size, the relative flows and the Reynolds number. Carrying out a sample calculation for $Re = 100$, and with 50 per cent of the flow to or from a branch of the same diameter, revealed that, approximately:

— for converging flow, straight ζ is four times that for turbulent flow

— for diverging flow, straight ζ is four times that for turbulent flow.

4.10.6.3 Tees: turbulent flow

The value of ζ is seen to vary considerably with the ratio of the respective flows so no simplistic values can be given. The friction loss differs considerably between converging and diverging flows. The effect of branch diameter relative to the diameter of the part carrying the combined flow, d_b/d_c, is appreciable and cannot be ignored but there are few data on this effect.

For flows straight across the tee, the values of ζ do not vary greatly with the relative flows, q_b/q_c.

A clear distinction is made between converging and diverging flows as follows.

Converging flows

There is little information on the effect of the upstream type of connection. However Idelchik[2] reports that when the flow from the branch is less than 80% of the combined flow, screwed branches give losses 10–20% more than for smooth connections. Conversely it would appear that when the branch flow is greater than 80% of the total, screwed branches give losses 10–20% less than for smooth connections.

It will be observed that in the case of converging flows, it is possible under certain flow conditions for the flow from the branch to experience a negative pressure loss factor, i.e. to experience a pressure gain.

For those who are unfamiliar with the concept of a negative pressure loss factor, a small explanation follows. With most of the flow going along the straight, this flow has the greater momentum. The flow arriving from the branch must be accelerated by frictional contact with the straight-flowing fluid, the effect more than counteracting the bend friction loss effect, and resulting in a pressure increase.

Diverging flows

For losses round to the branch, there is little difference between tees of smooth joints and those of screwed joints.

Table 4.28 Equal tees, converging flow, configuation A (see Figure 4.7): values for the straight factor, ζ_{s-c} (derived from Rahmeyer[29,30,33])

Type and diameter	Relative straight flow, q_s/q_c									
	0.1	0.2	0.3	0.4	0.5	0.6	0.7	0.8	0.9	1.0
(a) Screwed joint, malleable iron:										
— 50 mm	0.43	0.48	0.51	0.52	0.52	0.50	0.46	0.40	0.32	0.23
(b) Welded joint, forged steel:										
— 100 mm	−0.15	≠ −0.07	−0.01	0.05	0.11	0.15	0.17	0.16	0.12	0.06
(c) Butt-welded, wrought steel:										
— 300 mm	−0.05	0.02	0.08	0.14	0.18	0.20	0.21	0.18	0.13	0.07
— 400 mm	0.01	0.09	0.15	0.20	0.22	0.21	0.19	0.14	0.09	0.03
(d) PVC-U, moulded:										
— 50 mm	0.18	0.24	0.28	0.31	0.34	0.35	0.34	0.31	0.26	0.20
— 100 mm	0.22	0.26	0.30	0.32	0.33	0.33	0.31	0.27	0.21	0.13
— 150 mm	0.38	0.40	0.41	0.40	0.38	0.35	0.31	0.25	0.17	0.07
— 200 mm	0.24	0.27	0.30	0.31	0.30	0.28	0.25	0.21	0.15	0.07
(e) PVC-U, segmented:										
— 200 mm	0.64	0.68	0.70	0.67	0.63	0.57	0.48	0.37	0.26	0.14

Note: scatter between different manufacturers: (a) (b) (c) = ± 0.2; (d) (e) = ± 0.1; figures in italics are extrapolated values

Table 4.29 Equal tees, converging flow, configuation A (see Figure 4.7): values for the branch factor, $\zeta_{b\text{-}c}$ (derived from Rahmeyer[29,30,33])

Type and diameter	Relative branch flow, q_b/q_c									
	0.1	0.2	0.3	0.4	0.5	0.6	0.7	0.8	0.9	1.0
(a) Screwed joint, malleable iron:										
— 50 mm	−0.22	−0.06	0.10	0.27	0.43	0.59	0.74	0.88	1.00	1.10
(b) Welded joint, forged steel:										
— 100 mm	−0.65	−0.48	−0.34	−0.20	−0.06	0.08	0.20	0.30	0.42	0.54
(c) Butt–welded, wrought steel:										
— 300 mm	*−0.55*	*−0.39*	−0.23	−0.09	0.05	0.19	0.33	0.79	0.60	0.71
— 400 mm	*−0.49*	*−0.32*	−0.18	−0.02	0.12	0.26	0.39	0.51	0.63	0.75
(d) PVC–U, moulded:										
— 50 mm to 200 mm	−0.53	−0.30	−0.09	0.11	0.29	0.42	0.56	0.70	0.85	1.00

Note: scatter between different manufacturers: (a) (b) (c) = ± 0.2; (d) = ± 0.1; figures in italics are extrapolated values

Table 4.30 Equal tees, diverging flow, configuration A (see Figure 4.7): values for the straight factor, $\zeta_{s\text{-}c}$ (derived from Rahmeyer[29,30,33])

Type and diameter	Relative straight flow, q_s/q_c									
	0.1	0.2	0.3	0.4	0.5	0.6	0.7	0.8	0.9	1.0
(a) Screwed joint, malleable iron:										
— 50 mm	0.25	0.18	0.13	0.08	0.04	0.02	0.02	0.05	0.12	0.21
(b) Welded joint, forged steel:										
— 100 mm	0.45	0.35	0.26	0.18	0.11	0.06	0.03	0.01	0.02	0.06
(c) Butt-welded, wrought steel:										
— 300 mm	*0.30*	*0.21*	0.14	0.08	0.04	0.02	0.02	0.03	0.05	0.09
(d) PVC-U, moulded:										
— 50 mm	*0.22*	*0.17*	0.13	0.09	0.06	0.04	0.04	0.07	0.13	0.21
— 100 mm	*0.35*	*0.28*	0.22	0.16	0.11	0.07	0.04	0.05	0.08	0.14
— 150 mm	*0.34*	*0.27*	0.20	0.14	0.09	0.05	0.03	0.03	0.06	0.10
— 200 mm	*0.32*	*0.23*	0.16	0.10	0.06	0.03	0.02	0.02	0.04	0.07
(e) PVC-U, segmented:										
— 200 mm	*0.35*	*0.27*	0.21	0.16	0.11	0.07	0.06	0.06	0.09	0.13

Note: scatter between different manufacturers: (a) (b) (c) = ± 0.4; (d) (e) = ± 0.5; figures in italics are extrapolated values

Table 4.31 Equal tees, diverging flow, configuration A (see Figure 4.7): values for the branch factor, $\zeta_{c\text{-}b}$ (derived from Rahmeyer[29,30,33])

Type and diameter	Relative branch flow, q_b/q_c									
	0.1	0.2	0.3	0.4	0.5	0.6	0.7	0.8	0.9	1.0
(a) Screwed joint, malleable iron:										
— 50 mm	0.74	0.69	0.63	0.62	0.63	0.65	0.70	0.76	0.83	0.90
(b) Welded joint, forged steel:										
— 100 mm	0.93	0.82	0.74	0.67	0.62	0.60	0.61	0.64	0.68	0.74
(c) Butt–welded, wrought steel:										
— 300 mm	*0.80*	*0.72*	0.66	0.61	0.57	0.56	0.57	0.59	0.62	0.66
— 400 mm	*0.75*	*0.67*	0.60	0.54	0.51	0.50	0.51	0.52	0.53	0.54
(d) PVC–U, moulded:										
— 50 mm	*0.95*	*0.92*	0.90	0.89	0.90	0.95	1.02	1.10	1.18	1.26
— 100 mm	*0.95*	*0.87*	0.82	0.79	0.79	0.81	0.85	0.89	0.95	1.02
— 150 mm	*0.85*	*0.78*	0.73	0.70	0.69	0.72	0.75	0.79	0.84	0.89
(e) PVC–U, segmented:										
— 200 mm	*1.24*	*1.18*	1.14	1.12	1.12	1.15	1.20	1.27	1.36	1.47

Note: scatter between different manufacturers: (a) (b) (c) = ± 0.15; (d) (e) = ± 0.12; figures in italics are extrapolated values

Table 4.32 Equal tees, converging and diverging flow, configuration B (see Figure 4.7): values of ζ (derived from Rahmeyer[29])

Type	Flow ratio, q_b/q_c									
	0.1	0.2	0.3	0.4	0.5	0.6	0.7	0.8	0.9	1.0
Converging flow ($\zeta_{b\text{-}c}$)	0.09	0.26	0.45	0.56	0.55	0.47	0.39	0.37	0.49	0.80
Diverging flow ($\zeta_{c\text{-}b}$)	0.64	0.64	0.63	0.64	0.67	0.71	0.77	0.84	0.95	1.10

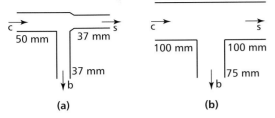

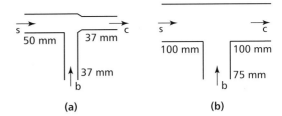

Figure 4.8 Unequal tees, diverging flow: configurations (Table 4.33)   **Figure 4.9** Unequal tees, converging flow: configurations (Table 4.34)

Table 4.33 Unequal tees, diverging flow: values of ζ; (a) for d_c = 50 mm, d_s = 37 mm, d_b = 37 mm, (b) d_c = 100 mm, d_s = 100 mm, d_b = 75 mm (see Figure 4.8) (derived from Rahmeyer[29])

Type	Flow ratio, q_b/q_c										
	0	0.1	0.2	0.3	0.4	0.5	0.6	0.7	0.8	0.9	1.0
Branch factors, $\zeta_{c\text{-}b}$:											
(a) 50 mm, screwed	—	0.78	0.78	0.86	1.04	1.30	1.64	2.05	2.55	3.11	3.75
(b) 100 mm, welded	—	0.91	0.89	0.90	0.94	1.11	1.33	1.64	2.06	2.59	3.26
Straight factors, $\zeta_{c\text{-}s}$:											
(a) 50 mm, screwed	2.55	2.02	1.56	1.16	0.83	0.57	0.38	0.25	0.20	0.22	—
(b) 100 mm, welded	0.04	0	0.01	0.01	0.05	0.11	0.17	0.24	0.31	0.39	—

Table 4.34 Unequal tees, converging flow: values of ζ; for (a) d_c = 50 mm, d_s = 37 mm, d_b = 37 mm, (b) d_c = 100 mm, d_s = 100 mm, d_b = 75 mm (see Figure 4.9) (derived from Rahmeyer[29])

Type	Flow ratio, q_b/q_c										
	0	0.1	0.2	0.3	0.4	0.5	0.6	0.7	0.8	0.9	1.0
Branch factors, $\zeta_{b\text{-}c}$:											
(a) 50 mm, screwed	—	2.26	2.54	2.73	2.86	2.98	3.08	3.174	3.24	3.30	3.36
(b) 100 mm, welded	—	−1.18	−0.82	−0.60	−0.55	−0.35	0.26	0.55	1.00	1.45	1.60
Straight factors, $\zeta_{s\text{-}c}$:											
(a) 50 mm, screwed	1.59	1.60	1.60	1.61	1.62	1.63	1.64	1.66	1.68	1.73	—
(b) 100 mm, welded	0.07	0.21	0.20	0.19	0.17	0.04	−0.04	−0.06	−0.14	−0.16	—

4.10.7   Valves

The value of the pressure loss factor for a valve will depend upon the type of valve and the configuration used by the manufacturer. The following approximate data are given to help in initial design calculations. The actual values, supplied by the manufacturer, should be used as soon as they are available.

A single value can only be given for the valve in the fully open position. (The value of ζ will be infinite when the valve is closed.) For regulating valves therefore, the manufacturer will generally prefer to give a value of the valve capacity (K) for the valve fully open, supplemented by a graph of the variation of the relative capacity with relative valve opening. (The value of K will be 0 when the valve is closed.) This is more useful than ζ when establishing the valve authority and overall control characteristic. The pressure drop due to the valve is easily calculated from equation 4.13 (see section 4.4.2), i.e:

$$q_v = K\sqrt{\Delta p}$$

4.10.7.1   Globe valves

See Table 4.35. As with balancing valves, these are designed to give a better control characteristic, for use in either balancing or control. Values of ζ are for the valve fully open. These vary with the internal design of the valve so are included here only for guidance and should be used with care.

4.10.7.2   Gate valves

These should be installed for use in the fully open position. They are designed to give a clear bore when fully open. In operation, therefore, the pressure drop through them should be quite small.

Although designs may vary, the following provides a rough estimate of the pressure drop:

— spherical-seal gates: $\zeta = 0.03$

— plain-parallel gates: $\zeta = 0.3$

Table 4.35 Globe valves: approximate values of ζ (taken from Idelchik[2])

Type	Value of ζ for stated diameter / mm							
	20	40	60	80	100	150	200	300
Standard globe valve, angular dividing walls	8	4.9	—	4	4.1	4.4	4.7	5.4
Angle globe valve	—	—	2.7	2.4	2.2	1.86	1.65	1.4

4.10.7.3   Non-return valves

See Tables 4.36 and 4.37. A single value of ζ cannot be given.

For the gravity flap type, the greater the flow, the more the valve flap opens and the lower becomes the value of ζ.

Spring-loaded non-return valves also behave in a very non-linear fashion, and so the manufacturer's characteristic must be used. The data in Table 4.37, taken from part of the performance characteristic of valves of a single manufacturer, may be used for the purpose of first estimates. It does not state what flow would result in these values of K.

Table 4.36 Non-return valves: approximate values of ζ (taken from Idelchik[2])

Type	Angle of opening / degree						
	20	30	40	50	60	70	75
Non-return valve	1.7	3.2	6.6	14	30	62	90

Table 4.37 Spring-loaded non-return valves: approximate values of K

Type	Value of K (/ m^3·h^{-1}·bar$^{-0.5}$) for stated diameter / mm		
	25	38	50
Spring-loaded non-return valve	15	38	55

4.10.8   Pipe joints

4.10.8.1   Welded and screwed metal tubes

The joints do not have a great effect and will generally be small in relation to the long tube lengths used. Therefore only brief guidance is given in Table 4.38. Screwed joints give a greater pressure drop due to the appreciable discontinuity of the surface at the joint, but no clear data are available.

4.10.8.2   Plastic joints

Tubes are likely to be shorter and smaller and the effects of joints can be significant. All of the values in Table 4.38 are taken from Idelchik[2] for Re values: $1.8 \times 10^5 < Re < 5 \times 10^5$.

4.10.9   Orifices

See Figure 4.10 and Table 4.39.

Orifice plates are generally used for flow measurement but may sometimes be installed to aid the balancing of flow. Although there is a gradual pressure recovery downstream of the orifice, they do incur a permanent pressure loss and permanent pumping costs. Thus if used for balancing purposes, consideration should be given to reducing the resistance of the parallel circuit instead.

Idelchik[2] gives data for various shapes of orifice and for the combination with a sudden contraction. In Table 4.39 the data for only one are given, namely for a thin sharp-edged orifice for which Re_o (within the orifice) $\geq 10^5$ and $\delta/d_o \leq 0.0075$, where δ is the plate thickness. Note that the values of ζ are to be used with the velocity pressure in the main pipe.

ζ is given by:

$$\zeta = \left(\frac{A}{A_o}\right)^2 \left[\left(1 - \frac{A_o}{A}\right) + 0.707\left(1 - \frac{A_o}{A}\right)^{0.375}\right]^2 \quad (4.28)$$

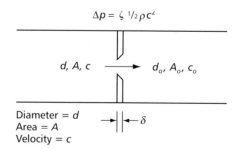

Figure 4.10 Orifice

Table 4.38 Pipe joints: values of ζ for $1.8 \times 10^5 < Re < 5 \times 10^5$ (from Idelchik[2])

Type	Pipe diameter / mm									
	50	75	100	150	200	250	300	400	500	600
Metal pipe, welded joints	—	—	—	—	0.026	—	0.0135	0.009	0.006	0.004
Plastic pipe:										
— welded joints	0.411	0.224	0.146	0.079	0.057	0.037	0.028	—	—	—
— flanged joints	0.131	0.13	0.114	0.096	0.079	0.062	0.045	—	—	—

Table 4.39 Sharp-edged orifice: values of ζ calculated from equation 4.28; for $Re_o > 10^5$ (Idelchik[2], diagram 4-14)

Type	Diameter ratio, d_o/d										
	0.15	0.2	0.25	0.3	0.35	0.4	0.5	0.6	0.7	0.8	0.9
Orifice	5565	1714	678	313	160	88.2	30.8	11.8	4.67	1.73	0.49

4.11 Pressure loss factors for ductwork components

4.11.1 General

An extensive review of pressure loss factors has been undertaken. Many sources give conflicting information. Note has been taken of recommended standard components given by HVCA[22], though in some instances no experimental data are given for these components. Best estimates are presented and are identified as such. Much of the experimental data were obtained long ago and original source data are therefore difficult to obtain. Tolerance on the published values is therefore impossible to estimate.

Technical names for components can vary but, for consistency, the HVCA labels are used.

Smith and Jones[32] found that bends having the seams against the flow gave rise to an additional 0.06 in the value of ζ in comparison with the value when the flow is with the seam. Surface effects associated with manufacture or installation could alter the values presented for ζ significantly. For flat-oval elbows the effect could give a variation of $\pm 25\%$.

No data are presented for laminar flow ($Re < 2 \times 10^3$).

The CIBSE is more confident about the data for circular ductwork than for rectangular ductwork. Only one source (Madison and Parker[31]) has been found giving evidence that rectangular ductwork has been tested, and one for square sections (Miller[37]). Much of the data for rectangular ductwork appears to have been adapted from results for circular ductwork.

For tees, ζ for branch losses and for the straight flow losses are based on use with the velocity pressure of the combined flow. The formula is included with each item as a reminder.

For tees, Eschman[24] shows that for diverging flow, the values of ζ vary very little with the branch area ratio A_b/A_c, but are very dependent on the velocity ratio c_b/c_c. However, since designers usually work with volume flow rates, much source data have been presented in terms of the relative branch flow q_b/q_c, and therefore also of A_b/A_c. This practice has been continued in this edition of Guide C.

Since publication of the 2001 edition of Guide C, the CIBSE has been able to obtain a copy of the report of the European Research Programme conducted in the 1990s[1]. The Programme investigated pressure losses in circular ductwork of two different sizes, over a considerable range of air speeds. Where appropriate, data have been amended in the light of this report. Major points to note are:

— for most components, ζ varies with diameter

— Reynolds number effects are significant.

Where data are available for a range of values of Reynolds number, and the variation of ζ is not large, the values quoted are for $Re = 2 \times 10^5$.

The radius of curvature of bends is standardised as that of the mean air stream (HVCA being the exception).

The data presented here are those which are considered most reliable. The CIBSE will continue to amend the data as more research results become available.

The data are presented as follows:

— *components for circular ductwork*: section 4.11.2

— *components for flat-oval ductwork*: section 4.11.3

— *components for rectangular ductwork*: section 4.11.4

— *transitions between circular and rectangular ductwork*: section 4.11.5.

4.11.2 Pressure loss factors for ductwork components: circular

Recent work by the United McGill Corporation[28], and by the European project[1] has shown that for bends, the value of ζ is dependent on the diameter. Work done on rectangular elbows by Madison and Parker[31], showed that size effects are appreciable for square bends of long radius and for those having a low aspect ratio (h/w).

The data for bends show that there is an optimum relative bend radius r/d. The phenomenon of the friction factor increasing with increasing radius may seem strange, but is explained by the fact that the bend inevitably becomes longer, for greater radiuses. In principle a sharper bend will introduce a greater pressure drop than a more gradual bend having less auxiliary ductwork associated with it. Although HVCA[22] suggests $r/d = 1.0$ as standard, the use of larger radius bends with $r/d = 1.5$ always results in appreciably less resistance, and is regarded as standard by ASHRAE[4]. The European Programme[1] confirms much earlier findings by Miller[25] that for medium size ducts (i.e. $d > 250$ mm) for minimum pressure loss, the optimum radius of a segmented bend is given by $r/d = 2$.

Values of ζ are now known to vary appreciably with Reynolds number. The variation is shown by Koch[38] to be greater than the variation of λ for straight ductwork, and should not therefore be ignored. Such data are provided where available.

Generally overlooked is that the direction of installation of a segmented bend matters. Smith and Jones[32], testing segmented oval bends, found that when the flow was 'against' the lap seam, the value of ζ was 23% higher than when the flow was 'with' the seam. CETIAT[39] tested segmented elbows from several different manufacturers and found ζ to vary by $\pm 25\%$, a variation which could easily be explained by the different states of projection of the butt welds on the inside. The condition and intrusion of joints might account for some of the discrepancy between certain research results.

The data are presented for the standard sizes recommended by HVCA[22].

The variation of ζ with bend angle (α) has been found by the European project[2] to be very different depending on the nature of the elbow/bend. This variation, relative to the value of ζ at 90° is given by the correction factor C_α and is shown in Figure 4.11. The rather older data of

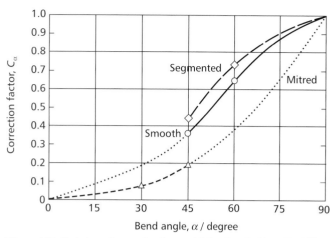

Figure 4.11 Variation of correction factor with bend angle (from Koch[38]); duct diameter d = 250 mm. Valid for $1.0 \times 10^5 < Re < 4.0 \times 10^5$; segmented and smooth bends ($r/d = 1.0$)

Miller[37] suggests that the curves for circular bends with $r/d > 1.0$ would be rather straighter. It is possible that this variation might be different for different sizes.

4.11.2.1 Smooth radius round bends (HVCA 127: 'pressed bend')

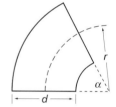

See Tables 4.40, 4.41 and 4.42.

Table 4.40 Smooth bends: variation of ζ with Reynolds number; for d = 250 mm, r/d = 1.0 (derived from European Programme Report[1] and Koch[38])

Bend angle, α / degree	Reynolds number, Re (/ 10^5)							
	0.5	1	1.5	2	2.5	3	3.5	4
30	—	—	0.048	0.044	0.044	0.043	0.043	0.042
45	0.119	0.101	0.094	0.087	0.086	0.085	0.084	0.083
60	0.221	0.187	0.175	0.161	0.160	0.158	0.156	0.155
75	0.298	0.252	0.238	0.217	0.216	0.213	0.211	0.209
90	0.343	0.290	0.271	0.250	0.248	0.245	0.242	0.240

Note: figures in italics were obtained by interpolation

Table 4.41 Smooth bends of any angle: value of ζ relative to that of a 90° bend; for d = 250 mm, r/d = 1.0; $1.0 \times 10^5 < Re < 2 \times 10^5$ (derived from the European Programme Report[1] and Koch[38])

Type	Value of ζ relative to 90° bend for stated bend angle, α				
	30°	45°	60°	75°	90°
Smooth bend	0.177	0.347	0.645	0.870	1

Note: figures in italics were obtained by interpolation

Table 4.42 Smooth 90° bends: variation of ζ with diameter; for Reynolds number = 1×10^5 (adapted from UMC[28])

Ratio, r/d	Diameter, d / mm							
	63	80	100	125	150	180	200	250
1.5	(0.35)	(0.28)	(0.21)	0.16	0.14	0.115	0.11	0.11

Notes: UMC also provides data for r/d = 1.0, but where a cross reference with Table 4.41 is possible a large contradiction is evident; these have therefore been omitted so as to avoid any confusion. Figures in parentheses were obtained by extrapolation. UMC gives the variation with diameter but gives no data on the variation with Re.

4.11.2.2 Pleated bends

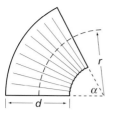

The only data available are for 90° bends, see Table 4.43. For bends of other angles (α) see Figure 4.11.

Table 4.43 Pleated 90° bends: variation of ζ with diameter; for r/d = 1.5, Reynolds number unknown (adapted from ASHRAE Handbook: *Fundamentals* 2005[4], chapter 35. © American Society of Heating, Refrigerating and Air-Conditioning Engineers Inc. (www.ashrae.org))

Type	Diameter, d / mm								
	100	125	150	180	200	250	300	350	400
Pleated 90° bend	0.57	0.495	0.43	0.375	0.34	0.28	0.26	0.11	0.25

Note: figures in italics were obtained by interpolation

4.11.2.3 Segmented bends (HVCA 128)

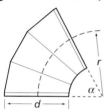

See Tables 4.44 to 4.48. Data from SMACNA[40] shows that the greater the number of segments, the smoother is the bend, and the lower is the value of ζ. Five or more segments are only likely to be used for large radius bends.

4.11.2.4 Mitred elbow (HVCA 128)

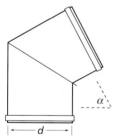

See Tables 4.49 to 4.51.

4.11.2.5 Bends and elbows in close proximity, in same plane ('gooseneck')

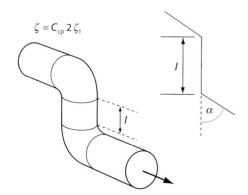

$$\zeta = C_{cp} \, 2 \zeta_1$$

See Table 4.52; ζ_1 is the factor for a single bend.

Table 4.44 Segmented 90° bends: variation of ζ with diameter; for $Re = 1 \times 10^5$ (adapted from UMC [28])

Ratio, r/d	Diameter, d / mm										
	80	100	125	150	200	250	300	400	500	800	1200
1.5 (5-segments)	(0.48)	(0.40)	(0.325)	0.28	0.23	0.20	0.18	0.16	0.14	0.12	0.12

Note: similar data are also provided for $r/d = 2.5$ (7-segments) by UMC and for $r/d = 1.0$ (5-segments) by ASHRAE but the values contradict those of Table 4.48 for $d = 250$ mm; to avoid confusion, these are omitted. Figures in parenthesis are extrapolated values.

Table 4.45 Segmented bends: variation of ζ with Reynolds number; for $r/d = 1.0$ (derived from European Programme Report[1] and Koch[38])

Diameter, d / mm	Bend angle, α / degree	Reynolds number, Re (/ 10^5)								
		0.5	1.0	1.5	2.0	2.5	3.0	4.0	5.0	6.0
250	45	0.159	0.143	0.129	0.122	0.120	0.118	0.114	—	—
	60	0.243	0.218	0.197	0.186	0.183	0.180	0.175	—	—
	75	*0.303*	*0.272*	*0.245*	*0.232*	*0.228*	*0.225*	*0.217*	—	—
	90	0.340	0.305	0.275	0.260	0.256	0.252	0.244	—	—
400	45	0.12	0.105	0.09	0.083	0.078	0.073	0.068	0.064	0.064
400	60	0.21	0.183	0.170	0.160	0.152	0.147	0.142	0.135	0.13
400	90	—	—	—	0.20★	—	—	—	—	—

★ estimated value

Note: figures in italics were obtained by interpolation

Table 4.46 Segmented bends of any angle: value of ζ relative to that of a 90° bend; for $d = 250$ mm, $r/d = 1.0$; $1.0 \times 10^5 < Re < 4 \times 10^5$ (derived from the European Programme Report[1] and Koch[38])

Type	Value of ζ relative to 90° bend for stated bend angle, α			
	45°	60°	75°	90°
Segmented bend	0.44	0.73	*0.90*	1

Note: figure in italics was obtained by interpolation

Table 4.47 Segmented bends (4 segments): variation of ζ with relative bend ratio (r/d); for $\alpha = 90°$, $d = 250$ mm; $Re = 2 \times 10^5$ (adapted from the European Programme Report[1])

Type	Relative bend ratio, r/d						
	0.7	1.0	1.5	2.0	2.5	3.0	5.0
Segmented bend (4 segments)	0.44	0.26	0.20	0.195	0.21	0.23	0.31

Table 4.48 Segmented bends: variation of ζ with Reynolds number, in terms of a multiplying factor C_{Re} to be applied to the values of Table 4.45; for $\alpha = 90°$, $d = 250$ mm (adapted from the European Programme Report[1])

Aspect ratio, r/d	Multiplying factor, C_{Re}, for stated Reynolds number, Re / 10^5						
	0.5	1.0	1.5	2.0	2.5	3.0	4.0
0.7	1.30	1.15	1.05	1.0	0.95	0.95	0.95
1.0	1.31	1.17	1.08	1.0	0.93	0.92	0.93
1.5	1.44	1.24	1.10	1.0	0.92	0.87	0.84
≥ 2.0	1.51	1.24	1.08	1.0	0.92	0.86	0.87

Table 4.50 Mitred elbows: variation of ζ with Reynolds number; for $d = 250$ mm (derived from European Programme Report[1] and Koch[38])

Diam., d / mm	Bend angle, α / degree	Reynolds number, Re (/ 10^5)						
		0.5	1.0	1.5	2.0	2.5	3.0	4.0
250	30	0.131	0.121	0.115	0.112	0.110	0.109	0.107
	45	0.269	0.253	0.239	0.233	0.229	0.227	0.223
	60	*0.526*	*0.488*	*0.461*	*0.450*	*0.448*	*0.432*	*0.431*
	75	*0.901*	*0.835*	*0.790*	*0.770*	*0.757*	*0.750*	*0.737*
	90	1.38	1.28	1.23	1.18	1.16	1.15	1.13
400	30	0.08	0.061	0.045	0.039	0.035	0.034	0.032

Note: figures in italics were obtained by interpolation

Table 4.51 Mitred elbows of any angle: values of ζ relative to that of a 90° elbow; for $d = 250$ mm; $1.0 \times 10^5 < Re < 4 \times 10^5$ (derived from European Programme Report[1] and Koch[38])

Type	Value of ζ relative to that of a 90° elbow, for stated elbow angle, α / degree					
	22.5	30	45	60	75	90
Mitred elbow	*0.05*	0.095	0.197	*0.381*	*0.653*	1

Note: figures in italics were obtained by interpolation

Table 4.49 Mitred elbows: variation of ζ with diameter; Re unknown (derived from UMC[28])

Bend angle, α / degree	Diameter, d / mm										
	80	100	125	150	200	250	300	400	500	800	1200
90	(1.44)	(1.4)	(1.36)	1.31	1.26	1.23	1.20	1.17	1.15	1.14	1.12

Note: figures in parentheses were obtained by extrapolation

Table 4.52 Two bends in close proximity in the same plane; values of interaction factor C_{cp}; for $d = 250$ mm, $r/d = 1$ (from European Programme Report[1] and Koch[38])

Bend angle, α, and type	Ratio, l/d	Value of C_{cp} for stated Reynolds number, $Re / 10^5$						
		0.5	1.0	1.5	2.0	2.5	3.0	4.0
30° mitred	$1 < l/d < 5$	0.83	0.82	0.82	0.82	0.82	0.81	0.80
30° smooth	$l/d = 1$	—	—	0.95	0.88	0.84	0.73	0.73
	$3 < l/d < 5$	—	—	1.12	1.02	0.93	0.87	0.79
45° segmented	$1 < l/d < 5$	1.45	1.16	1.10	1.07	1.04	1.02	0.96
45° smooth	$1 < l/d < 5$	0.96	0.99	0.97	0.92	0.88	0.84	0.85
60° segmented	$1 < l/d < 5$	1.03	1.11	1.10	1.07	1.08	1.09	1.09
60° smooth	$1 < l/d < 5$	1.05	0.94	0.93	0.87	0.86	0.84	0.83
75° segmented	$l/d = 1$	1.11	1.11	1.04	1.02	1.04	0.99	1.01
	$1 < l/d < 5$	1.10	0.97	0.93	0.93	0.95	0.93	0.81
75° smooth	$1 < l/d < 5$	1.07	1.00	0.96	0.92	0.92	0.91	0.89
90° smooth and segmented	$1 < l/d < 5$	1.07	0.96	0.95	1.02	1.04	1.02	1.10

Note: factors for close proximity C_{cp} are applied to the values of ζ_1 obtained from Tables 4.40 to 4.51, as appropriate.

The data given in Table 4.52 do not include the pressure drop of the length of separation. The separation (l) should be added to the length of straight ductwork of the same size.

4.11.2.6 Bends and elbows in close proximity, through perpendicular plane

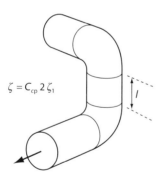

$$\zeta = C_{cp}\, 2\,\zeta_1$$

See Table 4.53; ζ_1 is the factor for a single bend.

The data given in Table 4.53 do not include the pressure drop of the length of separation. The separation l should be added to the length of straight ductwork of the same size.

Table 4.53 Two 90° bends in close proximity, out of plane: values of interaction factor C_{cp}; for $d = 250$ mm, $r/d = 1$ (derived from European Programme Report[1])

Type	Ratio, l/d	Value of C_{cp} for stated Reynolds number, Re (/ 10^5)						
		0.5	1.0	1.5	2.0	2.5	3.0	4.0
Smooth	1	1.14	0.91	0.83	0.82	0.83	0.83	0.84
	3	1.04	0.95	0.90	0.89	0.89	0.88	0.87
	5	1.16	0.96	0.90	0.89	0.89	0.89	0.89
Segmented	1	0.87	0.93	0.98	1.04	1.10	1.09	1.01
	3	0.94	0.99	1.04	1.09	1.15	1.15	1.02
	5	0.98	1.05	1.08	1.14	1.19	1.20	1.08

4.11.2.7 Symmetrical expansion (HVCA taper 132)

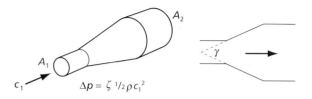

$$\Delta p = \zeta\, \tfrac{1}{2}\rho\, c_1^2$$

Laminar flow

For laminar flow through expansions of circular cross section, Idelchik[2] gives the following relationship, valid for $\zeta \leq 40°$:

$$\zeta = \frac{A}{Re} \tag{4.29}$$

where:

$$A = \frac{20\,(A_2/A_1)^{0.33}}{(\tan \gamma)^{0.75}} \tag{4.30}$$

Turbulent flow

See Tables 4.54 and 4.55.

For turbulent flow, Idelchik[2] reports that values of ζ are very dependent on flow separation which in turn is dependent on upstream flow conditions giving a velocity profile which may be symmetrical or asymmetrical. For small angles of divergence (γ) the length of travel of an unseparated core of flow will depend very much on the degree of asymmetry. Thus for small values of γ, prediction of the pressure drop becomes more difficult. Table 4.54 shows that even small values of γ result in appreciable pressure drop, and that abrupt expansions ($\gamma = 180°$) do not cause the pressure drop to be as great as might have been expected.

Contrary to the data of Idelchik[2], reproduced in other publications, the European Programme[1] shows that ζ

Table 4.54 Symmetrical expansion: values of ζ with no variation with Re; for $A_2/A_1 = 2.44$, $d_1 = 160$ mm, $d_2 = 250$ mm (derived from European Programme Report[1])

Type	Divergence angle, γ					
	30°	60°	90°	120°	150°	180°
Symmetrical expansion	0.168	0.280	0.353	*0.40*	*0.45*	0.49

Note: values in italics were obtained by interpolation

Table 4.55 Symmetrical expansion: values of ζ for various divergence angles (derived from Miller[37])

Divergence angle, γ	Area ratio, A_2/A_1							
	1.2	1.4	1.6	1.8	2.0	2.44	3.0	4.0
40°	0.058	0.095	0.13	0.17	0.20	—	0.38	0.55
30°	0.055	0.082	0.104	0.14	0.17	0.168*	0.31	0.49
20°	0.050	0.072	0.091	0.11	0.125	—	0.21	0.40

* value from the European Programme Report[1], see Table 4.54

does not vary with Reynolds number. The close agreement between the values Miller[37] and those of the European Programme enable Miller's data to be used for other expansion ratios, see Table 4.55.

The European Programme also tested abrupt expansions of different offsets. Even the maximum possible offset did not make a significant difference.

4.11.2.8 Symmetrical contractions, short tapers (HVCA 132 and 133)

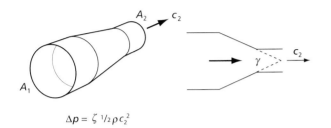

$$\Delta p = \zeta \; {}^{1}\!/_{2} \rho c_2{}^2$$

See Tables 4.56 and 4.57. It is clear from Table 4.56 that for contractions the values of ζ are small, but their relative variation with Re is appreciable. For other values of A_1/A_2 the only available data are from ASHRAE, but of unknown Reynolds number, see Table 4.57. There is an unresolved conflict between these two sets of data, especially evident for $\gamma = 90°$.

Table 4.56 Symmetrical contraction: values of ζ for various convergence angles; for $A_1/A_2 = 2.44$, $d_1 = 250$ mm, $d_2 = 160$ mm (derived from European Programme Report[1])

Convergence angle, γ	Reynolds number, Re (/ 10^5)							
	1.2	1.5	2.0	2.5	3.0	4.0	5.0	6.0
90°	0.084	0.075	0.059	0.048	0.042	0.040	0.044	0.051
60°	0.084	0.072	0.051	0.036	0.029	0.027	0.031	0.040
30°	0.084	0.073	0.054	0.039	0.033	0.030	0.034	0.045

Table 4.57 Symmetrical contraction: values of ζ; Reynolds number unknown (adapted from ASHRAE Handbook: *Fundamentals* 2005[4], chapter 35. © American Society of Heating, Refrigerating and Air-Conditioning Engineers Inc. (www.ashrae.org))

Ratio, A_1/A_2	Convergence angle, γ							
	15°	30°	45°	60°	90°	120°	150°	180°
2	0.05	0.05	0.06	0.06	0.12	0.18	0.24	0.26
4	0.04	0.04	0.06	0.07	0.17	0.27	0.35	0.41
6	0.04	0.04	0.06	0.07	0.18	0.28	0.36	0.42
10	0.05	0.05	0.07	0.08	0.19	0.29	0.37	0.43

4.11.2.9 Offset tapers (HVCA 131), contractions and expansions

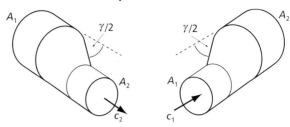

The European Programme[1] tested several different offsets for sudden expansions, $\gamma = 180°$, but found only a trivial difference from a symetrical expansion. It is reasonable to suppose that there would not have been a significant difference for offset sudden contractions. In the absence of other specific data concerning offset tapers, it seems reasonable to suppose no significant differences in the value of ζ from those given in Tables 4.54 to 4.57.

The angle γ to be used should be twice the angle of the part deviating most.

4.11.2.10 Bend coupled to short symmetrical expansion

The European project carried out no tests on bends coupled to contractions; only on bends close-coupled to expansions as shown below.

$$\Delta p_{tot} = \zeta_{tot} \; {}^{1}\!/_{2} \rho c_1{}^2$$

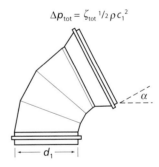

See Table 4.58. The values of ζ_{tot} for the combined assembly of bend plus expansion, always exceeds the sum of the values of ζ for the two individual components. Although the individual value of ζ for a bend varies considerably with Re, with the close-coupling, it is the effect of the expansion which dominates. ζ_{tot} is found to vary very little with Re.

Values for 90° bends were deemed unreliable. The figures in italics, are 'best advice' only.

Table 4.58 Segmented bend coupled to a symmetrical expansion: values of ζ_{tot}; for $d_1 = 250$ mm, $d_2 = 400$ mm, $A_2/A_1 = 2.44$, $r/d = 1.0$, Re / 10^5 (from the European Programme Report[1])

Bend angle, and type	Included angle of taper, γ			
	30°	60°	90°	180°
30° mitred	0.805	0.824	0.872	0.925
45°	0.645	0.815	0.834	0.925
60°	0.670	0.888	0.990	1.081
90°	*0.85*	*1.09*	*1.18*	*1.25*

4.11.2.11 Two bends coupled by a short symmetrical contraction, in same plane

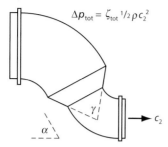

$$\Delta p_{tot} = \zeta_{tot} \, {}^{1}/_{2} \rho c_2^2$$

See Table 4.59. γ is the total included angle of the taper.

4.11.2.12 Two bends coupled by a short symmetrical expansion, in same plane

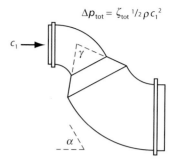

$$\Delta p_{tot} = \zeta_{tot} \, {}^{1}/_{2} \rho c_1^2$$

See Table 4.60. γ is the total included angle of the taper.

Table 4.59 Two bends coupled by a symmetrical contraction in same plane; values of ζ_{tot}; for $r/d = 1.0$ (derived from the European Programme Report[1])

Type	Taper angle, γ	Bend angle, α, and Reynolds number, Re									
		2 × 30°		2 × 45°		2 × 60°		2 × 75°		2 × 90°	
		1×10^5	2×10^5	1×10^5	2×10^5	1×10^5	2×10^5	1×10^5	2×10^5	1×10^5	2×10^5
(a) Contraction from $d_1 = 250$ mm, to $d_2 = 160$ mm; $A_1/A_2 = 2.44$											
Smooth*	30°	0.115	0.096	*0.160*	*0.134*	0.206	*0.199*	0.286	0.273	0.347	0.333
	60°	*0.115*	*0.097*	0.163	0.138	0.208	0.199	0.289	0.277	0.349	*0.338*
	90°	0.116	0.098	0.189	0.143	0.208	0.200	0.295	0.281	0.367	0.342
Segmented	30°	—	—	—	—	*0.250*	*0.263*	—	—	*0.455*	*0.465*
	60°	—	—	—	—	0.257	0.271	—	—	0.263	0.475
	90°	—	—	—	—	0.271	0.288	—	—	0.473	0.483
(b) Contraction from $d_1 = 400$ mm, to $d_2 = 250$ mm; $A_1/A_2 = 2.56$											
Mitred	30°	0.184	0.136	—	—	—	—	—	—	—	—
	60°	0.188	0.148	—	—	—	—	—	—	—	—
	90°	0.188	*0.150*	—	—	—	—	—	—	—	—
Segmented	30°	—	—	0.172	0.135	*0.300*	0.239	0.298	0.260	0.426	0.376
	60°	—	—	*0.192*	0.140	0.306	0.248	0.335	0.277	0.432	0.393
	90°	—	—	0.212	0.166	0.324	0.260	0.353	0.283	0.452	0.409

Note: figures in italics are 'best advice' figures, replacing experimental values which were much out of step, reflecting experimental problems.

Table 4.60 Two bends coupled by a symmetrical expansion in same plane; values of ζ_{tot}; for $r/d = 1.0$ (derived from the European Programme Report[1])

Type	Taper angle, γ	Bend angle, α, and Reynolds number, Re									
		2 × 30°		2 × 45°		2 × 60°		2 × 75°		2 × 90°	
		1×10^5	2×10^5	1×10^5	2×10^5	1×10^5	2×10^5	1×10^5	2×10^5	1×10^5	2×10^5
(a) Expansion from $d_1 = 160$ mm, to $d_2 = 250$ mm; $A_2/A_1 = 2.44$											
Smooth*	30°	0.513	0.495	0.503	0.482	0.417	0.373	0.475	0.436	0.465	0.420
	60°	*0.547*	0.503	0.717	0.685	0.654	0.588	0.634	0.582	0.589	0.590
	90°	0.562	0.529	0.761	0.743	0.755	0.758	0.743	0.687	0.717	0.671
Segmented	30°	—	—	—	—	0.916	0.854	—	—	0.742	0.748
	60°	—	—	—	—	—	—	—	—	0.830	0.475
	90°	—	—	—	—	0.849	0.819	—	—	0.889	0.876
(b) Expansion from $d_1 = 250$ mm, to $d_2 = 400$ mm; $A_2/A_1 = 2.56$											
Mitred	30°	0.727	0.731	—	—	—	—	—	—	—	—
	60°	0.746	0.735	—	—	—	—	—	—	—	—
	90°	0.760	0.739	—	—	—	—	—	—	—	—
Segmented	30°	—	—	0.722	0.730	0.750	0.740	0.580	0.538	0.625	0.624
	60°	—	—	0.855	0.844	1.072	1.010	0.805	0.769	0.890	0.870
	90°	—	—	1.154	1.120	1.145	1.106	0.856	0.816	1.012	0.921

Note: figures in italics are 'best advice' figures, replacing experimental values which were much out of step, reflecting experimental problems.

4.11.2.13 Two 90° bends coupled by a short symmetrical contraction, out of plane

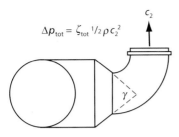

$$\Delta p_{tot} = \zeta_{tot} \,{}^1\!/_2 \rho c_2^2$$

See Table 4.61. γ is the total included angle of the taper.

Table 4.61 Two 90° bends coupled by a symmetrical contraction, out of plane; values of ζ_{tot} for $r/d = 1.0$ (derived from the European Programme Report[1])

Taper angle, γ	Type and Reynolds number, Re			
	Smooth		Segmented	
	1×10^5	2×10^5	1×10^5	2×10^5
(a) Contraction from $d_1 = 250$ mm, to $d_2 = 160$ mm; $A_2/A_1 = 2.44$				
30°	0.309	0.308	0.460	0.466
60°	0.304	0.303	0.441	0.454
90°	0.323	0.303	0.450	0.458
(b) Contraction from $d_1 = 400$ mm, to $d_2 = 250$ mm; $A_2/A_1 = 2.56$				
30°	—	—	0.461	0.406
60°	—	—	0.428	0.380
90°	—	—	0.460	0.403

4.11.2.14 Two 90° bends coupled by a short symmetrical expansion, out of plane

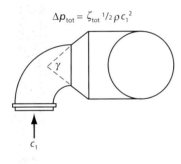

$$\Delta p_{tot} = \zeta_{tot} \,{}^1\!/_2 \rho c_1^2$$

See Table 4.62. γ is the total included angle of the taper.

Table 4.62 Two 90° bends coupled by a symmetrical expansion, out of plane; values of ζ_{tot} for $r/d = 1.0$ (derived from the European Programme Report[1])

Taper angle, γ	Type and Reynolds number, Re			
	Smooth		Segmented	
	1×10^5	2×10^5	1×10^5	2×10^5
(a) Expansion from $d_1 = 160$ mm, to $d_2 = 250$ mm; $A_2/A_1 = 2.44$				
30°	0.454	0.423	0.702	0.721
60°	0.560	0.544	0.783	0.771
90°	0.715	0.673	0.834	0.817
(b) Expansion from $d_1 = 250$ mm, to $d_2 = 400$ mm; $A_2/A_1 = 2.56$				
30°	—	—	0.616	0.604
60°	—	—	0.793	0.807
90°	—	—	0.946	0.948

4.11.2.15 90° branch tees, circular from circular (HVCA 139) and pressed equal tee (HVCA 130)

(a) Converging flows ($A_c = A_s$)

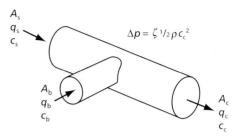

$$\Delta p = \zeta \,{}^1\!/_2 \rho c_c^2$$

See Tables 4.63 and 4.64. Re_c is based on the value for the combined flow.

It is now evident that the value of both the straight factor and the branch factor vary with the size of the tee (i.e. with the diameters of the main parts of the tee: A_c, A_s), and with Reynolds number. Values of the straight factor $\zeta_{s\text{-}c}$ appear generally to vary little with Re and not in a regular manner. In the interests of simplicity, the values of $\zeta_{s\text{-}c}$ given in Table 4.63 are mean values over the range $1 \times 10^5 < Re_c < 5 \times 10^5$. Values for $Re_c = 0.5 \times 10^5$ can be as much as 25% greater.

It is now evident that the value of the branch factor $\zeta_{b\text{-}c}$ varies with the size of the tee (i.e. with the diameters of the main parts of the tee: d_s, d_c), and with Reynolds number. For $Re > 1 \times 10^5$, the variation is not very great. In the interests of simplicity, the values of $\zeta_{b\text{-}c}$ given in Table 4.64 are mean values over the range $1 \times 10^5 < Re_c < 2 \times 10^5$. Values for $Re_c = 0.5 \times 10^5$ are generally about 8% greater[33].

(b) Diverging flows ($A_c = A_s$)

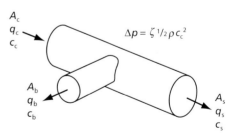

$$\Delta p = \zeta \,{}^1\!/_2 \rho c_c^2$$

See Tables 4.65 and 4.66. Values of the straight factor $\zeta_{s\text{-}c}$ appear generally to vary little with Reynolds number, and not in a regular manner. Mean values are therefore given below. Any possible variation with diameter is inconclusive at present.

It is now evident that the value of the branch factor $\zeta_{s\text{-}b}$ varies with the size of the tee (i.e. with the diameters of the main parts of the tee: d_c, d_s), and with Reynolds number. Re is based on the value for the combined flow. For $Re_c > 1 \times 10^5$, the variation is not very great. In the interests of simplicity, the values of ζ given in Table 4.66 are mean values over the range $1.0 \times 10^5 < Re_c < 5 \times 10^5$. Values for $Re_c = 0.5 \times 10^5$ are generally about 8% greater.

Table 4.63 90° tees, converging flow: values for the straight factor $\zeta_{s\text{-}c}$ (derived from the European Programme Report[1] and Koch[38])

Area ratio, A_b/A_c	Relative straight flow, q_s/q_c									
	0.1	0.2	0.3	0.4	0.5	0.6	0.7	0.8	0.9	1.0
(a) Main duct size: $d_s = d_c = 400$ mm										
0.0625★	0.45	0.60	0.80	1.1	1.4	0.85	0.55	0.25	0.04	0
0.10	1.2	1.1	1.15	1.08	1.0	0.60	0.35	0.22	0.10	0
0.1406★	1.65	1.5	1.25	1.0	0.74	0.50	0.31	0.20	0.09	0
0.20	1.4	1.3	1.10	0.83	0.62	0.43	0.285	0.19	0.10	0
0.25★	1.0	1.0	0.86	0.72	0.55	0.41	0.27	0.18	0.10	0
0.30	0.80	0.75	0.70	0.60	0.47	0.38	0.26	0.175	0.10	0
0.3906★	0.56	0.54	0.47	0.42	0.34	0.30	0.24	0.17	0.10	0
(b) Main duct size: $d_s = d_c = 250$ mm										
0.16†	1.55	1.7	1.6	1.53	1.09	0.87	0.56	0.4	0.2	0.02
0.2	1.50	1.5	1.4	1.2	1.0	0.75	0.55	0.39	0.21	0.02
0.3	1.3	1.2	1.05	0.90	0.75	0.60	0.47	0.36	0.22	0.03
0.36†	1.18	1.08	0.93	0.78	0.67	0.55	0.47	0.60	0.30	0.04
0.4	1.12	1.02	0.9	0.79	0.66	0.53	0.43	0.335	0.215	0.04
0.5	0.98	0.90	0.80	0.73	0.62	0.52	0.415	0.32	0.21	0.05
0.6	0.87	0.80	0.74	0.68	0.59	0.51	0.405	0.305	0.20	0.05
0.64†	0.84	0.78	0.68	0.66	0.58	0.49	0.43	0.31	0.19	0.05
0.7	0.81	0.75	0.71	0.66	0.58	0.50	0.40	0.30	0.17	0.05
0.8	0.78	0.74	0.70	0.65	0.58	0.50	0.40	0.30	0.14	0.06
1.00†	0.74	0.72	0.70	0.64	0.58	0.49	0.41	0.30	0.19	0.07

★ Values obtained using a main duct size: $d_s = d_c = 400$ mm; other values obtained by interpolation
† Values obtained using a main duct size: $d_s = d_c = 250$ mm; other values obtained by interpolation

Table 4.64 90° tees, converging flow: values for the branch factor $\zeta_{b\text{-}c}$; for $1 \times 10^5 < Re < 2 \times 10^5$ (derived from the European Programme Report[1] and Koch[38])

Area ratio, A_b/A_c	Relative branch flow, q_b/q_c									
	0.1	0.2	0.3	0.4	0.5	0.6	0.7	0.8	0.9	1.0
(a) Main duct size: $d_s = d_c = 400$ mm										
0.0625★	1.5	10	22	40	69	100	140	180	230	283
0.1	1.0	3.5	7.5	15	25	42	60	80	102	125
0.1406★	0.10	1.0	3.3	6.5	10.5	16	22.6	30.4	39.7	49.4
0.20	0	0.50	1.8	3.3	5.0	7.5	11	15	19	24
0.25★	0	0.43	1.1	2.0	3.3	5.1	7.2	9.5	12.2	14.7
0.30	0.10	0.30	0.70	1.3	2.0	3.0	4.4	6.1	8.0	10
0.3906★	−0.20	0	0.30	0.73	1.3	2.0	2.85	3.76	4.8	6.0
(b) Main duct size: $d_s = d_c = 250$ mm										
0.16†	0.05	1.2	3.24	6.1	10.4	15.5	22.5	30.3	39	46.7
0.2	0.40	0.85	2.0	3.5	6.1	9.6	13	17	23	30
0.3	0.40	0.30	0.90	1.8	2.8	4.0	5.2	6.8	8.2	9.8
0.36†	0	0.21	0.65	1.20	1.91	2.83	3.89	5.22	6.61	7.74
0.4	−0.20	0.17	0.55	1.0	1.6	2.3	3.2	4.35	5.2	6.3
0.5	0	0.13	0.40	0.78	1.15	1.6	2.3	3.0	3.8	4.5
0.6	0	0.85	0.30	0.61	0.9	1.2	1.7	2.2	2.6	3.0
0.64†	−0.12	0.07	0.27	0.55	0.82	1.10	1.43	1.87	2.26	2.61
0.7	−0.10	0.05	0.25	0.50	0.72	1.0	1.3	1.7	2.0	2.3
0.8	0	0.05	0.20	0.42	0.63	0.9	1.2	1.5	1.72	1.93
1.00†	−0.59	-0.24	0.15	0.36	0.56	0.76	0.95	1.07	1.19	1.26

★ Values obtained using a main duct size: $d_s = d_c = 400$ mm; other values obtained by interpolation
† Values obtained using a main duct size: $d_s = d_c = 250$ mm; other values obtained by interpolation

Table 4.65 90° tees, diverging flow; values for the straight factor $\zeta_{c\text{-}s}$ (derived from the European Programme Report[1] and Koch[38])

Diam. d_c, $(= d_s)$ / mm	Relative straight flow, q_s/q_c									
	0.1	0.2	0.3	0.4	0.5	0.6	0.7	0.8	0.9	1.0
250	0.24	0.20	0.14	0.08	0.04	0.01	−0.01	0	0.03	0.11
400	0.29	0.22	0.15	0.09	0.04	0.01	−0.01	−0.03	−0.02	0

Table 4.66 90° tees, diverging flow: values for the branch factor $\zeta_{\text{c-b}}$ (derived from the European Programme Report[1] and Koch[38])

Area ratio, A_b/A_c	Relative branch flow, q_b/q_c									
	0.1	0.2	0.3	0.4	0.5	0.6	0.7	0.8	0.9	1.0
(a) Main duct size: $d_s = d_c = 400$ mm										
0.0625★	2.0	3.0	3.6	4.2	4.5	6.0	9.0	12.0	16	21
0.1	1.5	1.8	2.4	3.0	3.4	4.5	6.0	8.1	10.4	12.5
0.1406★	1.25	1.3	1.7	2.2	2.7	3.4	4.3	5.4	6.6	7.8
0.20	1.1	1.2	1.4	1.65	2.0	2.3	2.7	3.3	3.75	4.5
0.25★	1.08	1.2	1.3	1.4	1.65	1.75	2.0	2.3	2.65	3.1
0.30	1.05	1.1	1.18	1.25	1.37	1.48	1.6	1.8	2.05	2.4
0.3906★	0.99	0.99	1.0	1.02	1.05	1.1	1.18	1.3	1.45	1.6
(b) Main duct size: $d_s = d_c = 250$ mm										
0.16†	1.6	2.3	3.0	4.0	5.7	7.9	10	13	16.8	21.5
0.2	1.45	2.0	2.5	3.3	4.4	6.5	7.6	9.0	10.5	14
0.3	1.25	1.5	1.8	2.2	2.7	3.3	4.1	5.0	6.0	7.0
0.36†	1.18	1.3	1.48	1.8	2.16	2.6	3.1	3.7	4.4	5.0
0.4	1.14	1.2	1.35	1.6	1.9	2.2	2.6	3.1	3.8	4.4
0.5	1.06	1.05	1.15	1.2	1.4	1.7	1.9	2.2	2.5	3.0
0.6	1.01	1.01	1.05	1.04	1.15	1.3	1.5	1.65	1.8	2.2
0.64†	1.0	1.0	1.0	1.0	1.1	1.2	1.35	1.5	1.7	2.0
0.7	0.98	0.98	0.98	0.98	1.05	1.1	1.2	1.3	1.5	1.7
0.8	0.97	0.97	0.97	0.97	1.0	1.0	1.1	1.15	1.3	1.4
1.00†	0.97	0.95	0.95	0.95	0.95	0.95	1.0	1.08	1.15	1.24

★ Values obtained using a main duct size: $d_s = d_c = 400$ mm; other values obtained by interpolation
† Values obtained using a main duct size: $d_s = d_c = 250$ mm; other values obtained by interpolation

4.11.2.16 Angle branch tees (HVCA 138)

(a) Converging flows

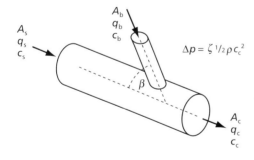

$$\Delta p = \zeta \tfrac{1}{2}\rho c_c^2$$

There are few data available for this simple component.

For the straight factor $\zeta_{\text{s-c}}$, the values given in section 4.11.2.21 may be used. These data are for an angle tee with a bend on the branch, but the bend on the branch is not expected to greatly affect the values of the straight factor.

Table 4.67 Angle branch tee, converging flow: values for branch factor $\zeta_{\text{b-c}}$ (derived from SMACNA[40] and partially confirmed by CETIAT[39])

Ratio, A_b/A_c	Relative branch flow, q_b/q_c									
	0.1	0.2	0.3	0.4	0.5	0.6	0.7	0.8	0.9	1
0.1	0.22	3.1	8	—	—	—	—	—	—	—
0.2	−0.37	0.31	1.5	3.2	5.3	—	—	—	—	—
0.3	—	−0.12	0.38	1.11	2.1	3.2	4.6	6.2	8	—
0.4	—	−0.21	0.08	0.44	1.02	1.6	2.4	3.2	4.3	5.4
0.6	—	—	−0.09	0.07	0.28	0.53	0.93	1.3	1.7	2.2
0.8	—	—	—	0.02	0.13	0.26	0.43	0.62	0.9	1.1
1	—	—	—	0.05	0.11	0.18	0.28	0.4	0.53	0.69

For the straight factor, $\zeta_{\text{s-c}}$:

— for $\beta = 60°$, use Table 4.77
— for $\beta = 45°$, use Table 4.79
— for $\beta = 30°$, use Table 4.81
— for $\beta = 15°$, use Table 4.83.

For the branch factor, see Table 4.67.

(b) Diverging flows

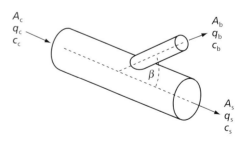

For the straight factor, $\zeta_{\text{s-c}}$, the values in section 4.11.2.22 may be used. These data are for an angle tee with a bend on the branch, but the bend on the branch is not expected to greatly affect the values of the straight factor.

For the straight factor:

— for $\beta = 60°$, use Table 4.85
— for $\beta = 45°$, use Table 4.87
— for $\beta = 30°$, use Table 4.89
— for $\beta = 15°$, use Table 4.91.

See Table 4.68 for the branch factor $\zeta_{\text{c-b}}$.

Table 4.68 Angle branch tee, diverging flow: values for branch factor $\zeta_{c\text{-}b}$ (derived from SMACNA[40])

Angle, α	Ratio, A_b/A_c	Relative branch flow, q_b/q_c								
		0.1	0.2	0.3	0.4	0.5	0.6	0.7	0.8	0.9
30°	0.1	0.28	1.5	—	—	—	—	—	—	—
	0.2	0.4	0.26	0.58	1.3	2.5	—	—	—	—
	0.4	0.59	0.33	0.21	0.20	0.27	0.40	0.62	0.92	1.3
	0.6	0.69	0.46	0.31	0.21	0.17	0.16	0.2	0.28	0.39
	0.8	0.75	0.55	0.4	0.28	0.21	0.16	0.15	0.16	0.19
45°	0.1	0.6	2.1	—	—	—	—	—	—	—
	0.2	0.56	0.56	1	1.8	—	—	—	—	—
	0.4	0.66	0.47	0.4	0.43	0.54	0.69	0.95	1.3	1.7
	0.6	0.74	0.56	0.44	0.37	0.35	0.36	0.43	0.54	0.68
	0.8	0.78	0.62	0.49	0.4	0.34	0.31	0.32	0.35	0.4
60°	0.1	1	2.9	—	—	—	—	—	—	—
	0.2	0.77	0.96	1.6	2.5	—	—	—	—	—
	0.4	0.76	0.65	0.65	0.74	0.89	1.1	1.4	1.8	2.3
	0.6	0.81	0.68	0.6	0.58	0.58	0.61	0.72	0.87	1.1
	0.8	0.83	0.71	0.62	0.56	0.52	0.50	0.53	0.60	0.68

4.11.2.17   90° tees, with enlargement taper for combined flow; converging flow

$$\Delta p = \zeta \tfrac{1}{2} \rho c_c^2$$

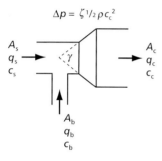

See Tables 4.69 and 4.70. Unusually these tables show lower values of ζ for the smaller tee than for the larger, even when taking into account the slightly different enlargement ratios. The two sizes were investigated by different research establishments. The data for the smaller size was contributed to the European Programme[1] by the National Engineering Laboratory (NEL) whose results were frequently found to give lower values than those of other contributors where a component had also been tested by another contributor. There is thus a strong possibility that the values listed below, for the smaller tee, may be on the low side.

Table 4.69 90° tees with expansion taper, converging flow: values for the straight factor $\zeta_{s\text{-}c}$; for $Re_c = 2 \times 10^5$ and correction for Reynolds number (derived from the European Programme Report[1])

Taper angle, γ	Relative straight flow, q_s/q_c								
	0.2	0.3	0.4	0.5	0.6	0.7	0.8	0.9	1.0
(a) Equal tees: 250/250/250 mm with expansion to 400 mm									
30°	5.4	5.4	5.2	5.0	4.8	4.4	3.7	2.7	1.4
60°	7.4	7.2	7.1	6.9	6.5	5.8	4.9	3.8	2.2
90°	8.0	8.0	7.9	7.7	7.2	6.4	5.5	4.3	2.8
(b) Equal tees: 160/160/160 mm with expansion to 250 mm									
30°	*5.0*	5.0	5.0	4.9	4.8	4.5	3.8	2.8	1.7
60°	6.1	6.1	6.0	5.9	5.7	5.3	4.4	3.4	2.2
90°	7.0	6.9	6.8	6.6	6.2	5.7	4.8	3.8	2.5
(c) Unequal tees: 250/200/250 mm with expansion to 400 mm									
30°	*5.0*	5.5	5.8	5.8	5.4	5.0	4.2	3.0	1.4
60°	6.6	7.2	7.4	7.4	7.0	6.4	5.3	3.9	2.1
90°	7.6	8.1	8.3	8.2	7.8	7.0	6.0	4.6	2.8
(d) Unequal tees: 160/100/160 mm with expansion to 250 mm									
30°	5.6	5.6	5.3	5.0	4.6	4.0	3.4	2.6	1.4
60°	*6.3*	6.3	6.3	6.2	5.8	5.2	4.4	3.4	1.9
90°	7.5	7.5	7.2	6.8	6.4	5.7	4.8	3.7	2.3

Diam. / mm	Correction factor for stated Reynolds number, Re_c				
	0.8×10^5	1.0×10^5	1.5×10^5	2.0×10^5	2.5×10^5
250/250	1.06	1.05	1.03	1.0	0.94
160/160	1.06	1.06	1.03	1.0	0.95
160/100		No correction required			

Note: area ratios as follows:
(a) $A_b/A_c = 1.0, A_c/A_s = 2.56$
(b) $A_b/A_c = 1.0, A_c/A_s = 2.44$
(c) $A_b/A_c = 0.64, A_c/A_s = 2.56$
(d) $A_b/A_c = 0.391, A_c/A_s = 2.44$

Figures in italics were obtained by extrapolation

Table 4.70 90° tees with expansion taper, converging flow: values for the branch factor $\zeta_{s\text{-}c}$; for $Re_c = 2 \times 10^5$ and correction for Reynolds number (derived from the European Programme Report[1])

Angle, γ	Relative branch flow, q_b/q_c									
	0.1	0.2	0.3	0.4	0.5	0.6	0.7	0.8	0.9	1.0
(a) Equal tees: 250/250/250 mm with expansion to 400 mm										
30°	*-1.5*	*0.4*	2.0	3.3	4.8	5.8	6.8	7.6	8.2	8.8
60°	*0.0*	*1.4*	3.0	4.5	5.8	7.4	8.7	9.5	10.2	10.7
90°	*1.0*	*2.4*	3.9	5.2	6.6	8.0	9.4	10.0	10.6	11.0
(b) Equal tees: 160/160/160 mm with expansion to 250 mm										
30°	*-1.0*	*0.5*	2.0	3.6	4.8	5.9	6.7	7.6	8.2	8.8
60°	*-0.4*	*1.2*	2.8	4.4	5.8	6.9	7.7	8.5	9.2	9.6
90°	*-0.1*	*1.5*	3.5	5.0	6.5	7.6	8.5	9.3	9.8	10.0
(c) Unequal tees: 250/200/250 mm with expansion to 400 mm										
30°	*0.2*	*1.8*	3.4	5.0	6.8	8.4	10	*11.7*	—	—
60°	*1.0*	*2.9*	4.6	6.4	8.2	10	12	*14*	—	—
90°	*1.2*	*3.2*	5.3	7.2	9.2	11	13	*15*	—	—

Diam. / mm	Correction factor for stated Reynolds number, Re_c				
	0.8×10^5	1.0×10^5	1.5×10^5	2.0×10^5	2.5×10^5
250/250	1.24	1.11	1.05	1	0.92
160/160	1.16	1.12	1.05	1	0.96

Note: area ratios as follows:
(a) $A_b/A_c = 1.0, A_c/A_s = 2.56$
(b) $A_b/A_c = 1.0, A_c/A_s = 2.44$
(c) $A_b/A_c = 0.64, A_c/A_s = 2.56$

Figures in italics were obtained by extrapolation

4.11.2.18 90° tees, with contraction taper for combined flow; diverging

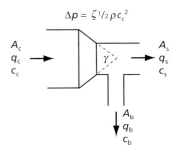

$$\Delta p = \zeta \, \tfrac{1}{2} \rho c_c^2$$

See Tables 4.71 and 4.72.

Table 4.71 90° tees with contraction taper, diverging flow: values for the straight factor $\zeta_{c\text{-}s}$; for $Re_c = 2 \times 10^5$ and correction for Reynolds number (derived from the European Programme Report[1])

Taper angle, γ	Relative straight flow, q_s/q_c								
	0.2	0.3	0.4	0.5	0.6	0.7	0.8	0.9	1.0
(a) For $d_c = 400$ mm; $d_b = 250$ mm; $d_s = 250$ mm ($A_c/A_s = 1.6$)									
30–90°	2.1	1.4	1.0	0.60	0.40	0.20	0.20	0.30	0.50
(b) For $d_c = 400$ mm; $d_b = 200$ mm; $d_s = 250$ mm ($A_c/A_s = 1.6$)									
30–90°	1.9	1.4	0.95	0.63	0.43	0.28	0.20	0.27	0.42

Type /mm	Correction factor for stated Reynolds number, Re_c				
	0.8×10^5	1.0×10^5	1.5×10^5	2.0×10^5	2.5×10^5
Equal	1.07	1.05	1.03	1	0.94
Unequal	No correction required				

Table 4.72 90° tees with contraction taper, diverging flow: values for the branch factor $\zeta_{c\text{-}b}$; for $Re_c = 2 \times 10^5$ (derived from the European Programme Report[1]) and correction for Reynolds number

Taper angle, γ	Relative branch flow, q_b/q_c								
	0.2	0.3	0.4	0.5	0.6	0.7	0.8	0.9	1.0
(a) For $d_c = 400$ mm; $d_b = 250$ mm; $d_s = 250$ mm ($A_c/A_s = 1.6$)									
30–90°	6.1	6.0	5.8	5.6	5.6	5.7	5.9	6.1	6.3
(b) For $d_c = 400$ mm; $d_b = 200$ mm; $d_s = 250$ mm ($A_c/A_s = 1.6$)									
30–90°	7.0	6.8	6.7	6.9	7.0	7.8	8.4	9.1	9.9

Type /mm	Correction factor for stated Reynolds number, Re_c				
	0.8×10^5	1.0×10^5	1.5×10^5	2.0×10^5	2.5×10^5
Equal	1.03	1.01	1.0	1.0	1.0
Unequal	No correction required				

4.11.2.19 Angle branch tees, with enlargement taper for combined flow; converging

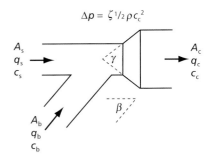

$$\Delta p = \zeta \, \tfrac{1}{2} \rho c_c^2$$

See Tables 4.73 and 4.74.

Data for the variation of ζ with Reynolds number were available only for full straight flow and full branch flow. The variation was sometimes found to be significant, so values of the correction factor C_{Re} are given in the tables. However, analysis for 90° tees[38] has shown that this is not necessarily an indication of what will occur for other flow rates.

Table 4.73 Angle tees with expansion taper, converging flow: values for the straight factor $\zeta_{s\text{-}c}$; for $Re_c = 2 \times 10^5$ and correction for Reynolds number (derived from the European Programme Report[1])

Branch angle, β	Taper angle, γ	Relative straight flow, q_s/q_c								
		0.2	0.3	0.4	0.5	0.6	0.7	0.8	0.9	1.0
30°	30°	*0.8*	*1.7*	*2.4*	3.0	3.4	3.5	3.4	2.8	1.8
	60°	*1.6*	*2.6*	*3.4*	3.9	4.1	4.1	3.9	3.45	2.7
	90°	2.5	3.4	4.2	4.5	4.5	4.4	4.2	3.8	3.3
45°	30°	2.5	3.2	3.6	3.9	3.9	3.7	3.3	2.6	1.8
	60°	4.2	4.9	5.2	5.4	5.2	4.9	4.3	3.4	2.3
	90°	4.6	5.2	5.6	5.8	5.7	5.4	4.9	4.1	2.9
60°	30°	5.8	6.8	7.0	7.1	6.8	6.1	5.0	3.6	1.7
	60°	7.0	7.7	8.2	8.1	7.8	7.0	5.8	4.2	2.3
	90°	7.2	8.0	8.3	8.4	8.0	7.3	6.2	4.8	2.9

Branch angle, β	Taper angle, γ	Correction factor for stated Reynolds number, Re_c				
		0.8×10^5	1.0×10^5	1.5×10^5	2.0×10^5	2.5×10^5
30°	30°	1.02	1.01	1.00	1.00	1.00
	60°	1.15	1.10	1.01	1.00	1.03
	90°	1.11	1.05	1.00	1.00	1.01
45°	30–90°	1.02	1.01	1.01	1.00	0.99
60°	30–90°	No correction required				

Note: using a size of $d_s = d_b = 250$ mm, $d_c = 400$ mm ($A_c/A_s = 2.56$). The figures in italics are extrapolations.

Table 4.74 Angle tees with expansion taper, converging flow: values for the branch factor $\zeta_{b\text{-}c}$; for $Re_c = 2 \times 10^5$ and correction for Reynolds number (derived from the European Programme Report[1])

Branch angle, β	Taper angle, γ	Relative branch flow, q_b/q_c								
		0.2	0.3	0.4	0.5	0.6	0.7	0.8	0.9	1.0
30°	30°	−0.4	1.0	2.1	3.0	3.8	4.4	4.9	5.15	5.4
	60°	0	1.5	2.7	3.8	4.7	5.4	6.0	6.35	6.4
	90°	−0.2	1.6	3.0	4.2	6.3	6.1	6.6	6.9	6.9
45°	30°	−1.0	1.2	2.7	4.0	5.0	5.8	6.2	6.4	6.3
	60°	0.3	2.4	4.0	5.6	6.6	7.6	8.0	8.1	8.0
	90°	0.9	2.8	4.5	5.9	7.1	7.9	8.6	9.0	9.1
60°	30°	1.9	3.8	5.5	6.9	8.0	8.8	9.4	9.7	9.6
	60°	3.0	5.0	6.6	7.9	9.2	10.1	11.0	11.4	11.5
	90°	3.0	5.0	6.7	9.0	9.2	10.5	11.2	11.8	12.2

Branch angle, β	Taper angle, γ	Correction factor for stated Reynolds number, Re_c				
		0.8×10^5	1.0×10^5	1.5×10^5	2.0×10^5	2.5×10^5
30°	30°	1.13	1.10	1.01	1.00	1.00
	60°	1.22	1.14	0.99	1.00	1.01
	90°	1.26	1.14	0.99	1.00	1.01
45°	30–90°	1.07	1.04	1.02	1.00	0.99
60°	30–90°	No correction required				

Note: using a size of $d_s = d_b = 250$ mm, $d_c = 400$ mm ($A_c/A_s = 2.56$).

Figures in italics were obtained by extrapolation

4.11.2.20 Angle branch tees, with contraction taper for combined flow; diverging

$$\Delta p = \zeta \tfrac{1}{2} \rho c_c^2$$

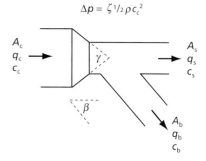

See Tables 4.75 and 4.76.

Table 4.75 Angle tees with contraction taper, diverging flow: values for the straight factor $\zeta_{c\text{-}s}$ (derived from the European Programme Report[1])

Branch angle, β	Taper angle, γ	Relative straight flow, q_s/q_c								
		0.2	0.3	0.4	0.5	0.6	0.7	0.8	0.9	1.0
(a) Equal tees: using $d_c = 400$ mm; $d_s = d_b = 250$ mm ($A_c/A_s = 2.56$)										
30°	30–60°	1.85	1.26	0.85	0.55	0.43	0.38	0.49	0.70	1.02
	90°	1.85	1.30	0.85	0.56	0.45	0.40	0.55	0.81	1.18
45°	30–90°	1.96	1.43	1.02	0.68	0.46	0.33	0.37	0.45	0.66
60°	30°	2.10	1.50	1.00	0.60	0.40	0.20	0.10	0.15	0.30
	60–90°	2.15	1.51	1.15	0.65	0.40	0.23	0.15	0.30	0.40
(b) Unequal tees: using $d_c = 400$ mm; $d_s = 250$ mm, $d_b = 200$ mm ($A_c/A_s = 2.56$)										
30°	30–90°	1.78	1.33	0.98	0.70	0.51	0.44	0.43	0.53	0.70
45°	30–90°	2.02	1.47	1.07	0.73	0.50	0.36	0.32	0.40	0.56
60°	30–90°	1.94	1.41	0.97	0.61	0.39	0.24	0.21	0.29	0.48

Note: figures in italics were obtained by extrapolation

Table 4.76 Angle tees with contraction taper, diverging flow: values for the branch factor $\zeta_{c\text{-}b}$ (derived from the European Programme Report[1])

Branch angle, β	Taper angle, γ	Relative branch flow, q_b/q_c								
		0.2	0.3	0.4	0.5	0.6	0.7	0.8	0.9	1.0
(a) Equal tees: using $d_c = 400$ mm; $d_s = d_b = 250$ mm ($A_c/A_s = 2.56$)										
30°	30–60°	5.6	4.4	3.5	2.8	2.4	2.3	2.3	2.7	3.2
45°	30–90°	5.9	4.8	3.9	3.2	2.8	2.5	2.5	2.7	3.1
60°	30–90°	6.3	5.6	5.0	4.4	4.0	3.8	3.8	3.9	4.1
(b) Unequal tees: using $d_c = 400$ mm; $d_s = 250$ mm, $d_b = 200$ mm ($A_c/A_s = 2.56$)										
30°	30–90°	4.5	3.1	2.2	1.9	2.0	2.6	3.7	5.4	7.0
45°	30–90°	5.1	3.8	3.0	2.6	2.6	3.0	4.0	5.2	6.8
60°	30–90°	6.4	5.2	4.4	4.0	3.8	4.0	4.6	5.5	6.5

Note: figures in italics were obtained by extrapolation

4.11.2.21 Angle branch tees, with bend on branch; converging flows

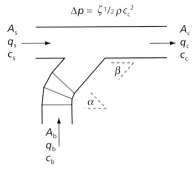

$$\Delta p = \zeta \, {}^1\!/_2 \, \rho \, c_c^2$$

All branch and bend pieces in same
plane, always giving: $\alpha + \beta = 90°$

See Tables 4.77 to 4.84.

Table 4.77 Angle tee, branch angle $\beta = 60°$, with bend on branch, $\alpha = 30°$, converging flow: values for the straight factor ζ_{s-c} (derived from the European Programme Report[1])

Area ratio, A_b/A_c	Relative straight flow, q_s/q_c									
	0.1	0.2	0.3	0.4	0.5	0.6	0.7	0.8	0.9	1.0
(a) Main duct size: $d_s = d_c = 400$ mm										
0.0625★	−12	−9.2	−6.9	−5.0	−3.3	−1.8	−0.8	−0.3	−0.05	0
0.1	−7.5	−5.5	−4.0	−2.8	−1.9	−1.1	−0.4	−0.1	−0.04	0
0.1406★	−4.5	−3.4	−2.5	−1.76	−1.04	−0.5	−0.2	0	0.05	0
0.20	−2.4	−1.6	−1.1	−0.75	−0.50	−0.30	−0.12	−0.05	−0.06	0
0.25★	−1.7	−1.1	−0.75	−0.50	−0.35	−0.20	−0.06	0.07	0.06	0
0.30	−1.4	−0.90	−0.60	−0.40	−0.25	−0.11	0	0.08	0.09	0
0.3906★	−1.07	−0.64	−0.43	−0.23	−0.10	0	0.09	0.10	0.08	0
0.4	−1.04	−0.61	−0.41	−0.21	−0.08	0.01	0.10	0.10	0.08	0
(b) Main duct size: $d_s = d_c = 250$ mm										
0.16†	−3.0	−2.3	−1.65	−1.15	−0.75	−0.35	−0.15	−0.03	0	0.03
0.2	−2.5	−1.8	−1.32	−0.90	−0.54	−0.26	−0.10	−0.02	0.01	0.03
0.3	−1.6	−1.1	−0.80	−0.48	−0.25	−0.1	0	0.02	0.03	0.04
0.36†	−1.16	−0.82	−0.53	−0.27	−0.13	0	0.07	0.05	0.04	0.04
0.4	−0.96	−0.66	−0.40	−0.17	−0.05	0.05	0.10	0.08	0.06	0.05
0.5	−0.58	−0.40	−0.22	−0.03	0.10	0.18	0.21	0.16	0.11	0.05
0.6	−0.40	−0.23	−0.10	−0.08	0.20	0.27	0.29	0.22	0.15	0.06
0.64†	−0.34	−0.18	−0.04	0.12	0.23	0.29	0.30	0.24	0.16	0.06
0.8	−0.23	−0.07	0.07	0.20	0.29	0.32	0.32	0.26	0.18	0.07
1.00†	−0.12	0.04	0.18	0.28	0.34	0.36	0.34	0.28	0.20	0.08

★ Values obtained using a main duct size: $d_s = d_c = 400$ mm; other values obtained by interpolation
† Values obtained using a main duct size: $d_s = d_c = 250$ mm; other values obtained by interpolation

Table 4.78 Angle tee, branch angle $\beta = 60°$, with bend on branch, $\alpha = 30°$, converging flow: values for the branch factor $\zeta_{b\text{-}c}$ (derived from the European Programme Report[1])

Area ratio, A_b/A_c	Relative branch flow, q_b/q_c									
	0.1	0.2	0.3	0.4	0.5	0.6	0.7	0.8	0.9	1.0
(a) Main duct size: $d_s = d_c = 400$ mm										
0.0625★	5.0	20	40	70	108	155	210	276	350	430
0.1	3.3	8.0	17	30	43	60	84	110	140	180
0.1406★	2.0	3.0	5.0	9.0	15	23	32	42	52	65
0.20	0.50	1.0	2.1	3.8	6.0	9.5	14	19	24	30
0.25★	−0.20	0.30	1.1	2.2	3.6	5.6	8.1	11	14	18
0.30	−0.30	0.10	0.60	1.3	2.2	3.5	5.1	7.0	9.0	11
0.3906★	−0.20	0	0.25	0.60	1.1	1.8	2.6	3.5	4.6	5.9
0.4	−0.18	0	0.22	0.60	1.0	1.7	2.4	3.3	4.3	5.6
(b) Main duct size: $d_s = d_c = 250$ mm										
0.16†	−2.0	0.01	3.3	6.5	11.0	16.0	22	29	37	45
0.2	−1.5	0	2.0	4.5	7.5	11.2	16	21	26	32
0.3	−0.80	0	1.0	1.8	3.0	4.6	6.5	9	12	15
0.36†	−0.50	0	0.54	1.1	1.8	2.8	3.9	5.3	7.0	9.6
0.4	−0.40	0	0.35	0.8	1.35	2.1	2.9	3.8	5.0	7.0
0.5	0.22	0	0.20	0.52	0.85	1.25	1.7	2.3	3.0	4.0
0.6	−0.14	0	0.15	0.40	0.62	0.85	1.15	1.5	1.9	2.4
0.64†	−0.10	0	0.14	0.36	0.56	0.77	1.06	1.33	1.67	2.0
0.8	−0.18	−0.05	0.10	0.25	0.40	0.55	0.70	0.90	1.1	1.2
1.00†	−0.40	−0.20	0	0.16	0.32	0.46	0.56	0.64	0.73	0.80

★ Values obtained using a main duct size: $d_s = d_c = 400$ mm; other values obtained by interpolation
† Values obtained using a main duct size: $d_s = d_c = 250$ mm; other values obtained by interpolation

Table 4.79 Angle tee, branch angle $\beta = 45°$, with bend on branch, $\alpha = 45°$, converging flow: values for the straight factor $\zeta_{s\text{-}c}$ (derived from the European Programme Report[1])

Area ratio, A_b/A_c	Relative straight flow, q_s/q_c									
	0.1	0.2	0.3	0.4	0.5	0.6	0.7	0.8	0.9	1.0
(a) Main duct size: $d_s = d_c = 400$ mm										
0.0625★	−16	−12	−8.8	−6.0	−3.9	−2.0	−1.0	−0.5	−0.2	0
0.1	−10.5	−8.0	−6.0	−4.1	−2.5	−1.4	−0.7	−0.35	−0.08	0
0.1406★	−6.6	5.0	−3.8	−2.6	−1.7	−1.0	−0.5	0.2	0	0
0.20	−3.7	−2.8	−2.1	−1.5	−1.0	−0.6	−0.3	−0.1	0	0
0.25★	−2.6	−2.1	−1.5	−1.1	−0.7	−0.4	−0.2	−0.05	0	0
0.30	−2.3	−1.8	−1.2	−0.85	−0.5	−0.25	−0.1	0.01	0.03	0
0.3906★	−2.1	−1.5	−1.0	−0.61	−0.29	−0.10	0	0.07	0.06	0
0.4	−2.0	−1.4	−0.98	−0.59	−0.27	−0.08	−0.01	0.08	0.06	0
(b) Main duct size: $d_s = d_c = 250$ mm										
0.16†	−4.6	−3.7	−2.8	−2.0	−1.4	−0.90	−0.44	−0.15	−0.02	0.03
0.2	−3.8	−3.0	−2.2	−1.6	−1.05	−0.65	−0.30	−0.09	0.01	0.03
0.3	−2.5	−1.9	−1.4	−0.90	−0.55	−0.28	−0.10	0	0.03	0.04
0.36†	−2.1	−1.5	−1.05	−0.68	−0.39	−0.16	0	0.05	0.05	0.04
0.4	−1.8	−1.3	−0.90	−0.55	−0.32	−0.10	0.04	0.07	0.06	0.04
0.5	−1.4	−0.95	−0.60	−0.32	−0.10	0.02	0.12	0.12	0.09	0.05
0.6	−1.0	−0.70	−0.42	−0.18	0	0.10	0.20	0.17	0.11	0.06
0.64†	−0.92	−0.61	−0.36	−0.12	0.04	0.15	0.22	0.20	0.13	0.06
0.8	−0.65	−0.40	−0.18	0	0.14	0.22	0.26	0.23	0.16	0.07
1.00†	−0.46	−0.24	−0.04	0.11	0.22	0.28	0.28	0.25	0.18	0.09

★ Values obtained using a main duct size: $d_s = d_c = 400$ mm; other values obtained by interpolation
† Values obtained using a main duct size: $d_s = d_c = 250$ mm; other values obtained by interpolation

Table 4.80 Angle tee, branch angle $\beta = 45°$, with bend on branch, $\alpha = 45°$, converging flow: values for the branch factor $\zeta_{b\text{-}c}$ (derived from the European Programme Report[1])

Area ratio, A_b/A_c	Relative branch flow, q_b/q_c									
	0.1	0.2	0.3	0.4	0.5	0.6	0.7	0.8	0.9	1.0
(a) Main duct size: $d_s = d_c = 400$ mm										
0.0625*	17	23	35	62	99	144	193	248	310	380
0.1	5.0	8.0	15	26	40	55	72	95	120	150
0.1406*	1.0	2.0	4.6	9.3	15	22	30	39	51	70
0.20	−0.50	0.35	1.9	3.7	6.4	9.7	13	17	22	30
0.25*	−0.70	0	1.0	2.2	3.8	5.5	7.7	10	13	17
0.30	−0.60	−0.1	0.60	1.4	2.3	3.6	5	6.8	9.0	12
0.3906*	−0.25	−0.06	0.20	0.5	1.0	1.7	2.5	3.4	4.4	5.5
0.4	−0.18	0	0.18	0.4	0.9	1.5	2.3	3.1	4.0	5.2
(b) Main duct size: $d_s = d_c = 250$ mm										
0.16†	−1.0	0.80	4.0	8.0	13	18	24	31	39	49
0.2	−0.50	0.60	2.5	4.5	7.5	11	16	21	27	34
0.3	−0.05	0.30	1.0	1.8	3.0	4.5	6.0	8.0	11	15
0.36†	0	0.20	0.50	1.0	1.7	2.5	3.4	4.6	5.9	7.4
0.4	0	0.15	0.35	0.80	1.3	1.9	2.8	3.7	4.5	5.0
0.5	0.	0.05	0.15	0.44	0.75	1.2	1.7	2.3	2.8	3.0
0.6	0	0	0.06	0.24	0.50	0.83	1.2	1.5	1.7	1.8
0.64†	−0.05	−0.04	0.03	0.20	0.45	0.76	1.0	1.2	1.4	1.6
0.8	−0.12	−0.08	0	0.16	0.40	0.50	0.60	0.70	0.85	1.0
1.00†	−0.25	−0.18	−0.17	0.10	0.22	0.32	0.40	0.46	0.51	0.56

* Values obtained using a main duct size: $d_s = d_c = 400$ mm; other values obtained by interpolation
† Values obtained using a main duct size: $d_s = d_c = 250$ mm; other values obtained by interpolation

Table 4.81 Angle tee, branch angle $\beta = 30°$, with bend on branch, $\alpha = 60°$, converging flow: values for the straight factor $\zeta_{s\text{-}c}$ (derived from the European Programme Report[1])

Area ratio, A_b/A_c	Relative straight flow, q_s/q_c									
	0.1	0.2	0.3	0.4	0.5	0.6	0.7	0.8	0.9	1.0
(a) Main duct size: $d_s = d_c = 400$ mm										
0.0625*	−19	−15	−11	−7.5	−4.7	−2.5	−0.9	−0.2	0	0
0.1	−13.5	−10.5	−8.0	−5.5	−3.3	−1.6	−0.7	−0.12	−0.05	0
0.1406*	−8.5	−6.7	−5.0	−3.6	−2.3	−1.1	−0.5	−0.10	−0.07	0
0.20	−5.5	−4.3	−3.2	−2.3	−1.5	−0.75	−0.3	−0.09	−0.06	0
0.25*	−4.4	−3.4	−2.5	−1.8	−1.1	−0.54	−0.18	−0.07	−0.05	0
0.30	−3.6	−2.7	−2.0	−1.40	−0.80	−0.37	−0.11	−0.04	0.02	0
0.3906*	−2.8	−2.1	−1.5	−0.97	−0.52	−0.20	−0.05	0	0	0
0.4	−2.7	−2.0	−1.4	−0.93	−0.49	0.18	0.04	0	0	0
(b) Main duct size: $d_s = d_c = 250$ mm										
0.16†	−7.0	−5.0	−3.6	−2.6	−1.8	−1.05	−0.56	−0.20	0	0.05
0.2	−5.7	−4.2	−2.9	−2.1	−1.4	−0.80	−0.37	−0.14	0.01	0.05
0.3	−3.9	−2.8	−2.0	−1.4	−0.83	−0.38	−0.09	−0.04	0.02	0.06
0.36†	−3.1	−2.3	−1.6	−1.0	−0.59	−0.25	0	0.02	0.04	0.06
0.4	−2.8	−2.0	−1.4	−0.90	−0.50	−0.19	0.03	0.04	0.06	0.06
0.5	−2.1	−1.5	−1.0	−0.60	−0.27	−0.06	0.11	0.13	0.09	0.06
0.6	−1.6	−1.1	−0.70	−0.40	−0.12	0.02	0.16	0.19	0.14	0.07
0.64†	−1.4	−0.98	−0.60	−0.33	−0.08	0.05	0.17	0.20	0.15	0.07
0.8	−1.0	−0.70	−0.04	−0.15	0.04	0.12	0.21	0.24	0.19	0.09
1.00†	−0.8	−0.50	−0.25	−0.05	0.11	0.18	0.23	0.25	0.20	0.12

* Values obtained using a main duct size: $d_s = d_c = 400$ mm; other values obtained by interpolation
† Values obtained using a main duct size: $d_s = d_c = 250$ mm; other values obtained by interpolation

Table 4.82 Angle tee, branch angle $\beta = 30°$, with bend on branch, $\alpha = 60°$, converging flow: values for the branch factor $\zeta_{b\text{-}c}$ (derived from the European Programme Report[1])

Area ratio, A_b/A_c	Relative branch flow, q_b/q_c									
	0.1	0.2	0.3	0.4	0.5	0.6	0.7	0.8	0.9	1.0
(a) Main duct size: $d_s = d_c = 400$ mm										
0.0625*	7.0	20	40	65	98	140	190	250	320	400
0.1	1.5	8	15	25	37	50	88	87	110	140
0.1406*	−0.20	2.0	6.0	10	16	23	31	40	50	60
0.20	−0.35	0.45	2.6	5.0	8.0	11	15	19	24	28
0.25*	−0.4	0.2	1.1	2.3	3.8	5.6	7.7	10	13	16
0.30	−0.45	0.10	0.60	1.2	1.8	2.6	3.6	4.8	6.5	8.7
0.3906*	−0.47	−0.12	0.28	0.77	1.3	2.0	2.65	3.45	4.35	5.4
0.4	−0.47	−0.13	0.25	0.75	1.3	1.9	2.6	3.4	4.3	5.1
(b) Main duct size: $d_s = d_c = 250$ mm										
0.16†	−1.0	1.0	4.1	7.7	12	17	23	30	38	47
0.2	−0.80	0.70	2.5	5.0	7.8	10.5	14	19	24	30
0.3	−0.50	0.20	0.85	1.85	2.9	4.0	5.4	7.0	9.3	12
0.36†	−0.40	0	0.50	1.1	1.7	2.4	3.2	4.2	5.3	6.4
0.4	−0.38	−0.08	0.37	0.85	1.35	1.9	2.6	3.4	4.2	4.8
0.5	−0.43	−0.18	0.18	0.47	0.80	1.2	1.65	2.1	2.5	2.9
0.6	−0.46	−0.23	0.05	0.30	0.55	0.80	1.05	1.3	1.5	1.7
0.64†	−0.48	−0.24	0	0.25	0.48	0.71	0.92	1.1	1.3	1.5
0.8	−0.54	−0.30	−0.08	0.11	0.26	0.40	0.55	0.65	0.75	0.85
1.00†	−0.56	−0.35	−0.16	0	0.15	0.27	0.37	0.42	0.45	0.46

* Values obtained using a main duct size: $d_s = d_c = 400$ mm; other values obtained by interpolation
† Values obtained using a main duct size: $d_s = d_c = 250$ mm; other values obtained by interpolation

Table 4.83 Angle tee, branch angle $\beta = 15°$, with bend on branch, $\alpha = 75°$, converging flow: values for the straight factor $\zeta_{s\text{-}c}$ (derived from the European Programme Report[1])

Area ratio, A_b/A_c	Relative straight flow, q_s/q_c									
	0.1	0.2	0.3	0.4	0.5	0.6	0.7	0.8	0.9	1.0
(a) Main duct size: $d_s = d_c = 400$ mm										
0.0625*	−27	−21	−16	−11	−7.1	−4.0	−2.0	−0.8	−0.3	0
0.1	−17	−12	−9	−6.5	−4.3	−2.6	−1.25	−0.45	−0.17	0
0.1406*	−10.5	−8.0	−6.0	−4.2	−2.9	−1.7	−0.70	−0.20	−0.05	0
0.20	−7.0	−5.3	−3.8	−2.7	−1.8	−0.90	−0.30	−0.13	−0.04	0
0.25*	−5.3	−4.1	−2.9	−2.0	−1.2	−0.60	−0.18	−0.07	−0.04	0
0.30	−4.0	−3.2	−2.3	−1.5	−0.90	−0.40	−0.10	−0.05	−0.03	0
0.3906*	−3.1	−2.3	−1.65	−1.05	−0.60	−0.20	−0.05	−0.03	−0.02	0
0.4	−3.0	−2.2	−1.6	−1.00	−0.57	−0.18	−0.04	−0.03	−0.02	0
(b) Main duct size: $d_s = d_c = 250$ mm										
0.16†	−9	−7	−5	−3.1	−1.75	−1.0	−0.46	−0.15	−0.02	0.07
0.2	−6.8	−5.5	−3.9	−2.45	−1.44	−0.80	−0.32	−0.10	0.01	0.08
0.3	−4.3	−3.3	−2.3	−1.5	−0.85	−0.37	−0.09	0.01	0.05	0.08
0.36†	−3.5	−2.6	−1.8	−1.15	−0.59	−0.20	0	0.06	0.08	0.09
0.4	−3.1	−2.3	−1.55	−0.95	−0.45	−0.13	0.04	0.08	0.09	0.10
0.5	−2.3	−1.64	−1.05	−0.60	−0.25	0	0.11	0.14	0.13	0.11
0.6	−1.7	−1.15	−0.75	−0.40	−0.12	0.06	0.16	0.18	0.16	0.12
0.64†	−1.5	−1.03	−0.66	−0.33	−0.08	0.08	0.18	0.20	0.18	0.13
0.8	−1.05	−0.70	−0.40	−0.18	0.04	0.13	0.22	0.24	0.23	0.16
1.00†	−0.76	−0.49	−0.26	−0.06	0.10	0.19	0.24	0.26	0.25	0.20

* Values obtained using a main duct size: $d_s = d_c = 400$ mm; other values obtained by interpolation
† Values obtained using a main duct size: $d_s = d_c = 250$ mm; other values obtained by interpolation

Table 4.84 Angle tee, branch angle $\beta = 15°$, with bend on branch, $\alpha = 75°$, converging flow: values for the branch factor ζ_{b-c} (derived from the European Programme Report[1])

Area ratio, A_b/A_c	Relative branch flow, q_b/q_c									
	0.1	0.2	0.3	0.4	0.5	0.6	0.7	0.8	0.9	1.0
0.0625★	20	35	55	78	108	146	192	247	310	380
0.1	5.0	15	20	27	35	47	65	90	120	150
0.1406★	–3.0	0.20	4.2	9.0	14.5	21	28.5	37	46	57
0.20	–1.0	0	1.7	4.0	6.5	9.5	13	17	21	25
0.25★	0.10	0.60	1.3	2.4	3.9	5.6	7.6	9.8	12	14.5
0.30	–0.20	0.20	0.80	1.5	2.3	3.3	4.4	5.5	7.0	9.0
0.3906★	–0.60	–0.20	0.30	0.80	1.3	1.9	2.5	3.1	3.8	4.5
0.4	–0.62	–0.22	0.28	0.70	1.2	1.8	2.4	3.0	3.6	4.0
0.16†	–1.3	1.4	4.6	8.6	13	18	25	32	41	50
0.2	–1.1	0.80	3.0	5.0	7.0	9.0	11	14	18	24
0.3	–0.80	0.10	1.0	2.0	3.0	4.0	5.0	6.3	8.0	10
0.36†	–0.7	0	0.52	1.2	1.9	2.7	3.5	4.4	5.3	6.3
0.4	–0.65	–0.12	0.38	1.0	1.6	2.2	2.9	3.7	4.5	5.1
0.5	0.55	–0.15	0.22	0.65	1.05	1.5	1.9	2.3	2.8	3.2
0.6	–0.50	–0.20	0.13	0.43	0.69	1.0	1.3	1.6	1.8	2.0
0.64†	–0.50	–0.20	0.10	0.35	0.60	0.88	1.1	1.3	1.5	1.7
0.8	–0.50	–0.25	0	0.15	0.32	0.50	0.62	0.80	0.90	1.0
1.00†	–0.52	–0.30	–0.11	0.06	0.19	0.28	0.36	0.44	0.49	0.52

★ Values obtained using a main duct size: $d_s = d_c = 400$ mm; other values obtained by interpolation
† Values obtained using a main duct size: $d_s = d_c = 250$ mm; other values obtained by interpolation

4.11.2.22 Angle branch tees, with bend on branch; diverging flow

$$\Delta p = \zeta \tfrac{1}{2} \rho c_c^2$$

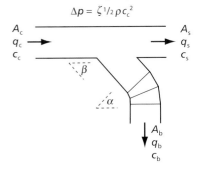

All branch and bend pieces in same plane, always giving: $\alpha + \beta = 90°$

See Tables 4.85 to 4.92.

Values of ζ are found to vary little with Reynolds number.
Values of the straight factors, ζ_{c-s}, do not vary with A_b/A_c.

Table 4.85 Angle tee, branch angle $\beta = 60°$, with bend on branch, $\alpha = 30°$, diverging flow: values for the straight factor ζ_{c-s} (derived from the European Programme Report[1])

Diam. d_c, ($= d_s$) / mm	Relative straight flow, q_s/q_c									
	0.1	0.2	0.3	0.4	0.5	0.6	0.7	0.8	0.9	1.0
250★	0.26	0.20	0.14	0.09	0.04	0.02	0.00	0.02	0.05	0.12
400†	0.30	0.23	0.16	0.10	0.05	0.02	–0.01	–0.02	–0.01	0.01

★ mean of values for $0.16 < A_b/A_c < 1.00$
† mean of values for $0.062 < A_b/A_c < 0.39$

Table 4.86 Angle tee, branch angle $\beta = 60°$, with bend on branch, $\alpha = 30°$, diverging flow: values for the branch factor $\zeta_{c\text{-}b}$ (derived from the European Programme Report[1])

Area ratio, A_b/A_c	Relative branch flow, q_b/q_c									
	0.1	0.2	0.3	0.4	0.5	0.6	0.7	0.8	0.9	1.0
(a) Main duct size: $d_s = d_c = 400$ mm										
0.0625*	0.48	6.0	16	30	46	65	88	110	136	160
0.1	0.48	3.0	7.0	14	24	33	44	59	79	92
0.1406*	0.48	0.90	3.0	6.0	9.6	14	20	28	36	44
0.20	0.48	0.55	1.2	2.5	4.0	6.0	8.8	12	16	21
0.25*	0.48	0.50	0.67	1.0	1.6	2.7	4.0	5.5	7.5	9.6
0.30	0.48	0.50	0.61	0.80	1.1	1.7	2.5	3.5	5.0	6.5
0.3906*	0.48	0.50	0.53	0.60	0.76	1.12	1.54	2.1	2.8	3.5
0.4	0.48	0.50	0.52	0.58	0.72	1.06	1.44	1.95	2.57	3.19
(b) Main duct size: $d_s = d_c = 250$ mm										
0.16†	1	1.3	2.0	4.0	6.4	10.0	14.7	21	28	38
0.2	1	1.0	1.5	2.8	4.5	7	10.5	15	20	26
0.3	1	0.80	0.90	1.3	1.8	2.5	4.0	6.5	9	11
0.36†	1	0.70	0.70	0.80	1.2	1.6	2.3	3.4	4.5	5.8
0.4	1	0.70	0.68	0.72	1.0	1.3	1.8	2.4	3.5	4.5
0.5	1.05	0.80	0.69	0.67	0.75	0.90	1.15	1.5	2.0	2.9
0.6	1.09	0.89	0.75	0.65	0.65	0.68	0.81	1.05	1.35	1.85
0.64†	1.10	0.90	0.76	0.65	0.64	0.65	0.76	0.95	1.2	1.6
0.8	1.10	0.91	0.79	0.66	0.63	0.63	0.66	0.74	0.85	1.05
1.00†	1.10	0.92	0.80	0.70	0.64	0.60	0.58	0.60	0.63	0.66

* Values obtained using a main duct size: $d_s = d_c = 400$ mm; other values obtained by interpolation
† Values obtained using a main duct size: $d_s = d_c = 250$ mm; other values obtained by interpolation

Table 4.87 Angle tee, branch angle $\beta = 45°$, with bend on branch, $\alpha = 45°$, diverging flow: values for the straight factor $\zeta_{c\text{-}s}$ (derived from the European Programme Report[1])

Diam., d_c ($= d_s$) / mm	Relative straight flow, q_b/q_c									
	0.1	0.2	0.3	0.4	0.5	0.6	0.7	0.8	0.9	1.0
250*	0.29	0.22	0.15	0.10	0.04	0.02	0	0.02	0.05	0.13
400†	0.28	0.21	0.14	0.09	0.04	0.01	–0.01	–0.03	–0.03	0

* Mean of values for $0.16 < A_b/A_c < 1.00$
† Mean of values for $0.062 < A_b/A_c < 0.39$

Table 4.88 Angle tee, branch angle $\beta = 45°$, with bend on branch, $\alpha = 45°$, diverging flow: values for the branch factor $\zeta_{c\text{-}b}$ (derived from the European Programme Report[1])

Area ratio, A_b/A_c	Relative branch flow, q_b/q_c									
	0.1	0.2	0.3	0.4	0.5	0.6	0.7	0.8	0.9	1.0
(a) Main duct size: $d_s = d_c = 400$ mm										
0.0625*	2.0	10	20	30	45	65	90	120	150	160
0.1	1.0	3.5	8.0	15	23	32	45	62	80	100
0.1406*	0.64	1.2	3.0	5.8	10	14.5	21	27	35	43
0.20	0.40	0.60	1.2	2.5	4.2	7.0	10	14	18	22
0.25*	0.30	0.56	0.74	1.4	2.3	3.8	5.6	8.0	10.5	13.3
0.30	0.30	0.40	0.65	1.0	1.5	2.4	3.5	5.0	6.8	8.5
0.3906*	0.50	0.50	0.50	0.60	0.80	1.1	1.6	2.2	3.0	3.8
0.4	–0.18	0	0.22	0.60	1.0	1.7	2.4	3.3	4.3	5.6
(b) Main duct size: $d_s = d_c = 250$ mm										
0.16†	1.0	1.5	2.3	4.0	7.0	11	16	23	31	42
0.2	0.90	1.2	1.7	2.9	5.0	7.5	11	16	22	30
0.3	0.70	0.65	0.80	1.2	2.0	3.0	4.2	6.0	9.0	13
0.36†	0.70	0.50	0.53	0.80	1.15	1.8	2.6	3.8	5.0	6.6
0.4	0.72	0.51	0.49	0.70	0.90	1.35	2.0	2.9	3.9	5.0
0.5	0.80	0.59	0.51	0.55	0.60	0.85	1.2	1.8	2.5	3.2
0.6	0.88	0.67	0.57	0.51	0.45	0.55	0.75	1.1	1.6	2.0
0.64†	0.90	0.70	0.60	0.50	0.42	0.50	0.65	0.90	1.3	1.7
0.8	0.95	0.78	0.65	0.50	0.42	0.40	0.45	0.55	0.70	0.90
1.00†	0.90	0.80	0.70	0.60	0.48	0.38	0.38	0.40	0.45	0.52

* Values obtained using a main duct size: $d_s = d_c = 400$ mm; other values obtained by interpolation
† Values obtained using a main duct size: $d_s = d_c = 250$ mm; other values obtained by interpolation

Table 4.89 Angle tee, branch angle $\beta = 30°$, with bend on branch, $\alpha = 60°$, diverging flow: values for the straight factor $\zeta_{c\text{-}s}$ (derived from the European Programme Report[1])

Diam., d_c ($= d_s$) / mm	Relative straight flow, q_s/q_c									
	0.1	0.2	0.3	0.4	0.5	0.6	0.7	0.8	0.9	1.0
250*	0.25	0.18	0.12	0.07	0.04	0.02	0.02	0.03	0.06	0.12
400†	0.27	0.19	0.13	0.07	0.03	0	−0.01	−0.02	−0.02	0

* Mean of values for $0.16 < A_b/A_c < 1.00$
† Mean of values for $0.062 < A_b/A_c < 0.39$

Table 4.91 Angle tee, branch angle $\beta = 15°$, with bend on branch, $\alpha = 75°$, diverging flow: values for the straight factor $\zeta_{c\text{-}s}$ (derived from the European Programme Report[1])

Diam., d_c ($= d_s$) / mm	Relative straight flow, q_s/q_c									
	0.1	0.2	0.3	0.4	0.5	0.6	0.7	0.8	0.9	1.0
250*	0.23	0.17	0.11	0.06	0.02	0	0	0.02	0.05	0.11
400†	0.24	0.17	0.11	0.06	0.02	0	−0.02	−0.02	−0.01	0.01

* Mean of values for $0.16 < A_b/A_c < 1.00$
† Mean of values for $0.062 < A_b/A_c < 0.39$

Table 4.90 Angle tee, branch angle $\beta = 30°$, with bend on branch, $\alpha = 60°$, diverging flow: values for the branch factor $\zeta_{c\text{-}b}$ (derived from the European Programme Report[1])

Area ratio, A_b/A_c	Relative branch flow, q_b/q_c									
	0.1	0.2	0.3	0.4	0.5	0.6	0.7	0.8	0.9	1.0
(a) Main duct size: $d_s = d_c = 400$ mm										
0.0625*	0.60	10	24	40	60	85	110	138	170	200
0.1	0.55	4.0	10	19	30	42	60	80	100	120
0.1406*	0.50	2.0	4.0	8.0	13	20	28	37	47	58
0.20	0.43	0.90	1.8	3.0	4.8	7.5	11	16	21	27
0.25*	0.40	0.55	0.90	1.5	2.5	4	6	8.2	11	15
0.30	0.37	0.48	0.60	0.90	1.5	2.3	3.5	5	7	9
0.3906*	0.35	0.40	0.50	0.70	1.0	1.6	2.3	3.1	4.0	4.9
0.4	0.35	0.39	0.49	0.69	0.97	1.5	2.2	3.0	3.8	4.6
(b) Main duct size: $d_s = d_c = 250$ mm										
0.16†	1.5	2.0	2.8	5.6	9.6	15	22	30	40	54
0.2	1.0	1.4	2.0	3.8	6.5	10	14	20	29	38
0.3	0.50	0.55	0.70	1.5	2.7	4.0	5.6	8.0	11	15
0.36†	0.30	0.30	0.41	0.80	1.4	2.3	3.2	4.7	6.3	8.0
0.4	0.32	0.33	0.41	0.65	1.1	1.8	2.6	3.7	4.8	6.5
0.5	0.42	0.41	0.43	0.48	0.62	1.0	1.4	1.9	2.6	4.0
0.6	0.51	0.48	0.48	0.46	0.45	0.70	0.95	1.3	1.8	2.5
0.64†	0.55	0.51	0.47	0.45	0.50	0.60	0.75	1.1	1.5	2.1
0.8	0.75	0.64	0.54	0.47	0.40	0.49	0.50	0.60	0.80	1.3
1.00†	1.0	0.82	0.63	0.50	0.39	0.34	0.34	0.40	0.50	0.61

* Values obtained using a main duct size: $d_s = d_c = 400$ mm; other values obtained by interpolation
† Values obtained using a main duct size: $d_s = d_c = 250$ mm; other values obtained by interpolation

Table 4.92 Angle tee, branch angle $\beta = 15°$, with bend on branch, $\alpha = 60°$, diverging flow: values for the branch factor $\zeta_{c\text{-}b}$ (derived from the European Programme Report[1])

Area ratio, A_b/A_c	Relative branch flow, q_b/q_c									
	0.1	0.2	0.3	0.4	0.5	0.6	0.7	0.8	0.9	1.0
(a) Main duct size: $d_s = d_c = 400$ mm										
0.0625*	2.0	12	24	36	54	78	107	145	190	250
0.1	0.80	5.0	10	15	22	35	52	75	100	130
0.1406*	0.50	1.6	3.6	6.8	13	20	28	36	47	59
0.20	0.32	0.60	1.4	3.0	5.3	8.0	12	17	22	27
0.25*	0.27	0.40	0.76	1.6	2.8	4.5	6.5	9.0	12	15
0.30	0.24	0.30	0.50	1.0	1.6	2.9	4.2	5.8	7.5	9.5
0.3906*	0.15	0.20	0.30	0.60	1.0	1.5	2.2	3.0	4.0	5.0
0.4	0.14	0.19	0.28	0.56	0.92	1.4	2.0	2.7	3.6	4.5
(b) Main duct size: $d_s = d_c = 250$ mm										
0.16†	1.4	2.0	3.9	7.6	12.5	20	28	39	52	66
0.2	1.0	1.5	2.5	5.0	8.5	13	19	28	38	47
0.3	0.55	0.60	0.78	1.5	3.0	5.0	7.5	11	16	21
0.36†	0.30	0.30	0.37	0.80	1.4	2.4	3.6	5.2	7.0	9.1
0.4	0.21	0.22	0.30	0.60	1.0	1.7	2.6	3.8	5.0	6.5
0.5	0.20	0.20	0.25	0.40	0.60	1.0	1.6	2.2	3.0	4.2
0.6	0.20	0.20	0.24	0.31	0.50	0.80	1.1	1.6	2.2	3.1
0.64†	0.20	0.20	0.25	0.30	0.45	0.70	1.0	1.4	1.9	2.6
0.8	0.41	0.30	0.29	0.28	0.27	0.40	0.60	0.85	1.2	1.7
1.00†	0.68	0.50	0.35	0.26	0.20	0.19	0.23	0.36	0.50	0.65

* Values obtained using a main duct size: $d_s = d_c = 400$ mm; other values obtained by interpolation
† Values obtained using a main duct size: $d_s = d_c = 250$ mm; other values obtained by interpolation

4.11.2.23 Angle branch tees, with bend on branch and expansion taper; converging flow

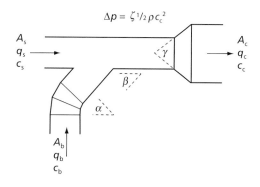

$$\Delta p = \zeta \tfrac{1}{2} \rho c_c^2$$

See Tables 4.93 and 4.94.

Table 4.93 Angle tees with bend on branch and expansion taper, converging flow: values for the straight factor $\zeta_{s\text{-}c}$ (derived from the European Programme Report[1])

Tee angle, β	Taper angle, γ	Relative straight flow, q_s/q_c								
		0.2	0.3	0.4	0.5	0.6	0.7	0.8	0.9	1.0
(a) Equal tees: 250/250/250 mm with expansion to 400 mm										
30°	30°	—	0.9	1.9	2.7	3.3	3.6	3.5	3.0	1.8
	60–90°	—	1.7	2.7	3.5	4.0	4.3	4.2	3.7	2.8
45°	30°	—	1.9	2.5	2.9	3.3	3.4	3.2	2.6	1.6
	60–90°*	—	3.9	4.5	4.9	4.9	4.7	4.3	3.5	2.4
60°	30°	—	6.0	6.5	6.6	6.4	5.8	4.8	3.4	1.5
	60–90°	—	7.6	8.1	8.1	7.8	7.2	6.2	4.6	2.6
(b) Equal tees: 160/160/160 mm with expansion to 250 mm										
30°	30°	-0.8	0.2	1.2	1.9	2.6	3.0	3.0	2.8	1.9
	60–90°	-0.4	0.8	1.8	2.6	3.1	3.4	3.5	3.2	2.6
45°	30°	0	1.2	2.0	2.7	3.1	3.4	3.4	3.0	2.2
	60–90°	0.9	1.9	2.7	3.2	3.6	3.8	3.7	3.4	2.8
60°	30°	1.4	2.1	2.6	3.0	3.1	3.1	2.8	2.3	1.7
	60–90°	2.6	3.2	3.5	3.7	3.8	3.8	3.6	3.2	2.4
(c) Unequal tees: 250/200/250 mm with expansion to 400 mm										
30°	30°	—	-2.5	-0.9	0.4	1.4	2.0	2.2	2.0	1.6
	60–90°	—	-1.7	0	1.3	2.3	3.0	3.4	3.3	2.6
45°	30°	—	-2.5	-0.6	0.8	1.8	2.5	2.7	2.4	1.4
	60–90°	—	-0.4	1.1	2.3	3.1	3.7	3.8	3.4	2.5
60°	30°	—	2.1	3.1	3.8	4.25	4.2	3.8	2.8	1.4
	60–90°	—	4.8	5.7	6.3	6.4	6.1	5.4	4.2	2.5
(d) Unequal tees: 160/100/160 mm with expansion to 250 mm										
30°	30°	-8.0	-5.7	-3.1	-1.2	0.2	1.1	1.6	1.8	1.8
	60–90°	-7.5	-5.0	-2.4	-0.5	0.9	1.9	2.5	2.7	2.4
45°	30°	-6.8	-3.9	-1.8	-0.2	1.0	1.6	1.8	1.4	0.5
	60–90°	-6.1	-3.4	-1.2	0.4	1.6	2.5	2.9	2.9	2.4
60°	30°	-1.4	0.1	1.4	2.4	3.0	3.3	3.2	2.6	1.7
	60–90°	-0.4	1.1	2.4	3.5	4.1	4.3	4.1	3.4	2.3

* Experimental results for $\beta = 45°$, $\gamma = 90°$ were rejected as unreliable; estimated values were assumed to be close to those for $\gamma = 60°$ as was the case for all the other results.

Note: area ratios as follows: (a) (c) $A_c/A_s = 2.56$; (b) (d) $A_c/A_s = 2.44$

Figures in italics were obtained by extrapolation

Table 4.94 Angle tees with bend on branch and expansion taper, converging flow: values for the branch factor $\zeta_{b\text{-}c}$ (derived from the European Programme Report[1])

Tee angle, β	Taper angle, γ	Relative branch flow, q_b/q_c								
		0.2	0.3	0.4	0.5	0.6	0.7	0.8	0.9	1.0
(a) Equal tees: 250/250/250 mm with expansion to 400 mm										
30°	30°	-0.2	1.0	1.9	2.7	3.5	4.1	4.6	5.0	5.3
	60–90°	0.4	1.5	2.5	3.5	4.3	5.0	5.6	6.2	6.6
45°	30°	-0.4	0.9	2.0	3.0	3.9	4.6	5.2	5.5	5.7
	60–90°	0.2	1.9	3.4	4.7	5.8	6.6	7.1	7.4	7.3
60°	30°	1.6	3.4	5.0	6.4	7.5	8.3	8.9	9.2	9.3
	60–90°	3.3	5.0	6.2	7.5	8.9	9.9	10.7	11.7	11.5
(b) Equal tees: 160/160/160 mm with expansion to 250 mm										
30°	30°	-0.4	0.7	1.6	2.3	2.9	3.4	3.7	4.0	4.3
	60–90°	-0.2	1.0	2.1	2.9	3.6	4.0	4.4	4.7	4.8
45°	30°	0	1.0	1.9	2.7	3.2	3.7	4.1	4.5	4.8
	60–90°	0.2	1.3	2.4	3.3	3.9	4.4	4.9	5.5	5.6
60°	30°	-0.2	0.9	2.0	3.0	3.9	4.7	5.4	6.0	6.5
	60–90°	0.2	1.5	2.7	3.8	4.7	5.5	6.3	7.0	7.4
(c) Unequal tees: 250/200/250 mm with expansion to 400 mm										
30°	30°	-0.7	0.8	2.2	3.8	5.4	7.1	—	—	—
	60–90°	0.1	1.7	3.4	4.9	6.5	8.1	—	—	—
45°	30°	-0.1	1.0	2.4	3.7	5.2	6.6	—	—	—
	60–90°	0.7	2.1	3.7	5.2	6.8	8.5	—	—	—
60°	30°	1.0	2.5	4.2	5.8	7.4	9.0	—	—	—
	60–90°	2.7	4.7	6.6	8.9	10.2	11.9	—	—	—
(d) Unequal tees: 160/100/160 mm with expansion to 250 mm										
30°	30°	1.0	3.3	7.0	11	16	21	29	37	45
	60–90°	1.8	4.1	7.8	12	17	23	31	39	48
45°	30–90°	2.0	4.0	8.0	12	18	24	32	42	52
60°	30°	4.0	6.0	8.5	13	19	26	35	45	56

Note: area ratios as follows: (a) (c) $A_c/A_s = 2.56$; (b) (d) $A_c/A_s = 2.44$

Figures in italics were obtained by extrapolation

4.11.2.24 Angle branch tees, with bend on branch and contraction taper; diverging flow

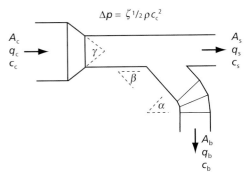

$$\Delta p = \zeta \tfrac{1}{2} \rho c_c^2$$

All branch and bend pieces in same plane, always giving: $\alpha + \beta = 90°$

See Tables 4.95 and 4.96.

Table 4.95 Angle tees with bend on branch and contraction taper, diverging flow: values for the straight factor ζ_{c-s} (derived from the European Programme Report[1])

Tee angle, β	Taper angle, γ	Relative straight flow, q_s/q_c								
		0.2	0.3	0.4	0.5	0.6	0.7	0.8	0.9	1.0
(a) Equal tees: 250/250/250 mm with contraction from 400 mm										
30°	30–90°	*2.10*	1.46	0.96	0.61	0.47	0.42	0.51	0.75	1.13
45°	30–90°	*1.91*	1.38	0.99	0.64	0.45	0.37	0.34	0.43	0.65
60°	30–90°	*2.17*	1.48	1.00	0.65	0.42	0.29	0.23	0.28	0.48
(c) Unequal tees: 250/200/250 mm with contraction from 400 mm										
30°	30–90°	*1.83*	1.35	0.97	0.66	0.47	0.38	0.41	0.50	0.72
45°	30–90°	*1.86*	1.34	0.95	0.63	0.43	0.33	0.30	0.39	0.58
60°	30–90°	*1.97*	1.41	0.98	0.63	0.43	0.35	0.32	0.38	0.52

Note: area ratio: $A_c/A_s = 2.56$

Figures in italics were obtained by extrapolation

Table 4.96 Angle tees with bend on branch and contraction taper, diverging flow: values for the branch factor ζ_{c-b} (derived from the European Programme Report[1])

Tee angle, β	Taper angle, γ	Relative branch flow, q_b/q_c								
		0.2	0.3	0.4	0.5	0.6	0.7	0.8	0.9	1.0
(a) Equal tees: 250/250/250 mm with contraction from 400 mm										
30°	30–90°	*5.53*	4.55	3.81	3.33	3.23	3.35	3.72	4.45	5.31
45°	30–90°	*5.67*	4.63	3.83	3.28	2.87	2.78	2.93	3.32	3.93
60°	30–90°	*6.07*	5.31	4.75	4.36	4.44	3.96	4.03	4.23	4.54
(c) Unequal tees: 250/200/250 mm with contraction from 400 mm										
30°	30–90°	*4.53*	3.47	3.00	2.85	3.40	4.90	6.70	9.03	12.2
45°	30–90°	*5.00*	3.87	3.15	2.97	3.30	4.43	6.00	8.13	10.3
60°	30–90°	*6.13*	4.98	4.17	3.80	3.83	4.33	5.27	6.67	8.07

Note: area ratio: $A_c/A_s = 2.56$

Figures in italics were obtained by extrapolation

4.11.2.25 90° 'Y' tees

(a) Converging flow:

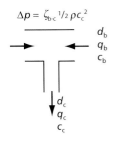

$$\Delta p = \zeta_{b-c} \tfrac{1}{2} \rho c_c^2$$

See Table 4.97.

Table 4.97 90° 'Y' tees, converging flow: values for the branch factor ζ_{b-c} (derived from the European Programme Report[1])

Diameter / mm	Ratio, A_b/A_c	Relative branch flow, q_b/q_c								
		0.2	0.3	0.4	0.5	0.6	0.7	0.8	0.9	1.0
100/250/100	0.16	7.6	7.75	8.0	9.1	12.7	17.4	23	31	38
160/250/160	0.41	*0.35*	0.50	0.75	1.07	1.50	2.10	2.85	3.76	4.86
100/250/100	0.64	*0.23*	0.28	0.36	0.47	0.65	0.87	1.17	1.47	1.81

Note: values determined at Reynolds numbers as follows:
100/250/100: $Re_c = 1.6 \times 10^5$
160/250/160: $Re_c = 2.0 \times 10^5$
100/250/100: $Re_c = 2.0 \times 10^5$

Figures in italics were obtained by extrapolation

(b) Diverging flow:

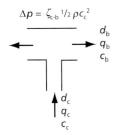

$$\Delta p = \zeta_{c-b} \tfrac{1}{2} \rho c_c^2$$

See Table 4.98.

Table 4.98 90° 'Y' tees, diverging flow: values for the branch factor ζ_{c-b}: for $Re_c = 2.0 \times 10^5$ (derived from the European Programme Report[1])

Diameter / mm	Ratio, A_b/A_c	Relative branch flow, q_b/q_c								
		0.2	0.3	0.4	0.5	0.6	0.7	0.8	0.9	1.0
100/250/100	0.16	*0.80*	1.31	2.05	3.11	4.25	5.6	7.05	9.00	11.6
160/250/160	0.41	*0.37*	0.50	0.68	0.87	1.15	1.51	2.00	2.52	3.17
100/250/100	0.64	*0.43*	0.48	0.55	0.66	0.80	1.00	1.23	1.55	2.00

Figures in italics were obtained by extrapolation

4.11.2.26 Angle 'Y' tees with bend on branch

(a) Converging flow

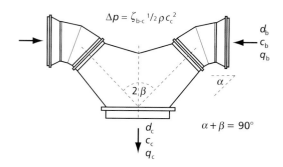

$$\Delta p = \zeta_{b\text{-}c} \, {}^1\!/_2 \, \rho \, c_c^2$$

$\alpha + \beta = 90°$

See Table 4.99.

(b) Diverging flow

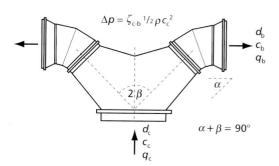

$$\Delta p = \zeta_{c\text{-}b} \, {}^1\!/_2 \, \rho \, c_c^2$$

$\alpha + \beta = 90°$

See Table 4.100.

Table 4.99 Angle 'Y' tees with bend on branch, converging flow: values for the branch factor $\zeta_{b\text{-}c}$ (derived from the European Programme Report[1])

Bend angle, α	Branch, angle, β	Relative branch flow, q_b/q_c								
		0.2	0.3	0.4	0.5	0.6	0.7	0.8	0.9	1.0
(a) 100/250/100 mm; $A_b/A_c = 0.16$										
30°	60°	*2.80*	3.80	5.40	8.05	12.2	17.8	24.2	32.4	40.8
45°	45°	*1.50*	3.00	5.45	9.00	13.6	18.3	23.5	29.5	36.6
60°	30°	*0*	1.90	4.35	7.69	12.0	16.5	21.5	27.0	32.7
(b) 160/250/160 mm; $A_b/A_c = 0.41$										
30°	60°	*0*	0.16	0.40	0.80	1.33	1.87	2.55	3.30	4.44
45°	45°	*–0.20*	*–0.03*	0.25	0.63	1.16	1.84	2.73	3.66	4.67
60°	30°	*–0.50*	*–0.25*	0.08	0.48	1.05	1.66	2.56	3.11	3.97
(c) 200/250/200 mm; $A_b/A_c = 0.64$										
30°	60°	*0.04*	0.10	0.21	0.36	0.53	0.70	0.88	1.05	1.22
45°	45°	*–0.08*	*0*	0.10	0.23	0.39	0.60	0.85	1.13	1.41
60°	30°	*–0.22*	*–0.12*	*0*	0.16	0.35	0.56	0.80	1.08	1.30
(d) 200/400/200 mm; $A_b/A_c = 0.25$										
30°	60°	*1.20*	1.27	1.50	2.10	3.75	5.95	8.60	12.0	15.5
45°	45°	*0.30*	0.55	1.10	2.09	4.00	6.40	9.55	13.0	16.4
60°	30°	*–1.30*	*–0.60*	0.54	0.246	4.84	7.61	10.9	14.2	18.1
(e) 250/400/250 mm; $A_b/A_c = 0.39$										
30°	60°	*0.05*	0.10	0.23	0.40	0.83	1.55	2.47	3.61	5.03
45°	45°	*–0.60*	*–0.47*	*–0.15*	0.38	1.00	1.90	2.97	4.31	5.92
60°	30°	*–0.80*	*–0.60*	*–0.20*	0.46	1.13	2.00	3.00	4.13	5.59
(f) 315/400/315 mm; $A_b/A_c = 0.62$										
30°	60°	*–0.05*	*0*	0.10	0.25	0.42	0.65	0.89	1.14	1.41
45°	45°	*–0.24*	*–0.19*	*–0.09*	0.01	0.15	0.35	0.57	0.77	0.99
60°	30°	*–0.20*	*–0.17*	*–0.07*	0.06	0.21	0.43	0.64	0.84	1.10

Note: values determined at Reynolds numbers as follows:
(a) (d): $Re_c = 1.6 \times 10^5$; (b) (c) (e) (f): $Re_c = 2.0 \times 10^5$

Figures in italics were obtained by extrapolation

Table 4.100 Angle 'Y' tees with bend on branch, diverging flow: values for the branch factor $\zeta_{c\text{-}b}$ (derived from the European Programme Report[1])

Bend angle, α	Branch, angle, β	Relative branch flow, q_b/q_c								
		0.2	0.3	0.4	0.5	0.6	0.7	0.8	0.9	1.0
(a) 100/250/100 mm; $A_b/A_c = 0.16$										
30°	60°	0.60	0.87	1.35	2.05	2.80	3.87	5.30	6.80	8.44
45°	45°	0.80	1.20	1.80	2.54	3.50	4.70	6.10	7.90	10.0
60°	30°	0.70	1.13	1.72	2.66	3.70	5.18	6.90	8.80	11.2
(b) 160/250/160 mm; $A_b/A_c = 0.41$										
30°	60°	0.41	0.42	0.45	0.50	0.55	0.64	0.78	0.94	1.16
45°	45°	0.35	0.31	0.30	0.30	0.38	0.51	0.66	0.88	1.16
60°	30°	0.25	0.24	0.27	0.33	0.48	0.67	0.87	1.13	1.48
(c) 200/250/200 mm; $A_b/A_c = 0.64$										
30°	60°	0.46	0.42	0.41	0.41	0.42	0.47	0.57	0.71	0.90
45°	45°	0.49	0.39	0.32	0.30	0.31	0.38	0.49	0.64	0.85
60°	30°	0.40	0.30	0.24	0.23	0.28	0.39	0.53	0.74	1.00
(d) 200/400/200 mm; $A_b/A_c = 0.25$										
45°	45°	0.10	0.13	0.18	0.27	0.37	0.49	0.64	0.83	1.06
60°	30°	0.10	0.18	0.30	0.44	0.61	0.80	1.01	1.26	1.5
(e) 250/400/250 mm; $A_b/A_c = 0.39$										
45°	45°	0.19	0.17	0.18	0.22	0.30	0.40	0.52	0.66	0.81
60°	30°	0.22	0.21	0.23	0.27	0.34	0.43	0.59	0.79	1.10
(f) 315/400/315 mm; $A_b/A_c = 0.62$										
45°	45°	0.37	0.29	0.24	0.22	0.21	0.24	0.31	0.41	0.53
60°	30°	0.39	0.27	0.20	0.17	0.20	0.26	0.36	0.55	0.76

Note: values determined at Reynolds numbers as follows:
(a) (b) (c) (e) (f): $Re_c = 2.0 \times 10^5$; (d): $Re_c = 1.6 \times 10^5$

Figures in italics were obtained by extrapolation

4.11.2.27 'Y' breech pieces, symmetrical (HVCA 150); converging and diverging flow

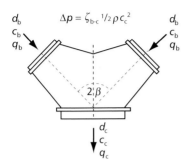

The preferred angle 2β is 60° to 90°, with manufacturers preferring 90°. No data are available for this item by itself. The nearest data available are that of item 4.11.2.26 above, where there is a bend on each branch. Thus values of ζ_{b-c} and ζ_{c-b} for the 'Y' breech alone can be expected to be less than those of Tables 4.99 and 4.100.

4.11.2.28 90° conical branch tees, circular from circular (HVCA 137 and 141)

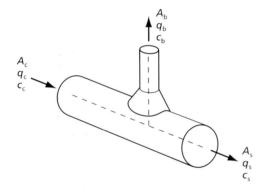

(a) Converging flows ($A_c = A_s$)

Miller[25] shows that, compared with a sharp tee, the slightest radius at the junction causes a reduction of at least 40% in the values of ζ_{s-c} and ζ_{b-c} over a range of normal flows $0.3 < q_b/q_c < 0.7$. The value of A_b/A_c was not given. Nevertheless the indication is that values less than those of Tables 4.63 and 4.64 may be used.

(b) Diverging flows ($A_c = A_s$)

Miller[25] shows that, compared with a sharp tee, the slightest radius at the junction causes a reduction of between 11% and 24% in the values of the branch factor ζ_{b-c} over a range of normal flows $0.3 < q_b/q_c < 0.7$. No data are given concerning the straight factor. The value of A_b/A_c was not given. Nevertheless the indication is that values less than those of Tables 4.65 and 4.66 may be used.

4.11.2.29 90° shoe branch tees, circular from circular (HVCA 139)

(a) Converging flows ($A_c = A_s$)

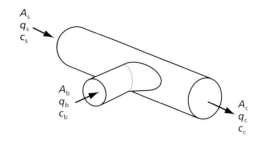

No data are available for a shoe on a circular branch. However, Miller[25] shows that a reduction of approximately 40% occurs for a trailing bevel on a circular branch on a rectangular duct and that a similar reduction occurs when a small radius ($r/d = 0.09$) is placed at the junction of a circular branch on a circular main duct. However it is not known over what range of A_b/A_c such reductions would apply. Nevertheless, the indication is that values less than those of Tables 4.63 and 4.64 may be used.

(b) Diverging flows ($A_c = A_s$)

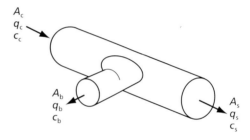

No data are available for a shoe on a circular branch. However, Miller[25] shows that a reduction of approximately 10% occurs for a leading bevel on a circular branch from a rectangular duct and that a 25% reduction occurs when a small radius ($r/d = 0.09$) is placed at the junction of a circular branch from a circular main duct. However it is not known over what range of A_b/A_c such reductions would apply. Nevertheless, the indication is that values less than those of Tables 4.65 and 4.66 may be used.

4.11.2.30 Angled off-sets, circular (HVCA 134)

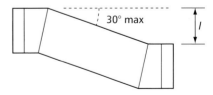

There are no specific data on mitred elbows in close proximity. A good approximation would be to use the sum of two mitres, and the length of straight duct between them. The value of ζ for mitre elbows of small angles can be obtained from Table 4.51 and Figure 4.11.

4.11.2.31   Exhaust vents with hood

Chinaman's hat

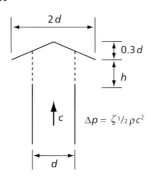

See Table 4.101.

Table 4.101 Exhaust vent with hood (Chinaman's hat): values of ζ (from Idelchik[2])

Item	Ratio, h/d									
	0.1	0.2	0.25	0.3	0.35	0.4	0.5	0.6	0.8	1.0
Exhaust vent (Chinaman's hat)	4	2.3	1.90	1.60	1.40	1.30	1.15	1.10	1.00	1.00

Plane baffle

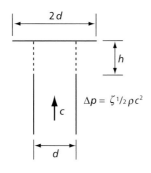

See Table 4.102.

Table 4.102 Exhaust vent with hood (plane baffle): values of ζ (from Idelchik[2])

Item	Ratio, h/d							
	0.25	0.3	0.35	0.4	0.5	0.6	0.8	1
Exhaust vent (plane baffle)	3.4	2.6	2.10	1.70	1.40	1.20	1.10	1.00

4.11.2.32   Plain extract

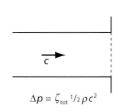

From Idelchik[2]:

$$\zeta_{tot} = 1.0 + \zeta_{mesh} \qquad (4.31)$$

4.11.2.33   Mesh screens; grids of circular metal wire

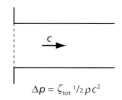

See Table 4.103. The value of ζ_{mesh} depends very much on the closeness of the mesh, or rather on the free or clear area ratio, being A_c/A.

For turbulent flow ($Re > 1000$) through the mesh, defined in this instance by:

$$Re = \rho c_m d / \eta \qquad (4.32)$$

where c_m is the mean velocity of air through the mesh and d is the diameter of the wire.

Idelchik[2] gives the following formula as a reasonable curve-fit for low values of A_c/A:

$$\zeta_{mesh} = 1.3 \left(1 - \frac{A_c}{A}\right) + \left(\frac{A}{A_c} - 1\right)^2 \qquad (4.33)$$

Table 4.103 Mesh screen: values of ζ (from Idelchik[2])

Item	Free area ratio, A_c/A							
	0.1	0.2	0.3	0.4	0.5	0.6	0.7	0.8
Mesh screen	82	17	6.4	3.03	1.65	0.97	0.58	0.32

4.11.2.34   Plain duct entries

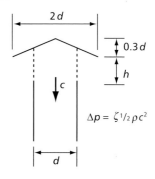

From Idelchik[2]:

$$\zeta_{tot} = 0.5 + \zeta_{mesh} \qquad (4.34)$$

4.11.2.35   Inlet vents with hood

Chinaman's hat

See Table 4.104.

Table 4.104 Inlet vent with hood (Chinaman's hat): values of ζ (from Idelchik[2])

Item	Ratio, h/d									
	0.1	0.2	0.3	0.4	0.5	0.6	0.7	0.8	0.9	1.0
Inlet vent (Chinaman's hat)	2.63	1.83	1.53	1.39	1.31	1.19	1.15	1.08	1.07	1.06

Plain baffle

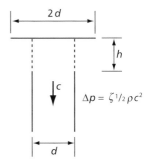

See Table 4.105.

Table 4.105 Inlet vent with hood (plane baffle): values of ζ (from Idelchik[2])

Item	Ratio, h/d							
	0.25	0.3	0.35	0.4	0.5	0.6	0.8	1.0
Inlet vent (plane baffle)	4.4	2.15	1.78	1.57	1.35	1.23	1.10	1.06

4.11.3 Pressure loss factors for ductwork components: flat-oval

4.11.3.1 90° segmented bends

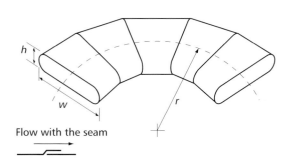

Flow with the seam

See Table 4.106. Smith and Jones[32] found that having the seams against the flow gave rise to an additional 0.06 in the value of ζ in comparison with the value when the flow is with the seam (approximately 23% extra). The values in Table 4.106 are for flow 'with the seam'. The values of ζ are greater than for a bend of circular cross section (see Table 4.47). It is to be expected that values of ζ for other values of r/w will be similarly greater than the circular equivalent.

For bends having the same aspect ratio h/w, the larger ducts have a slightly lower value of ζ.

4.11.3.2 Tees, flow diverging

All tees are circular off the oval duct, with branch diameter equal to the height of the oval duct ($d_b = h$). No data are available for the straight factor $\zeta_{c\text{-}s}$, nor for converging flow.

(*a*) 90° tee

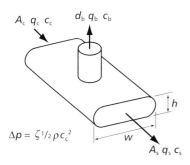

$$\Delta p = \zeta \tfrac{1}{2}\rho c_c^2$$

See Table 4.107 (page 4-52).

(*b*) 45° tee

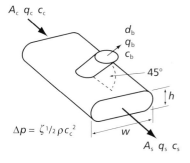

$$\Delta p = \zeta \tfrac{1}{2}\rho c_c^2$$

See Table 4.108 (page 4-52).

Table 4.106 90° segmented bends, flat-oval ($r/w = 1.5$): values of ζ; for $4 \times 10^5 < Re < 29 \times 10^5$ and 419 mm $< d_e <$ 794 mm (derived from Smith and Jones[32])

Item	Ratio, h/w									
	'Hard' ($w > h$)					'Easy' ($w < h$)				
	0.25	0.33	0.4	0.5	0.75	1	2	3	4	5
Seg. bend (flat-oval)	0.239	0.220	0.204	*0.192*	*0.171*	*0.170*	0.171	0.182	0.197	*0.214*

The figures in italics were obtained by interpolation

Table 4.107 90° tee, flat-oval, diverging: values of the branch factor, $\zeta_{c\text{-}b}$; for $4 \times 10^5 < Re_c < 29 \times 10^5$, and $255 \text{ mm} < d_{ec} < 550 \text{ mm}$ (derived from Smith and Jones[32])

Aspect, ratio, w/h	Equivalent diameter, d_{ec} / mm	Branch diameter, d_b / mm	Area ratio, A_b/A_c	Relative branch flow, q_b/q_c							
				0.1	0.2	0.3	0.4	0.5	0.6	0.7	0.8
2.0	255	150	0.279	0.921	1.05	1.21	1.53	1.95	2.42	3.03	—
3.2	300	150	0.196	0.958	1.17	1.64	2.26	3.12	—	—	—
4.1	550	150	0.157	1.00	1.37	2.11	3.12	—	—	—	—
2.0	423	250	0.282	0.937	1.04	1.26	1.53	1.90	2.37	3.00	3.69
2.9	484	250	0.210	0.947	1.16	1.53	2.11	2.84	3.69	—	—
4.1	550	250	0.159	1.00	1.37	2.05	3.03	—	—	—	—

Table 4.108 45° tee, flat-oval, diverging: values of the branch factor, $\zeta_{c\text{-}b}$; for $4 \times 10^5 < Re_c < 29 \times 10^5$, and $255 \text{ mm} < d_{ec} < 550 \text{ mm}$ (derived from Smith and Jones[32])

Aspect, ratio, w/h	Equivalent diameter, d_{ec} / mm	Branch diameter, d_b / mm	Area ratio, A_b/A_c	Relative branch flow, q_b/q_c							
				0.1	0.2	0.3	0.4	0.5	0.6	0.7	0.8
2.0	255	150	0.279	0.684	0.505	0.542	0.789	1.48	3.32	—	—
3.2	300	150	0.196	0.579	0.526	0.921	1.59	2.82	—	—	—
4.1	550	150	0.157	0.505	0.658	1.42	2.79	—	—	—	—
2.0	423	250	0.282	0.658	0.484	0.432	0.553	0.916	1.42	2.1	2.97
2.9	484	250	0.210	0.526	0.421	0.553	0.980	1.79	3.65	—	—
4.1	550	250	0.159	0.484	0.431	1.00	2.05	3.66	—	—	—

4.11.4 Pressure loss factors for ductwork components : rectangular

When Reynolds number is required for rectangular ducts, the hydraulic diameter (d_h) is to be used, being four times the hydraulic radius:

$$d_h = \frac{2\,w\,h}{(w + h)} \tag{4.35}$$

$$Re = \frac{\rho\,c\,d_h}{\eta} \tag{4.36}$$

where w and h are the width (mm) and height (mm) of the duct section.

Original source data are difficult to find. The primary source, Idelchik[2], is rather all-embracing and frequently too closely linked to data for circular ducts. Such data may have been derived using the hydraulic mean diameter. His original sources, generally in Russian, are neither readily available nor recent. Nevertheless, in the absence of other reliable data, we propose some of his data for guidance only and to be treated with circumspection.

4.11.4.1 90° radius bends without vanes (HVCA 86, 87)

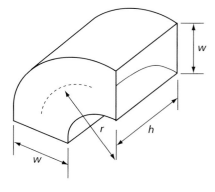

See Tables 4.109 and 4.110. The values in Table 4.109 are for $Re = 2 \times 10^5$.

For values of Re other than 2×10^5 the tabulated values should be multiplied by the correction factor C_{Re} given in Table 4.110. These data were obtained from the report of the European Programme on circular bends (see Table 4.48). It is expected to be similar for square bends $(r/d = 1)$, but may well be different for other values of h/w and r/w.

Appreciable savings in pressure drop are obtained by employing a radius r/d of 1.5 or greater. For 'tight' bends where $r/d \leq 1$, consideration should be given to using a guide vane (see section 4.11.4.2). It should be noted that for the same duct area $(w \times h)$ and for the same radius of the inner part of the bend, 'easy' bends $(h > w)$ give values of ζ which are appreciably less than for 'hard' bends $(h < w)$.

For bends of angles (α) other than 90°, Table 4.111 gives the angle factor, C_α, relative to the values of ζ for 90° bends. Miller[37] was not precise about the sizes used but the inference is that $w = 300 \text{ mm}$.

Table 4.109 90° bends, rectangular: values of ζ; for $Re = 2 \times 10^5$ (derived from Miller[37])

Ratio, r/w	Aspect ratio, h/w				
	0.5	0.75	1.0	1.5	2.0
0.8	—	—	—	—	0.359
1.0	0.232	*0.248*	0.254	*0.253*	0.243
1.5	*0.180*	*0.177*	*0.174*	*0.164*	0.137
2.0	0.164	*0.160*	0.155	*0.142*	0.121
2.5	*0.166*	*0.158*	*0.151*	*0.137*	0.124
3	0.170	*0.158*	0.150	*0.137*	0.128
4	—	—	—	—	0.135
6	—	—	—	—	0.153

Note: w is believed to be approximately 300 mm.

Figures in italics obtained by interpolation

Table 4.110 90° bends, rectangular: values of C_{Re} (derived from the European Programme Report[1])

Item	Value of C_{Re} for stated Reynolds number, $Re / 10^5$						
	0.5	1.0	1.5	2.0	3	4	10
90° bend, rect.	1.37	1.16	1.084	1.0	0.98	0.96	0.948

Table 4.111 Radius bends, rectangular: values of angle factor C_α; for $Re = 2 \times 10^5$ (derived from Miller[37])

Aspect ratio, h/w	Ratio, r/w	Value of C_α for stated bend angle, α					
		15°	30°	45°	60°	75°	90°
0.5	1	*0.150*	0.264	0.395	*0.636*	0.873	1
	2	*0.219*	0.400	0.568	*0.742*	0.897	1
	3	*0.224*	0.422	0.609	*0.776*	0.908	1
1.0	1	*0.124*	0.237	0.328	*0.498*	0.784	1
	2	*0.170*	0.367	0.531	*0.701*	0.857	1
	3	*0.204*	0.430	0.613	*0.775*	0.880	1
2.0	1	*0.088*	0.189	0.357	*0.617*	0.877	1
	2	*0.183*	0.391	0.583	*0.722*	0.852	1
	3	*0.182*	0.388	0.554	*0.711*	0.860	1

Figures in italics are interpolated values

Table 4.112 Short radius 90° bends, rectangular, with vanes: values of ζ (reproduced from *HVAC Systems Duct Design*[40] by permission of the Sheet Metal and Air-Conditioning Contractors' Association (SMACNA), Chantilly, Virginia, USA)

Ratio, r/w	Aspect ratio, h/w										
	0.25	0.5	1.0	1.5	2.0	3.0	4.0	5.0	6.0	7.0	8.0
(a) 1 turning vane											
0.55	0.52	0.40	0.43	0.49	0.55	0.66	0.75	0.84	0.93	1.01	1.09
0.60	0.36	0.27	0.25	0.28	0.30	0.35	0.39	0.42	0.46	0.49	0.52
0.65	0.28	0.21	0.18	0.19	0.20	0.22	0.25	0.26	0.28	0.30	0.32
0.70	0.22	0.16	0.14	0.14	0.15	0.16	0.17	0.18	0.19	0.20	0.21
0.75	0.18	0.13	0.11	0.11	0.11	0.12	0.13	0.14	0.14	0.15	0.15
0.80	0.15	0.11	0.09	0.09	0.09	0.09	0.10	0.10	0.11	0.11	0.12
0.90	0.11	0.08	0.07	0.06	0.06	0.06	0.06	0.07	0.07	0.07	0.07
1.00	0.09	0.06	0.05	0.05	0.04	0.04	0.04	0.05	0.05	0.05	0.05
(b) 2 turning vanes											
0.55	0.26	0.20	0.22	0.25	0.28	0.33	0.37	0.41	0.45	0.48	0.51
0.60	0.17	0.13	0.11	0.12	0.13	0.15	0.16	0.17	0.19	0.20	0.21
0.65	0.12	0.09	0.08	0.08	0.08	0.09	0.10	0.10	0.11	0.11	0.11
0.70	0.09	0.07	0.06	0.05	0.06	0.06	0.06	0.06	0.07	0.07	0.07
0.75	0.08	0.05	0.04	0.04	0.04	0.04	0.05	0.05	0.05	0.05	0.05
0.80	0.06	0.04	0.03	0.03	0.03	0.03	0.03	0.03	0.04	0.04	0.04
0.90	0.05	0.03	0.03	0.02	0.02	0.02	0.02	0.02	0.02	0.02	0.02
1.00	0.03	0.02	0.02	0.02	0.02	0.01	0.01	0.01	0.01	0.01	0.01
(c) 3 turning vanes											
0.55	0.11	0.10	0.12	0.13	0.14	0.16	0.18	0.19	0.21	0.22	0.23
0.60	0.07	0.05	0.06	0.06	0.06	0.07	0.07	0.08	0.08	0.08	0.09
0.65	0.05	0.04	0.04	0.04	0.04	0.04	0.04	0.04	0.04	0.05	0.05
0.70	0.03	0.03	0.03	0.03	0.03	0.03	0.03	0.03	0.03	0.03	0.03
0.75	0.03	0.02	0.02	0.02	0.02	0.02	0.02	0.02	0.02	0.02	0.02
0.80	0.03	0.02	0.02	0.02	0.02	0.01	0.01	0.01	0.01	0.01	0.01
0.90	0.02	0.01	0.01	0.01	0.01	0.01	0.01	0.01	0.01	0.01	0.01
1.00	0.01	0.01	0.01	0.01	0.01	0.01	0.01	0.01	0.01	0.01	0.01

Table 4.113 Short radius 90° bends, rectangular: recommended positions for splitters (from HVCA DW/144[22])

Dimension, w / mm	No. of splitters	Splitter position		
		1	2	3
400–800	1	$w/3$	—	—
801–1600	2	$w/4$	$w/2$	—
1601–2000	3	$w/8$	$w/3$	$w/2$

4.11.4.2 Short radius bends with vanes (splitters): rectangular (HVCA 88)

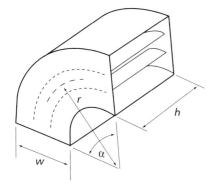

See Table 4.112. These data were published before size and Re were known to have an effect. Preferred positions for splitters are given in Table 4.113.

For bends of other angles, it is suggested that the angle factors given in Table 4.111 be used.

4.11.4.3 90° mitred throat bend (up to 400 mm wide) (HVCA 85)

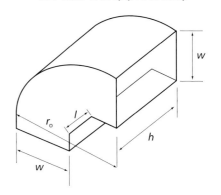

See Table 4.114. The figures have been based on an assumption of $l/w = 0.5$, where l is the length of the bevel, and $r_o/w = 1.5$, where r_o is the radius of the outer surface.

Table 4.114 90° mitred throat bend: values for ζ

Item	Aspect ratio, h/w										
	0.25	0.5	0.75	1	1.5	2	3	4	5	6	8
90° bend, mitred throat	0.31	0.29	0.27	0.26	0.24	0.23	0.22	0.22	0.22	0.23	0.23

Note: all values are estimates. No experimental values exist to justify them. They are based on the value of ζ lying between that for a mitred elbow with bevel inner, and that for a normal round bend. A confidence tolerance of ±30% would seem appropriate.

4.11.4.4   Elbow, mitred, rectangular, any angle

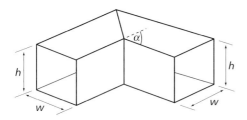

See Table 4.115. This table has been derived from data of Idelchik[2]. These data were published before size and *Re* were known to have an effect.

With the exception of small angles, similar values of ζ may be obtained using the following algorithm, being adapted from curve-fits by Idelchik[2]:

$$\zeta = \left(0.97 - 0.13 \ln \frac{h}{w}\right)\left(0.89 + \frac{40}{\alpha} \cos^2 (\alpha - 45)\right)$$

$$\times \left(0.95 \sin^2 \left(\frac{\alpha}{2}\right) + 2.05 \sin^4 \left(\frac{\alpha}{2}\right)\right) \quad (4.37)$$

Table 4.115 Mitred elbow, rectangular: values of ζ (from Idelchik[2])

Bend angle, α	Aspect ratio, h/w										
	0.25	0.5	0.75	1	1.5	2	3	4	5	6	8
20°	0.14	0.13	0.13	0.12	0.12	0.11	0.10	0.10	0.09	0.09	0.09
30°	0.17	0.17	0.16	0.16	0.15	0.14	0.13	0.12	0.12	0.11	0.11
45°	0.35	0.34	0.33	0.32	0.3	0.29	0.26	0.25	0.24	0.23	0.22
60°	0.61	0.59	0.58	0.56	0.53	0.50	0.46	0.43	0.42	0.40	0.39
75°	0.89	0.86	0.84	0.81	0.77	0.73	0.67	0.63	0.60	0.58	0.56
90°	1.31	1.27	1.24	1.19	1.13	1.07	0.99	0.93	0.89	0.86	0.83

4.11.4.5   Elbow, 90° rectangular, rounded inner corner

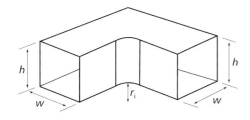

See table 4.116. This table has been derived from data of Idelchik[2]. It is to be expected that the values of ζ for the rounded inner corner should be lower than for a 90° mitred corner (see section 4.11.4.4). In most instances this

is the case, but there are a few contradictions. Although both sets of data have been derived from Idelchik, his information is derived from many other sources so some discrepancies may be expected. Comparing the values for the sharpest inner corner in Table 4.116 ($r_i/w = 0.05$) with those of a sharp mitre corner in Table 4.115 shows that for the slightest radius there is an optimum value of h/w, whereas for the sharp mitre elbow there is not. There is therefore some doubt about the validity of the values in Table 4.116 but they are the only data available.

Table 4.116 90° elbow, rectangular, with rounded inner corner: values of ζ (from Idelchik[2])

Ratio, r_i/w	Aspect ratio, h/w						
	0.5	0.75	1	2	3	4	6
0.05	1.31	1.22	1.12	0.95	0.95	1.01	1.10
0.1	1.05	0.98	0.90	0.77	0.77	0.81	0.88
0.2	0.85	0.79	0.73	0.62	0.62	0.66	0.72
0.3	0.67	0.64	0.59	0.51	0.51	0.53	0.58
0.5	0.60	0.56	0.52	0.45	0.45	0.47	0.51
0.7	0.65	0.51	0.47	0.41	0.41	0.43	0.46

4.11.4.6   90° rectangular mitred elbows of unequal areas

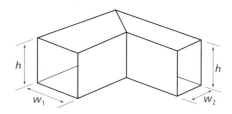

See Table 4.117. This table is a modification of that given in Idelchik's diagram 6–6[2].

Note that the value of ζ must be applied to the upstream velocity pressure, i.e.:

$$\Delta p = \zeta \tfrac{1}{2} \rho c_1^2 \quad (4.38)$$

Note that in the case of equal areas ($w_1/w_2 = 1$), there are slight discrepancies compared with the 90° mitred elbow (section 4.11.4.4).

Table 4.117 Mitred elbow, rectangular, of unequal areas: values of ζ (from Idelchik[2])

Ratio, h/w_1	Ratio, w_1/w_2						
	0.6	0.8	1	1.2	1.4	1.6	2
0.25	1.76	1.43	1.24	1.14	1.09	1.06	1.06
1	1.70	1.36	1.15	1.02	0.95	0.90	0.84
4	1.46	1.10	0.90	0.81	0.76	0.72	0.66
∞	1.50	1.04	0.79	0.69	0.63	0.60	0.60

4.11.4.7 Rectangular mitred elbows with vanes

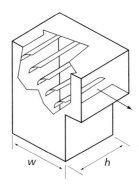

No reliable data are available. As an interim measure it is suggested that the values of Table 4.115 might be halved.

4.11.4.8 Bends in close proximity, rectangular ('gooseneck')

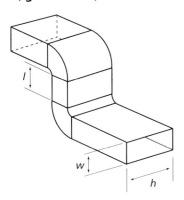

No data are available for the interaction factor C_{cp} of rectangular ductwork installed in close proximity. It is to be expected that C_{cp} would depend upon r/w and h/w of each bend as well as the separation l/w. We can also expect that it will vary with Reynolds number, and possibly also with size w.

Data for 'gooseneck' bends for circular ductwork are given in section 4.11.2.5 for close coupling of bends with $d = 250$ mm, and $r/d = 1.0$. Thus for close coupling of square bends of sides approximately 250 mm and with $r/d = 1.0$, it would seem reasonable to use the values of C_{cp} given in Table 4.52, in conjunction with values of ζ_1 from Table 4.109 in the equation:

$$\Delta p = 2\, C_{cp}\, \zeta_1\, {}^1/_2\, \rho\, c^2 \qquad (4.39)$$

Note that the above does not include for the pressure drop of the length of separation. The separation (l) should be added to the length of straight ductwork of the same size.

4.11.4.9 Bends in close proximity, rectangular, through perpendicular plane

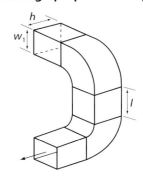

Since bends of this type involve one bend which is 'easy' and the other 'difficult', it is difficult to see which bend should be used for ζ. Use of ζ for a 'difficult' bend could give a conservative value.

No data are available for the interaction factor C_{cp} of rectangular ductwork installed in close proximity. It is to be expected that C_{cp} would depend upon r/w, r/h and h/w of each bend as well as the separation l/w. It is also expected that it will vary with Reynolds number, and possibly also with size w.

Data for bends in close proximity for circular ductwork are given in section 4.11.2.6 for bends with $d = 250$ mm, and $r/d = 1.0$. Thus for close coupling of square bends of sides approximately 250 mm and having $r/d = 1.0$, it would seem reasonable to use the values of C_{cp} given in Table 4.53, and use it in conjunction with values of ζ_1 from Table 4.109 in equation 4.39.

Note that the above does not include the pressure drop of the length of separation. The separation (l) should be added to the length of straight ductwork of the same size.

4.11.4.10 Elbows in close proximity, rectangular, in plane

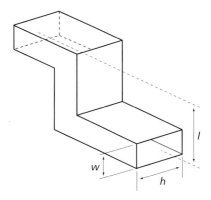

No recent data are available. Some tentative data are presented in Table 4.118. However, it is expected that ζ should vary with Reynolds number and with size.

Table 4.118 Combined double elbow, rectangular: values of ζ for the whole, including the separating length (derived from Idelchik[2], diagram 6–13)

Offset step, l/w	Aspect ratio, h/w							
	0.25	0.5	1	1.5	2	3	5	8
0.6	1.0	0.98	0.91	0.87	0.82	0.79	0.69	0.64
0.8	1.8	1.7	1.6	1.5	1.5	1.3	1.22	1.14
1	2.9	2.8	2.7	2.5	2.4	2.2	2.0	1.9
1.8	4.8	4.6	4.3	4.0	3.8	3.5	3.2	3.0
2	4.6	4.5	4.2	4.0	3.8	3.5	3.2	3.0
2.4	4.1	4.0	3.7	3.5	3.3	3.1	2.8	2.6
3	3.7	3.6	3.4	3.2	3.0	2.8	2.5	2.3
4	3.5	3.4	3.2	3.0	2.9	2.6	2.4	2.2
6	3.3	3.2	3.0	2.9	2.7	2.5	2.3	2.2
10	2.9	2.8	2.7	2.5	2.4	2.2	2.0	1.9

Notes:

(1) The maximum friction pressure loss occurs when the offset is around $l/w = 1.8$.

(2) In this instance l is defined as the step and not the separation.

4.11.4.11 Elbows in close proximity, rectangular, through perpendicular plane

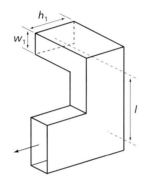

See Table 4.119.

No recent data are available. The data presented in Table 4.119 should be regarded as tentative. It is expected that ζ should vary with Reynolds number and with size.

Table 4.119 Double elbow, rectangular, through perpendicular plane: values of ζ for the whole, including the separating length (derived from Idelchik[2], diagram 6–13)

Offset step, l/w_1	Aspect ratio, h_1/w_1							
	0.25	0.5	1	1.5	2	3	5	8
0	1.26	1.23	1.15	1.09	1.04	0.95	0.86	0.81
0.6	2.7	2.6	2.4	2.3	2.2	2.0	1.8	1.7
1	3.8	2.6	3.5	2.3	2.2	2.0	1.8	1.7
1.5	3.6	3.5	3.2	3.0	2.9	2.7	2.4	2.3
2	3.5	3.4	3.2	3	2.8	2.6	2.4	2.2
3	3.5	3.5	3.2	3.1	2.9	2.7	2.4	2.3
5	3.3	3.2	3.0	2.8	2.6	2.5	2.3	2.1
7	3.1	3.0	2.8	2.7	2.6	2.4	2.2	2.0
10	2.9	2.8	2.6	2.5	2.4	2.2	2.0	1.9

Notes:

(1) In this instance l is defined as the step and not the separation.

(2) The outlet has the same dimensions h and w, but ζ is given in terms of w_1 and h_1.

(3) Although the data available are for any aspect ratio h/w, it is perhaps surprising that high values, implying that the second elbow is 'difficult', do not result in higher values of ζ. It is easier to have confidence in the values for a square or almost square duct.

4.11.4.12 90° rectangular tees (HVCA 104 and 106)

The only data available are from Miller[25,37]. For both the straight and branch factors, his values of ζ are consistently higher than his values for circular tees of the same area ratio A_b/A_c. However his values of ζ for rectangular tees were all a little lower than the more recently obtained data of the European Programme[1] for circular tees (see Tables 4.63 to 4.66). Therefore, for consistency, the original values produced by Miller have been increased so as to show, as he found, the increase in ζ compared to circular tees. The values printed in Tables 4.120 to 4.123, therefore, should be treated as 'best advice'. In the rectangular tees tested, w of the main duct remained constant ($w = h_c = h_s$), whereas $h_c \geq h_b$. Miller tested for various sizes of the shoe, b. The greater the size of the shoe the greater the reduction in ζ. The reduction in the valus of ζ due to the installation of a trailing or leading bevel ($\Delta\zeta$) is shown in the tables.

It is to be expected that values of ζ will vary considerably with A_b/A_c, as occurs for circular tees. It is expected that ζ will depend on the aspect ratios of both the main duct (h_c/w) and of the branch (h_b/w_b), and a little upon size but no experimental data are available.

(*a*) Converging flow

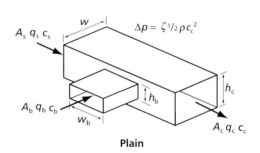

Plain

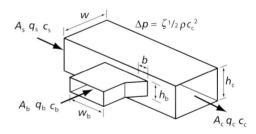

Trailing bevel

See Tables 4.120 and 4.121.

Table 4.120 90° rectangular tees, converging flow: values for the straight factor ζ_{s-c} and reduction in ζ obtained by inclusion of trailing bevel; for $w = h_c = h_s = 300$ mm, $Re_c > 10^5$ (derived from Miller[25,37])

Area ratio, A_b/A_c		Relative straight flow, q_s/q_c						
		0.2	0.3	0.4	0.5	0.6	0.7	0.8
0.79		0.75	0.71	0.66	0.60	0.53	0.44	0.35
1.00		0.74	0.70	0.65	0.59	0.52	0.43	0.33
	Bevel length, b	Reduction in straight factor, $\Delta\zeta_{s-c}$, due to trailing bevel						
0.79	$w/8$	0.26	0.24	0.22	0.20	0.17	0.15	0.11
1.00	$w/8$	0.26	0.24	0.25	0.26	0.19	0.11	0.06
1.00	$w/2$	0.54	0.45	0.35	0.27	0.19	0.11	0.06

Table 4.121 90° rectangular tees, converging flow: values for the branch factor ζ_{b-c} and reduction in ζ obtained by inclusion of trailing bevel; for $w = h_c = h_s = 300$ mm, $Re_c > 10^5$ (derived from Miller[25,37])

Area ratio, A_b/A_c		Relative branch flow, q_b/q_c						
		0.2	0.3	0.4	0.5	0.6	0.7	0.8
0.79			0.18	0.34	0.51	0.71	0.94	1.23	1.52
1.00			−0.10	0.19	0.42	0.62	0.83	1.01	1.13
	Bevel length, b	Reduction in branch factor, $\Delta\zeta_{b-c}$, due to trailing bevel						
0.79	$w/8$	—	0.23	0.21	0.23	0.25	0.27	0.30
1.00*	$w/8$	—	0.15	0.22	0.25	0.27	0.25	0.26
1.00	$w/2$	—	0.19	0.26	0.32	0.40	0.49	0.57

* Raw data is out of step with other data

(b) **Diverging flow**

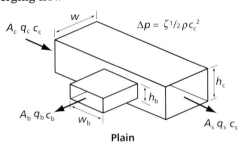

Plain

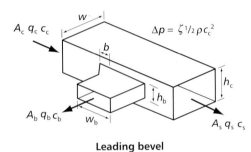

Leading bevel

See Tables 4.122 and 4.123.

Table 4.122 90° rectangular tees, diverging flow: values for the straight factor ζ_{c-s} and reduction in ζ obtained by inclusion of leading bevel; for $w = h_c = h_s = 300$ mm, $Re_c > 10^5$ (derived from Miller[37])

Area ratio, A_b/A_c		Relative straight flow, q_s/q_c						
		0.2	0.3	0.4	0.5	0.6	0.7	0.8
1.00		0.31	0.21	0.13	0.07	0.025	0	0
	Bevel length, b	Reduction in straight factor, $\Delta\zeta_{s-c}$, due to leading bevel						
1.00	$w/8$	No noticeable effect						
1.00	$w/2$	No noticeable effect						

Table 4.123 90° rectangular tees, diverging flow: values for the branch factor ζ_{c-b} and reduction in ζ obtained by inclusion of leading bevel; for $w = h_c = h_s = 300$ mm, $Re_c > 10^5$ (derived from Miller[25,37])

Area ratio, A_b/A_c		Relative branch flow, q_b/q_c						
		0.2	0.3	0.4	0.5	0.6	0.7	0.8
1.00*		*0.87*	*0.82*	*0.82*	*0.84*	*0.89*	*0.94*	*1.02*
	Bevel length, b	Reduction in branch factor, $\Delta\zeta_{b-c}$, due to leading bevel						
1.00	$w/8$	0.04	0.04	0.07	0.09	0.13	0.16	0.21
1.00	$w/2$	0.095	0.16	0.23	0.31	0.39	0.48	0.58

* Figures in italics are Miller's readings. They would be expected to be greater than for a circular tee (Table 4.66), but he did not make this comparison. The values as presented conflict with those for circular tees, thus there is possibly some doubt about these values.

4.11.4.13 Angled branch tees: rectangular from rectangular (HVCA 105)

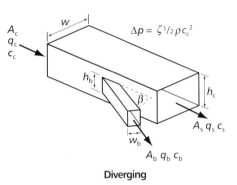

Converging

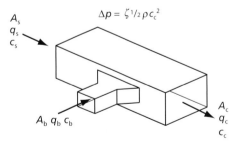

Diverging

The all-embracing data provided by Idelchik[2] is too simple to be true. For angle circular tees (cf Tables 4.77 and 4.78 for example) it is clear that, for the same value of A_b/A_c, size matters. From the limited data on flat-oval tees, (cf Tables 4.107 and 4.108) it is also clear that values of the branch factor depend upon h_c/w_c. We can also expect the branch factors in particular to depend upon w_b/w_c and h_b/h_c. In the absence of any data which takes account of these factors, it is impossible to present even simplified guidance. The data in this Guide which might point the designer towards an estimate of likely values of ζ are the data for angle branch tees, circular (section 4.11.2.16), 90° tees, flat-oval (section 4.11.3.2) and 90° tees, rectangular (section 4.11.4.12).

4.11.4.14 90° Tees: rectangular from rectangular; bell-mouth branch (HVCA 107)

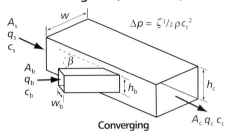

Converging and diverging flows ($A_c = A_s$)

No data can be found for this component. There is no reason to believe that the values of ζ will be any less than that for a shoe branch (section 4.11.4.12).

4.11.4.15 90° radiussed twin bend: rectangular (HVCA 91)

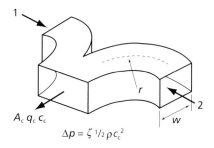

$$\Delta p = \zeta \, {}^1\!/_2 \, \rho \, c_c^2$$

Little information is available. Even for a symmetrical tee with an equal division of flow, values of ζ will depend upon A_1/A_c, r/w, h_b/w_b, h_c/w_c and size. Guidance should be taken from section 4.11.2.26 (Angle 'Y' tees with bend on branch, circular).

4.11.4.16 90° swept branch tee

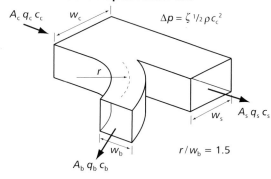

$$\Delta p = \zeta \, {}^1\!/_2 \, \rho \, c_c^2$$

$$r/w_b = 1.5$$

See Tables 4.124 and 4.125.

Table 4.124 90° swept tees, rectangular, diverging flow: values for the straight factor ζ_{c-s}; for $h_b = h_c = h_s$, $A_b + A_s \geq A_c$ (from ASHRAE Handbook: *Fundamentals* 2005[4], ch. 35. © American Society of Heating, Refrigerating and Air-Conditioning Engineers Inc. (www.ashrae.org))

A_s/A_c	A_b/A_c	Relative straight flow, q_s/q_c								
		0.1	0.2	0.3	0.4	0.5	0.6	0.7	0.8	0.9
0.50	0.25	8.75	1.62	0.50	0.17	0.05	0.00	−0.02	−0.02	0.00
	0.50	7.50	1.12	0.25	0.06	0.05	0.09	0.14	0.19	0.22
	1.00	5.00	0.62	0.17	0.08	0.08	0.09	0.12	0.15	0.19
0.75	0.25	19.13	3.38	1.00	0.28	0.05	−0.02	−0.02	0.00	0.06
	0.50	20.81	3.23	0.75	0.14	−0.02	−0.05	−0.05	−0.02	0.03
	1.00	16.88	2.81	0.63	0.11	−0.02	−0.05	0.01	0.00	0.07
1.00	0.25	46.00	9.50	3.22	1.31	0.52	0.14	−0.02	−0.05	−0.01
	0.50	35.00	6.75	2.11	0.75	0.24	0.00	−0.10	−0.09	−0.04
	1.00	38.00	7.50	2.44	0.81	0.24	−0.03	−0.08	−0.06	−0.02

Table 4.125 90° swept tees, rectangular, converging flow: values for the branch factor ζ_{c-b}; for $h_w = h_c = h_s$, $A_b + A_s \geq A_c$ (from ASHRAE Handbook: *Fundamentals* 2005[4], ch. 35. © American Society of Heating, Refrigerating and Air-Conditioning Engineers Inc. (www.ashrae.org))

A_s/A_c	A_b/A_c	Relative branch flow, q_b/q_c								
		0.1	0.2	0.3	0.4	0.5	0.6	0.7	0.8	0.9
0.50	0.25	3.44	0.70	0.30	0.20	0.17	0.16	0.16	0.17	0.18
	0.50	11.00	2.37	1.06	0.64	0.52	0.47	0.47	0.47	0.48
	1.00	60.00	13.00	4.78	2.06	0.96	0.47	0.31	0.27	0.26
0.75	0.25	2.19	0.55	0.35	0.31	0.33	0.35	0.36	0.37	0.39
	0.50	13.00	2.50	0.89	0.47	0.34	0.31	0.32	0.36	0.43
	1.00	70.00	15.00	5.67	2.62	1.36	0.78	0.53	0.41	0.36
1.00	0.25	3.44	0.78	0.42	0.33	0.30	0.31	0.40	0.42	0.46
	0.50	15.50	3.00	1.11	0.62	0.48	0.42	0.40	0.42	0.46
	1.00	67.00	13.75	5.11	2.31	1.28	0.81	0.59	0.47	0.46

The values of the branch factor ζ_{c-b} ought to depend on the aspect ratio h_b/w_b. The only available data are from ASHRAE[4].

4.11.4.17 Angled offsets (HVCA 96, 97, 98)

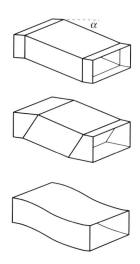

There are no specific data on rectangular elbows and bends in close proximity. A good approximation would be to use the sum of two bends or elbows, and the length of clear duct between. Values of ζ are given in Tables 4.109 to 4.111 for bends, and Table 4.115 for mitred elbows.

4.11.4.18 Opposed blade dampers

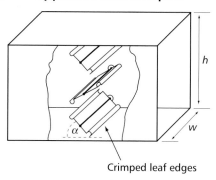

Crimped leaf edges

See Table 4.126. The parameter x is determined from:

$$x = \frac{n \, w}{2 \, (h + w)} \tag{4.40}$$

where n is the number of blades.

Table 4.126 Opposed blade damper: values of ζ from ASHRAE Handbook: *Fundamentals* 2005[4], ch. 35. © American Society of Heating, Refrigerating and Air-Conditioning Engineers Inc. (www.ashrae.org))

Value of x	Value of ζ for stated blade angle, α								
	0°	10°	20°	30°	40°	50°	60°	70°	80°
0.3	0.52	0.79	1.91	3.77	8.55	19.5	70.1	295	807
0.4	0.52	0.85	2.07	4.61	10.4	26.7	92.9	346	926
0.5	0.52	0.93	2.25	5.44	12.3	34.0	119	393	1045
0.6	0.52	1.00	2.46	5.99	14.1	41.3	144	440	1163
0.8	0.52	1.08	2.66	6.96	18.2	56.5	194	520	1325
1.0	0.52	1.17	2.91	7.31	20.2	71.7	245	576	1521
1.5	0.52	1.38	3.16	9.51	27.6	104.4	361	717	1804

4.11.4.19 Exhaust vents; lateral openings with and without side louvres

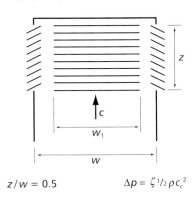

$z/w = 0.5$ $\Delta p = \zeta \tfrac{1}{2} \rho c_c^2$

The pressure drop through such exhaust vents will depend strongly on the geometry of the louvres so manufacturer's guidance should be sought. Table 4.127, taken from Idelchik[2], is intended for initial guidance only, when doing initial feasibility calculations.

Table 4.127 Exhaust vents, lateral openings: values of ζ (from Idelchik[2])

Number of openings	Layout	w/z	Value of ζ		
			Without louvres	30° louvres	45° louvres
One		1.5	15.5	22.0	—
Two		1.5	5.0	7.2	—
Three		1.5	3.5	5	—
Four		1.5	2.2	2.6	3.5
		1.0	5.3	7.0	10.0
		0.5	15.6	19.6	29

4.11.4.20 Inlet vents; lateral openings with and without side louvres

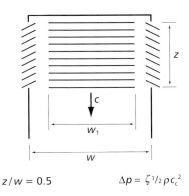

$z/w = 0.5$ $\Delta p = \zeta \tfrac{1}{2} \rho c_c^2$

The pressure drop through such exhaust vents will depend strongly on the geometry of the louvres so manufacturer's guidance should be sought. Table 4.128, derived from Idelchik[2], is intended for initial guidance only, when doing initial feasibility calculations.

Table 4.128 Inlet vents, lateral openings: values of ζ (from Idelchik[2])

Number of openings	Layout	w/z	Value of ζ		
			Without louvres	30° louvres	45° louvres
One		1.5	12.6	17.5	—
Two		1.5	3.6	5.4	—
Three		1.5	1.8	3.2	—
Four		1.5	1.2	2.5	3.8
		1.0	2.0	3.6	6.0
		0.5	8.0	13.7	21.5

4.11.4.21 Louvred duct entries

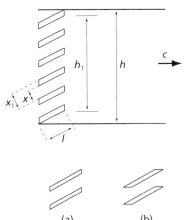

Table 4.129 gives values of ζ for the two idealised shapes of louvre blade, for values of $l/x_1 > 2.2$. Note that the angle of the blades would appear not to play a part, except insofar as it affects the value of h_1/h.

Table 4.129 Louvred duct entries: values of ζ (from Idelchik[2])

Louvre	x/x_1	Ratio, h_1/h					
		0.6	0.7	0.8	0.9	0.95	1.0
Type (a)	0.8	7.9	5.7	4.3	3.3	3.0	2.7
	0.9	6.7	4.8	3.7	2.9	2.6	2.3
Type (b)	0.8	4.8	3.4	2.6	2.0	1.8	1.6
	0.9	4.0	2.9	2.2	1.7	1.5	1.4

4.11.4.22 Plain outlets

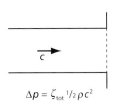

$\Delta p = \zeta_{tot} \tfrac{1}{2} \rho c^2$

From Idelchik[2]:

$$\zeta_{tot} = 1.0 + \zeta_{mesh} \qquad (4.41)$$

4.11.4.23 Mesh screens; grids of circular metal wire

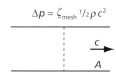

$$\Delta p = \zeta_{\text{mesh}} \, {}^{1}\!/_{2} \rho c^2$$

See Table 4.130. The value of ζ_{mesh} depends very much on the closeness of the mesh, or rather on the free or clear area ratio, A_c/A.

For turbulent flow ($Re > 1000$) through the mesh, defined in this instance by:

$$Re = \rho c_m d / \eta \qquad (4.42)$$

where c_m is the mean velocity of air through the mesh and d is the diameter of the wire.

Idelchik[2] gives the following formula as a reasonable curve-fit for low values of A_c/A:

$$\zeta_{\text{mesh}} = 1.3 \left(1 - \frac{A_c}{A}\right) + \left(\frac{A}{A_c} - 1\right)^2 \qquad (4.43)$$

Table 4.130 Mesh screen: values of ζ (from Idelchik[2])

Item	Free area ratio, A_c/A							
	0.1	0.2	0.3	0.4	0.5	0.6	0.7	0.8
Mesh screen	82	17	6.4	3.03	1.65	0.97	0.58	0.32

4.11.4.24 Plain duct entries

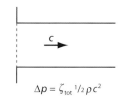

$$\Delta p = \zeta_{\text{tot}} \, {}^{1}\!/_{2} \rho c^2$$

From Idelchik[2]:

$$\zeta_{\text{tot}} = 0.5 + \zeta_{\text{mesh}} \qquad (4.44)$$

4.11.5 Transitions between circular and rectangular ductwork

4.11.5.1 Expansions, transitions

$$\Delta p = \zeta \, {}^{1}\!/_{2} \rho c_1^{\,2}$$

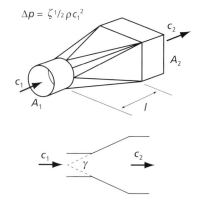

No recent experimental data can be found. ASHRAE reports that the same values of ζ apply for transitions circular-to-rectangular and rectangular-to-circular, and that for taper angles $\gamma > 30°$ these are very similar to those for circular-to-circular tapers. However the influence of aspect ratio h/w is not reported and has perhaps not been investigated. In the light of this, values of ζ should be taken from section 4.11.2.7.

For non-symmetrical expansions, vertical and horizontal projections will give two different taper angles, γ_1 and γ_2. The greater of these should be used when using the data of section 4.11.2.7.

It is expected that the expansion of rectangular sections, whether symmetrical or non-symmetrical, might have greater values of ζ than for circular-to-circular tapers.

4.11.5.2 Contractions, transitions

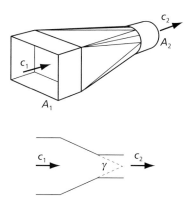

No recent experimental data can be found. ASHRAE reports that the same values of ζ apply for transitions circular-to-rectangular and rectangular-to-circular. However the influence of aspect ratio h/w is not reported and has perhaps not been investigated. In the light of this, values of ζ should be taken from section 4.11.2.8.

For non-symmetrical contractions, vertical and horizontal projections will give two different taper angles, γ_1 and γ_2. The greater of these should be used when using the data of section 4.11.2.8.

It is expected that the contraction of rectangular sections, whether symmetrical or unsymmetrical, might have greater values of ζ than for circular-to-circular tapers.

References

1   *Energy loss coefficients of components used in air distribution systems* EEC Programme Report No. 3401/1/0/110/90/8-BCR-D(30) (Brussels: Commission of the European Communities Directorate-General for Science, Research and Development) (1992) (obtainable from Eurovent, 62 Boulevard de Sébastopol, 75003 Paris) (www.eurovent-certification.com)

2   Idelchik I E *Handbook of hydraulic resistance* 3rd edn. (New York, NY: Begell House) (1996)

3   Lamont P 'The reduction with age of the carrying capacity of pipelines' *J. Inst. Water Engineers* **8** 53–92 (1954)

4   *Fundamentals* 2005 ASHRAE Handbook (Atlanta, GA: American Society of Heating, Refrigerating and Air-Conditioning Engineers) (2005)

5   Schneider K J *Bautabellen* (9th edn.) (Dusseldorf, Germany: Werner Verlag) (1990)

6   BS EN 10255: 2004: *Non-alloy steel tubes suitable for welding or threading. Technical delivery conditions* (London: British Standards Institution) (2004)

7   BS EN 10220: 2002: *Seamless and welded steel tubes. Dimensions and masses per unit length* (London: British Standards Institution) (2002)

8   BS 1211: 1958: *Specification for centrifugally cast (spun) iron pressure pipes for water, gas and sewage* (London: British Standards Institution) (1958)

9   BS EN 1057: 2006: *Copper and copper alloys. Seamless, round copper tubes for water and gas in sanitary and heating applications* (London: British Standards Institution) (2006)

10   BS EN 1452-2: 2000: *Plastics piping systems for water supply. Unplasticized poly(vinyl chloride) (PVC-U). Pipes* (London: British Standards Institution) (2000)

11   BS 7291: *Thermoplastics pipes and associated fittings for hot and cold water for domestic purposes and heating installations in buildings*: Part 1: 2006: *General requirements*; Part 2: 2006: *Specification for polybutylene (PB) pipes and associated fittings*; Part 3: 2006: *Specification for cross-linked polyethylene (PE-X) pipes and associated fittings*; Part 4: 1990: *Specification for chlorinated polyvinyl chloride (PVC-C) pipes and associated fittings and solvent cement* (London: British Standards Institution) (dates as indicated)

12   BS ISO 4065: 1996: *Thermoplastics pipes. Universal wall thickness table* (London: British Standards Institution) (1996)

13   BS 2782-11: Method 1121B: 1997 (ISO 161-1: 1996): *Methods of testing plastics. Thermoplastics pipes, fittings and valves. Thermoplastics pipes for the conveyance of fluids. Nominal outside diameters and nominal pressures. Metric series* (London: British Standards Institution) (1997)

14   Haaland S E 'Simple and explicit formulas for the friction factor in turbulent flow' *ASME J. of Fluids Eng.* **105** (3) 89–90 (March 1983)

15   *Rules of thumb UK/France* BSRIA TN 18/1995 (Bracknell: Building Services Research and Information Association) (1995)

16   Ball E F and Webster C 'Some measurements of water-flow noise in copper and ABS pipes' *Building Services Engineer* **44** (5) 33–40 (May 1976)

17   Rogers W L 'Noise and vibration in water piping systems' *ASHRAE J.* **1** (3) 83–86 (1959)

18   BS EN ISO 5167-1: 2003: *Measurement of fluid flow by means of pressure differential devices inserted in circular cross-section conduits running full. General principles and requirements* (London: British Standards Institution)

19   *Noise and vibration control for HVAC* ch. 5 in CIBSE Guide B: *Heating, ventilating, air conditioning and refrigeration* (London: Chartered Institution of Building Services Engineers) (2001–2)

20   Huebscher R G 'Friction equivalents for round square and rectangular ducts' *ASHVE Trans.* **54** 101–118 (1948)

21   Heyt J W and Diaz M J 'Pressure drop in flat oval spiral air duct' *ASHRAE Trans.* **81** (2) 221–232 (1975)

22   *Specification for sheet metal ductwork* HVCA DW/144 (London: Heating and Ventilating Contractors Association) (1998)

23   *Pressure losses in three-leg pipe junctions: combining flows* Engineering Sciences Data Unit Item 73023 (London: IHS ESDU International) (1973)

24   Eschman R and Lang W E 'A critical assessment of high velocity duct design information' *ASHRAE Trans.* **76** 157–176 (1970)

25   Miller D S *Internal flow systems* (Cranfield: British Hydromechanics Research Association) (1990)

26   Rahmeyer W J 'Pressure loss coefficients of pipe fittings for threaded and forged weld pipe fittings for ells, reducing ells, and pipe reducers' *ASHRAE Trans.* **105** (2) 334–354 (1999)

27   Rahmeyer W J 'Pressure loss data for large pipe ells, reducers and expansions' *ASHRAE Trans.* **108** (1) 360–375 (2002)

28   *An experimental study of the performance characteristics of 90° elbow* UMC Reports SRF 785 (1985) and 1285 (1986) (Westerville, OH: United McGill Corporation) (dates as indicated)

29   Rahmeyer W J 'Pressure loss coefficients of pipe fittings for threaded and forged weld pipe tees' *ASHRAE Trans.* **105** (2) 355–385 (1999)

30   Rahmeyer W J 'Pressure loss data for large pipe tees' *ASHRAE Trans.* **108** (1) 376–389 (2002)

31   Madison R D and Parker J R 'Pressure loss in rectangular elbows' *ASHRAE Trans.* **58** (1936)

32   Smith J R and Jones J W 'Pressure loss in high velocity flat oval duct fittings' *ASHRAE Trans.* **82** 157–176 (1976)

33   Rahmeyer W J 'Pressure loss data for PVC pipe tees' *ASHRAE Trans.* **109** (2) 230–251 (2003)

34   Koch P and Pierson P 'Et si le calcul des pertes de charge singulières n'était pas si juste qu'on pouvait le croire?' *Chaud Froid Plomberie* (661) 65–74 (2003)

35   Rahmeyer W J 'Pressure loss data for PVC pipe elbows, reducers and expansions' *ASHRAE Trans.* **109** (2) 230–251 (2003)

36   Rahmeyer W J 'Pressure loss coefficients for close-coupled pipe ell' *ASHRAE Trans.* **108** (1) 390–406 (2002)

37   Miller D S *Internal flow: A guide to losses in pipe and duct systems.* (Cranfield: British Hydromechanics Research Association) (1971)

38   Koch P ' The influence of Reynolds number and size effects on pressure loss factors of ductwork components' *Building Serv. Eng. Res. Technol.* **27** (4) 261–300 (2006)

39   Bersisparic S and Dagonnot J Catalogue des coefficients de perte d'énergie mécanique (Pressure loss coefficients) CETIAT NTO 90.307 (Villeurbanne, France: Centre Technique des Industries Aéraulique et Thermiques) (1990)

40   *HVAC systems duct design* (3rd edn.) (Chantilly, VA: Sheet Metal and Air Conditioning Contractors' National Association (SMACNA)) (1990)

41   Rogers G F C and Mayhew Y R *Thermodynamic and transport properties of fluids* (London: Blackwell) (1980)

42   Eckert E R and Drake R M *Analysis of heat and mass transfer* (New York, NY: McGraw-Hill) (1972)

43   National Engineering Laboratory *Viscosity of gases in metric units* (London: Her Majesty's Stationary Office) (1972)

44   The Engineering Toolbox *Ethylene glycol heat-transfer fluid* (available at http://www.engineeringtoolbox.com) (accessed 21 November 2006)

Bibliography

AiCVF *Aéraulique: Principes de l'aéraulique appliqués au génie climatique* (Paris: Association d'Ingénieurs de Climatisation Ventilation, et Froid) (1991)

ASHRAE *Duct Fitting Database* (Atlanta, GA: American Society of Heating, Refrigerating and Air-Conditioning Engineers) (2002)

BS EN 1505: 1998: *Ventilation for buildings. Sheet metal air ducts and fittings with rectangular cross-section. Dimensions* (London: British Standards Institution) (1998)

BS EN 1506: 1998: *Ventilation for buildings. Sheet metal air ducts and fittings with circular cross section. Dimensions* (London: British Standards Institution) (1998)

BS ISO 4065: 1996: *Thermoplastics pipes. Universal wall thickness table* (London: British Standards Institution) (1996)

Carlson L W and Irvine T F 'Fully developed pressure drop in triangular shaped ducts' *ASME J. Heat Transfer* **83** 441–444 (1961)

Carrier *Piping design* in *Carrier System Design Manual* (Syracuse, NY: Carrier Air Conditioning Company) (1960)

Crowder D *Calculation of pipework and ductwork friction loss from first principles* MRC Submission Report (September 2000)

Engineering Toolbox *Ethylene glycol based heat-transfer fluids.* http://www.engineeringtoolbox.com (March 2004)

Eurovent *Catalogue of energy loss coefficients of air handling components* (Paris: Eurovent) (1996) (This report is a simplified summary of the contents of the European Programme Report[1])

Griggs E I 'Resistance to flow of round galvanised ducts' *ASHRAE Trans.* **98** (1) (1987)

Hegberg R A 'Where did the k-factors for pressure loss in pipe fittings come from?' *ASHRAE Trans.* **101** (1) 1264–1278 (1995)

Hennington, Durham and Richardson *Design Guide* (Omaha, NE: Hennington, Durham and Richardson) (1981)

Hydraulic Institute *Engineering Data Book* (Parsippany, NJ: Hydraulic Institute) (1979)

Jones C D *Friction factor and roughness of United Sheet Metal Company spiral duct* (Westerville, OH: United McGill Corporation) (1979)

Koch P 'A survey of available data for pressure loss coefficients, ζ, for elbows and tees of pipework' *Building Serv. Eng. Res. Technol.* 153–160 (2000)

Koch P 'Comparisons and choice of pressure loss coefficients, ζ, for ductwork components' *Building Serv. Eng. Res. Technol.* **22** (3) 167–183 (2001)

Lamont P 'A review of pipe-friction data and formulae, with a proposed set of exponential formulae based on the theory of roughness' *Proc. Inst. Civil Eng.* III 248–255 (1954)

Moody L F 'Friction factors for pipe flow' *ASME Trans.* **66** 671 (1944)

Plastic Pipe Institute *Water flow characteristics of thermoplastic pipe* (Irving, TX: The Plastic Pipe Institute) (1971)

Sprenger F *Friction pressure drops in ducts and pipes* Undergraduate thesis (Coventry: Coventry University School of the Built Environment) (1995)

Townsend B S et al. 'Equivalent round diameter of spiral flat oval ducts' *ASHRAE Trans.* **100** (2) 389–395 (1994)

Appendix 4.A1 : Properties of various fluids

4.A1.1   Air and water

See Tables 4.A1.1 and 4.A1.2.

Note that values of density, being the reciprocal of the specific volume, are best obtained from the psychrometric data in chapter 1, which cover all values of humidity.

The variation of density with pressure can be obtained using a value ρ_0 from Table 4.A1.1 or the psychrometric data, and ideal gas equation, namely:

$$\rho = \rho_0 \left(\frac{p}{1.01325} \right) \qquad (4.A1.1)$$

Values of viscosity and specific thermal capacity do not vary significantly with pressure.

Although the preferred units of dynamic viscosity (η) are $kg \cdot m^{-1} \cdot s^{-1}$, the Poise still persists in some sources of data, for which the following conversion may be useful:

$$1 \text{ cP} = 0.01 \text{ Pa·s} = 10^{-2} \text{ kg·m}^{-1}\text{·s}^{-1}$$

Similarly, although the preferred units of dynamic viscosity (v) are $m^2 \cdot s^{-1}$, the Stoke still persists in some sources of data, for which the following conversion may be useful:

$$1 \text{ cSt} = 0.01 \text{ cm}^2\text{·s}^{-1} = 10^{-6} \text{ m}^2\text{·s}^{-1}$$

4.A1.2   Water–glycol mixtures

See Tables 4.A1.3 to 4.A1.6. The primary source for this data has been provided by Shell Chemicals. For low values of temperature this is supplemented in Tables 4.A1.4 and 4.A1.5 by some sparse internet data[44], the original source of which is not known, and which required interpolation from Imperial values.

Table 4.A1.1 Some properties of water

θ / °C	ρ / $kg \cdot m^{-3}$	η / $10^{-6}\ kg \cdot m^{-1} \cdot s^{-1}$	v / $10^{-6}\ kg \cdot m^{-1} \cdot s^{-1}$	c_p / $kJ \cdot kg^{-1} \cdot K^{-1}$
0.01	999.8	1752	1.7524	4.210
4	1000.0	1551	1.5510	4.205
10	999.7	1300	1.3004	4.193
20	999.8	1002	1.0022	4.183
30	995.6	797	0.8005	4.179
40	992.2	651	0.6561	4.179
50	988.0	544	0.5506	4.182
60	983.2	463	0.4709	4.185
70	977.8	400	0.4091	4.191
80	971.8	351	0.3612	4.198
90	965.3	311	0.3222	4.201
100	958.4	279	0.2911	4.219
110	950.6	252	0.2651	4.233
120	943.4	230	0.2438	4.248
130	934.6	216	0.2258	4.27
140	925.9	195	0.2106	4.29
150	916.6	181	0.1975	4.32
160	907.4	169	0.1862	4.35
170	897.7	158	0.1760	4.38
180	886.5	149	0.1681	4.42
190	875.6	141	0.1610	4.46
200	864.3	134	0.1550	4.51

Table 4.A1.3 Freezing temperature of ethylene-glycol–water mixture (derived from data provided by Shell Chemicals, Rotterdam)

Freezing temperature (/ °C) for ethylene-glycol solution at stated concentration (% by mass)						
25	30	40	50	90	95	100
–10.5	–13.7	–22.5	–33.7	–29.6	–21.8	–12.8

Note: the figure in italics was obtained by extrapolation.

Table 4.A1.4 Density of ethylene-glycol–water mixture

Temp. / °C	Density, ρ (/ $kg \cdot m^{-3}$), for stated concentration (% by mass)							
	0	20	30	40	50	60	80	100
60	983.2	1007.3	1019.4	1031.7	1042.3	1052.6	1071.4	1086.7
40	992.2	1017.3	1030.3	1042.5	1054.8	1065.5	1084.5	1100.0
20	999.8	1025.6	1040.4	1053.5	1066.4	1078.1	1098.6	1114.8
0	999.8	1031.8	1047.9	1063.9	1078.6	1091.1	1112.3	1129.1
	Density, ρ (/ $kg \cdot m^{-3}$) for stated concentration (% by volume)							
	0	20	30	40	50	60	80	100
–20	s	s	s	*1089*	*1103*	*1116*	*1142*	s
–40	s	s	s	s	s	*1121*	*1147*	s

Note: '% by mass' values adapted from data provided by Shell. '% by volume' values derived from unreferenced data[44]; values shown in italics are best estimates from that source.

's' denotes solid.

Table 4.A1.2 Some properties of air at a relative humidity of 50% and at a pressure of 1.012 bar (from Rogers and Mayhew[41])

θ / °C	ρ / $kg \cdot m^{-3}$	η / $10^{-6}\ kg \cdot m^{-1} \cdot s^{-1}$	c_p / $kJ \cdot kg^{-1} \cdot K^{-1}$
0	1.29	17.15	1.006
5	1.27	17.39	1.009
10	1.24	17.63	1.011
15	1.22	17.88	1.014
20	1.20	18.12	1.018
25	1.18	18.36	1.022
30	1.16	18.55	1.030
35	1.14	18.78	1.039
40	1.11	19.01	1.050

Table 4.A1.5 Kinematic viscosity of monoethylene-glycol–water mixture

Temp. / °C	Kinematic viscosity, v (/ $10^{-6} \cdot m^2 \cdot s^{-1}$), for stated concentration (/ % by mass)							
	0	20	30	40	50	60	80	100
100	0.291	0.382	0.457	0.555	0.680	0.790	1.19	2.02
60	0.471	0.675	0.812	1.00	1.27	1.56	2.54	4.54
40	0.656	0.956	1.20	1.54	2.00	2.50	4.35	8.59
20	1.002	1.56	2.01	2.60	3.38	4.44	8.41	17.9

	Kinematic viscosity, v (/ $10^{-6} \cdot m^2 \cdot s^{-1}$), for stated concentration (/ % by volume)							
	0	20	30	40	50	60	80	100
0	*1.75*	*6.0*	*8.6*	*12*	—	—		
−20	s	s	s	*16.8*	*24*	*38*	—	s

Note: '% by mass' values adapted from data provided by Shell. '% by volume' values derived from unreferenced data[44]; values shown in italics are best estimates from that source.

's' denotes solid.

Table 4.A1.6 Specific thermal capacity of monoethylene-glycol–water mixture

Temp. / °C	Specific thermal capacity, c_p (/ $kJ \cdot kg^{-1} \cdot K^{-1}$), for stated concentration (/ % by mass)							
	0	20	30	40	50	60	80	100
20–60	4.19	3.89	3.76	3.59	3.39	3.21	2.79	2.40

	Specific thermal capacity, c_p (/ $kJ \cdot kg^{-1} \cdot K^{-1}$), for stated concentration (/ % by volume)							
	0	20	30	40	50	60	80	100
0	4.21	3.91	3.72	3.53	3.32	3.11	2.72	2.33

Note: '% by mass' values adapted from data provided by Shell. '% by volume' values derived from unreferenced data[44]; values shown in italics are best estimates from that source.

4.A1.3   Gases

See Tables 4.A1.7 to 4.A1.11

Table 4.A1.7 Some properties of oxygen gas at 1 atm. (Eckert and Drake[42])

θ / °C	ρ / $kg \cdot m^{-3}$	η / $10^{-6}\ kg \cdot m^{-1} \cdot s^{-1}$	c_p / $kJ \cdot kg^{-1} \cdot K^{-1}$
150	2.619	11.49	0.9178
200	1.956	14.85	0.9131
250	1.562	17.87	0.9157
300	1.301	20.63	0.9203
350	1.113	23.16	0.9291
400	0.975	25.54	0.9420

Table 4.A1.8 Some properties of nitrogen gas at 1 atm. (Eckert and Drake[42])

θ / °C	ρ / $kg \cdot m^{-3}$	η / $10^{-6}\ kg \cdot m^{-1} \cdot s^{-1}$	c_p / $kJ \cdot kg^{-1} \cdot K^{-1}$
100	3.481	6.862	1.0722
200	1.711	12.95	1.0429
300	1.142	17.84	1.0408
400	0.8538	21.98	1.0459

Table 4.A1.9 Some properties of carbon dioxide gas at 1 atm. (Eckert and Drake[42])

θ / °C	ρ / $kg \cdot m^{-3}$	η / $10^{-6}\ kg \cdot m^{-1} \cdot s^{-1}$	c_p / $kJ \cdot kg^{-1} \cdot K^{-1}$
220	2.4733	11.10	0.783
250	2.1667	12.59	0.804
300	1.7973	14.96	0.871
350	1.5362	17.20	0.900
400	1.3424	19.32	0.942

Table 4.A1.10 Some properties of carbon monoxide gas at 1 atm. (Eckert and Drake[42])

θ / °C	ρ / $kg \cdot m^{-3}$	η / $10^{-6}\ kg \cdot m^{-1} \cdot s^{-1}$	c_p / $kJ \cdot kg^{-1} \cdot K^{-1}$
220	2.4733	11.10	0.783
220	1.5536	13.83	1.043
250	1.3668	15.40	1.042
300	1.1387	17.84	1.042
350	0.9742	20.09	1.043
400	0.8536	22.19	1.048

Table 4.A1.11 Some properties of ammonia gas at 1 atm. (Eckert and Drake[42])

θ / °C	ρ / $kg \cdot m^{-3}$	η / $10^{-6}\ kg \cdot m^{-1} \cdot s^{-1}$	c_p / $kJ \cdot kg^{-1} \cdot K^{-1}$
220	0.3828	7.255	2.198
273	0.7929	9.353	2.177
323	0.6487	11.03	2.177
373	0.5590	12.89	2.236
423	0.4934	14.67	2.315

4.A1.4   Fuel gases

See Table 4.A1.12.

Table 4.A1.12 Some properties of fuel gases at 1 atm. (from Eckert and Drake[42] and HMSO[43])

Fuel gas	θ / °C	ρ / $kg \cdot m^{-3}$	η / $10^{-6}\ kg \cdot m^{-1} \cdot s^{-1}$	c_p / $kJ \cdot kg^{-1} \cdot K^{-1}$
Butane (C_4H_{10})	273	2.66	6.8	—
	288	2.52	—	1.671
Methane (CH_4)	273	0.717	10.44	2.207
	288	0.680	10.80	—
	298	0.657	11.13	2.237
Propane (C_3H_8)	273	2.02	8.03	1.625
	288	1.91	—	—
	298	1.85	—	1.703

Note: values of η and c_p do not vary much with pressure; all the properties vary with temperature.

4.A1.5   Fuel oils

See Table 4.A1.13. The viscosity of fuel oils varies considerably with temperature. Even within a single grade of oil, properties can vary within a specified band. Thus the properties of a particular oil are best obtained from the manufacturer. Some approximate values are given in Table 4.A1.13, taken from the graphs in chapter 5 of this Guide.

Table 4.A1.13 Density and kinematic viscosity of fuel oils

Fuel oil	Class	Density, ρ / kg·m^{-3} at 15 °C	Kinematic viscosity, ν (/ 10^{-6}·m^2·s^{-1}), at stated temperature (/ °C)						
			−10	0	20	40	60	80	100
Kerosene	C2	803	0.34	2.75	1.0–2.0	—	—	—	
Gas oil	D	850	11	7.8	1.5–5.5	—	—	—	
Light fuel oil	E	940	—	600	160	58	25	13.5	8.2
Medium fuel oil	F	970	—	—	850	220	75	32	20.0 max
Heavy fuel oil	G	980	—	—	3400	705	205	75	40.0 max

Appendix 4.A2 : Pipe and duct sizing

4.A2.1 General

For a required mass flow, the constraint should normally be that the mean fluid velocity should not exceed a particular value, c_{max}. Such advice is given in section 4.5.1 for water, and in section 4.8.1 for air.

Values of pipe roughness are given in Table 4.1 and some typical values are shown in Table 4.A2.1. These do not necessarily constitute a recommendation for those wishing to compute new values. The values of k chosen for polymers are mid-range values, but for these materials the surface is so smooth that the value of k is not significant in the calculation.

Values of the fluid properties, i.e density ρ, and either dynamic viscosity η or kinematic viscosity ν ($\nu = \eta/\rho$), are required and may be obtained from Appendix 4.A1.

Step 1

The minimum internal pipe diameter is then given by:

$$d_{min} = \left(\frac{4\, q_m}{\pi\, \rho\, c_{max}} \right)^{0.5}$$ (4.A2.1)

Table 4.A2.1 Roughness coefficients (see also Table 4.1)

Material	Roughness coefficient, k / mm
Pipework (metal):	
— copper	0.0015
— heavy grade steel	0.046
— cast iron	1.0
— galvanised steel	0.15
Pipework (plastic):	
— PB	0.007
— PE-X	0.007
— PVC-U	0.007
— ABS	0.007
Ductwork:	
— galvanised steel	0.075
— spirally wound galvanised steel	0.090

The pipe to be selected can now be chosen, usually by rounding up to the next available internal diameter, d_i, from which the nominal size will also be evident.

The linear steps in the calculation are now as follows.

Step 2

The actual fluid mean velocity is given by:

$$c = \frac{4\, q_m}{\pi\, \rho\, d_i^2}$$ (4.A2.2)

Step 3

The Reynolds number is obtained from equation 4.2:

$$Re = \frac{c\, d_i}{\nu}$$ (4.A2.3)

Step 4

If the flow is laminar ($Re < 2000$), λ is obtained from equation 4.3, i.e:

$$\lambda = \frac{64}{Re}$$ (4.A2.4)

If the flow is turbulent ($Re > 3000$), λ is obtained from equation 4.5, i.e:

$$\frac{1}{\sqrt{\lambda}} = -1.8 \log\left[\frac{6.9}{Re} + \left(\frac{k/d}{3.71} \right)^{1.11} \right]$$ (4.A2.5)

Step 5

The pressure drop, or the pressure drop per unit length, is obtained from equation 4.1:

$$\frac{\Delta p}{l} = \lambda \frac{1}{d_i} \tfrac{1}{2}\, \rho\, c^2$$ (4.A2.6)

4.A2.1 Worked example: pipework

Problem

A mass flow of water of 5.74 kg·s^{-1} is required at a mean water temperature of 60 °C. Copper pipe is to be used.

Solution

From Appendix 4.A1, for water:

— ρ = 983.2 kg·m^{-3}

— v = 0.4709 x 10^{-6} m^2·s^{-1}

From Table 4.A2.1, for copper, k = 0.0015 mm

From Table 4.6, an approximate value of c_{max} might be 1.5 m·s^{-1}.

Using equation 4.A2.1:

$$d_{min} = \left(\frac{4\,q_m}{\pi\,\rho\,c_{max}}\right)^{0.5}$$

$$= \left(\frac{4 \times 5.74}{\pi \times 983.2 \times 1.5}\right)^{0.5} \quad \left[\frac{kg\cdot s^{-1}}{(kg\cdot m^{-3})(m\cdot s^{-1})}\right]^{0.5}$$

$$= 0.0704 \text{ m} = 70.4 \text{ mm}$$

A possible choice of pipe is copper pipe R290 76.1 × 1.5, having d_i = 73.1 mm.

The actual diameter and velocity may now be calculated.

Using equation 4.A2.2:

$$c = \frac{4\,q_m}{\pi\,\rho\,d_i^2}$$

$$= \frac{4 \times 5.74}{\pi \times 983.2 \times 0.0731^2} \quad \left[\frac{kg\cdot s^{-1}}{(kg\cdot m^{-3})\,m^2}\right]$$

$$= 1.391 \text{ m·s}^{-1}$$

The velocity pressure is given by:

$$p_v = \tfrac{1}{2}\,\rho\,c^2$$

Hence:

$$p_v = \tfrac{1}{2} \times 983.2 \times 1.391 \quad [(kg\cdot m^{-3})(m^2\cdot s^{-2})]$$

$$[= N\cdot m^{-2} = Pa]$$

$$= 951.3 \text{ Pa}$$

Using equation 4.A2.3:

$$Re = \frac{c\,d_i}{v}$$

$$Re = \frac{1.391 \times 0.0731}{0.4709 \times 10^{-6}} \quad \left[\frac{m\cdot s^{-1}\cdot m}{m^2\cdot s^{-1}}\right]$$

$$= 2.16 \times 10^5$$

The flow is turbulent, therefore equation (4.A2.5) applies:

$$\frac{1}{\sqrt{\lambda}} = -1.8 \log\left[\frac{6.9}{Re} + \left(\frac{k/d}{3.71}\right)^{1.11}\right]$$

$$\frac{1}{\sqrt{\lambda}} = -1.8 \log\left[\frac{6.9}{2.16 \times 10^5} + \left(\frac{0.0015 \div 73.1}{3.71}\right)^{1.11}\right]$$

$$= -1.8 \log\left[31.94 \times 10^{-6} + 1.4605 \times 10^{-6}\right]$$

$$= 8.057$$

Therefore:

$$\lambda = 0.01540$$

From equation 4.A2.6:

$$\frac{\Delta p}{l} = \lambda\,\frac{1}{d_i}\,\tfrac{1}{2}\,\rho\,c^2$$

$$\frac{\Delta p}{l} = 0.015405\,\frac{1}{0.0731}\,951.3 \quad \left[\frac{Pa}{m}\right]$$

$$= 200.5 \text{ Pa·m}^{-1}$$

In the event that a particularly long length of pipe were involved, pumping requirements could be much reduced by choosing the next larger pipe size. Equally, if only a short length of pipe were involved, the next size smaller could be chosen but the higher water velocity might lead to greater noise generation.

In summary:

— c = 1.391 m·s^{-1}

— p_v = 951.3 Pa

— $\Delta p\,/\,l$ = 200.5 Pa·m^{-1}

The method may easily be programmed as a spreadsheet. Table 4.A2.2 suggests a possible format for presenting the results.

Table 4.A2.2 Pipe sizing spreadsheet: possible format for displaying results of calculation

Input			Output		
Mass flow (kg·s^{-1})	Temp (°C)	Pipe size (mm × mm)	c (m·s^{-1})	$\Delta p\,/\,l$ (Pa·m^{-1})	$\tfrac{1}{2}\,\rho\,c^2$ (Pa)
Fluid: water					
5.74	60	66.7 × 1.2	1.80	372	1589
5.74	60	76.1 × 1.5	1.39	200	951
5.74	60	88.9 × 1.5	1.01	92	499
Choose another pipe diameter?					

4.A2.2 Worked example: ductwork

With airflow, the requirement may be in terms of mass flow (for heating or cooling requirements), or in terms of volume flow (for ventilation requirements), illogical though this may seem. In the following example, mass flow is specified.

Problem

A mass flow of 2.19 kg·s^{-1} of air is required at a mean water temperature of 27 °C and 30% saturation. Flat-oval galvanised ductwork is to be selected

Solution

The air conditions are assumed to be at a pressure of 101.3 kPa (unless otherwise specified). From the psychrometric tables in chapter 1:

— specific volume, $v = 0.86$ m^3/kg dry air

— moisture content, $g = 0.0068$ kg of steam/kg dry air.

Hence, the air density is:

$$\rho = \frac{1.0068}{0.86} \qquad \left[\frac{\text{kg·kg}^{-1}}{\text{m}^3\text{·kg}^{-1}}\right]$$

$$= 1.171 \text{ kg·m}^{-3}$$

From Appendix 4.A1, Table 4.A1.2, by interpolation:

$$\eta = 18.44 \times 10^{-6} \text{ kg·m}^{-1}\text{·s}^{-1}$$

But:

$$v = \frac{\eta}{\rho}$$

Hence:

$$v = \frac{18.44 \times 10^{-6}}{0.86} \qquad \left[\frac{\text{kg·m}^{-1}\text{·s}^{-1}}{\text{kg·m}^{-3}}\right]$$

$$= 15.49 \times 10^{-6} \text{ m}^2\text{·s}^{-1}$$

From Table 4.1, taking a mean value, for spirally wound galvanised ductwork, $k = 0.09$ mm

From Table 4.11, an approximate value of c_{max} might be 6 m·s^{-1}.

It is worthwhile calculating the volume flow:

$$q_v = \frac{q_m}{\rho} = \frac{2.19}{1.171} \qquad \left[\frac{\text{kg·s}^{-1}}{\text{kg·m}^{-3}}\right]$$

$$= 1.870 \text{ m}^3\text{·s}^{-1}$$

Thus, to find the minimum area, A_{min}:

$$A_{min} = \frac{q_v}{c_{max}} = \frac{1.870}{6} \qquad \left[\frac{\text{m}^3\text{·s}^{-1}}{\text{m·s}^{-1}}\right]$$

$$= 0.312 \text{ m}^2 = 312\,000 \text{ mm}^2$$

Consulting Table 4.17 for preferred dimensions of flat-oval pipe, the following sizes would seem possible: 300 × 1115, 400 × 895, 450 × 865, 500 × 755.

For reasons of space, 450 mm × 865 mm is chosen. The actual velocity must now be determined.

From Table 4.17:

$$A = 345\,793 \text{ mm}^2 = 0.345793 \text{ m}^2$$

From Table 4.18:

$$d_e = 653 \text{ mm}$$

Actual velocity, c, is given by:

$$c = \frac{q_v}{A} = \frac{1.870}{0.3458} \qquad \left[\frac{\text{m}^3\text{·s}^{-1}}{\text{m}^2}\right]$$

$$= 5.408 \text{ m·s}^{-1}$$

Everything can now be calculated as for the pipework example.

Note that the velocity calculated above is the real velocity of air in the flat-oval duct chosen. It is not the hypothetical velocity in the equivalent circular duct. However, for the purpose of calculating the equivalent Reynolds number, Re, it will be sufficient.

From equation 4.A2.3, using the equivalent diameter:

$$Re = \frac{c\, d_e}{v}$$

$$Re = \frac{5.408 \times 0.653}{15.49 \times 10^{-6}} \qquad \left[\frac{\text{m·s}^{-1}\text{·m}}{\text{m}^2\text{·s}^{-1}}\right]$$

$$= 2.28 \times 10^5$$

The flow is turbulent, therefore equation 4.A2.5 applies:

$$\frac{1}{\sqrt{\lambda}} = -1.8 \log\left[\frac{6.9}{Re} + \left(\frac{k/d}{3.71}\right)^{1.11}\right]$$

$$\frac{1}{\sqrt{\lambda}} = -1.8 \log\left[\frac{6.9}{2.28 \times 10^5} + \left(\frac{0.09 \div 652}{3.71}\right)^{1.11}\right]$$

$$= -1.8 \log\left[30.26 \times 10^{-6} + 12.12 \times 10^{-6}\right] = 7.871$$

Hence:

$$\lambda = 0.01614$$

From equation 4.20:

$$\frac{\Delta p}{l} = \lambda\, \frac{\rho}{2}\, \frac{16\, q_v^{\,2}}{\pi^2\, d_e^{\,5}}$$

$$= 0.01614 \frac{1.171}{2} \frac{16 \times 1.870^2}{\pi^2 \, 0.652^5} \quad \left[\frac{\text{kg·m}^{-3}\text{·m}^{6}\text{·s}^{-2}}{\text{m}^{5}} \right]$$

$$[= \text{N·m}^{-3} = \text{Pa·m}^{-1}]$$

$$= 0.455 \, \text{Pa·m}^{-1}$$

For use with ζ for ductwork components, the actual air velocity is used. Thus:

$$p_v = \tfrac{1}{2}\rho \, c^2$$

$$= \tfrac{1}{2} \times 1.171 \times 5.408^2 \quad [(\text{kg·m}^{-3})(\text{m}^2\text{·s}^{-2}) = \text{Pa}]$$

$$= 17.12 \, \text{Pa}$$

In the event that a particularly long length of duct were involved, fan power consumption could be much reduced by choosing the next larger duct size. Equally, if only a short length of duct were involved, the next smaller size could be chosen, but the higher air velocity might lead to greater noise generation.

In summary, for the chosen size of flat-oval duct (450 mm × 865 mm):

— $c = 5.408 \, \text{m·s}^{-1}$

— $p_v = 17.12 \, \text{Pa}$

— $\Delta p \,/\, l = 0.455 \, \text{Pa·m}^{-1}$

The method may easily be programmed as a spreadsheet. Table 4.A2.3 suggests a possible format for presenting the results.

Table 4.A2.3 Pipe sizing spreadsheet: possible format for displaying results of calculation

Input			Output		
Mass flow (kg·s^{-1})	Temp $(^\circ\text{C})$	Duct size $(\text{mm} \times \text{mm})$	c (m·s^{-1})	$\Delta p \,/\, l$ (Pa·m^{-1})	$\tfrac{1}{2}\rho \, c^2$ (Pa)
Fluid: air					
2.19	27	450 × 865	5.41	0.455	17.12
2.19	27	400 × 895	5.78	0.557	19.55
2.19	27	500 × 755	5.77	0.505	19.53
Choose another duct size?					
2.19	27	500 × 835	5.14	0.389	15.47

Appendix 4.A3 : Capacity (*K*) and complex networks

Whilst it is most common practice for components and fittings to have their pressure drop characteristic given in terms of the pressure loss factor ζ, most manufacturers of valves and dampers quote the performance in terms of the 'capacity' (*K*), defined in the following relationship:

$$q_v = K \sqrt{\Delta p} \qquad (4.A3.1)$$

This implies that *K* has units, usually of $m^3/(h \cdot bar^{0.5})$ for liquids, or $m^3/(s \cdot Pa^{0.5})$ for gases. Some manufacturers may quote values of *K* with different units, so care is needed.

There is a relation between *K* and ζ, but it is not really necessary to convert one to the other. Pressure drops are more simply calculated separately for those components for which *K* is given.

K is also useful when dealing with the authority of a valve, and in the prediction of flows in complex circuits.

For every branch of a circuit, once the value of pressure drop is known for a particular volume flow, the value of *K* for that branch can be obtained from equation 4.A3.1.

Elements in parallel

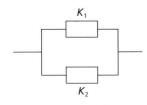

For elements of the circuit in parallel, the overall capacity K_o is given by:

$$K_o = K_1 + K_2 \qquad (4.A3.2)$$

Elements in series

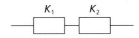

For elements of the circuit in series, the overall capacity K_o is given by:

$$\frac{1}{K_o} = \frac{1}{K_1} + \frac{1}{K_2} \qquad (4.A3.3)$$

Thus for a complex circuit, the entire circuit can be simplified until the circuit overall, 'total' capacity K_{tot} is obtained. Equation 4.A3.1 then permits the calculation of pressure drop for any value of total flow. Thus the pipework or ductwork pressure drop characteristic is obtained.

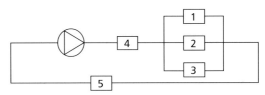

Figure 4.A3.1 Example of a complex circuit

For example, in Figure 4.A3.1, sub-circuits 1, 2 and 3 having capacities K_1, K_2 and K_3 respectively, can be simplified to give K_x using equation 4.A3.2 for circuits in parallel. Sub-circuits 4, 5 and *x* having capacities K_4, K_5 and K_x respectively, can be simplified to give K_{tot} using equation 4.A3.3 for circuits in series.

Equation 4.A3.1 can then be used to determine the characteristic for the system.

Appendix 4.A4 : Steam flow in pipes

4.A4.1 General

The calculation of pressure drops in flows of steam and natural gas is much more complex than that of water and of air. With water, the density remains constant irrespective of pressure in the system. With air, its use in ventilation systems is always at a pressure of about around 1 bar so some general predictions can be made. With both steam and natural gas, the density varies considerably with pressure and a wide range of pressures are used. Furthermore, large pressure drops along the pipework are generally acceptable, and these affect the fluid density as it flows along. The calculations are therefore best left to a specialist.

4.A4.2 Steam flow in pipes

The pressure drop due to friction in steel pipes may be calculated from:

$$\frac{Z_1 - Z_2}{l} = \frac{30.32\, q_m^{1.889}}{10^3\, d^{5.027}} \qquad (4.A4.1)$$

where Z is given by:

$$Z = p^{1.929} \qquad (4.A4.2)$$

where the following units must be used: q_m (kg·s⁻¹), d (m), l (m), p (kPa (absolute)) and Z (kPa$^{1.929}$).

These equations have been developed to cover initial steam pressures of between 100 kPa and 1000 kPa and for velocities ranging from 5 m·s⁻¹ to 50 m·s⁻¹. They may be used with less accuracy for conditions outside these limits.

Pre-calculated values of pressure drop are given in Table 4.A4.1 (pages 4.68 to 4.70). Values of the pressure factor Z are given in Table 4.A4.2.

The values used for density ρ and kinematic viscosity v were obtained from the following relationships:

— $\quad \rho = 7.83 \times 10^{-3}\, p^{0.94}$

— $\quad v = 9.79 \times 10^{-4}\, p^{-0.842}$

where the following units must be used: p (kPa (absolute)), ρ (kg·m⁻³) and v (m²·s⁻¹).

4.A4.2 Flow of condensate in pipes

The pressure drop of the condensate flow may be obtained in the same way as for hot water where:

(a)   thermostatic traps, having small pressure differentials between inlet and outlet, are employed and

(b)   air and other gases are prevented from entering the condensate drain by the use of automatic vents.

If air is required to traverse the condensate main and if flash steam is produced by the pressure drops in the trap and system then the resistance is greatly increased. The pressure drop in two-phase flow is always greater than for either phase individually, the calculation for which is beyond the scope of this Guide. In the absence of definite data it is recommended that where flash steam can occur the condensate mains should be sized for three times the normal hot water discharge.

Table 4.A4.2 Pressure factors Z for compressible flow (from equation 4.A4.2)

Pressure, p / kPa	Pressure factor, Z (/ kPa$^{1.929}$) for stated pressure, p / kPa									
	0	10	20	30	40	50	60	70	80	90
0	0	85	323	707	1230	1890	2690	3620	4690	5880
100	7210	8670	10 300	12 000	13 800	15 800	17 900	20 100	22 400	24 900
200	27 500	30 200	33 000	36 000	39 000	42 230	45 500	49 000	52 500	56 200
300	60 000	63 900	68 000	72 100	76 400	80 800	85 300	90 000	94 700	99 600
400	105 000	110 000	115 000	120 000	126 000	131 000	137 000	143 000	149 000	155 000
500	161 000	167 000	174 000	180 000	187 000	193 000	200 000	207 000	214 000	221 000
600	229 000	236 000	244 000	251 000	259 000	267 000	275 000	283 000	291 000	299 000
700	308 000	316 000	325 000	334 000	343 000	351 000	361 000	370 000	379 000	389 000
800	398 000	408 000	418 000	427 000	437 000	448 000	458 000	468 000	479 000	489 000
900	500 000	510 000	521 000	532 000	543 000	555 000	566 000	577 000	589 000	601 000
1000	612 000	—	—	—	—	—	—	—	—	—

Table 4.A4.1 Flow of saturated steam in heavy steel pipes

q_m = mass flow rate (kg·s^{-1})
p = pressure (absolute) (kPa)
$\Delta Z / l$ = pressure drop per unit length (Pa$^{1.929}$·m^{-1})

HEAVY GRADE STEEL

SATURATED STEAM

$\Delta Z / l$	p	Mass flow rate, q_m, for stated nominal outside diameter						p	$\Delta Z / l$
		10 mm	15 mm	20 mm	25 mm	32 mm	40 mm		
1		0.0001	0.0003	0.0007	0.001	0.003	0.004		1
2	10	0.0002	0.0004	0.001	0.002	0.004	0.006	30	2
4		0.0003	0.0006	0.001	0.003	0.006	0.009		4
6		0.0004	0.0008	0.001	0.003	0.007	0.011	50	6
8		0.0004	0.0009	0.002	0.004	0.008	0.013		8
10		0.0005	0.001	0.002	0.004	0.009	0.014		10
12		0.0005	0.001	0.002	0.005	0.010	0.016		12
14	30	0.0006	0.001	0.003	0.005	0.011	0.017		14
16		0.0006	0.001	0.003	0.005	0.012	0.018		16
18		0.0007	0.001	0.003	0.006	0.013	0.019		18
20		0.0007	0.001	0.003	0.006	0.013	0.020		20
25		0.0008	0.002	0.004	0.007	0.015	0.023	100	25
30		0.0009	0.002	0.004	0.008	0.017	0.025		30
35	50	0.0009	0.002	0.004	0.008	0.018	0.027		35
40		0.001	0.002	0.005	0.009	0.019	0.029		40
45		0.001	0.002	0.005	0.009	0.021	0.031		45
50		0.001	0.002	0.005	0.010	0.022	0.033		50
55		0.001	0.002	0.006	0.011	0.023	0.035		55
60		0.001	0.003	0.006	0.011	0.024	0.037		60
65		0.001	0.003	0.006	0.012	0.025	0.038		65
70		0.001	0.003	0.006	0.012	0.026	0.040		70
75		0.001	0.003	0.007	0.012	0.027	0.041		75
80		0.001	0.003	0.007	0.013	0.028	0.043		80
85		0.001	0.003	0.007	0.013	0.029	0.044		85
90		0.002	0.003	0.007	0.014	0.030	0.045		90
95	100	0.002	0.003	0.008	0.014	0.031	0.047		95
100		0.002	0.003	0.008	0.014	0.031	0.048		100
200		0.002	0.005	0.011	0.021	0.045	0.069	300	200
300		0.003	0.006	0.014	0.026	0.056	0.086		300
400		0.003	0.007	0.016	0.030	0.065	0.100	500	400
500		0.004	0.008	0.018	0.034	0.074	0.112		500
600		0.004	0.009	0.020	0.037	0.081	0.124		600
700		0.005	0.010	0.022	0.041	0.088	0.134		700
800	300	0.005	0.010	0.024	0.043	0.094	0.144		800
900		0.005	0.011	0.025	0.046	0.101	0.153		900
1000		0.005	0.011	0.026	0.049	0.106	0.162	1000	1000
2000	500	0.008	0.017	0.038	0.071	0.153	0.234		2000
3000		0.010	0.021	0.047	0.086	0.190	0.290		3000
4000		0.011	0.024	0.055	0.102	0.222	0.338		4000
5000		0.013	0.027	0.062	0.115	0.249	0.380		5000
6000		0.014	0.030	0.068	0.126	0.275	0.418		6000
7000	1000	0.015	0.032	0.074	0.137	0.298	0.454		7000
8000		0.017	0.034	0.080	0.147	0.320	0.487		8000
9000		0.018	0.037	0.085	0.157	0.340	0.519		9000
10 000		0.019	0.039	0.090	0.166	0.360	0.548	3000	10 000
20 000		0.027	0.056	0.129	0.239	0.519	0.791		20 000
30 000		0.033	0.069	0.160	0.296	0.644	0.981		30 000
40 000		0.039	0.081	0.187	0.345	0.750	1.14		40 000
50 000	3000	0.044	0.091	0.210	0.388	0.844	1.29		50 000
60 000		0.048	0.100	0.231	0.428	0.929	1.42		60 000

Table continues

Table 4.A4.1 Flow of saturated steam in heavy steel pipes — *continued*

q_m = mass flow rate (kg·s^{-1})
p = pressure (absolute) (kPa)
$\Delta Z / l$ = pressure drop per unit length (Pa$^{1.929}$·m^{-1})

HEAVY GRADE STEEL
SATURATED STEAM

$\Delta Z / l$	p	Mass flow rate, q_m, for stated nominal outside diameter						p	$\Delta Z / l$
		50 mm	65 mm	80 mm	90 mm	100 mm	125 mm		
1		0.008	0.016	0.025	0.037	0.051	0.092		1
2	50	0.011	0.023	0.036	0.054	0.074	0.133	50	2
4		0.017	0.034	0.052	0.077	0.107	0.192		4
6		0.021	0.042	0.065	0.096	0.132	0.238	100	6
8		0.024	0.049	0.076	0.112	0.154	0.277		8
10		0.027	0.055	0.085	0.126	0.173	0.312		10
12		0.030	0.060	0.094	0.138	0.191	0.344		12
14		0.032	0.065	0.102	0.150	0.207	0.373		14
16		0.035	0.070	0.109	0.161	0.222	0.400		16
18	100	0.037	0.075	0.116	0.172	0.237	0.426		18
20		0.039	0.079	0.123	0.181	0.250	0.450		20
25		0.044	0.089	0.138	0.204	0.281	0.507		25
30		0.048	0.098	0.152	0.225	0.310	0.558		30
35		0.052	0.106	0.165	0.244	0.336	0.606		35
40		0.056	0.114	0.177	0.262	0.361	0.650	300	40
45		0.060	0.121	0.189	0.279	0.384	0.692		45
50		0.063	0.128	0.200	0.295	0.406	0.732		50
55		0.066	0.135	0.210	0.310	0.427	0.769		55
60		0.069	0.141	0.220	0.324	0.447	0.806		60
65		0.072	0.147	0.229	0.339	0.467	0.841		65
70		0.075	0.153	0.239	0.352	0.485	0.874		70
75		0.078	0.159	0.247	0.365	0.504	0.907		75
80		0.081	0.165	0.256	0.378	0.521	0.938		80
85		0.084	0.170	0.264	0.390	0.538	0.969		85
90		0.086	0.175	0.273	0.402	0.555	0.999		90
95		0.089	0.180	0.280	0.414	0.571	1.03	500	95
100	300	0.091	0.185	0.288	0.425	0.586	1.06		100
200		0.131	0.267	0.416	0.614	0.846	1.52		200
300	500	0.163	0.331	0.516	0.761	1.05	1.89		300
400		0.190	0.386	0.600	0.886	1.22	2.20	1000	400
500		0.213	0.434	0.676	0.997	1.37	2.48		500
600		0.235	0.478	0.744	1.10	1.51	2.73		600
700		0.255	0.519	0.807	1.12	1.64	2.96		700
800		0.274	0.557	0.866	1.28	1.76	3.17		800
900		0.291	0.593	0.922	1.36	1.88	3.38		900
1000	1000	0.308	0.627	0.975	1.44	1.98	3.57		1000
2000		0.445	0.905	1.41	2.08	2.86	5.16		2000
3000		0.551	1.12	1.74	2.57	3.55	6.39	3000	3000
4000		0.642	1.31	2.03	3.00	4.13	7.44		4000
5000		0.722	1.47	2.29	3.34	4.65	8.38		5000
6000		0.795	1.62	2.52	3.71	5.12	9.22		6000
7000		0.863	1.76	2.73	4.03	5.56	10.0		7000
8000	3000	0.926	1.88	2.93	4.33	5.97	10.7		8000
9000		0.986	2.01	3.12	4.60	6.35	11.4		9000
10 000		1.04	2.12	3.23	4.87	6.71	12.1		10 000
20 000		1.50	3.06	4.76	7.03	9.69	17.4		20 000
30 000		1.86	3.79	5.90	8.71	12.0	21.6		30 000
40 000		2.17	4.42	6.87	10.1	14.0	25.2		40 000
50 000		2.44	4.97	7.74	11.4	15.7	28.3		50 000
60 000		2.69	5.48	8.52	12.6	17.3	31.2		60 000

Table continues

Table 4.A4.1 Flow of saturated steam in heavy steel pipes — *continued*

q_m = mass flow rate (kg·s^{-1})
p = pressure (absolute) (kPa)
$\Delta Z / l$ = pressure drop per unit length (Pa$^{1.929}$·m^{-1})

HEAVY GRADE STEEL

SATURATED STEAM

$\Delta Z / l$	p	\multicolumn{6}{c}{Mass flow rate, q_m, for stated nominal outside diameter}	p	$\Delta Z / l$
		150 mm	175 mm	200 mm	225 mm	250 mm	300 mm		
1		0.149	0.235	0.327	0.445	0.600	0.965		1
2		0.215	0.339	0.472	0.642	0.866	1.39	100	2
4	100	0.310	0.489	0.681	0.926	1.25	2.01		4
6		0.385	0.606	0.844	1.15	1.55	2.49		6
8		0.448	0.705	0.983	1.34	1.80	2.90		8
10		0.504	0.794	1.11	1.50	2.03	3.26		10
12		0.555	0.874	1.22	1.66	2.24	3.59		12
14		0.602	0.949	1.32	1.80	2.43	3.90	300	14
16		0.647	1.02	1.42	1.93	2.60	4.19		16
18		0.688	1.08	1.51	2.05	2.77	4.46		18
20		0.728	1.15	1.60	2.17	2.93	4.71		20
25		0.819	1.29	1.80	2.44	3.30	5.30		25
30	300	0.902	1.42	1.98	2.69	3.63	5.84		30
35		0.979	1.54	2.15	2.92	3.94	6.34	500	35
40		1.05	1.65	2.30	3.13	4.23	6.80		40
45		1.12	1.76	2.45	3.34	4.50	7.24		45
50		1.18	1.86	2.59	3.53	4.76	7.65		50
55		1.24	1.96	2.73	3.71	5.00	8.05		55
60		1.30	2.05	2.86	3.88	5.24	8.43		60
65		1.36	2.14	2.98	4.05	5.47	8.79		65
70		1.41	2.22	3.10	4.22	5.69	9.14		70
75		1.46	2.31	3.21	4.37	5.90	9.48		75
80	500	1.52	2.39	3.33	4.52	6.10	9.81		80
85		1.57	2.46	3.43	4.67	6.30	10.1		85
90		1.61	2.54	3.54	4.81	6.49	10.4		90
95		1.66	2.61	3.64	4.95	6.68	10.7		95
100		1.71	2.69	3.74	5.09	6.87	11.0	1000	100
200		2.46	3.88	5.40	7.35	9.91	15.9		200
300	1000	3.05	4.81	6.70	9.11	12.3	19.8		300
400		3.55	5.60	7.80	10.6	14.3	23.0		400
500		4.00	6.30	8.77	11.9	16.1	25.9		500
600		4.40	6.94	9.66	13.1	17.7	28.5		600
700		4.78	7.52	10.5	14.3	19.2	30.9		700
800		5.13	8.08	11.3	15.3	20.6	33.2		800
900		5.46	8.60	12.0	16.3	22.0	35.3	3000	900
1000		5.77	9.09	12.7	17.2	23.2	37.4		1000
2000	3000	8.33	13.1	18.3	24.9	33.5	53.9		2000
3000		10.3	16.3	22.7	30.8	41.6	66.8		3000
4000		12.0	18.9	26.4	35.9	48.4	77.8		4000
5000		13.5	21.3	29.7	40.4	54.5	87.6		5000
6000		14.9	23.5	32.7	44.5	60.0	96.5		6000
7000		16.2	25.5	35.5	48.3	65.1	105		7000
8000		17.4	27.3	38.1	51.8	69.9	112		8000
9000		18.5	29.1	40.5	55.1	74.4	120		9000
10 000		19.5	30.8	42.9	58.3	78.6	126		10 000
20 000		28.2	44.4	61.9	84.1	113	182		20 000
30 000		34.9	55.0	76.7	104	141	226		30 000
40 000		40.7	64.1	89.3	121	164	263		40 000
50 000		45.8	72.1	101	137	184	296		50 000
60 000		50.4	79.4	111	151	203	326		60 000

Appendix 4.A5 : Compressible flow

In the case of compressible fluids flowing under conditions where the pressure drop is considerable in proportion to the initial pressure (greater than 10 per cent), the change in density between the initial and final condition should be taken into account.

For determining Reynolds number ($Re = \rho c d / \eta$) there is no problem. For a particular mass flow and constant pipe diameter, c is inversely proportional to density; thus density change has no effect on Reynolds number. Viscosity η varies little with pressure (though varying considerably with temperature). Thus, despite large changes in pressure, Re and λ will remain constant, and the calculation of total pressure drop need take into account only the variation of density and velocity between the inlet and outlet:

$$\int_1^2 \mathrm{d}p = \frac{\lambda}{2\,d} \int_1^2 \rho\, c^2 \,\mathrm{d}l \qquad (4.A5.1)$$

Still considering isothermal flow, where despite pressure loss there is sufficient heat transfer to maintain the fluid at the temperature of the surroundings, the pressure loss may be represented by:

$$p_1^2 - p_2^2 = \frac{32\, q_m^2\, RT}{\pi^2\, d^4} \left(\frac{\lambda l}{2\,d} + \ln \frac{p_1}{p_2} \right) \qquad (4.A5.2)$$

In other cases the theoretical equations become complex and use is made of approximate formula derived empirically.

In all of the following equations, x, y, K_1, K_2 and K_3 are experimentally determined.

The equations are generally of the form:

$$\frac{\mathrm{d}p}{\mathrm{d}l} = K_1 \frac{q_m^x}{d^{(2x+y)}\, \rho^{(x-1)}} \qquad (4.A5.3)$$

Variation of density is of the form:

$$\rho = K_2\, p^n \qquad (4.A5.4)$$

Substitution into the previous equation gives:

$$\frac{p_1^m - p_2^m}{l} = K_3 \frac{q_m^x}{d^{(2x+y)}} \qquad (4.A4.5)$$

Table 4.A5.1 gives some values of the constants for steam and compressed air.

Table 4.A5.1 Values of constants for steam and compressed air

Fluid	x	y	m	K_3
Steam	1.889	1.249	1.929	3.032×10^{-3}
Compressed air	1.889	1.249	1.929	4.268×10^{-3}

5   Fuels and combustion

5.1   Introduction

There have been no significant changes in the classification or properties of fossil fuels since the 2001 edition of this chapter. In addition there have been no changes in air pollution regulations relevant to Local Authority supervision and the Clean Air Act 1993[1]. Following the ratification of the Kyoto treaty by Russia, new impetus has been given to global greenhouse gas abatement in line with Treaty obligations. The UK's target is to reduce emissions by 12.5% below 1990 levels by 2008–2012. A further goal is to cut the UK's emission of carbon dioxide by 20% below 1990 levels by 2010. Major economic and other measures have been introduced by the UK government to limit fossil fuel usage and hence carbon emissions. These include the Climate Change Levy[2,3] on non-domestic users, promotion of energy conservation with renewed emphasis on combined heat and power, emissions trading and financial incentives for renewable energy utilisation*. Building Regulations Approved Document L2A (2006)[4] introduced a target CO_2 emission rate for new buildings other than dwellings.

As noted in earlier editions of this chapter, the data presented are limited to those required by a practising building services engineer. They are not intended to represent full property specifications for each class of fuel and reference should be made to suppliers and standard literature for further information. A bibliography is included at the end of the chapter. In some places sources of information are included in brackets at the end of a sentence. If appropriate these are intended to be accessed using internet search engine(s). The familiar structure of the previous edition has been retained and data assembled according to the previous format.

---

* Up-to-date information may be obtained from the Carbon Trust (www.carbontrust.co.uk).

5.2   Classification of fuels

Fossil fuels may be classified into primary and secondary groups. Primary fuels occur naturally and are formed within a geological time scale from the decay of animal and vegetable matter. In general secondary fuels are prepared from primary fuels, with the intention of modifying the properties to suit particular applications. Electricity is sometimes classed as a secondary fuel.

The carbon to hydrogen ratio of the fuel can also be used as a means of classification. This ratio varies on a mass basis from about 3:1 for natural gas, 7.6:1 for heavy fuel oil, up to 30:1 for anthracites. Properties such as gross calorific value and stoichiometric air requirement are seen to vary in a regular manner with carbon to hydrogen ratio. The ratio can also affect flame parameters such as luminosity.

5.3   Primary fuels

5.3.1   Coal

British coals are classified according to caking properties (Gray King Assay) and percentage volatile matter content. These and other properties are related to the rank or age of the coal. The Coal Rank Code (CRC) classification divides coals into groups numbered in hundreds from 100 to 900, the groups being sub-divided into classes and sub-classes for a closer definition of property ranges.

Caking propensity increases from zero at both ends of the scale (groups 100 and 900) to a maximum in groups 300 and 400. Coals in group 100 are the anthracites; those in group 200 comprise the low volatile steam coals (coals in these two groups are natural smokeless fuels); coals in groups 300 to 900 are generally known as bituminous coals of which those in the groups 300 to 600 are generally used as coking coals, with the lower ranking groups (600–900) being general purpose coals for domestic and commercial burning.

5.3.2   Natural gas

Most natural gas distributed in the UK stems from underground deposits beneath the North Sea and Irish Sea. As these gas fields decline in output increasing quantities will become available from Norway and the Russian Federation. Gas quality is controlled under the auspices of the Gas Act 1986[5]. Calorific value must be declared as gas is costed on the basis of number of units of energy supplied. Similar restrictions apply to the uniformity of calorific value, supply pressure, Wobbe number, hydrogen sulphide content and smell. The unit of energy 'therm' is 10^5 British Thermal Units (BTU) and this is equivalent to 105.5 MJ.

5.4   Secondary fuels

5.4.1   Smokeless solid fuels

Manufactured smokeless fuels are cokes and bonded briquettes. In the heating field these are usually burned in hand-fired or gravity-fed appliances. The use of briquetted fuels is restricted to domestic appliances.

5.4.2   Petroleum fuel oils

All fuel oils are refinery products. Crude oils, which are obtained from the oil wells as mixtures of hydrocarbons, are processed in the refinery to produce many hundreds of commercial products, including fuel oil. The numerous hydrocarbon compounds have different boiling points and, by controlled heating of the crude oil, the various fractions are distilled and condensed, producing gasolines, kerosenes and gas oils which are termed distillates. Blending of the residual oils with a suitable distillate enables the production of the various grades of residual fuel oils, which are commercially available for application to the larger heating plants. Nitrogen and asphaltene contents of residual fuel oils are significant in determining levels of nitrogen oxide and particulate emissions to the atmosphere. Careful selection of the appropriate equipment, boilers, burners and flues will enable the most effective grade of fuel oil to be applied to the particular plant requirements.

5.4.3   Liquefied petroleum gases

Liquefied petroleum gases, commonly known as LPG, are the C3 and C4 members of the hydrocarbon family. They are readily liquefied by the application of moderate pressure at ambient temperature. These are marketed in the UK as two grades, known as 'commercial propane' and 'commercial butane' under various brand names given by the distributing companies. They are transported and stored in the liquid phase but are used and handled as a gas.

5.4.4   Electricity

Electricity is distributed over a high voltage grid system which is reduced at the user to standard conditions of 415 V, three phase, 50 Hz for normal purposes and small demands, but at higher voltages for large power requirements.

5.5   Specification of fuels

5.5.1   Solid fuels

5.5.1.1   Coal

The average properties of coals for the UK are given in Table 5.1 for typical 'as fired' fuel. This is the form in which the data are normally used for calculation. Physical data are given in Tables 5.2 to 5.7.

Coal size is identified according to metric screen sizes appropriate to BS 1016: Part 109[6]. Sizes for various graded coals are given in Tables 5.2 to 5.5.

Graded coals are separated into five standard groups for which the upper and lower limits have a permitted range (Table 5.2). Smalls are specified in terms of an upper size only; for stoker firing smalls have a top size of either 25 mm or 50 mm. Treated smalls are washed or dry cleaned. A guide to coal storage and handling is given in reference 7.

Calorific values

The following definitions are adopted in this chapter for gross and net calorific values:

— *Gross calorific value*: the calorific value of the fuel including the latent heat of condensation of all water vapour in the products of combustion.

— *Net calorific value*: the calorific value of the fuel when no water vapour is condensed from the products of combustion.

The calorific values of the fuels are tabulated for certain moisture contents. When the fuel has a different moisture content from that tabulated, the calorific value can be found from:

$$h_g = \frac{(100 - m)\, h_{gt}}{(100 - m_t)} \tag{5.1}$$

$$h_n = \frac{(100 - m)\, h_{nt}}{(100 - m_t)} - 24.5\,(m_t - m) \tag{5.2}$$

where h_g is the gross calorific value (mass basis) at moisture content m (kJ·kg^{-1}), h_{gt} is the tabulated gross calorific value (mass basis) (kJ·kg^{-1}), m is the moisture content of the fuel (%), m_t is the tabulated moisture content of the fuel (%), h_{nt} is the tabulated net calorific value (mass basis) (kJ·kg^{-1}) and h_n is the net calorific value (mass basis) at moisture content m (kJ·kg^{-1}).

Table 5.1 Average 'as fired' properties of coal

Fuel	Coal rank code	Moisture content / %		Constituent parts by mass / %							Calorific value / MJ·kg⁻¹	
		Air dried	96% RH 30 °C	Moisture	Ash	Carbon	Hydrogen	Nitrogen	Sulphur	Oxygen	Gross	Net
(a) Washed smalls												
Anthracite	101	2	4	8	8	78.2	2.4	0.9	1.0	1.5	29.65	28.95
	102	1	2	7	8	77.9	3.1	1.1	1.0	1.9	30.35	29.30
Dry steam coals	201	1	1	7	8	77.4	3.4	1.2	1.0	2.0	30.60	29.65
Coking steam coals	202	1	1	7	8	77.1	3.5	1.2	1.0	2.2	30.70	29.75
	204	1	1	7	8	76.8	3.8	1.2	1.0	2.2	30.80	29.80
Medium volatile coking coals	301a	1	1	7	8	75.8	4.1	1.3	1.2	2.6	30.80	29.75
	301b	1	1	7	8	74.8	4.2	1.3	1.2	3.5	30.45	29.40
Heat altered coals	302H	1	2	7	8	74.4	4.2	1.7	1.2	3.5	30.35	29.25
	303H	2	3	8	8	72.7	4.2	1.4	1.2	4.5	29.75	28.60
High volatile coking coals:												
— very strongly caking	401	2	2	9	8	71.6	4.3	1.6	1.7	3.8	29.55	28.40
— strongly caking	501	2	3	9	8	71.0	4.3	1.5	1.7	4.6	29.20	28.05
	502	3	4	10	8	68.8	4.4	1.5	1.7	5.5	28.60	27.40
— medium caking	601	4	6	11	8	67.8	4.3	1.4	1.7	5.9	27.80	26.60
	602	4	5	11	8	67.0	4.4	1.4	1.7	6.1	27.80	26.55
General purpose coals:												
— weakly caking	701	5	6	13	8	65.7	4.0	1.4	1.7	6.2	26.75	25.50
	702	5	7	13	8	65.0	4.2	1.3	1.7	6.8	26.75	25.50
— very weakly caking	802	8	11	16	8	61.3	4.0	1.3	1.7	7.7	25.25	23.95
— non-caking	902	10	13	18	8	59.0	3.7	1.2	1.7	8.4	23.85	22.60
Manufactured fuels:												
— domestic and industrial coke	—	—	—	8–12	7	82.0	0.4	1.7	—	—	27.90	26.30
— low temperature coke	—	—	—	15	6	71.0	2.4	2.4	—	3.2	27.45	25.40
(b) Washed singles												
Anthracite	101	2	4	4	5	84.7	2.6	1.0	1.1	1.6	32.10	31.45
	102	1	2	3	5	84.3	3.4	1.2	1.1	2.0	32.85	31.80
Dry steam coals	201	1	1	3	5	83.7	3.7	1.3	1.1	2.2	33.10	32.20
Coking steam coals	202	1	1	3	5	83.4	3.8	1.3	1.1	2.4	33.20	32.30
	204	1	1	3	5	83.1	4.1	1.3	1.1	2.4	33.30	32.35
Medium volatile coking coals	301a	1	1	3	5	82.1	4.4	1.4	1.3	2.8	33.30	32.30
	301b	1	1	3	5	81.0	4.5	1.4	1.3	2.8	32.95	31.90
Heat altered coals	302H	1	2	3	5	80.6	4.5	1.8	1.3	3.8	32.85	31.75
	303H	2	3	4	5	78.7	4.6	1.5	1.3	4.9	32.20	31.10
High volatile coking coals:												
— very strongly caking	401	2	2	4	5	78.5	4.7	1.7	1.9	4.2	32.40	31.25
— strongly caking	501	2	3	5	5	77.0	4.7	1.5	1.8	5.0	31.65	30.50
	502	3	4	5	5	75.5	4.8	1.6	1.9	6.2	31.40	30.20
— medium caking	601	4	6	6	5	74.5	4.6	1.5	1.9	6.5	30.60	29.35
	602	4	5	7	5	73.2	4.8	1.5	1.9	6.6	30.15	28.95
General purpose coals:												
— weakly caking	701	5	6	9	5	71.5	4.4	1.5	1.8	6.8	29.15	27.80
	702	5	7	9	5	70.8	4.6	1.4	1.8	7.4	29.15	27.90
— very weakly caking	802	8	11	11	5	67.8	4.4	1.4	1.9	8.5	27.90	26.60
— non-caking	902	10	13	16	5	63.0	3.9	1.3	1.8	9.0	24.45	24.10

Table 5.2 Standard size groups for graded coals

Name of group	Round hole screen size / mm	
	Upper limit	Lower limit
Large cobbles	>150	75
Cobbles	100–150	50–100
Trebles/large nuts	63–100	38–63
Doubles/nuts	38–63	25–38
Singles	25–38	13–18

Table 5.3 Size limits and bulk density of Welsh anthracite

Name	Size limits / mm	Bulk density / kg·m⁻³
Cobbles	80–125	770–800
French nuts	63–80	770–800
Stove nuts	36–63	770–800
Stovesse	20/16–36	750–785
Beans	10–20	750–785
Peas	10–16	750–785
Grains	5–10	750–785
Washed duff	0–5	785–820

Table 5.4 Size limits and bulk density of Welsh dry steam coal

Name	Size limits / mm	Bulk density / kg·m^{-3}
Cobbles	80–125	720–750
Large nuts	56–80	720–750
Small nuts	18–56	720–750
Beans	16–18	705–735
Peas	10–18	705–735
Washed duff	0–10	705–735

Table 5.5 Size limits and bulk density of hard coke

Name	Size limits / mm	Bulk density / kg·m^{-3}
Large	Over 90	433
Cobbles	64–90	448
Trebles	40–64	464
Doubles	25–40	464
Singles	16–25	481
Beans	10–16	497

Table 5.6 Natural angle of repose of solid fuels

Approximate size of fuel / mm	Angle of repose (measured from the horizontal)
20–30	408
12–20	428
6–12	528
0–6	588

Table 5.7 Bulk density of loosely packed dry coal

Nature and size of coal	Bulk density / kg·m^{-3}
Graded coal	640 ± 60
Small coal	770 ± 60
Coal dust (‚3 mm)	530 ± 50
Pulverised fuel (50–90% passing 76 × 76 μm square mesh sieve)	450 ± 50

Note: The bulk density depends on a number of factors and is not reproducible within 65% except under laboratory conditions. Compaction may increase the density by up to 20%, whereas freshly formed pulverised fuel has a wide variation in range and may be less than 50% of the quoted figure.

5.5.1.2 Pelletised refuse derived fuel (d-RDF)

Pelletised refuse derived fuel remains a suitable energy source for small boilers despite some problems in manufacture and market viability. Table 5.8[8] compares the properties of d-RDF with a typical coal used for stoker firing. The calorific value of d-RDF is about two-thirds that of coal and ash yields on combustion significantly higher. Appreciable fuel glass contents may provide low d-RDF ash fusion temperatures and possible clinker formation under adverse combustion conditions.

5.5.1.3 Properties of wood fuels

The sustainable use of wood fuels can provide environmental benefits in terms of reduced carbon dioxide, nitrogen oxide and sulphur oxide emissions in comparison to coal. Short rotation coppice (SRC) wood fuels, based on fast growing poplar and willow species, are becoming more available in the form of dried chips.

Wood chips are divided into grades of super, fine and coarse covering size ranges of 2 mm to 25 mm. A European classification system for wood sizes is given in CEN/TS 1496[9]. For small boiler plant operation it is recommended that fuel moisture content does not exceed 35% (British Biogen).

Wood fuels contain high percentage volatile matter and oxygen compositions with low ash. These properties influence smoke emission and the stoichiometric air requirement respectively. Table 5.9 gives an indicative composition of a chipped wood fuel.

5.5.2 Liquid fuels

5.5.2.1 Petroleum oils

British Standard specifications are published for all grades of petroleum oil fuels and are accepted as the basic requirements for the UK (BS 2869[10]). The five classes shown in Table 5.10 cover the fuels normally used in fixed appliances. Class C1 is a paraffin type fuel for use in free-standing, flueless domestic burners, and is not detailed in this section. Class C2 is a distillate fuel of the kerosene type for vapourising and small atomising burners.

Class D is a distillate grade for larger atomising burners in both domestic and industrial use, generally known as gas oil. Under the Sulphur Content of Liquid Fuels Regulations 2000[11] the maximum sulphur content of Class D oils should not exceed 0.1% from January 2008.

Classes E, F and G are residual or blended fuel oils for atomising burners and generally need pre-heating before combustion. These will normally require storage and

Table 5.8 Properties of a commercial coal and d-RDF[8]

Fuel	Moisture / %	Volatile matter / %	Ash / %	Calorific value, as fired / MJ·kg^{-1}	Bulk density / kg·m^{-3}
Coal	8.4	25.9	10.2	27.2	900
d-RDF	7.3	67.5	15.0	18.7	600

Table 5.9 Indicative composition of a chipped wood fuel

Moisture content as fired by mass / %	Ash as fired, by mass / %	Volatile matter, dry as fired, by mass / %	O$_2$ dry as fired, by mass / %	Gross calorific value, dry as fired / MJ·kg^{-1}
15	0.6	80	48	19.7

Table 5.10 Properties of petroleum burner fuels (BS 2869[10])

Property	Class C2	Class D	Class E	Class F	Class G
Kinematic viscosity (m²·s⁻¹) at 40 °C	1.00–2.00 × 10⁻⁶ (min–max)	1.5–5.5 × 10⁻⁶ (min–max)	—	—	—
Kinematic viscosity (m²·s⁻¹) at 100 °C	—	—	8.2 × 10⁻⁶ (max)	20.0 × 10⁻⁶ (max)	40.0 × 10⁻⁶ (max)
Carbon residue (% mass); Ramsbottom on 10% residue	—	0.3 (max)	15.0 (max)	18.0 (max)	20.0 (max)
Minimum closed flash point (°C):					
— Abel	38	—	—	—	—
— Pensky–Martens	—	56	66	66	66
Maximum water content	—	200 mg·kg⁻¹	0.5% v/v	0.75% v/v	1.0% v/v
Maximum sediment content by mass (%)	—	0.01	0.10	0.15	0.15
Maximum ash content by mass (%)	—	0.01	0.10	0.10	0.15
Maximum sulphur content by mass (%)	0.20	0.20	3.50	3.50	3.50

Table 5.11 Properties of typical petroleum fuel oils

Property	Kerosene Class 2	Gas oil Class D	Light fuel oil Class E	Medium fuel oil Class F	Heavy fuel oil Class G
Relative density at 15 °C	0.803	0.850	0.940	0.970	0.980
Minimum closed flash point (°C)	38	60	66	66	66
Kinematic viscosity (m²·s⁻¹):					
— at 40 °C	—	3.2 × 10⁻⁶	—	—	—
— at 100 °C	—	—	8 × 10⁻⁶	16 × 10⁻⁶	35 × 10⁻⁶
Freezing point (°C)	< −40	—	—	—	—
Maximum pour point (°C)	—	—	26	24	30
Maximum cloud point (°C)	—	−5 (Mar/Sep) −16 (Oct/Feb)	—	—	—
Gross calorific value (MJ·kg⁻¹)	46.4	45.5	42.5	41.8	42.7
Net calorific value (MJ·kg⁻¹)	43.6	42.7	40.1	39.5	40.3
Maximum sulphur content by mass (%)	0.2	0.2	3.2	3.5	3.5
Maximum water content by volume (%)	negligible	0.05	0.5	0.75	1.0
Maximum sediment content by mass (%)	—	0.01	0.10	0.15	0.15
Maximum ash content by volume (%)	—	0.01	0.05	0.07	0.10
Mean specific heat capacity, 0–100 °C (kJ·kg⁻¹·K⁻¹)	2.1	2.06	1.93	1.89	1.89

handling plant with heating facilities. Under the Sulphur Content of Liquid Fuels Regulations 2000[11] the maximum sulphur content of Class G oils should not exceed 1% by mass unless an exemption is granted.

Commercial specifications follow the pattern shown in Table 5.11 but usually include additional information so that all points governing fuel performance can be assessed. More detailed property data and updated information may be obtained from the fuel supplier.

BS 799: Part 5[12] provides specifications for oil storage tank installations.

Viscosity

Kinematic viscosity is a measure of resistance of the liquid to flow and may be defined as the force needed to shear a unit cube at unit speed and was formerly expressed in units of centistokes (cSt), where 1 cSt = 1 mm²·s⁻¹. The SI unit is m²·s⁻¹. (Thus 1 cSt = 1 mm²·s⁻¹ = 1 × 10⁻⁶ m²·s⁻¹).

Figure 5.1 (page 5-6) shows the relationship between kinematic viscosity and temperature for fuel oils of grades E, F G and H.

Maximum viscosities of 500 × 10⁻⁶ m²·s⁻¹ for pumping and 12 to 15 × 10⁻⁶ m²·s⁻¹ for pressure atomisation are normally used. Rotary cup atomisers employ a viscosity range of 50 to 80 × 10⁻⁶ m²·s⁻¹.

Pour point

Pour point (Table 5.11) is a laboratory test by which the lowest temperature at which an oil will flow under carefully defined conditions is measured. In order to ensure mobility of the fuel, minimum storage temperatures are required for class E, F and G oil fuels. The distillate grades require no heating.

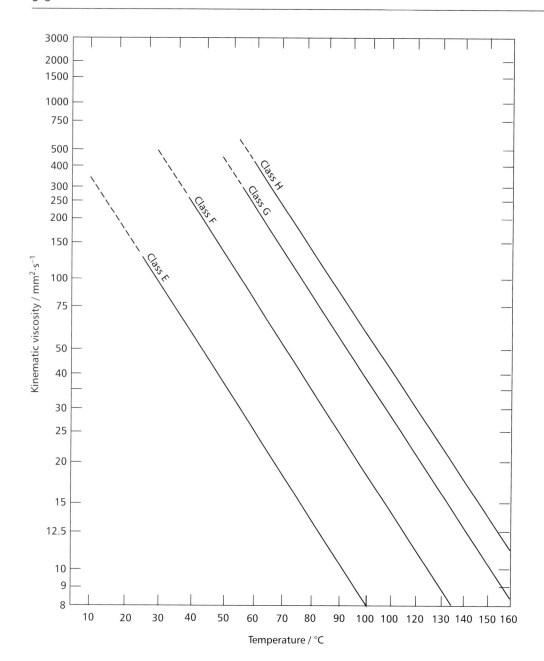

Figure 5.1 Viscosity–temperature chart for class E, F, G and H fuel oils (reproduced from BS 2869[10] by permission of the British Standards Institution)

Heating requirements

Fuel of classes C2 and D may be stored, handled and atomised at ambient temperatures, but exposure for a long period to extreme cold should be avoided otherwise restrictions in the flow of oil from the tank may result. The appropriate temperatures for the storage and handling of fuels of classes E, F and G are given in Table 5.12.

Normally oil burners require that residual fuel oils should be presented to the burner at a viscosity between 12 and 15×10^{-6} m^2·s^{-1}. The burner manufacturer's actual requirements should be ascertained at the design stage.

5.5.3   Gaseous fuels

5.5.3.1   Liquefied petroleum gas (LPG)

Typical properties of commercial butane and commercial propane are given in Table 5.13. Limiting requirements for the properties of commercial butane and commercial propane are given in BS 4250[13].

Latent heat of vapourisation

Reference to Table 5.13 shows that on a mass basis the latent heats of vapourisation for propane and butane are similar and equivalent to 0.75% of the calorific value of the fuel. Unless the latent heat is supplied artificially with a vapouriser it can only be taken from the atmosphere through the walls of the container; this places a limit on the rate at which gas can be taken off under natural, ambient temperature conditions.

Table 5.12 Storage and handling temperatures of fuel oils (BS 799: Part 5[12])

Class of fuel	Minimum storage temperature / °C	Minimum handling or outflow from storage temperature / °C
E	10	10
F	25	30
G	40	50

Table 5.13 Typical properties of commercial butane and commercial propane

Property	Butane (C_4H_{10})	Propane (C_3H_8)
Density at 15 °C (kg·m^{-3})	570	500
Relative density of liquid at 15 °C	0.570–0.580	0.500–0.510
Relative density of gas compared with air at STP	1.90–2.10	1.40–1.55
Volume of gas per kg of liquid at STP (m^3)	0.41–0.43	0.53–0.54
Ratio of gas volume to liquid volume at STP	233	−274
Boiling point (°C)	0	−45
Absolute vapour pressure at stated temperature (for products of the maximum specified vapour pressure) (kPa):		
— −40.0 °C	—	140
— −17.8 °C	—	320
— 0 °C	200	560
— 37.8 °C	580	1570
— 45.0 °C	690	1810
Latent heat of vapourisation at 15 °C (kJ·kg^{-1})	370	357
Specific heat of liquid (kJ·kg^{-1}·K^{-1})	2.4	2.52
Sulphur content	Negligible to 0.02% by mass	Negligible to 0.02% by mass
Limits of flammability (percentage by volume of gas in gas/air mixture)	9.0 (upper) 1.8 (lower)	10.0 (upper) 2.2 (lower)
Calorific values (dry volumetric basis) (MJ·m^{-3}):		
— gross	122	93
— net	113	86
Calorific values (mass basis) (MJ.kg^{-1}):		
— gross	49.5	50
— net	46	46.5
Air required for combustion (m^3 per m^3 of gas)	30	24

Note: values of density and specific volume are given at STP, being 15 °C and 101.3 kPa; similarly values of relative density are given relative to dry air at STP; the density of dry air to normalise gas density to relative density is 1.16 m^3·kg^{-1}.

Relative density

Both propane and butane are heavier than air and the vapour will therefore tend to collect at a low level in the event of a leak. This point must be borne in mind when designing storage and handling systems. Conversely the liquid density is low and this is important when considering transportation and filling of containers of known internal volume.

Sulphur content

LPG has a low sulphur content controlled by specification limits (BS 4250) to 200 mg·kg^{-1} (0.02% by mass).

5.5.3.2 Natural gas

Typical analyses and properties of natural gas are given in Tables 5.14 and 5.15.

Where gas volume data are given they are based on conventional reference conditions of 15 °C and 101.3 kPa.

Calorific value

The legal requirement is for the public gas transporter to calculate each day in accordance with the Gas (Calculation of Thermal Energy) Regulations[14], a 'flow weighted average' calorific value (FWAC) which is passed to all gas shippers for all charging areas.

Table 5.14 Typical volume analysis and properties of natural gas

Components and properties	Value
Components:	
— methane	92.6%
— ethane	3.6%
— propane	0.8%
— butane	0.2%
— pentane and above	0.1%
— hydrogen	—
— carbon monoxide	—
— carbon dioxide	0.1%
— nitrogen	2.6%
Properties:	
— gross calorific value (MJ·m^{-3})	38.7
— net calorific value (MJ·m^{-3})	34.9
— relative density	0.602
— Wobbe No. (dry)	49.9
— air required for combustion (m^3 per m^3 gas)	9.73

Table 5.15 Operating properties of natural gas

Property	Value
Declared calorific value	≈ 38.7 MJ·m^{-3}
Relative density	0.59–0.61
Wobbe No.	45.7–55.0 (Gas Group H)
Distribution pressure	1750–2750 Pa★

★Legal requirement: must not fall below 1250 Pa

Sulphur compounds

The contract specification for natural gas limits the total sulphur content to 35 parts per million expressed as hydrogen sulphide. As distributed the sulphur content of natural gas is approximately 0.0011 per cent by volume.

Relative density

There is no legal requirement for relative density and the average value is given in Tables 5.14 and 5.15.

Wobbe number

The thermal input of an appliance (e.g. central heating boiler) for a given pressure and burner orifice is a function of the Wobbe number. This number is defined as:

$$W = \frac{h_g}{d^{0.5}} \tag{5.3}$$

where W is the Wobbe number ($MJ \cdot m^{-3}$), h_g is the gross calorific value (volume basis) ($MJ \cdot m^{-3}$) and d is the relative density.

Natural gases all have Wobbe numbers falling within a narrow range and all appliances are designed to operate on gas corresponding to the mean of that range.

5.5.3.3   Landfill gas

There is significant potential for landfill gas as a fuel for direct boiler firing or in CHP applications. Gas may require cleaning and dewatering before use. The composition is approximately 60 per cent methane and 40 per cent carbon dioxide and also includes many other gases in trace concentrations. The calorific value is in the range 15–25 $MJ \cdot m^{-3}$ depending upon the inert gas content and the extent of raw gas conditioning[8].

5.6   Combustion data

5.6.1   Combustion air and waste gas volume

It is necessary to determine combustion air requirements and waste gas volumes for boiler plant and chimney/flue designs. In order to simplify this assessment, charts are reproduced below for various fuels where the required volume under various CO_2 per cent (excess air) conditions can be read off. Percentage CO_2 values are expressed on a dry gas basis.

Note that all volumes are standardised at 15 °C, 101.3 kPa. For volumes at other temperatures the following formula may be used:

$$V_g = \frac{V(\theta_g + 273)}{288} \tag{5.4}$$

where V_g is the volume at temperature θ_g (m^3), θ_g is the actual air or flue gas temperature (°C) and V_g is the standard volume read from charts (m^3).

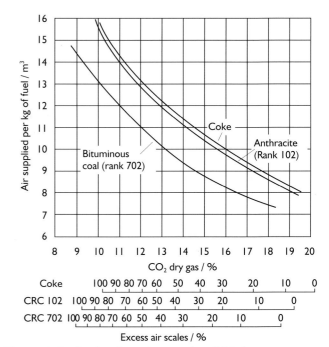

Figure 5.2 Combustion air requirements for solid fuels

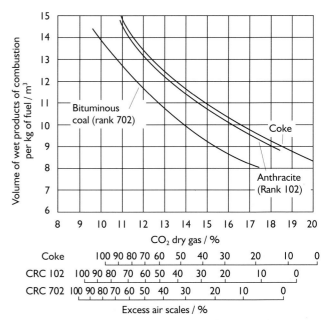

Figure 5.3 Volumes of products of combustion for solid fuels

5.6.1.1   Solid fuels

The average figures given in Table 5.16 may be taken for CO_2 per cent, excess air, total air and gas requirements per kilogram of fuel for plant working under normal conditions of combustion efficiency.

Where the anticipated CO_2 per cent (and excess air values) varies considerably from the averaged conditions listed in Table 5.16, refer to the appropriate curves on Figures 5.2 and 5.3, which are accurate for practical design purposes.

5.6.1.2   Fuel oils

The average figures in Table 5.16 may be taken for CO_2 per cent, excess air, total air and flue gas volume requirements per kilogram of fuel with plant working under normal conditions of combustion efficiency.

Table 5.16 Combustion conditions

Fuel	CO_2 / %	Excess air / %	Total air volume / $m^3 \cdot kg^{-1}$	Flue gas volume / $m^3 \cdot kg^{-1}$
Solid fuels:				
— coke	13.7	50	11.7	11.9
— anthracite	12.7	50	12.3	12.7
— bituminous coal	12.3	50	10.8	11.4
Fuel oils:				
— classes C and D	11.6	30	15.4	16.3
— classes E, F and G	12.1	30	14.1	14.7

Where the anticipated CO_2 per cent (excess air) varies considerably from the above averaged figures, refer to the appropriate curves on Figures 5.4 and 5.5, which are sufficiently accurate for practical design purposes.

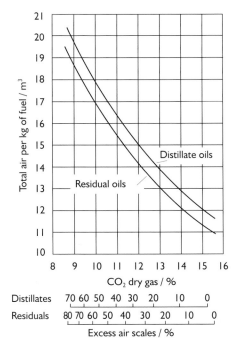

Figure 5.4 Combustion air requirements for petroleum fuel oils

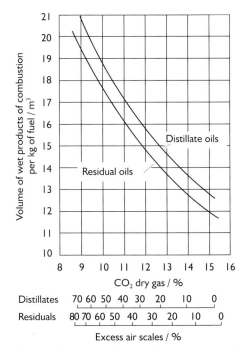

Figure 5.5 Volumes of products of combustion for petroleum fuel oils

5.6.1.3 Gaseous fuels

With gas fired boilers the flue gas/air volumes depend on the type of boiler/burner unit installed and the design of the union between the boiler exhaust gas outlet flue and chimney.

The average figures given in Table 5.17 for natural gas have been obtained from site tests. Two types are given:

(a) boilers fitted with a naturally inspirated burner and a draught diverter

(b) boilers fitted with a forced draught burner and a direct flue connection.

Excess air data are given in Figure 5.6. It is important to note that it is possible to have an air deficiency when measuring CO_2 percentage alone. Since natural gas does not produce black smoke when combustion is incomplete it is necessary to measure the CO content in addition to CO_2 to determine if there is sufficient combustion air. For example, from Figure 5.6 it is seen that 10.3% CO_2 could mean either 14% excess air or 15% air deficiency; measuring the CO content will show which air value is correct.

The water dew point of natural gas exhaust gases, appropriate to typical operating conditions of forced draught condensing boilers, is approximately 55 °C.

Table 5.17 Percentage volumes of combustion products for boilers burning natural gas

Type of burner	CO_2 / %	CO / %	Flue gas temp. / °C
Natural inspirated burner and draught diverter (values measured in primary flue)	7.5–9	0.001–0.008	190–290
Forced draught burner with direct flue connection	8–11	0.001–0.006	55–320

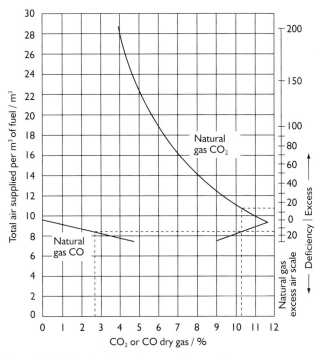

Figure 5.6 Combustion air requirements for natural gas

5.7 Stack losses

The major heat loss from combustion appliances is the heat carried away in the flue gases. Several formulae have been proposed for assessing these losses based mainly upon variations to the 'Siegert' expression. In order to simplify the assessment for practical requirements, graphs are included in this section which give the stack losses based upon the gross calorific value of the fuel. They do not include any unburned gas loss, i.e. it is assumed that there is no CO in the flue gases.

5.7.1 Solid fuels

The curves given in Figures 5.7, 5.8 and 5.9 show the total flue gas heat loss for various CO_2 per cent values (excess air quantities) expressed as a per cent of gross calorific value. They are provided for general guidance because

variables such as rank, grade and moisture content will affect the gross heat loss. CO_2 per cent values are denoted on the basis of dry flue products.

5.7.2 Liquid fuels

The curves given in Figures 5.10 and 5.11 show the total flue gas loss at various flue gas temperatures for various CO_2 per cent values (excess air quantities) expressed as a per cent of gross calorific value.

5.7.3 Gaseous fuels

The curves given in Figure 5.12 show the total flue gas loss at various flue gas temperatures for various CO_2 per cent values (excess air quantities) expressed as a per cent of gross calorific value.

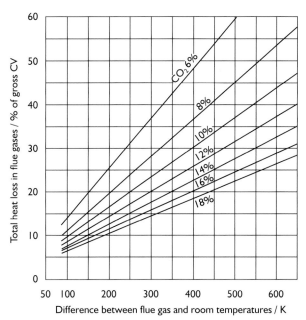

Figure 5.7 Flue gas losses: bituminous coal (CRC 702)

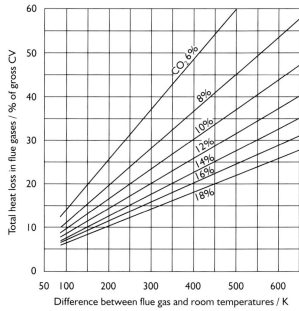

Figure 5.9 Flue gas losses: anthracite (CRC 102)

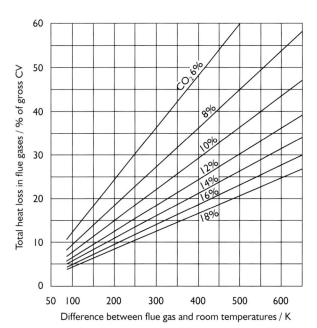

Figure 5.8 Flue gas losses: coke

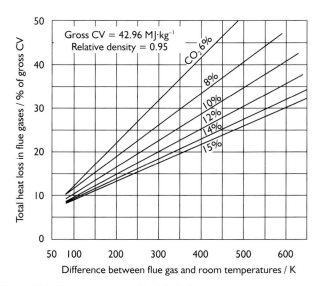

Figure 5.10 Flue gas losses: residual fuel oils

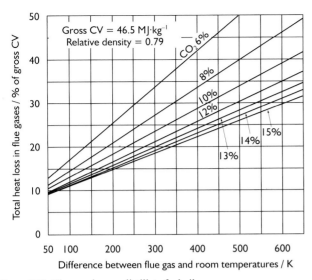

Figure 5.11 Flue gas losses: distillate fuel oils

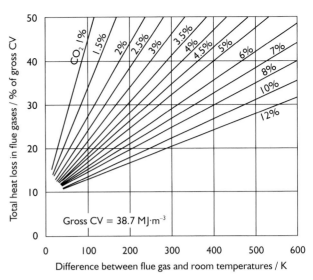

Figure 5.12 Flue gas losses: natural gas

References

1   Clean Air Act 1993 (London: Her Majesty's Stationery Office) (1993)

2   Climate Change Agreements and the Climate Change Levy (London: Department for Environment, Food and Rural Affairs) (2005) (http://www.defra.gov.uk/environment/ccl/intro.htm)

3   *The practical guide to the Climate Change Levy — energy efficient solutions for industry, commerce and the public sector* (Association for the Conservation of Energy/Journal of Water, Energy and the Environment) (2001)

4   *Conservation of fuel and power in existing buildings other than dwellings* The Building Regulations 2000 Approved Document L2B (London: The Stationery Office) (2006)

5   Gas Act 1986 (London: Her Majesty's Stationery Office) (1986)

6   BS 1016: *Methods for analysis and testing of coal and coke*: Part 109: 1995 (ISO 1953: 1994): *Size analysis of coal* (London: British Standards Institution) (1995)

7   Vesma V (ed.) *Industrial Coal Handbook* 1st edn. (Energy Publications) (1985)

8   Williams P T *Waste treatment and disposal* (London: Wiley) (1998)

9   DD CEN/TS 14961: 2005: *Solid biofuels. Fuel specifications and classes* (London: British Standards Institution) (2005)

10   BS 2869: 2006: *Fuel oils for agricultural, domestic and industrial engines and boilers. Specification* (London: British Standards Institution) (2006)

11   The Sulphur Content of Liquid Fuels (England and Wales) Regulations 2000 Statutory Instruments 2000 No. 1460; The Sulphur Content of Liquid Fuels Regulations (Northern Ireland) 2002 Statutory Rules of Northern Ireland 2002 No. 28; The Sulphur Content of Liquid Fuels (Scotland) Regulations 2000 Scottish Statutory Instruments 2000 No. 169 (London: The Stationery Office) (dates as indicated)

12   BS 799: *Oil burning equipment*: Part 5: 1987: *Specification for oil storage tanks* (London: British Standards Institution) (1987)

13   BS 4250: 1997: *Specification for commercial butane and commercial propane* (London: British Standards Institution) (1997)

14   The Gas (Calculation of Thermal Energy) Regulations 1996 Statutory Instruments 1996 No. 439 (London: Her Majesty's Stationery Office) (1996)

Bibliography

Breag G R, Joseph P G and Tariq A S Biomass Combustion Systems — Flue Gas Losses and Equipment Efficiency (Greenwich: University of Greenwich Natural Resources Institute) (1992)

BS 799: *Oil burning equipment*: Part 3: 1981: *Automatic and semi-automatic atomizing burners up to 36 litres per hour*; Part 4: 1991: *Specification for atomizing burners (other than monobloc type) together with associated equipment for single burner and multi burner installations*; Part 5: 1987: *Specification for oil storage tanks* (London: British Standards Institution) (1981/1987/1991)

BS 845: *Methods for assessing thermal performance of boilers for steam, hot water and high temperature heat transfer fluids*: Part 1: 1987: *Concise procedure*; Part 2: 1987: *Comprehensive procedure* (London: British Standards Institution) (1987)

BS 1016: *Methods for the analysis and testing of coal and coke*: Parts 1–21 (1970–1998 with earlier parts withdrawn); Parts 100–113 (1991–1998); Part 100: 1994: *General introduction and methods for reporting results* (London: British Standards Institution) (dates as indicated)

Digest of United Kingdom Energy Statistics (London: Government Statistical Service (published annually) (www.dti.gov.uk/energy/statistics/publications/dukes/page19311.html)

Dryden I G C (ed.) *The efficient use of energy* 2nd edn. (Oxford: Butterworth Scientific) (1982)

Energy Institute Yearbook and Directory 2006 (London: Energy Institute) (published annually)

Environmental Protection Act 1990 (London: Her Majesty's Stationery Office) (1990; reprinted with corrections 1998, 2004)

Establishing guidelines for wood fuel standards DTI Project Summary 369 (1st. issue) (London: Department of Trade and Industry) (October 1994)

Fuel and energy abstracts (London: Energy Institute/Elsivier) (bi-monthly)

Gunn D and Horton R *Industrial boilers* 1st edn. (London: Longman Scientific and Technical) (1989)

IP Standard Methods for analysis and testing of petroleum and related products, and British Standard 2000 Parts (2 vols.) (London: Energy Institute) (2006)

Pollution Handbook 2006 (Brighton: National Society for Clean Air and Environmental Protection) (published annually)

Rose J W and Cooper J R (eds.) *Technical data on fuel* 7th edn. (Edinburgh: Scottish Academic Press) (1977)

6 Units, standard and mathematical data

6.1 Introduction

This section contains information which, although essential to engineers and designers does not on the whole belong exclusively to any other chapter of the Guide. Inevitably, therefore, a large part of the section is devoted to SI units, which are used throughout the Guide but are not explained elsewhere. The development of SI is traced and the definitions of the base and supplementary units are given. There is also an explanation of how the units adopted by the European Union differ from SI. Comprehensive tables then list the conversion factors for changing from old units to their practical SI equivalents.

Although SI units have been the official standard units in Europe (including the UK) since 1971, conversion from other units is still regularly required for three reasons:

— some countries, notably the USA, have not fully adopted SI units

— some UK engineers still think in imperial units

— much of the UK heritage of plant and buildings was built to imperial unit designs.

6.2 The International System of Units (SI)

All international matters concerning the metric system have been the responsibility of the Conférence Générale des Poids et Mesures (CGPM) since the signing of the Metre Convention in 1875. Under the authority of CGPM are the Comité International des Poids et Mesures (CIPM) and the Bureau International des Poids et Mesures (BIPM). UK participation in CGPM work is through the Department of Trade and Industry (DTI). The International Standards Organisation (ISO) provides recommendations and advice and, more recently, International Standards on the use and selection of SI units in industry and technology. UK participation in ISO work is through the British Standards Institution (BSI). The relevant standards are BS ISO 31/0 to 31/13 and BS ISO 1000.

At its 10th meeting in 1954, CGPM adopted a coherent system of units based on the metre, kilogram, second, ampere, kelvin and candela. At its 14th meeting in 1971, the mole was added as the seventh base unit. The 11th meeting in 1960 gave the system its formal title 'Le Système International d'Unités — commonly abbreviated to SI. The SI comprises:

— seven named base units (Table 6.1)

— two named supplementary units.

These units are defined below. Each unit has been allocated an internationally agreed symbol. All other units may be derived from these base and supplementary units. The supplementary units have since 1981 been redefined as 'derived units'.

Certain derived units have been given internationally agreed names and symbols. The allocation of a name to a derived unit has:

(a) the advantage of simplicity in written and verbal communication

(b) the disadvantage of masking the derivation of the unit.

Table 6.1 SI base units

Quantity	Name	Symbol
Length	metre	m
Mass	kilogram	kg
Time	second	s
Electric current	ampere	A
Thermodynamic temperature	kelvin	K
Luminous intensity	candela	cd
Amount of substance	mole	mol

6.2.1 Definitions of base units

6.2.1.1 Unit of length

Name: metre   *Symbol*: m

The metre is the length of the path travelled in a vacuum by light during 1/299 792 458 seconds. (17th CGPM (1983), Resolution 1.)

6.2.1.2 Unit of mass

Name: kilogram   *Symbol*: kg

With the object of removing the ambiguity which still occurred in the common use of the word 'weight', the 3rd CGPM (1901) declared: 'the kilogram is the unit of mass (and not of weight or of force); it is equal to the mass of the international prototype of the kilogram'. This international prototype made of platinum–iridium is kept at the BIPM under conditions specified by the 1st CGPM in 1889.

6.2.1.3 Unit of time

Name: second   *Symbol*: s

The second is the duration of 9 192 631 770 periods of the radiation corresponding to the transition between the two hyperfine levels of the ground state of the caesium-133 atom. (13th CGPM (1967), Resolution 1.)

6.2.1.4 Unit of electric current

Name: ampere   *Symbol*: A

The ampere is that constant current which, if maintained in two straight parallel conductors of infinite length, of negligible circular cross-section, and placed 1 metre apart in a vacuum, would produce between these conductors a force equal to 2×10^{-7} newton per metre of length. (CPIM (1946), Resolution 2 approved by the 9th CGPM 1948.)

6.2.1.5 Unit of thermodynamic temperature

Name: kelvin   *Symbol*: K

The kelvin, the unit of thermodynamic temperature, is the fraction 1/273.16 of the thermodynamic temperature of the triple point of water. (3th CGPM (1967), Resolution 4.)

The 13th CGPM (1967), Resolution 3, also decided that the unit kelvin and its symbol K should be used to express an interval or a difference of temperature.

In addition to the thermodynamic temperature expressed in kelvins, use is also made of Celsius temperature defined by:

$$\theta = T - T_0 \qquad (6.1)$$

where θ is the Celsius temperature (°C), T is the thermodynamic temperature (K) and $T_0 = 273.15$ K by definition.

The Celsius temperature is in general expressed in degree Celsius (symbol °C). The unit 'degree Celsius' is thus equal to the unit 'kelvin' and an interval or a difference of Celsius temperature may also be expressed in degrees Celsius.

6.2.1.6 Unit of luminous intensity

Name: candela   *Symbol*: cd

The candela is the luminous intensity in a given direction of a source emitting monochromatic radiation at 50×10^{12} H$_3$ with a radiant intensity in that direction of 1/683 watt per steradian. (16th CGPM (1979), Resolution 3.)

6.2.1.7 Unit of amount of substance

Name: mole   *Symbol*: mol

The mole is the amount of substance of a system which contains as many elementary entities as there are atoms in 0.012 kilogram of carbon 12. (14th CGPM (1971), Resolution 3.)

Note: when the mole is used, the elementary entities must be specified and may be atoms, molecules, ions, electrons, other particles, or specified groups of such particles.

6.2.2 Definitions of supplementary units

6.2.2.1 Unit of plane angle

Name: radian   *Symbol*: rad

The radian is the angle between two radii of a circle which cuts off on the circumference an arc equal in length to the radius.

6.2.2.2 Unit of solid angle

Name: steradian   *Symbol*: sr

The steradian is the solid angle which, having its vertex in the centre of a sphere, cuts off an area of the surface of the sphere equal to the square of the radius of the sphere.

6.2.3 Derived units

Derived units are expressed algebraically in terms of base and/or supplementary units, see Table 6.2. Certain of these have been given special names, see Table 6.3.

Table 6.2 Examples of SI derived units expressed in terms of base units

Quantity	Name	Symbol
Area	square metre	m^2
Volume	cubic metre	m^3
Velocity	metre per second	$m{\cdot}s^{-1}$
Specific volume	cubic metre per kilogram	$m^3{\cdot}kg^{-1}$
Thermal conductivity	watt per metre kelvin	$W{\cdot}m^{-1}{\cdot}K^{-1}$
Luminance	candela per square metre	$cd{\cdot}m^{-2}$

6.2.4 Prefixes for multiples and submultiples

The magnitude of SI units may be increased or decreased by the use of named prefixes. Each prefix is allocated an internationally agreed symbol which may be added (in front) of the unit symbol.

Table 6.3 SI derived units with special names

Quantity	Name of SI derived unit	Symbol	Expressed in terms of SI base or supplementary units or in terms of other SI derived units
Plane angle	radian	rad	—
Solid angle	steradian	sr	—
Frequency	hertz	Hz	$1\ Hz = 1\ s^{-1}$
Force	newton	N	$1\ N = 1\ kg \cdot m \cdot s^{-2}$
Pressure and stress	pascal	Pa	$1\ Pa = 1\ N \cdot m^{-2}$
Work, energy, quantity of heat	joule	J	$1\ J = 1\ N \cdot m$
Power	watt	W	$1\ W = 1\ J \cdot s^{-1}$
Apparent power	volt ampere	V·A	$1\ V \cdot A = 1\ J \cdot s^{-1}$
Quantity of electricity	coulomb	C	$1\ C = 1\ A \cdot s$
Electrical potential, potential difference, electromotive force	volt	V	$1\ V = 1\ W \cdot A^{-1} = 1\ J \cdot C^{-1}$
Electrical capacitance	farad	F	$1\ F = 1\ A \cdot s \cdot V^{-1} = 1\ C \cdot V^{-1}$
Electrical resistance	ohm	Ω	$1\ \Omega = 1\ V \cdot A^{-1}$
Electrical conductance	siemens	S	$1\ S = 1\ \Omega^{-1}$
Magnetic flux, flux of magnetic induction	weber	Wb	$1\ Wb = 1\ V \cdot s$
Magnetic flux density, magnetic induction	tesla	T	$1\ T = 1\ Wb \cdot m^{-2}$
Inductance	henry	H	$1\ H = 1\ V \cdot s \cdot A^{-1} = 1\ Wb \cdot A^{-1}$
Luminous flux	lumen	lm	$1\ lm = 1\ cd \cdot sr$
Illuminance	lux	lx	$1\ lx = 1\ lm \cdot m^{-2}$
Celsius temperature	degree Celsius	°C	$1\ °C = 1\ K$
Activity	becquerel	Bq	$1\ Bq = 1\ s^{-1}$
Specific energy imparted	gray	Gy	$1\ Gy = 1\ J \cdot kg^{-1}$
Dose equivalent	sievert	Sv	$1\ Sv = 1\ J \cdot kg^{-1}$
Catalytic activity	katal	kat	$1\ kat = 1\ mol \cdot s^{-1}$

The prefixes given in Table 6.4 may be used to construct decimal multiples of units.

Table 6.4 SI prefixes

Multiplying factor	Prefix	Symbol
10^{24}	yotta	Y
10^{21}	zetta	Z
10^{18}	exa	E
10^{15}	peta	P
10^{12}	tera	T
10^{9}	giga	G
10^{6}	mega	M
10^{3}	kilo	k
10^{2}	hecto	h
$10^{1} = 10$	deca	da
$10^{-1} = 0.1$	deci	d
10^{-2}	centi	c
10^{-3}	milli	m
10^{-6}	micro	μ
10^{-9}	nano	n
10^{-12}	pico	p
10^{-15}	femto	f
10^{-18}	atto	a
10^{-21}	zepto	z

6.2.5 Explanatory notes

The following notes are intended as a guide to some quantities and units.

6.2.5.1 Pressure and stress

In terms of the SI base units the quantity pressure may be expressed in the units ($kg \cdot m^{-1} \cdot s^{-2}$). This derived unit has been given the name pascal (Pa). Pressure can also be expressed as $N \cdot m^{-2}$, $J \cdot m^{-3}$, $W \cdot s \cdot m^{-3}$ etc.

A non-SI unit in common use is the bar ($1\ bar = 10^5\ Pa$).

Since the bar is a special authorised EU multiple of the pascal it is anticipated that the bar (and mbar) will remain in use indefinitely.

The Institution has adopted the pascal (and the internationally agreed multiples and sub-multiples) for expressing both pressure and stress in documents published after 1973. Operating pressures are usually expressed in kilopascals, and sometimes followed by the quantity in bars in parentheses; e.g. 60 kPa (0.6 bar). It should be noted that operating pressures should be in terms of 'gauge pressure' and should be unambiguously stated, e.g. gauge pressure 600 kPa (6 bar).

6.2.5.2 Weight and mass

The term 'weight' has for many years been used in two different senses. In common parlance and in the Weights and Measures Act 1963 it is used to mean 'mass', whereas in some technical work the word 'weight' is used in the sense of 'gravitational force'. There is no explicit SI unit of weight. When 'weight' is used to mean 'mass', then the correct SI unit is the kilogram. When 'weight' is used to mean 'force', the correct SI unit is the newton.

6.2.5.3 Specific heat capacity

Due to the original definitions of British thermal unit and calorie, the quantity 'specific heat capacity' of water approximated to unity when expressed in imperial or technical metric units.

In SI units the specific heat capacity of water is 4.185 5 kJ·kg^{-1}·K^{-1} at a reference temperature of 15 °C.

6.2.5.4 Temperature

When adopting the kelvin as the unit of thermodynamic temperature or for expressing temperature difference, the 13th CGPM recognised that the term degree Celsius (°C) would continue in everyday use for as long as could be foreseen. The degree Celsius is defined by equation 6.1.

Celsius temperature is in general expressed in degrees Celsius (°C). The unit 'degree Celsius' is equal to the unit 'kelvin' and an interval of, or a difference of, Celsius temperature may also be expressed in degrees Celsius. In the CIBSE Guide temperature differences, particularly in compound units, are expressed in kelvins, e.g. W·m^{-1}·K^{-1}.

6.2.5.5 Sound

The decibel is a unit which compares power and its derivatives. When used in the context of sound, it is known as a measure of sound level defined, in the case of power, as:

$$L_{\mathrm{w}} = 10 \log_{10} \frac{W_1}{W_2} \qquad (6.2)$$

where L_{w} is the sound power level (dB), W_1 is sound power 1 (W) and W_2 is sound power 2 (usually a reference value) (W).

Sound intensity level and sound pressure level are defined by similar equations which take into account their relationship with sound power. Table 6.12 gives standard reference values which are used in sound measurement.

6.2.5.6 Radioactivity

The activity of a radioactive source is the number of nuclear transformations occurring in a small time interval divided by that time interval. The unit of activity is the Becquerel second.

Concentrations in air are expressed in reciprocal seconds per cubic metre.

The radiation dose absorbed by any material is defined as the mean energy imparted by ionising radiation per unit mass at the point of interest and is expressed in J·kg^{-1}. The special unit gray for the quantity absorbed dose is defined as:

$$1\ \mathrm{Gy} = 1\ \mathrm{J \cdot kg^{-1}} \qquad (6.3)$$

Doses to people are expressed as dose equivalent, which is obtained by multiplying the absorbed dose at the point of interest in tissue by various modifying factors, which among other things take account of the energy and type of the ionising radiation. Where the radiation dose is measured in grays the dose equivalent is measured in sieverts.

6.2.5.7 Clothing insulation

The clo is a dimensionless factor expressing the insulation of clothing and is defined as:

$$I_{\mathrm{cl}} = \frac{R_{\mathrm{cl}}}{R_{\mathrm{r}}} \qquad (6.4)$$

where I_{cl} is the insulation factor (clo), R_{cl} is the total thermal resistance from skin to outer surface of the clothed bodies (m^2·K·W^{-1}) and R_{r} is the reference thermal resistance (= 0.155) (m^2·K·W^{-1})

A clo value of 1 is the insulation given by a typical business suit with waistcoat.

6.3 Quantities, units and numbers

A physical quantity is an attribute which can be measured. The measurement is described in terms of a number multiplied by a unit. The algebraic relationship:

physical quantity = number × unit

must always be maintained.

Examples of physical quantities expressed as number of units are:

— height of Nelson's Column = 43.211 75 metres

— velocity of light in vacuo = 299 792 500 metres per second.

— thermal conductivity of balsa wood = 0.040 watts per metre kelvin.

6.3.1 Some rules for physical quantities

(1) The algebraic symbol should be a single letter of the Latin or Greek alphabet.

(2) When necessary, subcripts, superscripts, or other modifying signs may be attached.

(3) The symbol should, if possible, be printed in sloping (italic) type.

(4) The word 'specific' is restricted to mean divided by mass.

(5) The word 'molar' is restricted to mean divided by amount of substance.

6.3.2 Some rules for units

(1) There is one and one only SI unit for each physical quantity.

(2) To find the units of physical quantities other than the base physical quantities:

    (*a*) define the physical quantity in terms of the base physical quantities

    (*b*) obtain the units of the physical quantity by mutiplying and/or dividing the constituent base units.

(3) Only agreed symbols must be used.

(4) The symbol should be printed in upright (i.e. not italic) type.

(5) The symbol for a unit derived from a proper name begins with a capital letter.

(6) When written in full, all units are written in lower case letters (e.g. newton, pascal) with the exception of Celsius, which starts with a capital letter.

(7) A product of two units may be represented in a number of ways:

$$m\ s \qquad m.s \qquad m{\cdot}s$$

but not ms without the space.

(8) A quotient of two units may be represented in a number of ways:

$$m\ s^{-1} \qquad m{\cdot}s^{-1} \qquad m/s \qquad \frac{m}{s}$$

but not ms^{-1}, i.e. there must always be a space between the unit symbols.

(9) More than one solidus (/) should not appear in the same expression unless parentheses are used to eliminate ambiguity.

6.3.3 Some rules for numbers

(1) Numbers should be printed in upright type.

(2) The decimal sign can be a point (.) on the line, e.g. 2.6 (as has been adopted for CIBSE Guides and current British Standards), or raised above the line, e.g. 2·6; in other European countries a comma is normally used, i.e. 2,6.

(3) Digits should be grouped in threes about the decimal sign, separated by a space, e.g:

$$2\,576.392\,72$$

(4) When the decimal sign is before the first digit a zero should be placed before the decimal sign, e.g:

$$0.292\ \textit{not}\ .292$$

(5) The multiplication sign between numbers should be a cross (×) and not the mathematical (.) as may be used with unit symbols, e.g:

$$2.3 \times 3.4$$

(6) Division of one number by another may be indicated in a number of ways.

$$\frac{129}{298}\ \text{or}\ 129/298\ \text{or}\ 129 \times (298)^{-1}$$

(7) More than one solidus should never be used in the same expression unless parentheses are used to eliminate ambiguity, e.g:

$$(129/298)/2.62\ \text{or}\ 129/(298 \times 2.62)$$

but never 129/298/2.62.

6.3.4 Some rules for prefixes

A combination of prefix and symbol is regarded as a single symbol:

$$cm^2\ \text{means}\ (0.01\ m)^2\ \text{not}\ 0.01\ m^2$$

Compound prefixes should not be used:

$$10^{-9}\ m = nm\ \textit{not}\ m\mu m$$

Note: decimal multiples of the kilogram are formed by attaching an SI prefix to gram and not kilogram:

$$mg\ \textit{not}\ \mu kg\ \text{for}\ 10^{-6}\ kg$$

$$Mg\ \textit{not}\ kkg\ \text{for}\ 10^3\ kg$$

6.3.5 Some rules for labelling graphs and tables

When labelling the co-ordinate axes of graphs or the column headings of tables it is essential to distinguish between the quantity itself and the numerical value of the quantity expressed in a particular unit. In graphs or tables it is sets of numbers that are plotted or tabulated. The normal presentation is to enclose the unit in brackets. However, since:

$$\text{number} = \text{physical quantity}/\text{unit}$$

the label may comprise 'quantity/unit'. For clarity the unit may be enclosed in brackets.

6.4 Metrication in the European Union

6.4.1 Legislative background

Use of metric and other units within the EU is governed by Council Directive 80/181/EEC of 20th December 1979 as modified 3rd January 1985 and 7th December 1989. This Directive approved the use of metric units as defined in ISO standard 2955 of 1st March 1974, authorising continued use of certain other units in certain circumstances, and repealed Directive 71/354/EEC of 18th October 1971, the original directive on metric units.

6.4.2 Obligatory units

The obligatory units for use within the EU are the SI base, supplementary and derived units, as given in Tables 6.1 and 6.2. Some special names, given in Table 6.5, are authorised.

6.4.3 Special authorised units

Certain non-SI units are specially authorised for use within member states either for general use or for specific purposes. Each state is entitled to select any or all of these for internal use. These units are given in Table 6.6.

6.4.4 Forbidden units

All other units are forbidden although they may be retained for use for products already on the market at the time of decision and for spares for these and obsolete products. They may still be used as supplementary indications but may be no larger than the approved indications, which must predominate.

6.5 Conversion factors

The tables of conversion factors (Tables 6.7 and 6.8) are arranged in five columns: physical quantity, previous unit, factor, SI unit, SI symbol. To convert a quantity in previous units to the equivalent quantity in SI units, multiply by the factor. To convert a quantity in SI units to the equivalent quantity in old units, divide by the factor.

Table 6.5 EU units with special names

Description	Quantity	Unit		
		Name	Symbol	Value
Decimal multiples of SI units	Volume	litre*	l	$1 \, l = 1 \, dm^3$
	Mass	tonne*	t	$1 \, t = 1 \, Mg$
	Pressures and stress	bar*	bar	$1 \, bar = 10^5 \, Pa$
Units for special fields of application	Area of farmland and real estate	are*	a	$1 \, a = 100 \, m^2$
	Vergency of optical systems	dioptre		$1 = 1 \, m^{-1}$
	Mass of precious stones	metric carat		$1 = 2 \times 10^{-4} \, kg$
	Mass/unit length (textile yarns and threads)	tex	tex	$1 \, tex = 10^{-6} \, kg{\cdot}m^{-1}$
Defined from SI units but not decimal multiples	Plane angle	revolution	r†	$1 \, r = 2\pi \, rad$
		gon*	gon	$1 \, gon = \pi/200 \, rad$
		degree	°	$1° = \pi/180 \, rad$
		minute of angle‡	′	$1′ = \pi/10\,800 \, rad$
		second of angle‡	″	$1″ = \pi/648\,000 \, rad$
	Time	minute	min	$1 \, min = 60 \, s$
		hour	h	$1 \, h = 3600 \, s$
		day	d	$1 \, d = 86\,400 \, s$
Defined independently of SI units	Mass	atomic mass unit*	u	$1 \, u \approx 1.660\,565\,5 \times 10^{-27} \, kg$ §
	Energy	electronvolt*	eV	$1 \, eV \approx 1.602\,189\,2 \times 10^{-19} \, J$ §

* SI prefixes apply to these units
† UK symbol
‡ BS ISO 31: 1992 recommends use of decimal division of the degree, e.g. $30′ = 0.5°$
§ Values from CODATA bulletin No. 11, December 1973

Table 6.6 Special EU authorised units

Quantity	Use	Unit		
		Name	Symbol	Value
Length	Road traffic signs, distance and speed measures	inch	in	$2.540 \times 10^{-1} \, mm$
	Road traffic signs, distance and speed measures	foot	ft	$3.048 \times 10^{-1} \, m$
	Road traffic signs, distance and speed measures	yard	yd	$9.144 \times 10^{-1} \, m$
	Road traffic signs, distance and speed measures	mile		$1.609 \, km$
	Marine navigation	fathom		$1.829 \, m$
Area	Land registration	acre		$4.047 \times 10^3 \, m^2$
Volume	Drinks in returnable containers	fluid ounce	fl oz	$2.841 \times 10^{-2} \, dm^3$
	Spirits	gill		$1.421 \times 10^{-1} \, dm^3$
	Draught beer and cider, milk; drinks in returnable containers	pint	pt	$5.683 \times 10^{-1} \, dm^3$
Mass	Loose bulk goods	ounce	oz	$2.835 \times 10^1 \, g$
	Precious metals	troy ounce	oz tr	$3.110 \times 10^1 \, g$
	Loose bulk goods	pound	lb	$4.536 \times 10^{-1} \, kg$
Pressure	Blood pressure	mm mercury	mm hg	$1.333 \times 10^2 \, Pa$

Table 6.7 Conversion factors

Physical quantity	Previous unit	×	Factor	=	SI unit	SI symbol
SPACE AND TIME						
Length	micron		1	E	micrometre	μm
	thou' (mil)		2.54×10^1	E	micrometre	μm
	inch		2.54×10^1	E	millimetre	mm
	foot		3.048×10^{-1}	E	metre	m
	yard		9.144×10^{-1}	E	metre	m
	mile		1.609		kilometre	km
Area	square inch		6.452×10^2		square millimetre	mm²
			6.452		square centimetre	cm²
	square foot		9.290×10^{-2}		square metre	m²
	square yard		8.361×10^{-1}		square metre	m²
	are		1×10^2	E	square metre	m²
	acre		4.047×10^3		square metre	m²
	hectare		1×10^4	E	square metre	m²
	square mile		2.590		square kilometre	km²
Volume	cubic inch		1.639×10^1		cubic centimetre	cm³
	US pint		4.732×10^{-1}		cubic decimetre	dm³
	pint		5.683×10^{-1}		cubic decimetre	dm³
	litre		1	E	cubic decimetre	dm³
	US gallon		3.785		cubic decimetre	dm³
	gallon		4.546		cubic decimetre	dm³
	cubic foot		2.832×10^1		cubic decimetre	dm³
			2.832×10^{-2}		cubic metre	m³
	US barrel (petroleum)		1.590×10^{-1}		cubic metre	m³
	cubic yard		7.646×10^{-1}		cubic metre	m³
Second moment of area	quartic inch		4.162×10^1		quartic centimetre	cm⁴
	quartic foot		8.631×10^{-3}		quartic metre	m⁴
Time	minute		6×10^1	E	second	s
	hour		3.6×10^3	E	second	s
	day		8.64×10^4	E	second	s
Angle	second		4.848		microradian	μrad
	minute		2.909×10^{-1}		milliradian	mrad
	grade		1.571×10^{-2}		radian	rad
	gon		1.571×10^{-2}		radian	rad
	degree		1.745×10^{-2}		radian	rad
	right angle		1.571		radian	rad
	revolution		6.283		radian	rad
Velocity	foot/minute		5.080×10^{-3}	E	metre/second	m·s⁻¹
	kilometre/hour		2.778×10^{-1}		metre/second	m·s⁻¹
	foot/second		3.048×10^{-1}	E	metre/second	m·s⁻¹
	mile/hour		4.470×10^{-1}		metre/second	m·s⁻¹
	knot		5.148×10^{-1}		metre/second	m·s⁻¹
Angular velocity	revolution per minute		1.047×10^{-1}		radian/second	rad·s⁻¹
	revolution per second		6.283		radian/second	rad·s⁻¹
Acceleration	foot/square second		3.048×10^{-1}	E	metre/square second	m·s⁻²
Frequency	cycle/second		1	E	hertz	Hz
MASS AND DENSITY						
Mass	grain		6.480×10^1		milligram	mg
	ounce		2.835×10^1		gram	g
	pound		4.536×10^{-1}		kilogram	kg
	slug		1.459×10^1		kilogram	kg
	hundredweight		5.080×10^1		kilogram	kg
	ton (short)		9.072×10^{-1}		megagram	Mg
	tonne		1	E	megagram	Mg
	ton		1.016		megagram	Mg
Mass per unit length	pound/foot		1.488		kilogram/metre	kg·m⁻¹
	pound/inch		1.786×10^1		kilogram/metre	kg·m⁻¹
Mass per unit area	pound/square foot		4.882		kilogram/square metre	kg·m⁻²
Concentration	grain/cubic foot		2.288		gram/cubic metre	g·m⁻³
Density	pound/cubic foot		1.602×10^1		kilogram/cubic metre	kg·m⁻³
	pound/gallon		9.978×10^1		kilogram/cubic metre	kg·m⁻³
	pound/cubic inch		2.768×10^1		megagram/cubic metre	Mg·m⁻³
Specific volume	cubic foot/pound		6.243×10^{-2}		cubic metre/kilogram	m³·kg⁻¹

E — exact conversion factor
The word 'litre' may be employed as a special name for dm³

Table 6.7 Conversion factors — *continued*

Physical quantity	Previous unit	×	Factor	=	SI unit	SI symbol
FLOW RATE						
Mass flow rate	pound/hour		1.260×10^{-1}		gram/second	$g \cdot s^{-1}$
	kilogram/hour		2.778×10^{-1}		gram/second	$g \cdot s^{-1}$
	pound/minute		7.560×10^{-3}		kilogram/second	$kg \cdot s^{-1}$
	kilogram/minute		1.667×10^{-2}		kilogram/second	$kg \cdot s^{-1}$
Volume flow rate	cubic inch/minute		2.732×10^{-4}		cubic decimetre/second	$dm^3 \cdot s^{-1}$
	litre/hour		2.778×10^{-4}		cubic decimetre/second	$dm^3 \cdot s^{-1}$
	US gallon/hour		1.052×10^{-3}		cubic decimetre/second	$dm^3 \cdot s^{-1}$
	gallon/hour		1.263×10^{-3}		cubic decimetre/second	$dm^3 \cdot s^{-1}$
	cubic foot/hour		7.886×10^{-3}		cubic decimetre/second	$dm^3 \cdot s^{-1}$
	cubic inch/second		1.639×10^{-2}		cubic decimetre/second	$dm^3 \cdot s^{-1}$
	litre/minute		1.667×10^{-2}		cubic decimetre/second	$dm^3 \cdot s^{-1}$
	US gallon/minute		6.309×10^{-2}		cubic decimetre/second	$dm^3 \cdot s^{-1}$
	gallon/minute		7.577×10^{-2}		cubic decimetre/second	$dm^3 \cdot s^{-1}$
	cubic metre/hour		2.778×10^{-1}		cubic decimetre/second	$dm^3 \cdot s^{-1}$
	cubic foot/minute		4.719×10^{-1}		cubic decimetre/second	$dm^3 \cdot s^{-1}$
	cubic metre/minute		1.667×10^{1}		cubic decimetre/second	$dm^3 \cdot s^{-1}$
	cubic foot/second		2.832×10^{-2}		cubic metre/second	$m^3 \cdot s^{-1}$
MOMENTUM						
Momentum	pound foot/second		1.383×10^{-1}		kilogram metre/second	$kg \cdot m \cdot s^{-1}$
Moment of inertia	pound square foot		4.214×10^{-2}		kilogram square metre	$kg \cdot m^2$
Moment of momentum	pound square foot/second		4.214×10^{-2}		kilogram square metre/second	$kg \cdot m^2 \cdot s^{-1}$
FORCE AND TORQUE						
Force	dyne		1×10^{1}	E	micronewton	μN
	poundal		1.383×10^{-1}		newton	N
	pound force		4.448		newton	N
	kilogram force		9.807		newton	N
	kilopond		9.807		newton	N
Torque	pound force foot		1.356		newton metre	$N \cdot m$
PRESSURE AND STRESS						
Pressure	millimetre of water		9.807		pascal	Pa
	pound force/square foot		4.788×10^{1}		pascal	Pa
	millimetre of mercury		1.333×10^{2}		pascal	Pa
	torr		1.333×10^{2}		pascal	Pa
	inch of water		2.491×10^{2}		pascal	Pa
	foot of water		2.989		kilopascal	kPa
	inch of mercury		3.386		kilopascal	kPa
	pound force/square inch		6.895		kilopascal	kPa
	kilogram force/square centimetre		9.807×10^{1}		kilopascal	kPa
	bar		1×10^{2}	E	kilopascal	kPa
			1×10^{-1}	E	megapascal	MPa
	standard atmosphere		1.013×10^{2}		kilopascal	kPa
			1.013×10^{-1}		megapascal	MPa
Pressure drop per unit length	inch of water/hundred feet		8.176		pascal/metre	$Pa \cdot m^{-1}$
	foot of water/hundred feet		9.810×10^{1}		pascal/metre	$Pa \cdot m^{-1}$
Stress	pound force/square foot		4.788×10^{1}		pascal	Pa
	pound force/square inch		6.895		kilopascal	kPa
	ton force/square foot		1.073×10^{2}		kilopascal	kPa
	ton force/square inch		1.544×10^{1}		megapascal	MPa
VISCOSITY						
Dynamic viscosity	pound/hour foot		4.134×10^{-1}		millipascal second	$mPa \cdot s$
	centipoise		1×10^{-3}	E	pascal second	$Pa \cdot s$
	poise		1×10^{-1}	E	pascal second	$Pa \cdot s$
	pound force second/square foot		4.788×10^{1}		pascal second	$Pa \cdot s$
	pound force hour/square foot		1.724×10^{2}		kilopascal second	$kPa \cdot s$
Kinematic viscosity	stokes		1	E	square centimetre/second	$cm^2 \cdot s^{-1}$
	square metre/hour		2.778		square centimetre/second	$cm^2 \cdot s^{-1}$
	square inch/second		6.452		square centimetre/second	$cm^2 \cdot s^{-1}$
	square foot/minute		1.548×10^{-3}		square metre/second	$m^2 \cdot s^{-1}$
	Redwood No. 1 and No. 2 seconds		No direct conversion			
	SAE grades		No direct conversion			

E — exact conversion factor.   The word 'litre' may be employed as a special name for dm^3

Table 6.7 Conversion factors — *continued*

Physical quantity	Previous unit	×	Factor	=	SI unit	SI symbol
ENERGY						
Energy, work, quantity of heat	erg		1×10^{-1}	E	microjoule	µJ
	foot pound force		1.356		joule	J
	calorie*		4.187		joule	J
	metre kilogram force		9.807		joule	J
	British thermal unit		1.055		kilojoule	kJ
	frigorie†		4.186		kilojoule	kJ
	kilocalorie*		4.187		kilojoule	kJ
	horsepower hour		2.685		megajoule	MJ
	kilowatt hour		3.6	E	megajoule	MJ
	thermie†		4.186		megajoule	MJ
	therm		1.055×10^{-1}		gigajoule	GJ
POWER						
Power, heat flow rate	British thermal unit/hour		2.931×10^{-1}		watt	W
	kilocalorie/hour		1.163	E	watt	W
	foot pound force/second		1.356		watt	W
	calorie/second		4.187		watt	W
	metric horsepower (cheval vapeur)		7.355×10^{-1}		kilowatt	kW
	horsepower		7.457×10^{-1}		kilowatt	kW
	ton of refrigeration		3.517		kilowatt	kW
	Lloyd's ton of refrigeration		3.884		kilowatt	kW
Intensity of heat flow rate	kilocalorie/hour square metre		1.163	E	watt/square metre	W·m⁻²
	Btu/hour square foot		3.155		watt/square metre	W·m⁻²
	watt/square foot		1.076×10^{1}		watt/square metre	W·m⁻²
Heat emission	Btu/hour cubic foot		1.035×10^{1}		watt/cubic metre	W·m⁻³
Thermal conductivity	Btu inch/hour square foot degree Fahrenheit		1.442×10^{-1}		watt/metre kelvin	W·m⁻¹·K⁻¹
	kilocalorie/hour metre degree Celsius		1.163	E	watt/metre kelvin	W·m⁻¹·K⁻¹
	Btu/hour foot degree Fahrenheit		1.731		watt/metre kelvin	W·m⁻¹·K⁻¹
	calorie/second centimetre degree Celsius		4.187×10^{2}		watt/metre kelvin	W·m⁻¹·K⁻¹
Thermal conductance	kilocalorie/hour square metre degree Celsius		1.163	E	watt/square metre kelvin	W·m⁻²·K⁻¹
	Btu/hour square foot degree Fahrenheit		5.678		watt/square metre kelvin	W·m⁻²·K⁻¹
	calorie/second square centimetre degree Celsius		4.187×10^{1}		kilowatt/square metre kelvin	kW·m⁻²·K⁻¹
Thermal resistivity	centimetre second degree Celsius/calorie		2.388×10^{-3}		metre kelvin/watt	m·K·W⁻¹
	foot hour degree Fahrenheit/Btu		5.778×10^{-1}		metre kelvin/watt	m·K·W⁻¹
	metre hour degree Celsius/kilocalorie		8.598×10^{-1}		metre kelvin/watt	m·K·W⁻¹
	square foot hour degree Fahrenheit/Btu inch		6.933		metre kelvin/watt	m·K·W⁻¹
Thermal resistance	square centimetre second degree Celsius/calorie		2.388×10^{-5}		square metre kelvin/watt	m²·K·W⁻¹
	square foot hour degree Fahrenheit/Btu		1.761×10^{-1}		square metre kelvin/watt	m²·K·W⁻¹
	square metre hour degree Celsius/kilocalorie		8.598×10^{-1}		square metre kelvin/watt	m²·K·W⁻¹
Thermal diffusivity	square inch/hour		1.792×10^{-1}		square millimetre/second	mm²·s⁻¹
	square foot/hour		2.581×10^{-5}		square metre/second	m²·s⁻¹
	square metre/hour		2.778×10^{-4}		square metre/second	m²·s⁻¹
ENERGY CONTENT						
Heat capacity	Btu/degree Fahrenheit		1.899		kilojoule/kelvin	kJ·K⁻¹
	kilocalorie/degree Celsius		4.187		kilojoule/kelvin	kJ·K⁻¹
Specific enthalpy	Btu/pound		2.326	E	kilojoule/kilogram	kJ·kg⁻¹
	kilocalorie/kilogram		4.187		kilojoule/kilogram	kJ·kg⁻¹
Specific heat capacity	Btu/pound degree Fahrenheit		4.187		kilojoule/kilogram kelvin	kJ·kg⁻¹·K⁻¹
	kilocalorie/kilogram degree Celsius		4.187		kilojoule/kilogram kelvin	kJ·kg⁻¹·K⁻¹
Entropy	Btu/degree Rankine		1.899		kilojoule/kelvin	kJ·K⁻¹
	kilocalorie/kelvin		4.187		kilojoule/kelvin	kJ·K⁻¹

E — exact conversion factor

The word 'litre' may be employed as a special name for dm³

* Based on the international calorie defined as 4.1868 J

† Based on the 15 °C calorie determined as 4.1855 J

Table 6.7 Conversion factors — *continued*

Physical quantity	Previous unit	×	Factor	=	SI unit	SI symbol
Specific entropy	Btu/pound degree Rankine		4.187		kilojoule/kilogram kelvin	$kJ \cdot kg^{-1} \cdot K^{-1}$
	kilocalorie/kilogram kelvin		4.187		kilojoule/kilogram kelvin	$kJ \cdot kg^{-1} \cdot K^{-1}$
Latent heat	foot pound force/pound		2.989		joule/kilogram	$J \cdot kg^{-1}$
	Btu/pound		2.326	E	kilojoule/kilogram	$kJ \cdot kg^{-1}$
	kilocalorie/kilogram		4.187		kilojoule/kilogram	$kJ \cdot kg^{-1}$
Volumetric calorific value	kilocalorie/cubic metre		4.187		kilojoule/cubic metre	$kJ \cdot m^3$
	Btu/cubic foot		3.726×10^1		kilojoule/cubic metre	$kJ \cdot m^3$
Specific heat (volume basis)	kilocalorie/cubic metre degree Celsius		4.187		kilojoule/cubic metre kelvin	$kJ \cdot m^{-3} \cdot K^{-1}$
	Btu/cubic foot degree Farenheit		6.707×10^1		kilojoule/cubic metre kelvin	$kJ \cdot m^{-3} \cdot K^{-1}$

MOISTURE CONTENT

Physical quantity	Previous unit	×	Factor	=	SI unit	SI symbol
Vapour permeability	grain inch/hour square foot inch of mercury (perminch)		1.45		nanogram metre/newton second	$ng \cdot m \cdot N^{-1} \cdot s^{-1}$
			1.45		nanogram/second pascal metre	$ng \cdot s^{-1} \cdot Pa^{-1} \cdot m^{-1}$
	pound foot/hour pound force		8.620		milligram metre/newton second	$mg \cdot m \cdot N^{-1} \cdot s^{-1}$
			8.620		milligram/second pascal metre	$mg \cdot s^{-1} \cdot Pa^{-1} \cdot m^{-1}$
Vapour permeance	grain/square foot hour inch of mercury (perm)		5.72×10^1		nanogram/newton second	$ng \cdot N^{-1} \cdot s^{-1}$
	grain/ square foot hour millibar		1.940		microgram/newton second	$\mu g \cdot N^{-1} \cdot s^{-1}$
	pound square inch/square foot hour pound force		1.965×10^{-1}		milligram/newton second	$mg \cdot N^{-1} \cdot s^{-1}$
	pound/hour pound force		2.834×10^1		milligram/newton second	$mg \cdot N^{-1} \cdot s^{-1}$
Moisture content	grain/pound		1.428×10^{-1}		gram/kilogram	$g \cdot kg^{-1}$
	pound/pound		1	E	kilogram/kilogram	$kg \cdot kg^{-1}$
Moisture flow rate	pound/square foot hour		1.357		gram/square metre second	$g \cdot m^{-2} \cdot s^{-1}$
	grain/square foot hour		1.94×10^{-1}		milligram/square metre second	$mg \cdot m^{-2} \cdot s^{-1}$
Mass transfer coefficient	foot/hour		8.47×10^{-2}		millimetre/second	$mm \cdot s^{-1}$

LIGHT

Physical quantity	Previous unit	×	Factor	=	SI unit	SI symbol
Luminous intensity	candle		9.810×10^{-1}		candela	cd
Illumination	foot candle		1.076×10^1		lux	lx
	lumen/square foot		1.076×10^1		lux	lx
Luminance	foot lambert		3.426		candela/square metre	$cd \cdot m^{-2}$
	candela/square inch		1.550×10^3		candela/square metre	$cd \cdot m^{-2}$

ELECTRICTY AND MAGNETISM

Physical quantity	Previous unit	×	Factor	=	SI unit	SI symbol
Conductance	mho		1	E	siemens	S
Magnetic field strength	oersted		7.958×10^1		ampere/metre	$A \cdot m^{-1}$
Magnetic flux	maxwell		1×10^{-2}	E	microweber	μWb
Magnetic flux density	gauss		1×10^{-1}	E	millitesla	mT

RADIOACTIVITY

Physical quantity	Previous unit	×	Factor	=	SI unit	SI symbol
Activity of a radioactive source	curie		3.7×10^1		nanosecond^{-1}	ns^{-1}
Absorbed dose	rad		1×10^{-2}	E	joule/kilogram	$J \cdot kg^{-1}$
Equivalent absorbed dose	rem		1×10^{-2}	E	joule/kilogram	$J \cdot kg^{-1}$
Exposure to ionisation	roentgen		2.58×10^{-1}		milllicoulomb/kilogram	$mC \cdot kg^{-1}$

E — exact conversion factor

Example 1

A boiler is rated at 150 000 Btu·h^{-1}. In SI units this is 150 000 × (2.931 × 10^{-1}) = 43 965 W = 43.965 kW.

Example 2

A heating plant has an annual energy consumption of 500 GJ. In imperial units this is 500/(1.055 × 10^{-1}) = 4740 therms. In technical metric units the factor quoted is for converting between thermies and megajoules. Thus, 500 GJ must be transposed to MJ before being divided by the conversion factor, i.e. (500 × 10^3)/4.186 = 119 446 thermies.

Table 6.8 Conversion factors in alphbetical subject order

Physical quantity	Previous unit ×	Factor =	SI unit	SI symbol
Absorbed dose	rad	1×10^{-2} E	joule/kilogram	$J{\cdot}kg^{-1}$
Acceleration	foot/square second	3.048×10^{-1} E	metre/square second	$m{\cdot}s^{-2}$
Angle	second	4.848	microradian	μrad
	minute	2.909×10^{-1}	milliradian	mrad
	grade	1.571×10^{-2}	radian	rad
	gon	1.571×10^{-2}	radian	rad
	degree	1.745×10^{-2}	radian	rad
	right angle	1.571	radian	rad
	revolution	6.283	radian	rad
Angular velocity	revolution per minute	1.047×10^{-1}	radian/second	$rad{\cdot}s^{-1}$
	revolution per second	6.283	radian/second	$rad{\cdot}s^{-1}$
Area	square inch	6.452×10^{2}	square millimetre	mm^2
		6.452	square centimetre	cm^2
	square foot	9.290×10^{-2}	square metre	m^2
	square yard	8.361×10^{-1}	square metre	m^2
	are	1×10^{2} E	square metre	m^2
	acre	4.047×10^{3}	square metre	m^2
	hectare	1×10^{4} E	square metre	m^2
	square mile	2.590	square kilometre	km^2
Concentration	grain/cubic foot	2.288	gram/cubic metre	$g{\cdot}m^{-3}$
Conductance, electrical	mho	1 E	siemens	S
Conductance, thermal	kilocalorie/hour square metre degree Celsius	1.163 E	watt/square metre kelvin	$W{\cdot}m^{-2}{\cdot}K^{-1}$
	Btu/hour square foot degree Fahrenheit	5.678	watt/square metre kelvin	$W{\cdot}m^{-2}{\cdot}K^{-1}$
	calorie/second square centimetre degree Celsius	4.187×10^{1}	kilowatt/square metre kelvin	$kW{\cdot}m^{-2}{\cdot}K^{-1}$
Conductivity, thermal	Btu inch/hour square foot degree Fahrenheit	1.442×10^{-1}	watt/metre kelvin	$W{\cdot}m^{-1}{\cdot}K^{-1}$
	kilocalorie/hour metre degree Celsius	1.163 E	watt/metre kelvin	$W{\cdot}m^{-1}{\cdot}K^{-1}$
	Btu/hour foot degree Fahrenheit	1.731	watt/metre kelvin	$W{\cdot}m^{-1}{\cdot}K^{-1}$
	calorie/second centimetre degree Celsius	4.187×10^{2}	watt/metre kelvin	$W{\cdot}m^{-1}{\cdot}K^{-1}$
Density	pound/cubic foot	1.602×10^{1}	kilogram/cubic metre	$kg{\cdot}m^{-3}$
	pound/gallon	9.978×10^{1}	kilogram/cubic metre	$kg{\cdot}m^{-3}$
	pound/cubic inch	2.768×10^{1}	megagram/cubic metre	$Mg{\cdot}m^{-3}$
Diffusivity, thermal	square inch/hour	1.792×10^{-1}	square millimetre/second	$mm^2{\cdot}s^{-1}$
	square foot/hour	2.581×10^{-1}	square centimetre/second	$cm^2{\cdot}s^{-1}$
	square metre/hour	2.778	square centimetre/second	$cm^2{\cdot}s^{-1}$
Energy, work, quantity of heat	erg	1×10^{-1} E	microjoule	μJ
	foot pound force	1.356	joule	J
	calorie*	4.187	joule	J
	metre kilogram force	9.807	joule	J
	British thermal unit	1.055	kilojoule	kJ
	frigorie†	4.186	kilojoule	kJ
	kilocalorie*	4.187	kilojoule	kJ
	horsepower hour	2.685	megajoule	MJ
	kilowatt hour	3.6 E	megajoule	MJ
	thermie†	4.186	megajoule	MJ
	therm	1.055×10^{-1}	gigajoule	GJ
Enthalpy, specific	Btu/pound	2.326 E	kilojoule/kilogram	$kJ{\cdot}kg^{-1}$
	kilocalorie/kilogram	4.187	kilojoule/kilogram	$kJ{\cdot}kg^{-1}$
Entropy	Btu/degree Rankine	1.899	kilojoule/kelvin	$kJ{\cdot}K^{-1}$
	kilocalorie/kelvin	4.187	kilojoule/kelvin	$kJ{\cdot}K^{-1}$
Entropy, specific	Btu/pound degree Rankine	4.187	kilojoule/kilogram kelvin	$kJ{\cdot}kg^{-1}{\cdot}K^{-1}$
	kilocalorie/kilogram kelvin	4.187	kilojoule/kilogram kelvin	$kJ{\cdot}kg^{-1}{\cdot}K^{-1}$
Equivalent absorbed dose	rem	1×10^{-2} E	joule/kilogram	$J{\cdot}kg^{-1}$
Exposure to ionisation	roentgen	2.58×10^{-1}	millicoulomb/kilogram	$mC{\cdot}kg^{-1}$
Flow rate, mass	pound/hour	1.260×10^{-1}	gram/second	$g{\cdot}s^{-1}$
	kilogram hour	2.778×10^{-1}	gram/second	$g{\cdot}s^{-1}$
	pound/minute	7.560×10^{-3}	kilogram/second	$kg{\cdot}s^{-1}$
	kilogram/minute	1.667×10^{-2}	kilogram/second	$kg{\cdot}s^{-1}$

E — exact conversion factor
* Based on the international calorie defined as 4.186 8 J
† Based on the 15°C calorie determined as 4.185 5 J

Table 6.8 Conversion factors in alphbetical subject order — *continued*

Physical quantity	Previous unit	×	Factor	=	SI unit	SI symbol
Flow rate, volume	cubic inch/minute		2.3732×10^{-4}		cubic decimetre/second	$dm^3 \cdot s^{-1}$
	litre/hour		2.778×10^{-4}		cubic decimetre/second	$dm^3 \cdot s^{-1}$
	US gallon/hour		1.052×10^{-3}		cubic decimetre/second	$dm^3 \cdot s^{-1}$
	gallon/hour		1.263×10^{-3}		cubic decimetre/second	$dm^3 \cdot s^{-1}$
	cubic foot/hour		7.866×10^{-3}		cubic decimetre/second	$dm^3 \cdot s^{-1}$
	cubic inch/second		1.639×10^{-2}		cubic decimetre/second	$dm^3 \cdot s^{-1}$
	litre/minute		1.667×10^{-2}		cubic decimetre/second	$dm^3 \cdot s^{-1}$
	US gallon/minute		6.309×10^{-2}		cubic decimetre/second	$dm^3 \cdot s^{-1}$
	gallon/minute		7.577×10^{-2}		cubic decimetre/second	$dm^3 \cdot s^{-1}$
	cubic metre/hour		2.778×10^{-1}		cubic decimetre/second	$dm^3 \cdot s^{-1}$
	cubic foot/minute		4.719×10^{-1}		cubic decimetre/second	$dm^3 \cdot s^{-1}$
	cubic metre/minute		1.667×10^{1}		cubic decimetre/second	$dm^3 \cdot s^{-1}$
	cubic foot/second		2.832×10^{-2}		cubic metre/second	$m^3 \cdot s^{-1}$
Force	dyne		1×10^{1}	E	micronewton	μN
	poundal		1.383×10^{-1}		newton	N
	pound force		4.448		newton	N
	kilogram force		9.807		newton	N
	kilopond		9.807		newton	N
Frequency	cycle/second		1	E	hertz	Hz
Heat capacity	Btu/degree Fahrenheit		1.899		kilojoule/kelvin	$kJ \cdot K^{-1}$
	kilocalorie/degree Celsius		4.187		kilojoule/kelvin	$kJ \cdot K^{-1}$
Heat capacity, specific	Btu/pound degree Fahrenheit		4.187		kilojoule/kilogram kelvin	$kJ \cdot kg^{-1} \cdot K^{-1}$
	kilocalorie/kilogram degree Celsius		4.187		kilojoule/kilogram kelvin	$kJ \cdot kg^{-1} \cdot K^{-1}$
Heat emission	Btu/hour cubic foot		1.035×10^{1}		watt/cubic metre	$W \cdot m^{-3}$
Illumination	foot candle		1.076×10^{1}		lux	lx
	lumen/square foot		1.076×10^{1}		lux	lx
Intensity of heat flow rate	kilocalorie/hour square metre		1.163	E	watt/square metre	$W \cdot m^{-2}$
	Btu/hour square foot		3.155		watt/square metre	$W \cdot m^{-2}$
	watt/square foot		1.076×10^{1}		watt/square metre	$W \cdot m^{-2}$
Latent heat	foot pound force/pound		2.989		joule/kilogram	$J \cdot kg^{-1}$
	Btu/pound		2.326	E	kilojoule/kilogram	$kJ \cdot kg^{-1}$
	kilocalorie/kilogram		4.187		kilojoule/kilogram	$kJ \cdot kg^{-1}$
Length	micron		1	E	micrometre	μm
	thou' (mil)		2.54×10^{1}	E	micrometre	μm
	inch		2.54×10^{1}	E	millimetre	mm
	foot		3.048×10^{-1}	E	metre	m
	yard		9.144×10^{-1}	E	metre	m
	mile		1.609		kilometre	km
Luminance	foot lambert		3.426		candela/square metre	$cd \cdot m^{-2}$
	candela/square inch		1.550×10^{3}		candela/square metre	$cd \cdot m^{-2}$
Luminous intensity	candle		9.810×10^{-1}		candela	cd
Magnetic field strength	oersted		7.958×10^{1}		ampere/metre	$A \cdot m^{-1}$
Magnetic flux	maxwell		1×10^{-2}	E	microweber	μWb
Magnetic flux density	gauss		1×10^{-1}	E	millitesla	mT
Mass	grain		6.480×10^{1}		milligram	mg
	ounce		2.835×10^{1}		gram	g
	pound		4.536×10^{-1}		kilogram	kg
	slug		1.459×10^{1}		kilogram	kg
	hundredweight		5.080×10^{1}		kilogram	kg
	ton (short)		9.072×10^{-1}		megagram	Mg
	tonne		1	E	megagram	Mg
	ton		1.016		megagram	Mg
Mass per unit area	pound/square foot		4.882		kilogram/square metre	$kg \cdot m^{-2}$
Mass per unit length	pound/foot		1.488		kilogram/metre	$kg \cdot m^{-1}$
	pound/inch		1.786×10^{1}		kilogram/metre	$kg \cdot m^{-1}$
Mass transfer coefficient	foot/hour		8.47×10^{-2}		millimetre/second	$mm \cdot s^{-1}$
Moisture content	grain/pound		1.428×10^{-1}		gram/kilogram	$g \cdot kg^{-1}$
	pound/pound		1	E	kilogram/kilogram	$kg.kg^{-1}$
Moisture flow rate	pound/square foot hour		1.357		gram/square metre second	$g \cdot m^{-2} \cdot s^{-1}$
	grain/square foot hour		1.94×10^{-1}		milligram/square metre second	$mg \cdot m^{-2} \cdot s^{-1}$
Moment of inertia	pound square foot		4.214×10^{-2}		kilogram square metre	$kg \cdot m^2$

E — exact conversion factor

The word 'litre' may be employed as a special name for dm^3

Table 6.8 Conversion factors in alphbetical subject order — *continued*

Physical quantity	Previous unit ×	Factor	=	SI unit	SI symbol
Moment of momentum	pound square foot/second	4.214×10^{-2}		kilogram square metre/ second	$kg \cdot m^2 \cdot s^{-1}$
Momentum	pound foot/second	1.383×10^{-1}		kilogram metre/second	$kg \cdot m \cdot s^{-1}$
Permeability, vapour	grain inch/hour square foot inch of mercury (perminch)	1.45		nanogram metre/newton second	$ng \cdot m \cdot N^{-1} \cdot s^{-1}$
		1.45		nanogram/second pascal metre	$ng \cdot s^{-1} \cdot Pa^{-1} \cdot m^{-1}$
	pound foot/hour pound force	8.620		milligram metre/newton second	$mg \cdot m \cdot N^{-1} \cdot s^{-1}$
		8.620		milligram/second pascal metre	$mg \cdot s^{-1} \cdot Pa^{-1} \cdot m^{-1}$
Permeance, vapour	grain/square foot hour inch of mercury (perm)	5.72×10^{1}		nanogram/newton second	$ng \cdot N^{-1} \cdot s^{-1}$
	grain/square foot hour millibar	1.940		microgram/newton second	$\mu g \cdot N^{-1} \cdot s^{-1}$
	pound square inch/square foot hour pound force	1.965×10^{-1}		milligram/newton second	$mg \cdot N^{-1} \cdot s^{-1}$
	pound/hour pound force	2.834×10^{1}		milligram/newton second	$mg \cdot N^{-1} \cdot s^{-1}$
Power, heat flow rate	British thermal unit/hour	2.931×10^{-1}		watt	W
	kilocalorie/hour	1.163	E	watt	W
	foot pound force/second	1.356		watt	W
	calorie/second	4.187		watt	W
	metric horsepower (cheval vapeur)	7.355×10^{-1}		kilowatt	kW
	horsepower	7.457×10^{-1}		kilowatt	kW
	ton of refrigeration	3.517		kilowatt	kW
	Lloyd's ton of refrigeration	3.884		kilowatt	kW
Pressure	millimetre of water	9.807		pascal	Pa
	pound force/square foot	4.788×10^{1}		pascal	Pa
	millimetre of mercury	1.333×10^{2}		pascal	Pa
	torr	1.333×10^{2}		pascal	Pa
	inch of water	2.491×10^{2}		pascal	Pa
	foot of water	2.989		kilopascal	kPa
	inch of mercury	3.386		kilopascal	kPa
	pound force/square inch	6.895		kilopascal	kPa
	kilogram force/square centimetre	9.807×10^{1}		kilopascal	kPa
	bar	1×10^{2}	E	kilopascal	kPa
		1×10^{-1}	E	megapascal	MPa
	standard atmosphere	1.013×10^{2}		kilopascal	kPa
		1.013×10^{-1}		megapascal	MPa
Pressure drop per unit length	inch of water/hundred feet	8.176		pascal/metre	$Pa \cdot m^{-1}$
	foot of water/hundred feet	9.810×10^{1}		pascal/metre	$Pa \cdot m^{-1}$
Radioactivity	curie	3.7×10^{1}		nanosecond^{-1}	ns^{-1}
Resistance, thermal	square centimetre second degree Celsius/calorie	2.388×10^{1}		square decimetre kelvin/ watt	$dm^2 \cdot K \cdot W^{-1}$
	square foot hour degree Fahrenheit/Btu	1.761×10^{-1}		square metre kelvin/watt	$m^2 \cdot K \cdot W^{-1}$
	square metre hour degree Celsius/ kilocalorie	8.598×10^{-1}		square metre kelvin/watt	$m^2 \cdot K \cdot W^{-1}$
Resistivity, thermal	centimetre second degree Celsius/calorie	2.388×10^{-3}		metre kelvin/watt	$m \cdot K \cdot W^{-1}$
	foot hour degree Fahrenheit/Btu	5.778×10^{-1}		metre kelvin/watt	$m \cdot K \cdot W^{-1}$
	metre hour degree Celsius/kilocalorie	8.598×10^{-1}		metre kelvin/watt	$m \cdot K \cdot W^{-1}$
	square foot hour degree Fahrenheit/Btu inch	6.933		metre kelvin/watt	$m \cdot K \cdot W^{-1}$
Second moment of area	quartic inch	4.162×10^{5}		quartic decimetre	dm^4
	quartic foot	8.631×10^{-3}		quartic metre	m^4
Specific heat (volume basis)	kilocalorie/cubic metre degree Celsius	4.187		kilojoule/cubic metre kelvin	$kJ \cdot m^{-3} \cdot K^{-1}$
	Btu/cubic foot degree Fahrenheit	6.707×10^{1}		kilojoule/cubic metre kelvin	$kJ \cdot m^{-3} \cdot K^{-1}$
Specific volume	cubic foot/pound	6.243×10^{-2}		cubic metre/kilogram	$m^3 \cdot kg^{-1}$
Stress	pound force/square foot	4.788×10^{1}		pascal	Pa
	pound force/square inch	6.895		kilopascal	kPa
	ton force/square foot	1.073×10^{2}		kilopascal	kPa
	ton force/square inch	1.544×10^{1}		megapascal	MPa
Time	minute	6×10^{1}	E	second	s
	hour	3.6×10^{3}	E	second	s
	day	8.64×10^{4}	E	second	s

E — exact conversion factor

Table 6.8 Conversion factors in alphbetical subject order — *continued*

Physical quantity	Previous unit	×	Factor	=	SI unit	SI symbol
Torque	pound force foot		1.356		newton metre	N·m
Velocity	foot/minute		5.080×10^{-3}	E	metre/second	m·s^{-1}
	kilometre/hour		2.778×10^{-1}		metre/second	m·s^{-1}
	foot/second		3.048×10^{-1}	E	metre/second	m·s^{-1}
	mile/hour		4.470×10^{-1}		metre/second	m·s^{-1}
	knot		5.148×10^{-1}		metre/second	m·s^{-1}
Viscosity, dynamic	pound/hour foot		4.134×10^{-1}		millipascal second	mPa·s
	centipoise		1×10^{-3}	E	pascal second	Pa·s
	poise		1×10^{-1}	E	pascal second	Pa·s
	pound force second/square foot		4.788×10^{1}		pascal second	Pa·s
	pound force hour/square foot		1.724×10^{2}		kilopascal second	kPa·s
Viscosity, kinematic	stokes		1×10^{-2}	E	square decimetre/second	dm^2·s^{-1}
	square metre/hour		2.778×10^{-2}		square decimetre/second	dm^2·s^{-1}
	square inch/second		6.452		square decimetre/second	dm^2·s^{-1}
	square foot/minute		1.548×10^{-3}		square metre/second	m^2·s^{-1}
	Redwood No. 1 and No. 2 seconds		No direct conversion			
	SAE grades		No direct conversion			
Volume	cubic inch		1.639×10^{-2}		cubic decimetre	dm^3
	US pint		4.732×10^{-1}		cubic decimetre	dm^3
	pint		5.683×10^{-1}		cubic decimetre	dm^3
	litre		1	E	cubic decimetre	dm^3
	US gallon		3.785		cubic decimetre	dm^3
	gallon		4.546		cubic decimetre	dm^3
	cubic foot		2.832×10^{1}		cubic decimetre	dm^3
			2.832×10^{-2}		cubic metre	m^3
	US barrel (petroleum)		1.590×10^{-1}		cubic metre	m^3
	cubic yard		7.646×10^{-1}		cubic metre	m^3
Volumetric calorific value	kilocalorie/cubic metre		4.187		kilojoule/cubic metre	kJ·m^{-3}
	Btu/cubic foot		3.726×10^{1}		kilojoule/cubic metre	kJ·m^{-3}

E — exact conversion factor   The word 'litre' may be employed as a special name for dm^3

Table 6.9 The Beaufort scale

Beaufort number	Description of wind	Observations	Limit of wind speed / m·s^{-1}
0	Calm	Smoke rises vertically	Less than 0.5
1	Light air	Direction of wind shown by smoke drift but not by wind vanes	0.5 to 1.5
2	Light breeze	Wind felt on face; leaves rustle; ordinary vane moved by wind	1.5 to 3.0
3	Gentle breeze	Leaves and small twigs in constant motion; wind extends light flag	3 to 6
4	Moderate breeze	Raises dust and loose paper; small branches are moved	6 to 8
5	Fresh breeze	Small trees in leaf begin to sway	8 to 11
6	Strong breeze	Large branches in motion; umbrellas used with difficulty	11 to 14
7	Moderate gale	Whole trees in motion; inconvenience felt when walking into wind	14 to 17
8	Fresh gale	Twigs broken off trees; generally impedes progress	17 to 21
9	Strong gale	Slight structural damage occurs (slates and chimney pots removed from roofs)	21 to 24
10	Whole gale	Seldom experienced inland; trees uprooted; considerable structural damage occurs	24 to 28
11	Storm	Very rarely experienced; accompanied by widespread damage	28 to 32
12	Hurricane	(Yacht crews take up golf)	32 to 36

With acknowledgement to P. Heaton

Table 6.10 SI units for catalogues

Quantity	Unit	Quantity	Unit
Boilers:		Fuels:	
— heat output	kW	— calorific value (solid)	MJ·kg⁻¹
— heat input	kW	— calorific value (gaseous)	MJ·m⁻³
— steam generation rate	kg·s⁻¹	— calorific value (liquid)	MJ·kg⁻¹
— fuel firing rate (solid)	kg·s⁻¹		
— fuel firing rate (gaseous)	dm³·s⁻¹★	Heat exchangers:	
— fuel firing rate (liquid)	kg·s⁻¹	— heat output	kW
— volume flow rate (combustion products)	m³·s⁻¹	— mass flow rate	kg·s⁻¹
— power to input (to drives)	kW	— hydraulic resistance	Pa
— operating pressure	kPa (bar)	— operating pressure	kPa (bar)
— hydraulic resistance	Pa	— flow velocity	m·s⁻¹
— draught conditions	Pa	— heat exchange surface area	m²
Coil (cooling and heating):		Induction terminals:	
— heat, exchange rate	kW	— heating or cooling output	kW
— mass flow rate (primary medium)	kg·s⁻¹	— volume flow rate (primary air)	m³·s⁻¹
— hydraulic resistance (primary medium)	Pa	— static pressure loss (primary air)	Pa
— air volume flow rate	m³·s⁻¹	— mass flow rate (secondary water)	kg·s⁻¹
— air flow static pressure loss	Pa	— hydraulic resistance (secondary water)	Pa
Controls and instruments:		Pumps:	
— mass flow rate	kg·s⁻¹	— mass flow rate	kg·s⁻¹
— volume flow rate	m³·s⁻¹	— volume flow rate	dm³·s⁻¹★
— operating pressure	kPa (bar)	— power input (to drive)	kW
— hydraulic resistance	Pa	— developed pressure	Pa
— rotational frequency	rev·s⁻¹	— operating pressure	kPa (bar)
		— rotational frequency	rev·s⁻¹
Cooling towers:			
— heat extraction rate	kW	Space heating apparatus:	
— volume flow rate (air)	m³·s⁻¹	— heat output	kW
— volume flow rate (water)	dm³·s⁻¹★	— air flow volume flow rate	m³·s⁻¹
— power input (to drive)	kW	— power input (to drive)	kW
		— mass flow rate (primary medium)	kg·s⁻¹
Diffusers and grilles:		— hydraulic resistance	Pa
— air volume flow rate	m³·s⁻¹	— operating pressure	kPa (bar)
— air flow pressure loss	Pa	— air flow static pressure loss	Pa
— specific velocity	m·s⁻¹		
		Vessels:	
Fans		— operating pressure	kPa (bar)
— air volume flow rate	m³·s⁻¹	— volumetric capacity	dm³★ or m³
— power input (to drive)	kW		
— fan static pressure	Pa	Washers (air):	
— fan total pressure	Pa	— volume flow rate (air)	m³·s⁻¹
— rotational frequency	rev·s⁻¹	— volume flow rate (water)	dm³·s⁻¹★
— outlet velocity	m·s⁻¹	— mass flow rate (water)	kg·s⁻¹
		— power input (to drive)	kW
Filters:		— air flow static pressure loss	Pa
— air volume flow rate	m³·s⁻¹	— hydraulic resistance	Pa
— liquid volume flow rate	dm³·s⁻¹★		
— static pressure loss	Pa	Water chillers:	
		— cooling capacity	kW
		— mass flow rate (water)	kg·s⁻¹
		— power input (to drive)	kW
		— refrigerant pressure	kPa (bar)
		— hydraulic resistance	Pa

★ The word 'litre' may be employed as a special name for dm³

Table 6.11 Birmingham gauge and standard wire gauge thickness

BG	SWG	Thickness / mm	BG	SWG	Thickness / mm
52	—	0.024	20	—	0.996
—	50	0.025	—	18	1.219
50	—	0.030	18	—	1.257
48	—	0.039	16	—	1.588
—	48	0.041	—	16	1.626
46	—	0.049	14	—	1.994
44	46	0.061	—	14	2.032
42	—	0.078	12	—	2.517
—	44	0.081	—	12	2.642
40	—	0.098	10	—	3.175
—	42	0.102	—	10	3.251
38	40	0.122	8	—	3.988
—	38	0.152	—	8	4.064
36	—	0.155	—	6	4.877
—	36	0.193	6	—	5.032
34	—	0.196	—	4	5.893
—	34	0.234	4	—	6.350
32	—	0.249	—	2	7.010
—	32	0.274	2	—	7.993
30	—	0.312	—	0	8.230
—	30	0.315	—	2/0	8.839
—	28	0.376	—	3/0	9.449
28	—	0.397	0	—	10.07
—	26	0.457	—	4/0	10.16
26	—	0.498	—	5/0	10.97
—	24	0.559	2/0	—	11.31
24	—	0.629	—	6/0	11.79
—	22	0.711	3/0	7/0	12.70
22	—	0.794	4/0	—	13.76
—	20	0.914	5/0	—	14.94

Table 6.13 Standard values and reference values

Physical quantity	Value	Unit
Air (CIBSE reference conditions):		
— density	1.200	$kg \cdot m^{-3}$
— pressure	101.325	kPa
— relative humidity	43	%
— specific heat capacity	1.02	$kJ \cdot kg^{-1} \cdot K^{-1}$
— temperature (dry bulb)	20	°C
Avogadro's number	$6.022\,17 \times 10^{23}$	mol^{-1}
Base of natural logarithms (e)	2.718 28	—
Gas constants:		
— universal	8.314	$J \cdot mol^{-1} \cdot K^{-1}$
— dry air	287	$J \cdot kg^{-1} \cdot K^{-1}$
— steam	461	$J \cdot kg^{-1} \cdot K^{-1}$
Gravitational acceleration	9.806 65	$m \cdot s^{-2}$
Gravitational constant	66.7	$pN \cdot m^2 \cdot kg^{-2}$
Light, speed of (in vacuo)	299.792	$Mm \cdot s^{-1}$
Planck's constant	6.626×10^{-34}	J·s
Permeability of free space	1.257	$\mu H \cdot m^{-1}$
Permittivity of free space	8.854	$pF \cdot m^{-1}$
Sound, reference level:		
— intensity	1	$pW.m^{-2}$
— reference power	1	pW
— reference pressure	20	μPa
Sound, speed of:		
— in dry air at 20 °C	343.6	$m \cdot s^{-1}$
— in water at 20 °C	1497	$m \cdot s^{-1}$
— in copper	4760	$m \cdot s^{-1}$
— in mild steel	5960	$m \cdot s^{-1}$
Stefan–Boltzmann constant	56.696	$nW \cdot m^{-2} \cdot K^{-4}$
Circle, ratio of circumference to diameter (π)	3.141 59	—

Table 6.12 Preferred ISO metric screw thread sizes

Nominal diam. / mm	Pitch / mm	
	Coarse	Fine
1.0	0.25	0.20
1.2	0.25	0.20
1.6	0.35	0.20
2.0	0.40	0.25
2.5	0.45	0.35
3.0	0.50	0.35
4.0	0.70	0.50
5.0	0.80	0.50
6.0	1.0	0.75
8.0	1.25	0.75
10	1.5	0.75; 1.0; 1.25
12	1.75	1.0; 1.25; 1.5
16	2.0	1.0; 1.5
20	2.5	1.0; 1.5; 2.0
24	3.0	1.0; 1.5; 2.0
30	3.5	1.0; 1.5; 2.0; 3.0
36	4.0	1.5; 2.0; 3.0
42	4.5	1.5; 2.0; 3.0; 4.0
48	5.0	1.5; 2.0; 3.0; 4.0
56	5.5	1.5; 2.0; 3.0; 4.0
64	6.0	1.5; 2.0; 3.0; 4.0

Note: hexagon head bolts and screws are classified as 'M' followed by the nominal diameter, e.g. M10 is a 10 mm diameter bolt.

Table 6.14 Velocity pressure of wind

Velocity / m·s⁻¹	Pressure / Pa	Velocity / m·s⁻¹	Pressure / Pa
0.5	1.56×10^{-1}	10	6.25×10
1	6.25×10^{-1}	11	7.55×10
2	2.5	15	1.39×10^2
3	5.6	20	2.5×10^2
4	10	25	3.9×10^2
5	1.56×10	30	5.63×10^2
6	2.25×10	35	7.61×10^2
7	3.05×10	40	1.0×10^3
8	4.0×10	45	1.27×10^3
9	5.05×10	50	1.56×10^3

Table 6.15 Dimensionless constants

Field	Name	Symbol	Definition
Momentum transport	Reynolds number	Re	$Re = \dfrac{\rho\, v\, l}{\eta} = \dfrac{v\, l}{v}$
	Euler number	Eu	$Eu = \dfrac{\Delta p}{\rho\, v^2}$
	Froude number	Fr	$Fr = \dfrac{v}{\sqrt{l\, g}}$
	Grashof number	Gr	$Gr = \dfrac{l^3\, g\, \gamma\, \Delta\theta}{v^2}$
	Weber number	We	$We = \dfrac{\rho\, v^2\, l}{\sigma}$
	Mach number	Ma	$Ma = \dfrac{v}{c}$
	Knudsen number	Kn	$Kn = \dfrac{\lambda^\star}{l}$
	Strouhal number	Sr	$Sr = \dfrac{l\, f}{v}$
Transport of heat	Fourier number	Fo	$Fo = \dfrac{\lambda\, t}{c_p\, \rho\, l^2} = \dfrac{a\, t}{l^2}$
	Péclet number	Pe	$Pe = \dfrac{\rho\, c_p\, v\, l}{\lambda} = \dfrac{v\, l}{e} = Re \times Pr$
	Rayleigh number	Ra	$Ra = \dfrac{l^3\, \rho^2\, c_p\, g\, \gamma\ \Delta\theta}{\eta\, \lambda} = \dfrac{l^3\, g\, \gamma\, \Delta\theta}{v\, a} = Gr \times Pr$
	Nusselt number	Nu	$Nu = \dfrac{h\, l}{\lambda}$
	Stanton number	St	$St = \dfrac{h}{\rho\, v\, c_p} = Nu/Pe$
Transport of matter in binary mixture	Fourier number for mass transfer	$Fo\star$	$Fo\star = \dfrac{D\, t}{l^2} = Fo/Le$
	Péclet number for mass transfer	$Pe\star$	$Pe\star = \dfrac{v\, l}{D} = Pe \times Le$
	Grashof number for mass transfer	$Gr\star$	$Gr\star = \dfrac{l^3\, g\, \beta\, \Delta x}{v^2}$
	Nusselt number for mass transfer	$Nu\star$	$Nu\star = \dfrac{k\, l}{\rho\, D}$
	Stanton number for mass transfer	$St\star$	$St\star = \dfrac{k}{\rho\, v} = \dfrac{Nu\star}{Pe\star}$
Constants of matter	Prandtl number	Pr	$Pr = \dfrac{\eta\, c_p}{\lambda} = \dfrac{v}{\alpha}$
	Schmidt number	Sc	$Sc = \dfrac{\eta}{\rho\, D} = \dfrac{v}{D}$
	Lewis number	Le	$Le = \dfrac{\lambda}{\rho\, c_p\, D} = \dfrac{\alpha}{D} = \dfrac{Sc}{Pr}$

Symbols used in table:

D	diffusion coefficient	$\Delta\theta$	characteristic temperature difference
c	velocity of sound	α	thermal diffusivity: $\alpha = \lambda/\rho\, c_p$
c_p	specific heat capacity at constant pressure	β	$\beta = -\dfrac{1}{\rho}\left(\dfrac{\partial\rho}{\partial x}\right)_{\theta,p}$
f	characteristic frequency		
g	acceleration due to gravity		
h	coefficient of heat transfer:	γ	cubic expansion coefficient: $\gamma = -\dfrac{1}{\rho}\left(\dfrac{\partial\rho}{\partial\theta}\right)_p$
	heat/(time × cross-sectional area × temperature difference)	η	viscosity (dynamic viscosity)
k	mass transfer coefficient:	θ	temperature
	mass/(time × cross-sectional area × mole fraction difference)	λ	thermal conductivity
		$\lambda^\star$	mean free path
l	characteristic length	v	kinematic viscosity ($= \eta/\rho$)
t	characteristic time interval	ρ	density (mass density)
v	characteristic velocity	σ	surface tension
Δp	pressure difference		
Δx	characteristic difference of mole fraction		

Table 6.16 Geometric formulae

Shape	Plan area, A	Centre of gravity (G)	Radius of gyration, k ($I = A\,k^2$)
Triangle	$\dfrac{a\,h}{2}$	$\dfrac{h}{3}$ up from base $\dfrac{2\,a_1 + a_2}{3}$ across	About G, in x-plane: $k^2 = \dfrac{h^2}{18}$ About G, in y-plane: $k^2 = \dfrac{a_1^2 + a_1 a_2 + a_2^2}{18}$
Square	a^2	At centre	About base: $k^2 = \dfrac{a^2}{3}$ About G: $k^2 = \dfrac{a^2}{12}$
Rectangle	$a\,b$	At centre	About base: $k^2 = \dfrac{b^2}{3}$ About G, in x-plane: $k^2 = \dfrac{b^2}{12}$
Hollow square tube	$A^2 - a^2$	At centre	About G: $k^2 = \dfrac{A^4 - a^4}{12\,(A^2 - a^2)}$
Hollow rectangular tube	$A\,B - a\,b$	At centre	About G, in x-plane: $k^2 = \dfrac{A\,B^3 - a\,b^3}{12\,(A\,B - a\,b)}$ About G, in y-plane: $k^2 = \dfrac{A^3\,B - a^3\,b}{12\,(A\,B - a\,b)}$
I-section	$A\,B - 2\,a\,b = a\,t + 2\,B\,T$	At centre	About G, in x-plane: $k^2 = \dfrac{B^3\,(A - a) + a\,(B - 2\,b)^3}{12\,(A\,B - 2\,a\,b)}$ About G, in y-plane: $k^2 = \dfrac{A^3\,B - 2\,a^3\,b}{12\,(A\,B - 2\,a\,b)}$
Circle	$\dfrac{\pi\,d^2}{4}$	At centre	About G: $k^2 = \dfrac{d^2}{16}$

Table 6.16 Geometric formulae — *continued*

Shape	Volume, V	Plan area, A	Centre of gravity (G)	Radius of gyration, k $(I = A k^2)$
Sector of circle θ in radians		$\dfrac{d^2\,\theta}{8}$	$\dfrac{2\,d\,\sin\,(\theta/2)}{3\,\theta}$	About G, in x-plane: $k^2 = \dfrac{d^2}{4}\left(\dfrac{\theta - \sin\theta}{4\,\theta}\right)$ About G, in y-plane: $k^2 = \dfrac{d^2}{4}\left(\dfrac{\theta + \sin\theta}{4\,\theta} - \dfrac{16\,\sin^2(\theta/2)}{9\,\theta^2}\right)$
Cone 	$\dfrac{\pi\,d^2\,h}{12}$	$\dfrac{d\,h}{2}$	$\dfrac{h}{4}$ up from base On axis	About G, in x-plane: $k^2 = \dfrac{3\,(h^2 + d^2)}{80}$ About tip: $k^2 = \dfrac{3\,d^2}{40}$
Cylinder 	$\dfrac{\pi\,h\,d^2}{4}$	$\dfrac{\pi\,d^2}{4}$ (x-plane) $d\,h$ (z-plane)	At centre	About G, in x-plane: $k^2 = \dfrac{(4\,h^2 + 3\,d^2)}{48}$ About G, in z-plane: $k^2 = \dfrac{d^2}{8}$
Hollow cylinder 	$\dfrac{\pi\,h\,(D^2 - d^2)}{4}$	$\dfrac{\pi\,(D^2 - d^2)}{4}$ (x-plane) $h\,(D - d)$ (z-plane)	At centre	About G, in x-plane: $k^2 = \dfrac{4\,h^2 + 3\,(D^2 + d^2)}{48}$ About G, in z-plane: $k^2 = \dfrac{D^2 + d^2}{8}$
Sphere 	$\dfrac{\pi\,d^3}{6}$	$\dfrac{\pi\,d^2}{4}$	At centre	About G: $k^2 = \dfrac{d^2}{10}$
Rectangular block 	$a\,b\,c$	$b\,c$ (x-plane)	At centre	About G, in x-plane $k^2 = \dfrac{a^2 + c^2}{12}$

Bibliography

BS 350: 2004: *Conversion factors for units* (London: British Standards Institution) (2004)

BS ISO 31: *Specifications for quantities, units and symbols*: Part 0: 1992: *General principles*; Part 1: 1992: *Space and time*; Part 2: 1992: *Periodic and related phenomena*; Part 3: 1992: *Mechanics*; Part 4: 1992: *Heat*; Part 5: 1992: *Electricity and magnetism*; Part 6: 1992: *Light and related electromagnetic radiations*; Part 7: 1992: *Acoustics*; Part 8: 1992: *Physical chemistry and molecular physics*; Part 9: 1992: *Atomic and nuclear physics*; Part 10: 1992: *Nuclear reactions and ionizing radiations*; Part 11: 1992: *Mathematical signs and symbols for use in physical sciences and technology*; Part 12: 1992: *Characteristic numbers*; Part 13: 1992: *Solid state physics* (London: British Standards Institution) (dates as indicated)

BS ISO 1000: 1992: *SI units and recommendations for the use of their multiples and of certain other units* (London: British Standards Institution) (1992)

Council Directive 80/181/EEC of 20 December 1979 on the aproximation for the laws of the Member States relating to units of measurement and on the repeal of Directive 71/354/EEC *Official J. of the European Communities* **L39** 40–50 (15.2.1980) (Brussels: Commission for the European Communities) (1980)

Council Directive 85/1/EEC of 18 December 1984 amending Directive 80/181/EEC on the approximation of the laws of the Member States relating to units of measurement *Official J. of the European Communities* **L2** 11–12 (3.1.1985) (Brussels: Commission for the European Communities) (1985)

Council Directive 89/617/EEC of 27 November 1989 amending Directive 80/181/EEC on the approximation of the laws of the Member States relating to units of measurement *Official J. of the European Communities* **L357** 28–30 (7.12.1989) (Brussels: Commission for the European Communities) (1989)

Index